# Statistics 1: Introduction to ANOVA, Regression, and Logistic Regression

Course Notes

*Statistics 1: Introduction to ANOVA, Regression, and Logistic Regression Course Notes* was developed by Danny Modlin. Additional contributions were made by Chris Daman, Marc Huber, Dan Kelly, Bob Lucas, Paul Marovich, Azhar Nizam, Mike Patetta, Jill Tao, Catherine Truxillo, and artwork by Stanley Goldman. Editing and production support was provided by the Curriculum Development and Support Department.



**Statistics 1: Introduction to ANOVA, Regression, and Logistic Regression Course Notes**



---

Book code E2095, course code LWST193/ST193, prepared date 21Mar2012. LWST193_001

ISBN 978-1-61290-125-1

# Table of Contents

## Course Description

This course is for SAS software users who perform statistical analyses using SAS/STAT software. The focus is on *t* tests, ANOVA, linear regression, and logistic regression. This course (or equivalent knowledge) is a prerequisite to many of the courses in the statistical analysis curriculum.

### To learn more…

For information about other courses in the curriculum, contact the SAS Education Division at 1-800-333-7660, or send e-mail to training@sas.com. You can also find this information on the Web at support.sas.com/training/ as well as in the Training Course Catalog.

For a list of other SAS books that relate to the topics covered in this Course Notes, USA customers can contact our SAS Publishing Department at 1-800-727-3228 or send e-mail to sasbook@sas.com. Customers outside the USA, please contact your local SAS office.

Also, see the Publications Catalog on the Web at support.sas.com/pubs for a complete list of books and a convenient order form.

# Prerequisites

Before attending this course, you should

- have completed the equivalent of an undergraduate course in statistics covering *p*-values, hypothesis testing, analysis of variance, and regression.
- be able to execute SAS programs and create SAS data sets. You can gain this experience by completing the SAS® Programming 1: Essentials course.

# Chapter 1 Introduction to Statistics

# 1.1 Fundamental Statistical Concepts

## Objectives

- Decide what tasks to complete before analyzing the data.
- Use the MEANS procedure to produce descriptive statistics.

3

## Defining the Problem

The purpose of the study is to determine whether the average combined Math and Verbal scores on the Scholastic Aptitude Test (SAT) at Carver County magnet high schools is 1200 – the goal set by the school board.

4

As a project, students in Ms. Chao's statistics course must assess whether the students at magnet schools (schools with special curricula) in their district accomplished a goal of the Board of Education. The board wants the graduating class to attain a combined score of 1200 on the Math and Verbal portions of the SAT (the Scholastic Aptitude Test, a college admissions exam). Each section of the SAT has a maximum score of 800. Eighty students are selected at random from among magnet school students in the district. The total scores are recorded and each sample member is assigned an identification number.

## Variable Type and Level of Measurement

Before analyzing, identify the variable type (continuous or categorical) and level of measurement (nominal or ordinal).

5

There are a variety of statistical methods for analyzing data. To choose the appropriate method, you must determine the type and level of measurement for your variables.

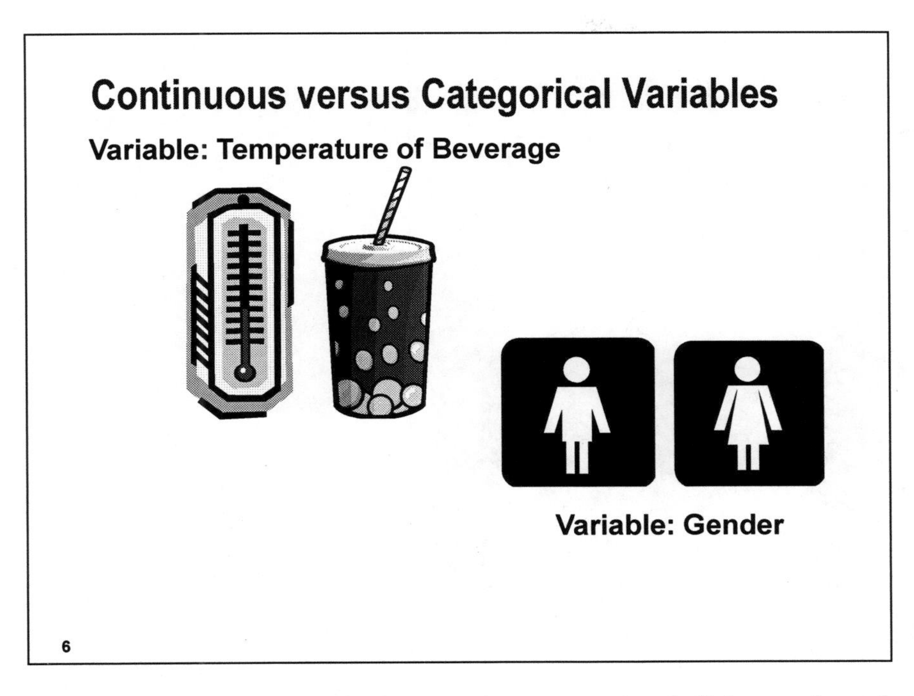


*Continuous variables* can, in theory, take on any of an infinite number of possible values between two numbers. An example of a continuous variable would be temperature of a beverage. There is no restriction to the number of values between 22° and 23°. You could have a temperature of 22.45° or 22.98° Fahrenheit. Notice that a variable can be continuous even if your measurement system has finite intervals.

Some numeric variables are not continuous. These include variables such as counts that can only take on specific values (for example, integers). In many statistical applications, methods for continuous data can be applied to these variables as well.

*Categorical variables* are variables that represent groupings. Categorical variables can be stored as numeric or non-numeric values in SAS. Examples of categorical variables include **gender** (**`male`** or **`female`**) and **size** of a product (**`Small`**, **`Medium`**, **`Large`**).

 It should be noted that continuous variables, through the process of binning, could be made into categorical variables.

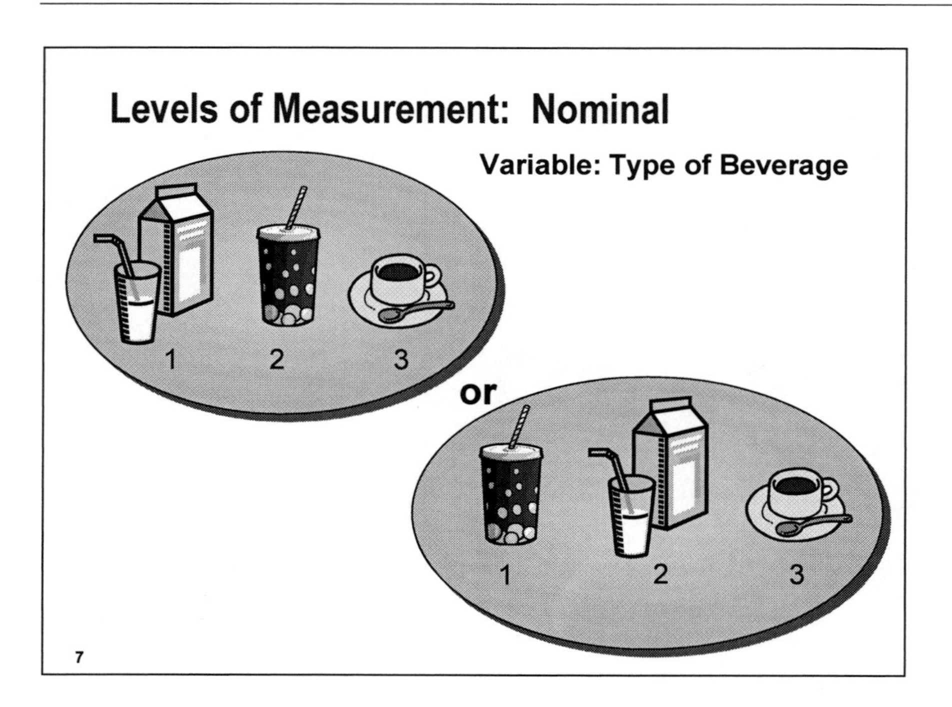


*Nominal variables* have values with no logical ordering. In this example, drink **type** is a nominal variable, even though numeric values are assigned to the categories.

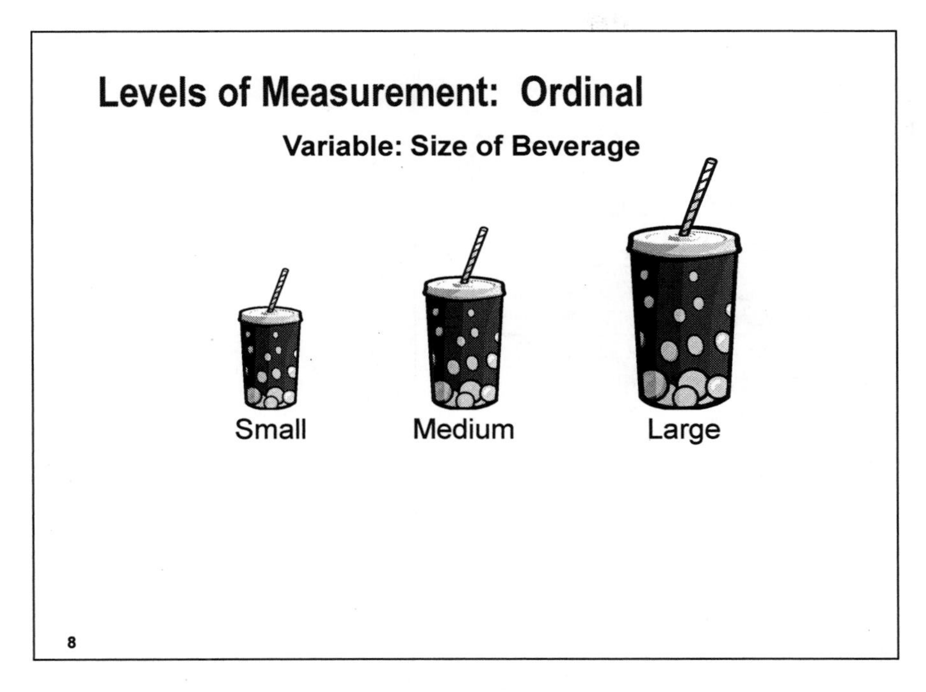


*Ordinal variables* have values with a logical order. However, the relative distances between the values are not clear. In this example, drink **size** is categorical. The number assignments to the categories convey information of the relative size of the drinks, but not precise information about the quantitative differences.

For mathematical completion, there are two other levels of measurement (interval and ratio). Interval and ratio variables have a shared property that we are able to calculate the distance between two ranked values. Ratio variables differ from that of interval in the existence of a "true" zero point. This zero point allows ratios to be calculated.

The SAT score variable used in this chapter is not truly continuous. It is argued that educational test scores have a linear relationship with measures that truly are continuous and therefore can be analyzed as if they were continuous. An SAT score is treated as a continuous, interval-level measure in this course.

## Overview of Statistical Models

| Type of Response \ Type of Predictors | Categorical | Continuous | Continuous and Categorical |
|---|---|---|---|
| **Continuous** | Analysis of Variance (ANOVA) | Ordinary Least Squares (OLS) Regression | Analysis of Covariance (ANCOVA) |
| **Categorical** | Contingency Table Analysis or Logistic Regression | Logistic Regression | Logistic Regression |

9

This course deals with statistical modeling. The type of modeling depends on the level of measurement of two types of variables.

The first type of variable is called *Response Variables*. These are the variables that generally are the focus of business or research. They are also known as *outcome variables* or *target variables* or (in designed experiments) *dependent variables*.

The second type of variable is referred to as *Predictor Variables*. These are the measures that are theoretically associated with the response variables. They can therefore be used to "predict" the value of the response variables. They are also known as *independent variables* in analysis of data from designed experiments.

*Categorical data analysis* is concerned with categorical responses, regardless of whether the predictor variables are categorical or continuous. Categorical responses have a measurement scale consisting of a set of categories.

*Continuous data analysis* is concerned with the analysis of continuous responses, regardless of whether the predictor variables are categorical or continuous

## Populations and Samples

**Population** – the entire collection of individual members of a group of interest.

**Sample** – a subset of a population drawn to enable inferences to the population.

**Assumption for This Course – The sample that is drawn is *representative* of the population.**

10

A *population* is a collection of all objects about which information is desired, for example:

- all potential customers of a bank
- all copper wires of 1/8" diameter and 36" length
- all students in Carver schools magnet programs

A *sample* is a subset of the population. The sample should be ***representative*** of the population, meaning that the sample's characteristics are similar to the population's characteristics. Examples of samples are as follows:

- 500 bank customers responding to a survey
- 50 randomly selected copper wires of 1/8" diameter and 36" length
- 80 students in Carver schools magnet programs

*Simple random sampling*, a technique in which each member of the population has an equal probability of being selected, is used by Ms. Chao's students. Random sampling can help ensure that the sample is representative of the population.

In a simple random sample, every member of the population has an equal chance of being included. In the test scores example, each student has an equal chance of being selected for the study.

 See the appendix for information about how to generate random samples without replacement and with replacement.

Why not select only the students from Ms. Chao's class?

When you only select students that are easily available to you, you are using *convenience sampling*. Convenience sampling can lead to biased samples. A *biased* sample is one that is not representative of the population from which it is drawn.

In the example, the average test scores of only Ms. Chao's students might not be close to the true average of the population. This can cause the students to reach incorrect conclusions about the true average score and the variability of scores in the school district. This would not impress Ms. Chao.

## Parameters and Statistics

Statistics are used to approximate population parameters.

| | Population Parameters | Sample Statistics |
|---|---|---|
| Mean | $\mu$ | $\bar{x}$ |
| Variance | $\sigma^2$ | $s^2$ |
| Standard Deviation | $\sigma$ | $s$ |

11

*Parameters* are characteristics of populations. Because populations usually cannot be measured in their entirety, parameter values are generally unknown. *Statistics* are quantities calculated from the values in the sample.

Suppose you have $x_1, x_2, \ldots, x_n$, a sample from some population.

$$\bar{x} = \frac{1}{n}\sum x_i$$

The mean is an average, a typical value in the distribution.

$$s^2 = \frac{1}{n-1}\sum (x_i - \bar{x})^2$$

The variance measures the sample variability.

$$s = \sqrt{\frac{1}{n-1}\sum (x_i - \bar{x})^2}$$

The standard deviation measures variability. It is reported in the same units as the mean.

## Describing Your Data

When you describe data, your goals are as follows:

- characterize the central tendency
- inspect the spread and shape of continuous variables
- screen for unusual data values

12

After you select a random sample of the population, you can start describing the data. Although you want to draw conclusions about your population, you first want to explore and describe your data before you use inferential statistics.

Why?

- Data must be as error-free as possible.
- Unique aspects, such as data values that cluster or show some unusual shape, must be identified.
- An extreme value of a variable, if not detected, could cause gross errors in the interpretation of the statistics.

## 1.01 Multiple Answer Poll

A sample from a population should be which of the following?

a. Random
b. Representative
c. Normal

14

## Test Score Data Set

| Gender | SATScore | IDNumber |
|---|---|---|
| Male | 1170 | 61469897 |
| Female | 1090 | 33081197 |
| Male | 1240 | 68137597 |
| Female | 1000 | 37070397 |
| Male | 1210 | 64608797 |
| Female | 970 | 60714297 |
| Male | 1020 | 16907997 |
| Female | 1490 | 9589297 |
| Male | 1200 | 93891897 |
| Female | 1260 | 5859397 |
| ... | ... | ... |

16

Example: The identification number of each student (**IDNumber**) and the total score on the SAT (**SATScore**) are recorded. The data are stored in the **sasuser.testscores** data set.

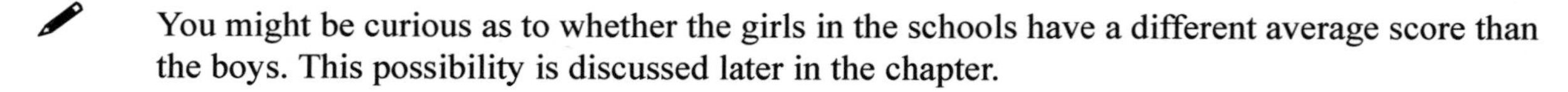

You might be curious as to whether the girls in the schools have a different average score than the boys. This possibility is discussed later in the chapter.

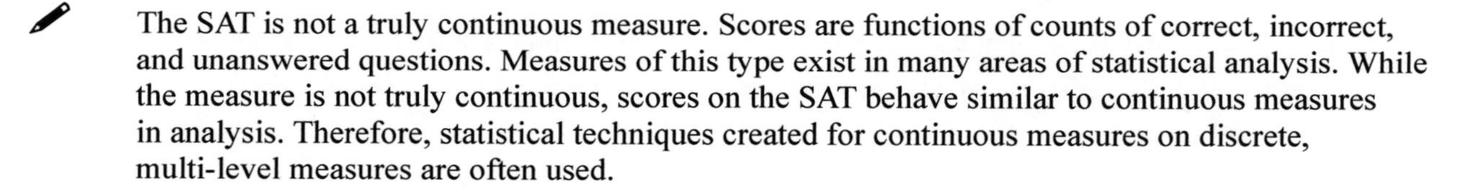

The SAT is not a truly continuous measure. Scores are functions of counts of correct, incorrect, and unanswered questions. Measures of this type exist in many areas of statistical analysis. While the measure is not truly continuous, scores on the SAT behave similar to continuous measures in analysis. Therefore, statistical techniques created for continuous measures on discrete, multi-level measures are often used.

## Distributions

When you examine the distribution of values for the variable **SATScore**, you can determine the following:

- the range of possible data values
- the frequency of data values
- whether the data values accumulate in the middle of the distribution or at one end

17

A *distribution* is a collection of data values that are arranged in order, along with the relative frequency. For any type of data, it is important that you describe the location, spread, and shape of your distribution using graphical techniques and descriptive statistics.

For the example, these questions can be addressed using graphical techniques.

- Are the values of **SATScore** symmetrically distributed?
- Are any values of **SATScore** unusual?

You can answer these questions using descriptive statistics.

- What is the best estimate of the average of the values of **SATScore** for the population?
- What is the best estimate of the average spread or dispersion of the values of **SATScore** for the population?

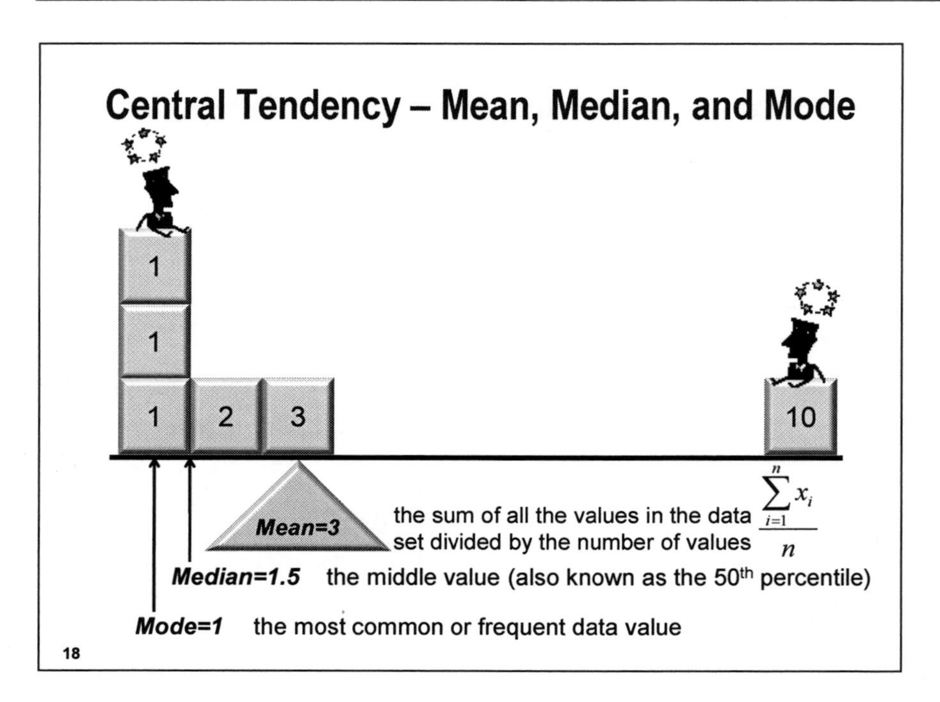


Descriptive statistics that locate the center of your data are called *measures of central tendency*. The most commonly reported measure of central tendency is the sample mean. It is most appropriate for variables measured on an interval or ratio scale with an approximately symmetrical distribution.

A property of the sample mean is that the sum of the differences of each data value from the mean is always 0. That is, $\sum(x_i - \bar{x})=0$.

The *mean* is the arithmetic balancing point of your data.

The *median* is the data point in the middle of a sorted sequence. It is appropriate for either rank scores (variables measured on an ordinal scale) or variables measured on an interval or ratio scale with a skewed distribution.

The *mode* is the data point that occurs most frequently. It is most appropriate for variables measured on a nominal scale. There might be several modes in a distribution.

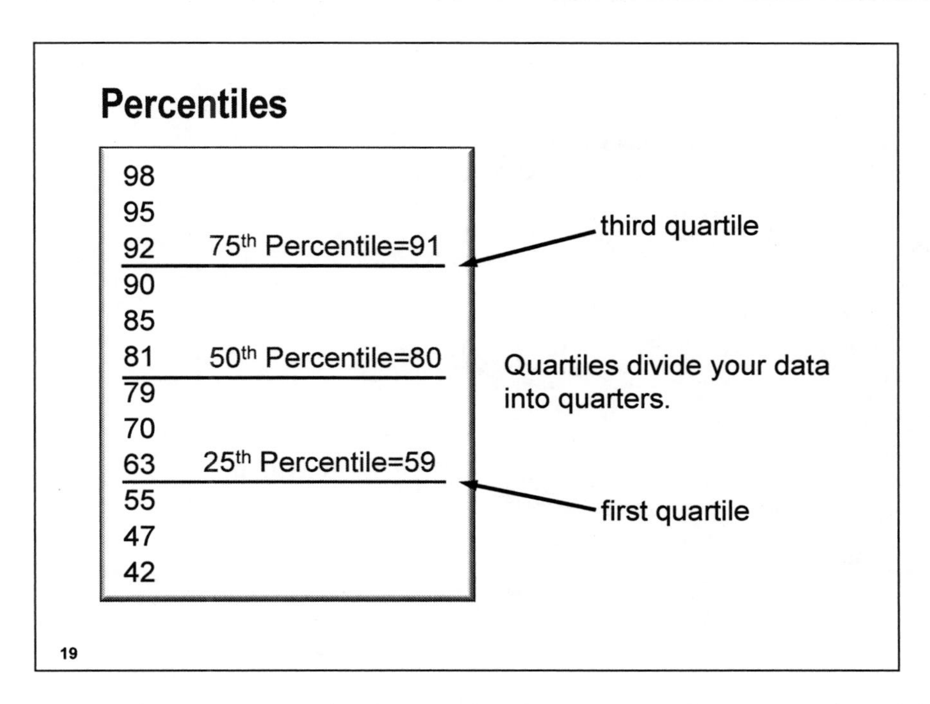


*Percentiles* locate a position in your data larger than a given proportion of data values.

Commonly reported percentile values are the following:

- the 25th percentile, also called the first quartile
- the 50th percentile, also called the median
- the 75th percentile, also called the third quartile.

## The Spread of a Distribution: Dispersion

| Measure | Definition |
|---|---|
| **Range** | the difference between the maximum and minimum data values |
| **Interquartile Range** | the difference between the 25th and 75th percentiles |
| **Variance** | a measure of dispersion of the data around the mean |
| **Standard Deviation** | a measure of dispersion expressed in the same units of measurement as your data (the square root of the variance) |

20

Measures of dispersion enable you to characterize the dispersion, or spread, of the data.

Formula for sample variance: $s^2 = \frac{1}{n-1}\Sigma(x_i - \bar{x})^2$

Another measure of variation is the coefficient of variation (C.V.), which is the standard deviation as a percentage of the mean.

It is defined as $\frac{s}{\bar{x}} \times 100$.

The variance and standard deviation are typically reported where the measure of central tendency is the mean. Where the distribution is skewed, the data contains several extreme outliers, or the variable is measured on an ordinal scale, a value better suited to reflect dispersion is the *interquartile range*. The interquartile range shows the range of the middle 50% of data values.

## The MEANS Procedure

General form of the MEANS procedure:

```
PROC MEANS DATA=SAS-data-set <options>;
      CLASS variables;
      VAR variables;
RUN;
```

21

The MEANS procedure is a Base SAS procedure for generating descriptive statistics for your data.

Selected MEANS procedure statements:

CLASS specifies the variables whose values define the subgroup combinations for the analysis. Class variables are numeric or character. Class variables can have continuous values, but they typically have a few discrete values that define levels of the variable. ***You do not have to sort the data by CLASS variables.***

VAR specifies numeric variables for which you want to calculate descriptive statistics. If no VAR statement appears, all numeric variables in the data set are analyzed.

For assistance with the correct syntax and options for a SAS procedure, you can type **help** in the command box. This opens the Help window, which accesses SAS documentation. After you locate the appropriate procedure, select **syntax** to see all options available for that procedure.

## Descriptive Statistics

Example: Use the PRINT procedure to list the first 10 observations in the **sasuser.testscores** data set. Then use PROC MEANS to generate descriptive statistics for **SATScore**.

Submit the program **st100d01.sas** before running the programs in this course. Formats for the data sets are written there.

Partial Code

```
options nodate nonumber ls=95 ps=80 formdlim='-';
ods noproctitle;

proc format;
...

data sasuser.testscores;
   input Gender $ 1-6 SATScore 8-11 IDNumber 13-20;
   datalines;
...
```

Selected SAS system options:

| | |
|---|---|
| NODATE | specifies that the date and the time are not printed. |
| NONUMBER | specifies that SAS not print the page number on the first title line of each page of SAS output. |
| LINESIZE= (LS=)*n* | specifies the line size (printer line width) in characters for the SAS log and the SAS output that are used by the DATA step and procedures. |
| PAGESIZE= (PS=)*n* | specifies the number of lines that compose a page. |
| FORMDLIM= | specifies in quotation marks a character written to delimit pages. Normally, the delimit character is null. |

Selected ODS statement options.

| | |
|---|---|
| NOPROCTITLE | suppresses the writing of the title of the procedure that produces the results. |

Code for the demonstration starts here:

```
/*st101d01.sas*/  /*Part A*/
proc print data=sasuser.testscores (obs=10);
   title 'Listing of the SAT Data Set';
run;
```

| Obs | Gender | SATScore | IDNumber |
|---|---|---|---|
| 1 | Male | 1170 | 61469897 |
| 2 | Female | 1090 | 33081197 |
| 3 | Male | 1240 | 68137597 |
| 4 | Female | 1000 | 37070397 |
| 5 | Male | 1210 | 64608797 |
| 6 | Female | 970 | 60714297 |
| 7 | Male | 1020 | 16907997 |
| 8 | Female | 1490 | 9589297 |
| 9 | Male | 1200 | 93891897 |
| 10 | Female | 1260 | 85859397 |

```
/*st101d01.sas*/  /*Part B*/
proc means data=sasuser.testscores;
   var SATScore;
   title 'Descriptive Statistics Using PROC MEANS';
run;
```

| Analysis Variable : SATScore | | | | |
|---|---|---|---|---|
| N | Mean | Std Dev | Minimum | Maximum |
| 80 | 1190.63 | 147.0584466 | 890.0000000 | 1600.00 |

By default, PROC MEANS prints the number of nonmissing observations (N), the mean, the standard deviation, the minimum value, and the maximum value. You can add options to the MEANS statement to request additional or alternate statistics. When you add options to request specific statistics, only the requested statistics appear in the output. In addition, you can control the number of decimal places that are displayed.

```
/*st101d01.sas*/  /*Part C*/
proc means data=sasuser.testscores
           maxdec=2
           n mean median std q1 q3 qrange;
   var SATScore;
   title 'Selected Descriptive Statistics for SAT Scores';
run;
```

Selected PROC MEANS statement options:

MAXDEC= specifies the maximum number of decimal places to use when printing numeric values.

| Analysis Variable : SATScore | | | | | | |
|---|---|---|---|---|---|---|
| N | Mean | Median | Std Dev | Lower Quartile | Upper Quartile | Quartile Range |
| 80 | 1190.63 | 1170.00 | 147.06 | 1085.00 | 1280.00 | 195.00 |

## Exercises

1. **Calculating Basic Statistics in PROC MEANS**

The data in **sasuser.NormTemp** comes from an article in the *Journal of Statistics Education* by Dr. Allen L. Shoemaker from the Psychology Department at Calvin College. The data are based on an article in a 1992 edition of *JAMA* (*Journal of the American Medical Association*), which questions the notion that the true mean body temperature is 98.6. There are 65 males and 65 females. There is also some question about whether mean body temperatures for women are the same as for men. The variables in the data set are as follows:

| | |
|---|---|
| **ID** | Identification number |
| **BodyTemp** | Body temperature (degrees Fahrenheit) |
| **Gender** | Coded (`Male`, `Female`) |
| **HeartRate** | Heart rate (beats per minute) |

Use PROC MEANS to answer these questions:

**a.** What is the overall mean and standard deviation of body temperature in the sample?

**b.** What is the interquartile range of body temperature?

**c.** Do the mean values seem to differ between men and women?

Hint: Use the CLASS statement in PROC MEANS, with **Gender** as the class variable.

# 1.2 Picturing Distributions

## Objectives

- Look at distributions of continuous variables.
- Describe the normal distribution.
- Use the UNIVARIATE procedure to generate histograms and normal probability plots and to produce descriptive statistics.
- Use the SGPLOT procedure to generate box plots.

26

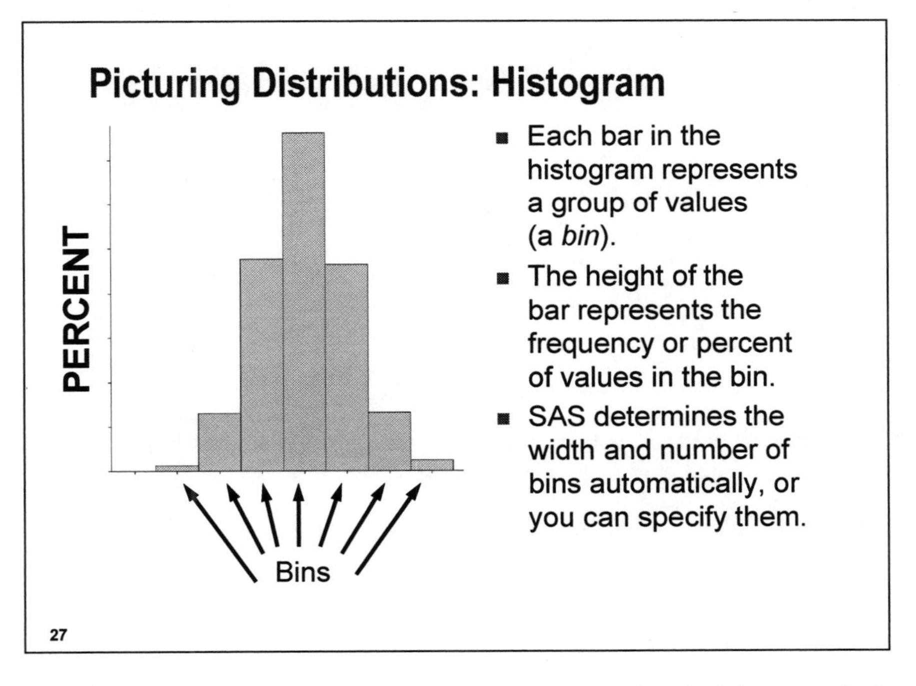


Most elementary statistical procedures assume some underlying population probability distribution. It is a good idea to look at your data to see whether the distribution of your sample data can reasonably be assumed to come from a population with the assumed distribution. A histogram is a good way to determine how the probability distribution is shaped.

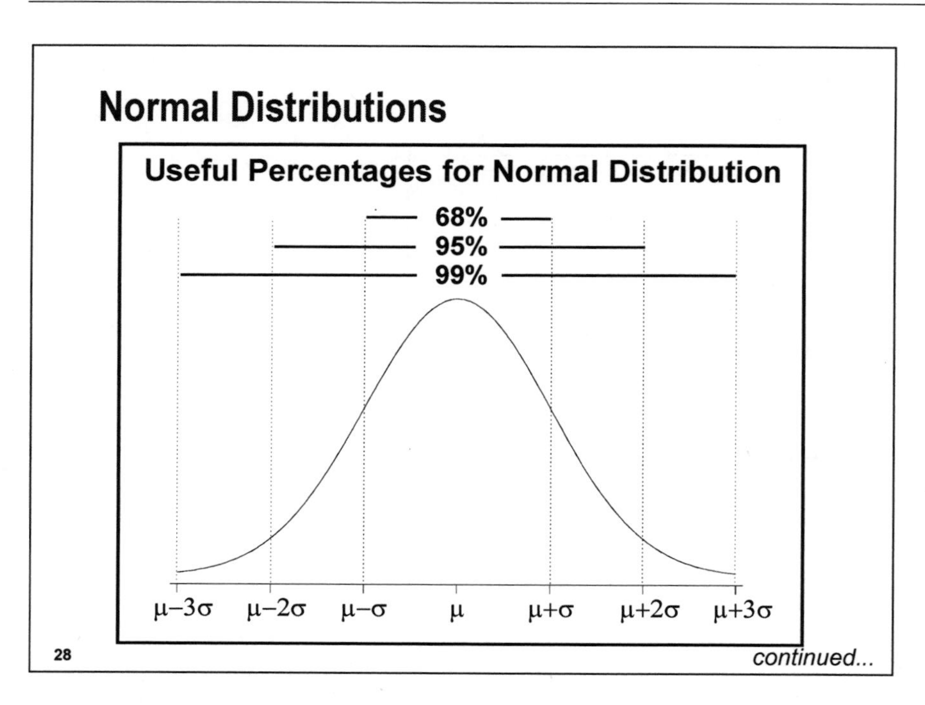


Quite often in analysis, although not always, a normal distribution is assumed.

The normal distribution is a mathematical function. The height of the function at any point on the horizontal axis is the "probability density" at that point. Normal distribution probabilities (which can be thought of as the proportion of the area under the curve) tend to be higher near the middle. The center of the distribution is the population mean ($\mu$). The standard deviation ($\sigma$) describes how variable the distribution is about $\mu$. A larger standard deviation implies a wider normal distribution. The mean locates the distribution (sets its center point) and the standard deviation scales it.

An observation value is considered unusual if it is far away from the mean. How far is far? You can use the mathematical properties of the normal probability density function (PDF) to determine that. If a population follows a normal distribution, then approximately the following is true:

- 68% of the data fall within 1 standard deviation of the mean.
- 95% of the data fall within 2 standard deviations of the mean.
- 99.7% of the data fall within 3 standard deviations of the mean.

Often, values that are more than two standard deviations from the mean are regarded as unusual. Now you can see why. Only about 5% of all values are at least that far away from the mean.

You use this information later when you discuss the concepts of confidence intervals and hypothesis tests.

## Normal Distributions

A *normal distribution*

- is ***symmetric***. If you draw a line down the center, you get the same shape on either side.
- is ***fully characterized*** by the mean and standard deviation. Given the values of those two parameters, you know all there is to know about the distribution.
- is bell shaped.
- has mean=median=mode.

The line on each of the following graphs represents the shape of the normal distribution with the mean and variance estimated from the sample data.

29

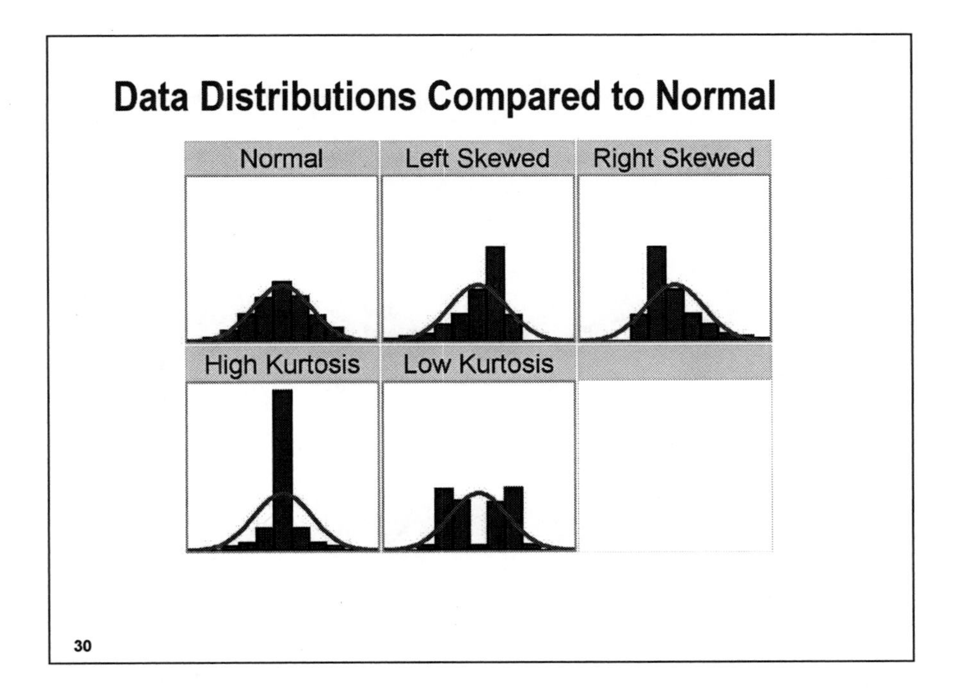


The distribution of your data might not look normal. There are an infinite number of different ways that a population can be distributed. When you look at your data, you might notice the features of the distribution that indicate similarity or difference from the normal distribution.

In evaluating distributions, it is useful to look at statistical measures of the shape of the sample distribution compared to the normal.

Two such measures are skewness and kurtosis.

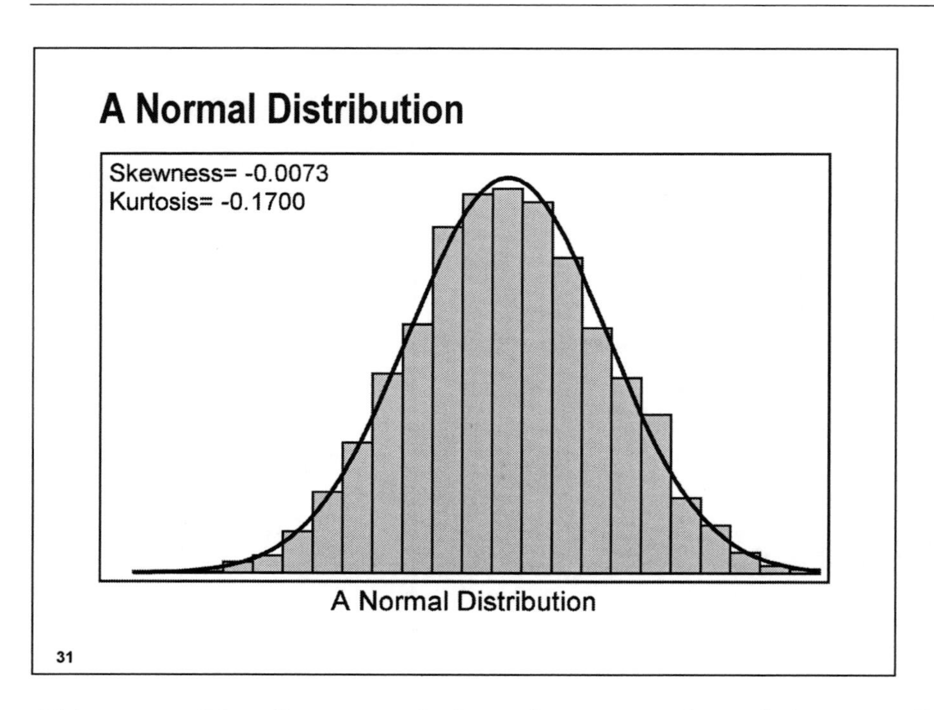


A histogram of data from a sample drawn from a normal population generally shows values of skewness and kurtosis near 0 in SAS output.

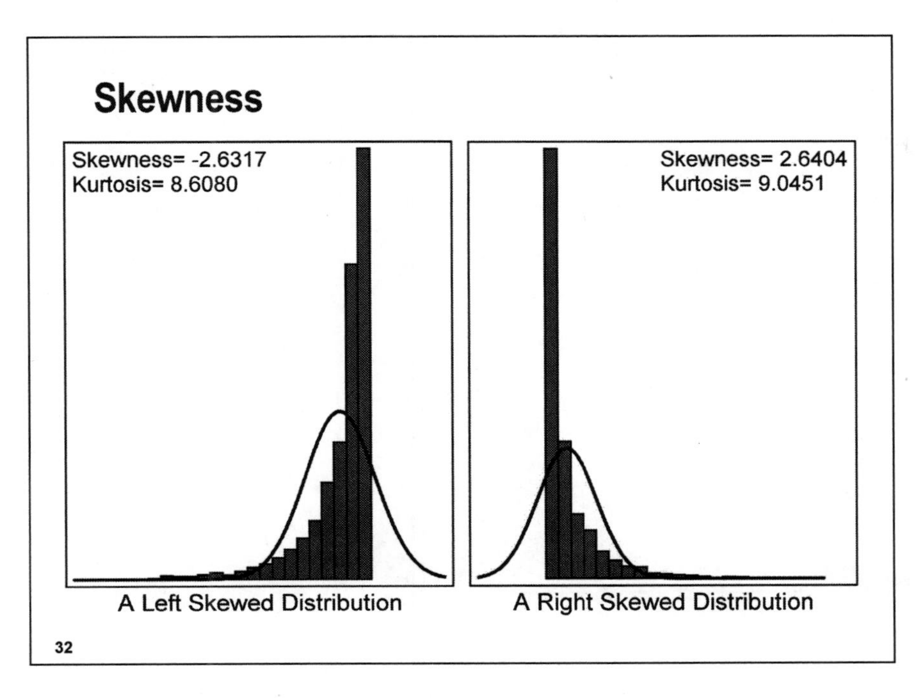


One measure of the shape of a distribution is skewness. The *skewness* statistic measures the tendency of your distribution to be more spread out on one side than the other. A distribution that is approximately symmetric has a skewness statistic close to 0.

If your distribution is more spread out on the

- ***left*** side, then the statistic is negative, and the mean is less than the median. This is sometimes referred to as a *left-skewed* or *negatively skewed* distribution.
- ***right*** side, then the statistic is positive, and the mean is greater than the median. This is sometimes referred to as a *right-skewed* or *positively skewed* distribution.

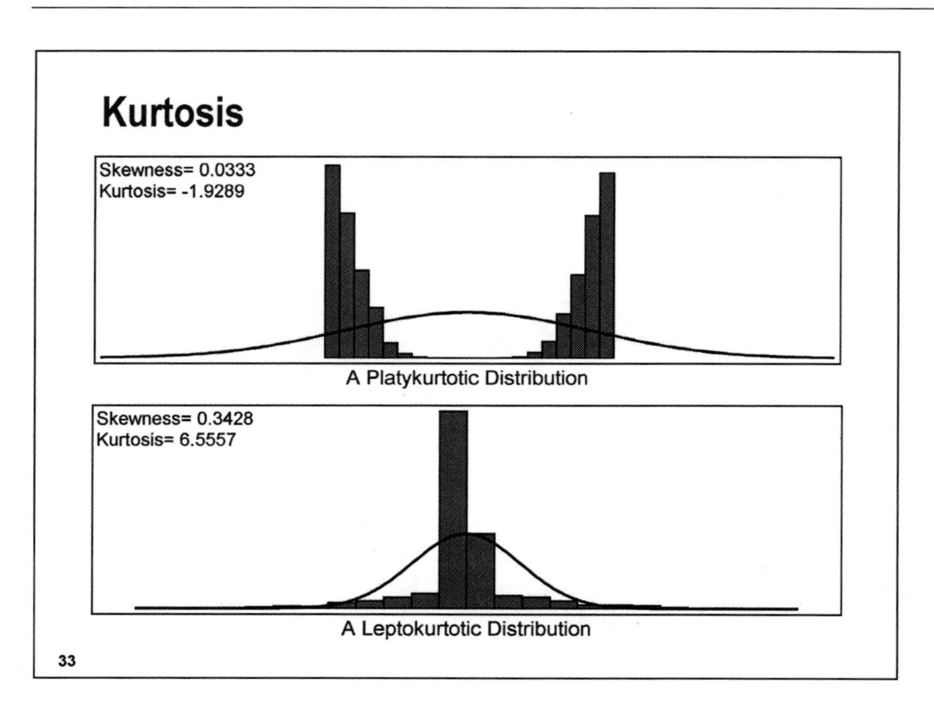


*Kurtosis* measures the tendency of your data to be distributed toward the center or toward the tails of the distribution. A distribution that is approximately normal has a kurtosis statistic close to 0 in SAS. Kurtosis is often very difficult to assess visually.

If the value of your kurtosis statistic is negative, the distribution is said to be *platykurtic*. If the distribution is both symmetric and platykurtic, then there tends to be a smaller-than-normal proportion of observations in the tails and/or a somewhat flat peak. Rectangular, bimodal, and multimodal distributions tend to have low (negative) values of kurtosis.

If the value of the kurtosis statistic is positive, the distribution is said to be *leptokurtic*. If the distribution is both symmetric and leptokurtic, then there tends to be a larger-than-normal proportion of observations in the extreme tails and/or a taller peak than the normal. A leptokurtic distribution is often referred to as *heavy-tailed*. Leptokurtic distributions are also sometimes referred to as *outlier-prone distributions*.

Distributions that are asymmetric also tend to have nonzero kurtosis. In these cases, understanding kurtosis is considerably more complex than in situations where the distribution is approximately symmetric.

The normal distribution actually has a kurtosis value of 3, but SAS subtracts a constant of 3 from all reported values of kurtosis, making the constant-modified value for the normal distribution 0 in SAS output. That is the value against which to compare a sample kurtosis value in SAS when assessing normality. This value is often referred to as *relative kurtosis*.

## Graphical Displays of Distributions

You can produce three types of plots for examining the distribution of your data values:

- histograms
- normal probability plots
- box plots

34

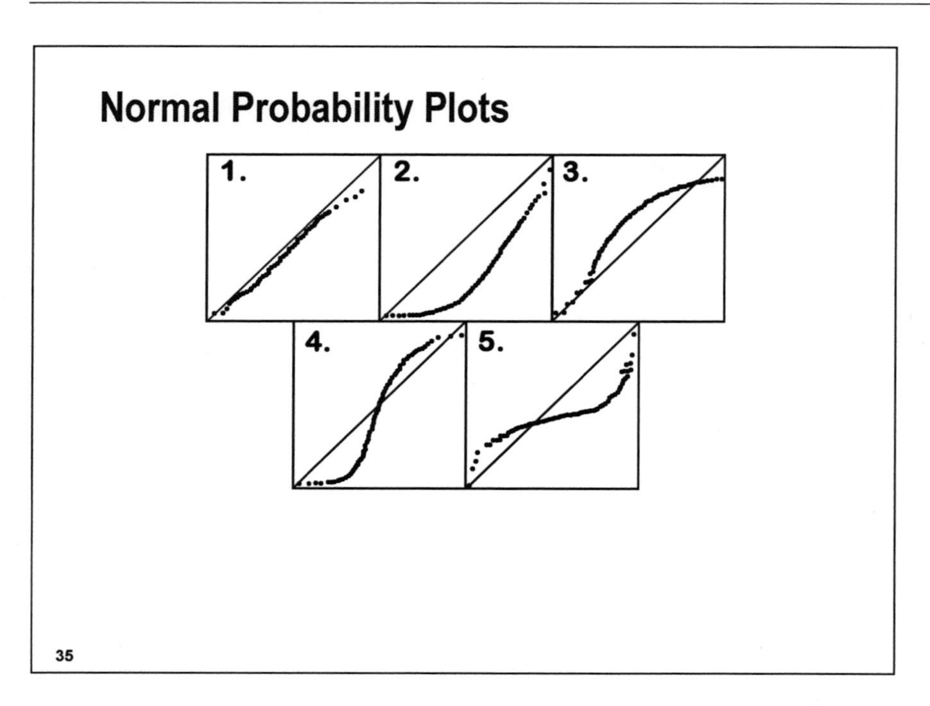


A *normal probability plot* is a visual method for determining whether your data come from a distribution that is approximately normal. The vertical axis represents the actual data values, and the horizontal axis displays the expected percentiles from a standard normal distribution.

The above diagrams illustrate some possible normal probability plots for data from the following:

1. normal distribution (the observed data follow the reference line)
2. skewed-to-the-right distribution
3. skewed-to-the-left distribution
4. light-tailed distribution
5. heavy-tailed distribution

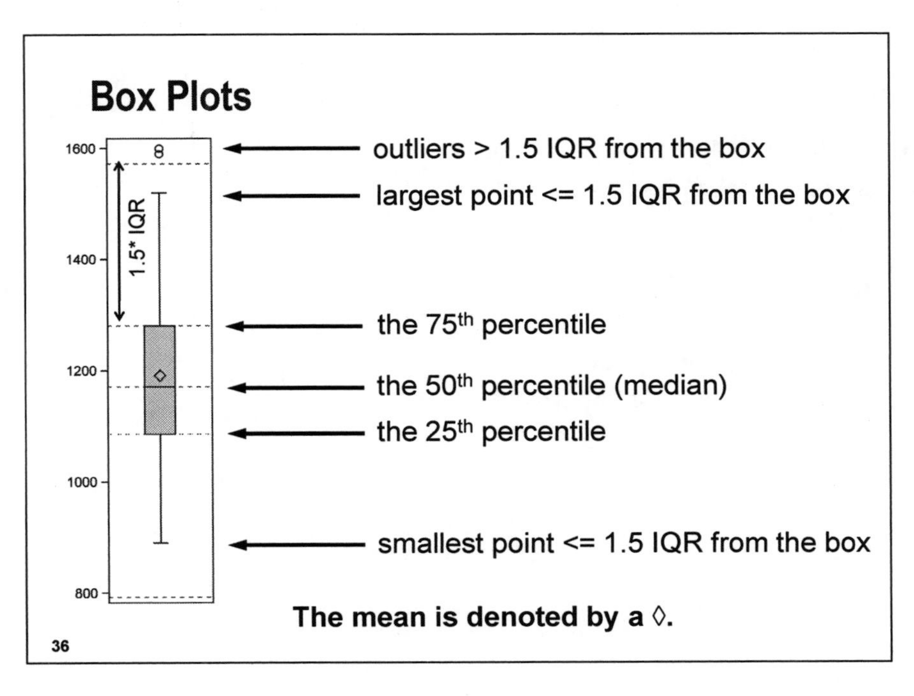


*Box plots* (Tukey 1977) (sometimes referred to as *box-and-whisker plots*) provide information about the variability of data and the extreme data values. The box represents the middle 50% of your data (between the 25th and 75th percentile values). You get a rough impression of the symmetry of your distribution by comparing the mean and median, as well as assessing the symmetry of the box and whiskers around the median line. The whiskers extend from the box as far as the data extends, to a distance of, at most, 1.5 interquartile range (IQR) units. If any values lay more than 1.5 IQR units from either end of the box, they are represented in SAS by individual plot symbols.

The plot above shows that the data are approximately symmetric.

## ODS Graphics Output

- Some graphs are created by default.
- Procedure options (such as PLOTS=) are used to specify which graphs to create.
- You can specify where you want your graphs displayed by using ODS destination statements (for example, LISTING, HTML, RTF).
- ODS SELECT and ODS EXCLUDE statements can be used to select and exclude information from your output.

37

In this course, you use ODS Statistical Graphics for graphical analysis of data. ODS Statistical Graphics were first made available in SAS 9.2. In SAS 9.3, statistical graphics from SAS statistical procedures are produced unless the ODS GRAPHICS OFF statement is submitted. This statement only needs to be submitted once within an interactive SAS session (or batch job) and remains in effect until the ODS GRAPHICS ON (ODS GRAPHICS) statement is submitted.

The SAS documentation lists the available graphics in the description of the SAS procedure.

ODS templates can be used to modify the layout and details of each graph.

ODS Statistical Graphics can also be toggled on and off by checking and unchecking the appropriate box by selecting **Tools** ⇨ **Options** ⇨ **Preferences** ⇨ **Results**.

## Some Recommended ODS Styles

| Style | Description |
|---|---|
| HTMLBLUE | This lighter color scheme for HTML content is the default for the HTML destination. |
| STATISTICAL | Color style recommended for output in Web pages or color print media. |
| ANALYSIS | Color style with a somewhat different appearance from STATISTICAL. |
| JOURNAL and JOURNAL2 | Gray-scale and pure black-and-white styles, respectively; recommended for graphs in black-and-white publications. |
| RTF | Used to produce graphs to insert into a Microsoft Word document or a Microsoft PowerPoint slide. |

38

ODS styles are used to control the general appearance and consistency of all graphs and tables. (You can use a variety of styles and destinations throughout this course.)

## Statistical Graphics Procedures in SAS

- PROC SGSCATTER creates single-cell and multi-cell scatter plots and scatter plot matrices with optional fits and ellipses.
- PROC SGPLOT creates single-cell plots with a variety of plot and chart types.
- PROC SGPANEL creates single-page or multi-page panels of plots and charts conditional on classification variables.
- PROC SGRENDER provides a way to create plots from graph templates that you modified or wrote yourself.

39

## The UNIVARIATE Procedure

General form of the UNIVARIATE procedure:

```
PROC UNIVARIATE DATA=SAS-data-set <options>;
      VAR variables;
      ID variable;
      HISTOGRAM variables </ options>;
      PROBPLOT variables </ options>;
      INSET keywords </ options>;
RUN;
```

40

The UNIVARIATE procedure not only computes descriptive statistics, but also provides greater detail about the distributions of the variables.

Selected UNIVARIATE procedure statements:

VAR
specifies numeric variables to analyze. If no VAR statement appears, then all numeric variables in the data set are analyzed.

ID
specifies a variable used to label the five lowest and five highest values in the output.

HISTOGRAM
creates high-resolution histograms.

PROBPLOT
creates a high-resolution probability plot, which compares ordered variable values with the percentiles of a specified theoretical distribution.

INSET
places a box or table of summary statistics, called an *inset*, directly in a graph created with a CDFPLOT, HISTOGRAM, PPPLOT, PROBPLOT, or QQPLOT statement. The INSET statement must follow the PLOT statement that creates the plot that you want to augment.

Selected option for HISTOGRAM and PROBPLOT statements:

NORMAL<(*options*)>
creates a normal probability plot. Options (MU= SIGMA=) determine the mean and standard deviation of the normal distribution used to create reference lines (normal curve overlay in HISTOGRAM and diagonal reference line in PROBPLOT).

## The SGPLOT Procedure

General form of the SGPLOT procedure:

```
PROC SGPLOT <option(s)>;
     DOT category-variable </option(s)>;
     HBAR category-variable < /option(s) >;
     HBOX response-variable </option(s)>;
     HISTOGRAM response-variable < /option(s)>;
     NEEDLE X= variable Y= numeric-variable </option(s)>;
     REG X= numeric-variable Y= numeric-variable
              </option(s)>;
     SCATTER X= variable Y= variable </option(s)>;
     VBAR category-variable < /option(s)>;
     VBOX response-variable </option(s)>;
RUN;
```

41

The SGPLOT procedure creates one or more plots and overlays them on a single set of axes. You can use the SGPLOT procedure to create statistical graphics such as histograms and regression plots, in addition to simple graphics such as box plots, scatter plots, and line plots.

Selected SGPLOT procedure statements:

VBOX creates a vertical box plot that shows the distribution of your data.

## Examining Distributions

```
/*st101d02.sas*/  /*Part A*/
proc univariate data=sasuser.testscores;
   var SATScore;
   histogram SATScore / normal(mu=est sigma=est) kernel;
   inset skewness kurtosis / position=ne;
   probplot SATScore / normal(mu=est sigma=est);
   inset skewness kurtosis;
   title 'Descriptive Statistics Using PROC UNIVARIATE';
run;
```

Selected HISTOGRAM statement options:

KERNEL — superimposes kernel density estimates on the histogram.

NORMAL — displays fitted normal density curves on the histogram. MU=__ specifies mean $\mu$ for normal curve. SIGMA=__ specifies standard deviation $\sigma$ for normal curve. The EST option requests that the value be estimated from the data.

Optional ODS statement:

ODS LISTING (*action*) — opens, manages, or closes the LISTING destination.

GPATH=*file-specification* <(url=*'Uniform-Resource-Locator'* | NONE)>
specifies the location for all graphics output that is generated while the destination is open.

By default, output goes to the HTML destination. Other options are RTF, LISTING, and PDF destinations, which can also be opened, managed, and closed by ODS RTF, ODS LISTING, and ODS PDF, respectively. If graphical output is requested for either HTML or LISTING destinations, it is sent to the user's default location. You can select a different location with the GPATH= option.

Selected Output

| Moments | | | |
|---|---|---|---|
| **N** | 80 | **Sum Weights** | 80 |
| **Mean** | 1190.625 | **Sum Observations** | 95250 |
| **Std Deviation** | 147.058447 | **Variance** | 21626.1867 |
| **Skewness** | 0.64202018 | **Kurtosis** | 0.42409987 |
| **Uncorrected SS** | 115115500 | **Corrected SS** | 1708468.75 |
| **Coeff Variation** | 12.3513656 | **Std Error Mean** | 16.4416342 |

| Basic Statistical Measures | | | |
|---|---|---|---|
| Location | | Variability | |
| Mean | 1190.625 | Std Deviation | 147.05845 |
| Median | 1170.000 | Variance | 21626 |
| Mode | 1050.000 | Range | 710.00000 |
| | | Interquartile Range | 195.00000 |

<table>
<tr><th colspan="5">Tests for Location: Mu0=0</th></tr>
<tr><th>Test</th><th colspan="2">Statistic</th><th colspan="2">p Value</th></tr>
<tr><td>Student's t</td><td>t</td><td>72.41525</td><td>Pr > |t|</td><td><.0001</td></tr>
<tr><td>Sign</td><td>M</td><td>40</td><td>Pr >= |M|</td><td><.0001</td></tr>
<tr><td>Signed Rank</td><td>S</td><td>1620</td><td>Pr >= |S|</td><td><.0001</td></tr>
</table>

| Quantiles (Definition 5) | |
|---|---|
| Quantile | Estimate |
| 100% Max | 1600 |
| 99% | 1600 |
| 95% | 1505 |
| 90% | 1375 |
| 75% Q3 | 1280 |
| 50% Median | 1170 |
| 25% Q1 | 1085 |
| 10% | 1020 |
| 5% | 995 |
| 1% | 890 |
| 0% Min | 890 |

| Extreme Observations | | | |
|---|---|---|---|
| Lowest | | Highest | |
| Value | Obs | Value | Obs |
| 890 | 69 | 1490 | 8 |
| 910 | 74 | 1520 | 42 |
| 970 | 6 | 1520 | 54 |
| 990 | 51 | 1590 | 70 |
| 1000 | 4 | 1600 | 25 |

The tabular output indicates the following:

- The mean of the data is 1190.625. This is approximately equal to the median (1170), which indicates the distribution is fairly symmetric.
- The standard deviation is 147.058447, which means that the average variability around the mean is approximately 147 points.
- The distribution is slightly skewed to the right.
- The distribution has slightly heavier tails than the normal distribution.
- The student with the lowest score is observation 69, with a score of 890. The student with the highest score is number 25, with a score of 1600 (highest possible score for the SAT).

In the Quantiles table, Definition 5 indicates that PROC UNIVARIATE uses the default definition for calculating percentile values. You can use the PCTLDEF= option in the PROC UNIVARIATE statement to specify one of five methods. These methods are listed in an appendix.

In order to view the graphical output when you use the SAS windowing environment with the Listing destination active, follow these steps:

1. Expand the output from the Results window by right-clicking on the name of the procedure in the Results window and selecting **Expand All** in the drop-down menu.

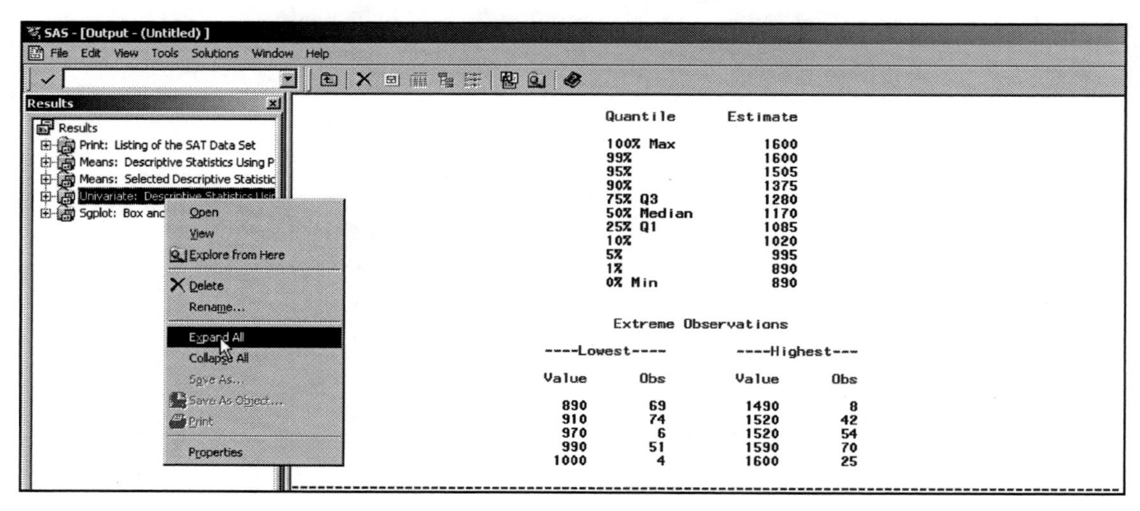


2. Double-click on the image icon to open the image in the user's default graphics software window.

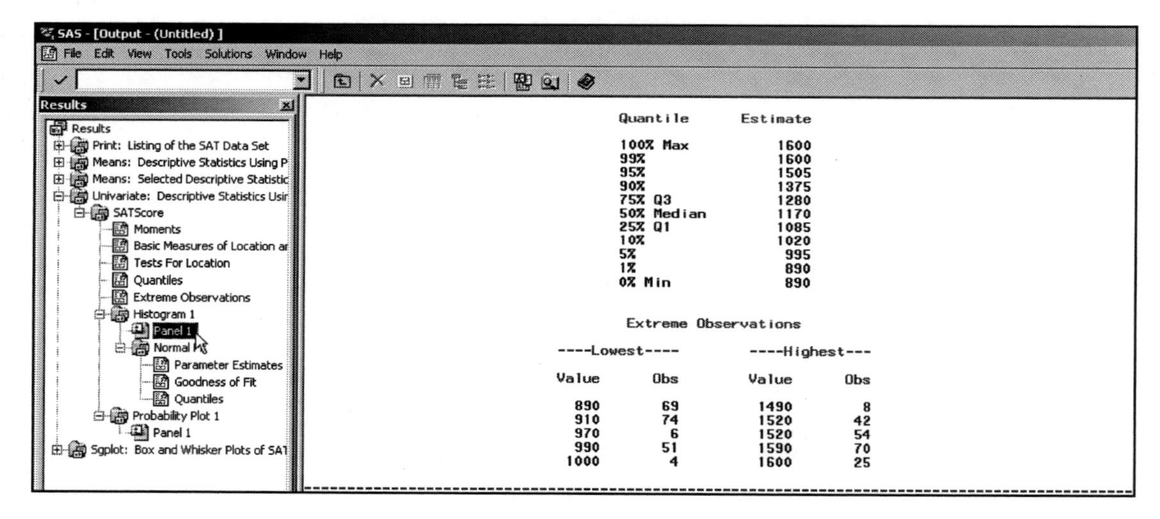

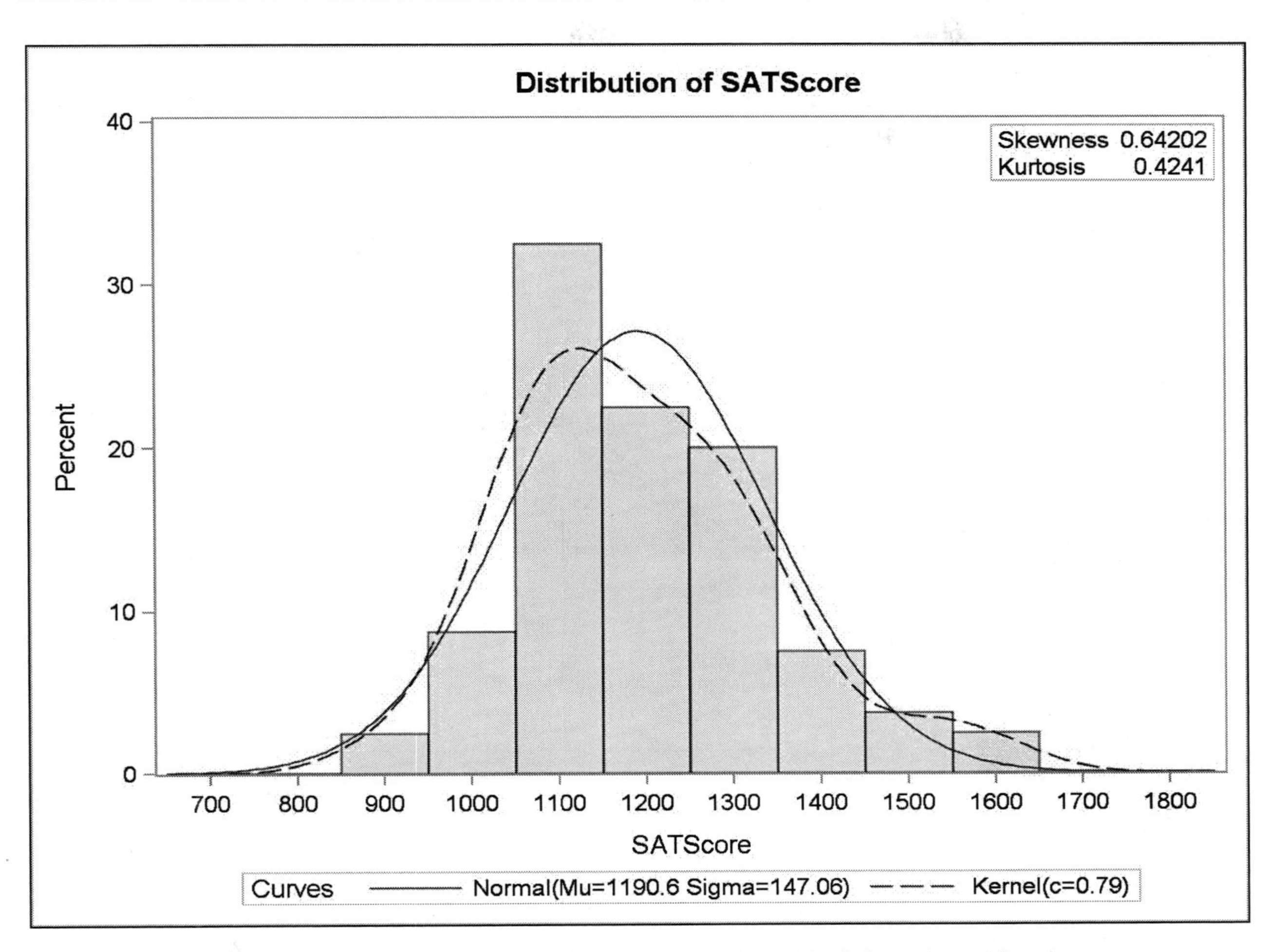


The bin identified with the midpoint of 1100 has approximately 33% of the values. The skewness and kurtosis values are reported in the inset. The kernel density curve is a smoothed version of the histogram and can be used to compare the approximate sample distribution to a normal distribution. In this case, the distribution of the observed data seems to approach normality.

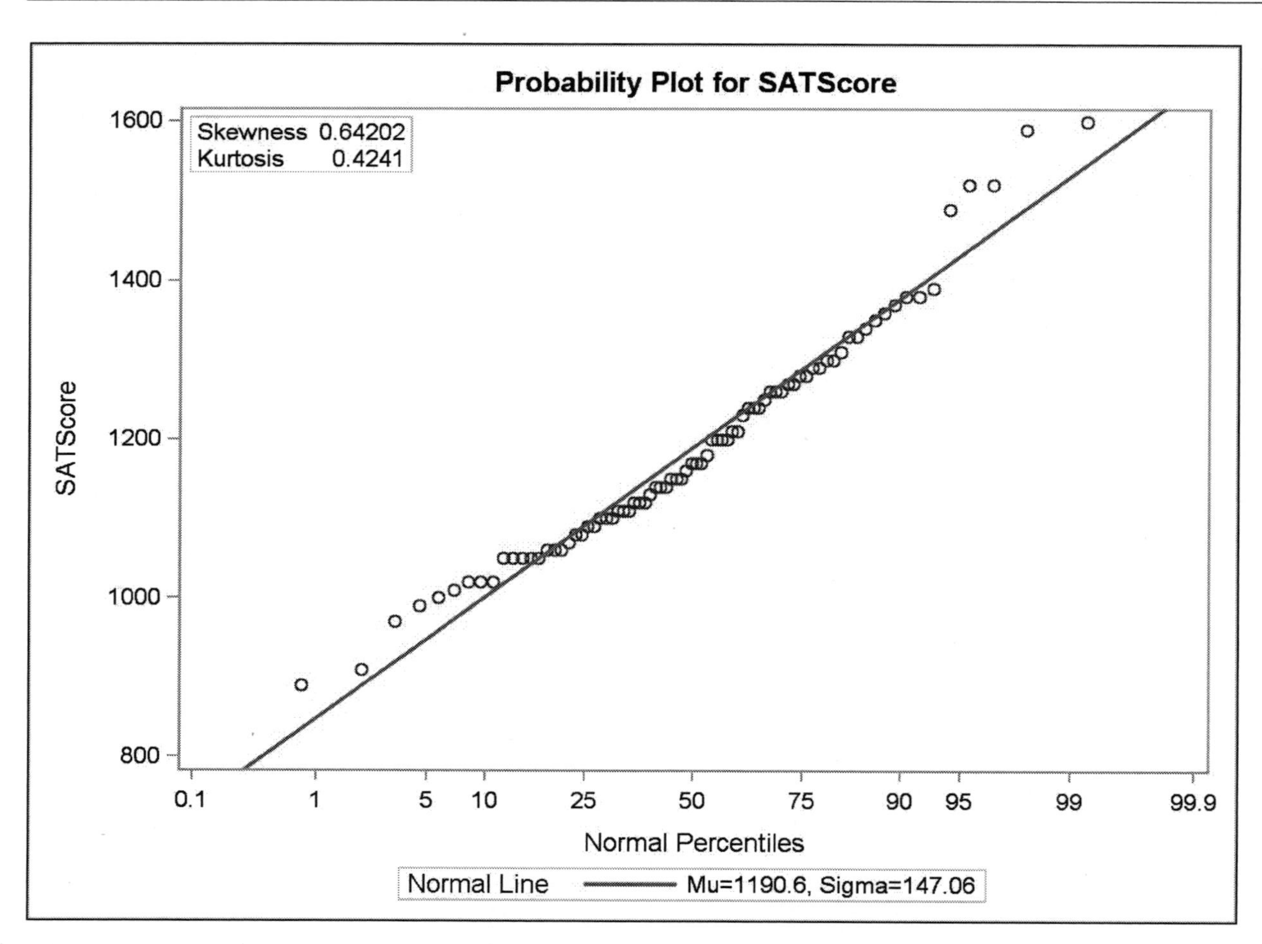


The normal probability plot is shown above. The 45-degree line represents where the data values would fall if they came from a normal distribution. The circles represent the observed data values. Because the circles follow the 45-degree line in the graph, you can conclude that there does not appear to be any severe departure from normality.

Asking for the normal reference curve for the histogram also produces a set of tables relating to assessing whether the distribution is normal or not. There is a table with three tests presented: Kolmogorov-Smirnov, Anderson-Darling, and Cramér-von Mises. In each case, the null hypothesis is that the distribution is normal. Therefore, high *p*-values are desirable.

| **Parameters for Normal Distribution** | | |
|---|---|---|
| **Parameter** | **Symbol** | **Estimate** |
| **Mean** | Mu | 1190.625 |
| **Std Dev** | Sigma | 147.0584 |

| **Goodness-of-Fit Tests for Normal Distribution** | | | | |
|---|---|---|---|---|
| **Test** | **Statistic** | | **p Value** | |
| **Kolmogorov-Smirnov** | **D** | 0.08382224 | **Pr > D** | >0.150 |
| **Cramer-von Mises** | **W-Sq** | 0.09964577 | **Pr > W-Sq** | 0.114 |
| **Anderson-Darling** | **A-Sq** | 0.70124822 | **Pr > A-Sq** | 0.068 |

| Quantiles for Normal Distribution | | |
|---|---|---|
| | Quantile | |
| Percent | Observed | Estimated |
| **1.0** | 890.000 | 848.516 |
| **5.0** | 995.000 | 948.735 |
| **10.0** | 1020.000 | 1002.162 |
| **25.0** | 1085.000 | 1091.436 |
| **50.0** | 1170.000 | 1190.625 |
| **75.0** | 1280.000 | 1289.814 |
| **90.0** | 1375.000 | 1379.088 |
| **95.0** | 1505.000 | 1432.515 |
| **99.0** | 1600.000 | 1532.734 |

All three tests have high *p*-values (greater than 0.05). This is known as the *alpha level* of the test and is explained in a later section. The high *p*-values imply that the distribution of **SATScore** is approximately normal.

```
/*st101d02.sas*/  /*Part B*/
proc sgplot data=sasuser.testscores;
   vbox SATScore / datalabel=IDNumber;
   format IDNumber 8.;
   refline 1200 / axis=y label;
   title "Box-and-Whisker Plots of SAT Scores";
run;
```

Selected PROC SGPLOT statements and options:

VBOX *response-variable* </ *option(s)*>;
creates a vertical box plot that shows the distribution of your data.

[VBOX Statement] DATALABEL= *option*
adds data labels for the outlier markers. If you specify a variable, then the values for that variable are used as data labels. If you do not specify a variable, then the values of the response variable are used.

REFLINE *variable* | *value*-1 <... *value-n*> </ *option(s)*>;
creates a horizontal or vertical reference line.

[REFLINE Statement] LABEL= *option*
creates labels for each reference line. If you do not specify a label for a line, the reference value for that line is used as the label.

A reference line is requested at 1200 on the Y axis. Because this is a vertical box plot, the Y-axis is the **SATScore** axis. A DATALABEL option is used to identify potential outliers. If there are no outliers, that option has no effect.

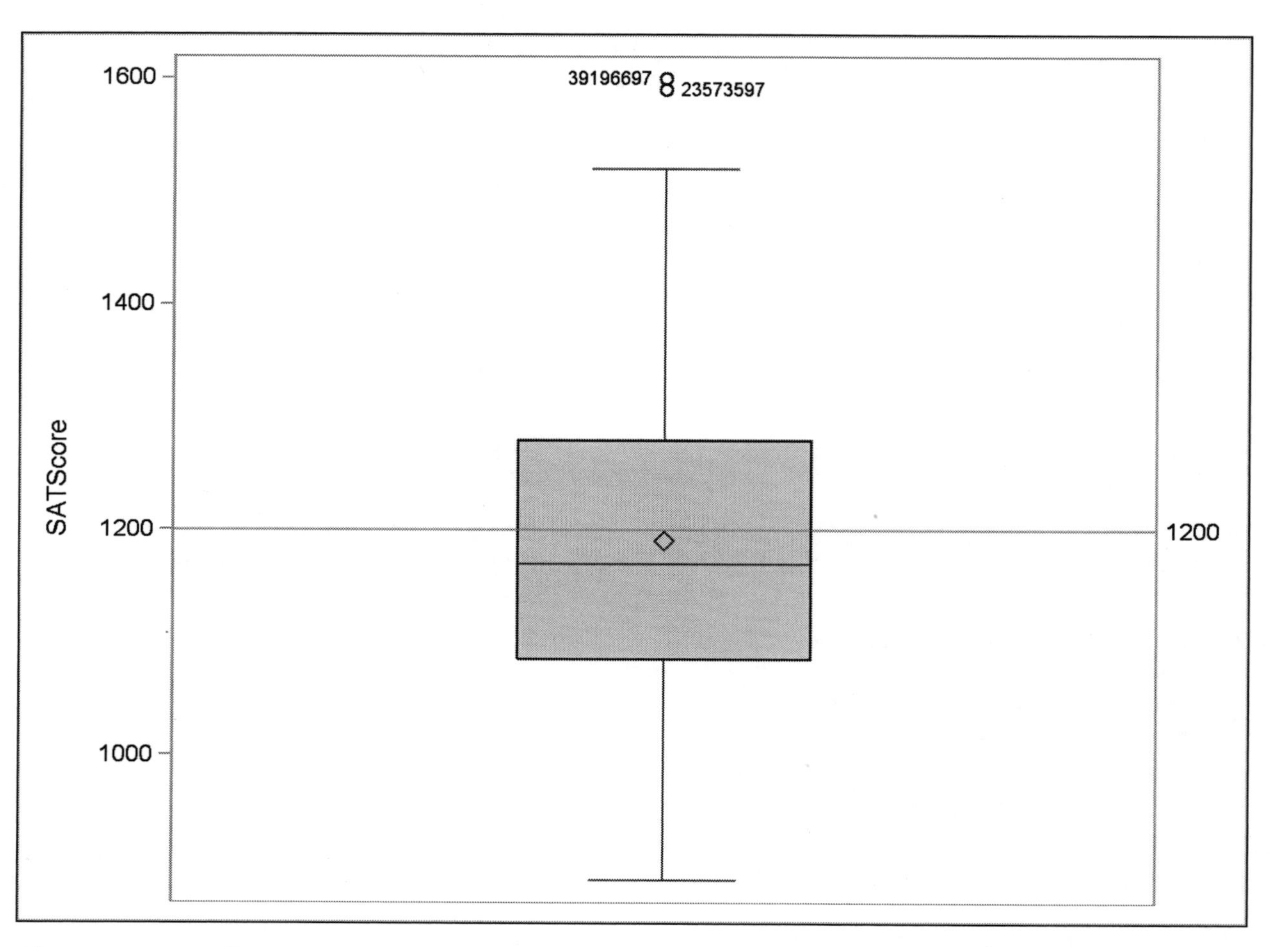


There are two outliers (values beyond 1.5 interquartile units from the box). The **IDnumber** values are displayed.

## Exercises

**2. Producing Descriptive Statistics**

Use the **sasuser.NormTemp** data set to answer the following:

**a.** What are the minimum, the maximum, the mean, and the standard deviation for **BodyTemp**? Does the variable appear to be normally distributed?

| | **BodyTemp** |
|---|---|
| **Minimum** | |
| **Maximum** | |
| **Mean** | |
| **Standard Deviation** | |
| **Skewness** | |
| **Kurtosis** | |
| **Distribution: Normal** | Yes/No |

**b.** Create box plots for **BodyTemp**. Use **ID** to identify outliers. Display a reference line at 98.6 degrees. Does the average body temperature seem to be 98.6 degrees?

## 1.02 Multiple Choice Poll

In the **NormTemp** data set, the distribution of **BodyTemp** seemed to be which of the following?

a. Close to normal
b. Left skewed
c. Right skewed
d. Having high positive kurtosis
e. Having high negative kurtosis

46

# 1.3 Confidence Intervals for the Mean

## Objectives

- Explain and interpret the confidence intervals for the mean.
- Explain the central limit theorem.
- Use PROC MEANS to calculate confidence intervals.

49

## Point Estimates

$\bar{X}$ estimates $\mu$

$S$ estimates $\sigma$

50

A *point estimate* is a sample statistic that is used to estimate a population parameter.

- An estimate of the average **SATScore** is 1190.6, and an estimate of the standard deviation is 147.06.
- Because you only have an estimate of the unknown population mean, you need to know the variability of your estimate.

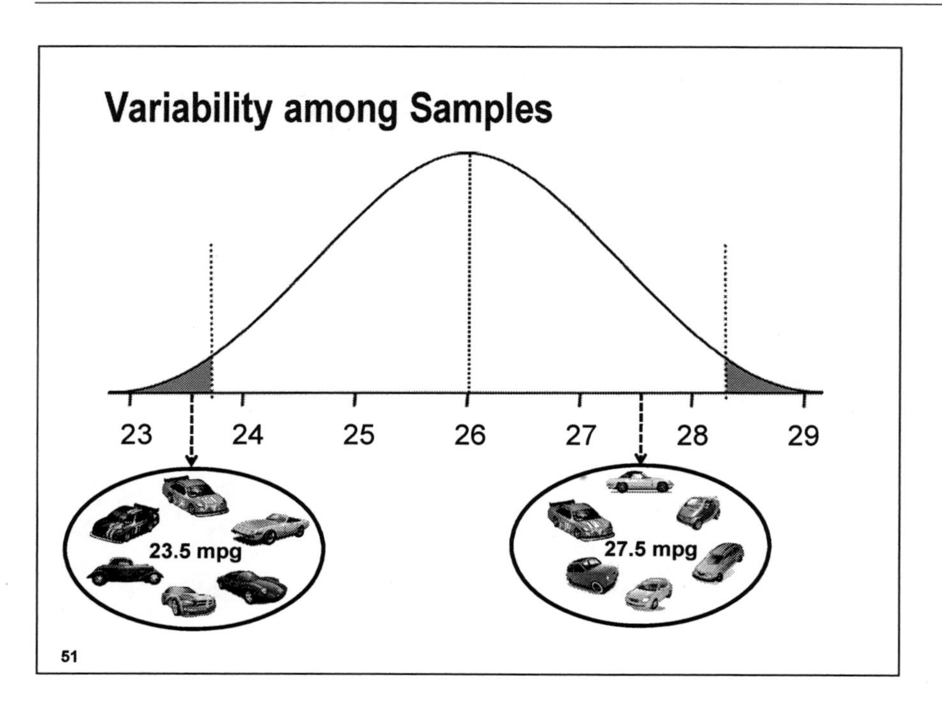


Why can you not be absolutely certain that the average SAT Math+Verbal score for students in Carver County magnet schools is 1190.6? The answer is because the sample mean is only an estimate of the population mean. If you collected another sample of students, you would likely obtain another estimate of the mean.

Different samples yield different estimates of the mean for the same population. Your mean can be thought of as a selection from a distribution of all possible means. Another sample would likely yield a different value from that distribution.

For example, you could take a random sample of size 6 of cars in your town and measure highway gas mileage. The sample that you choose today might have a mean of 23.5 miles per gallon. Tomorrow's sample from the same population might result in a mean of 27.5.

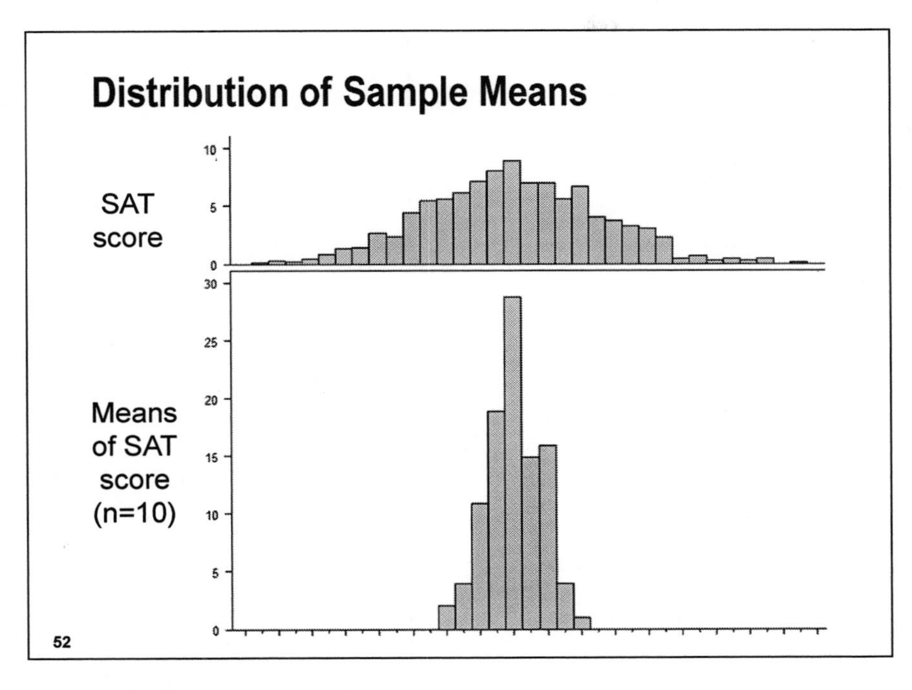


What is a distribution of sample means? It is a distribution of many mean values, each of a common sample size.

Suppose 1000 random samples, all with the same sample size of 10, are taken from an identified population.

- The top histogram shows the distribution of all 5000 ***observations***.
- The bottom histogram, however, represents the distribution of the 1000 ***sample means***.

The variability of the distribution of sample means is smaller than the variability of the distribution of the 5000 observations. That should make sense. It seems relatively likely to find one student with an SAT score of 1550 (out of a maximum of 1600), but not likely that a mean of a sample of 10 students would be 1550.

The samples in the 1000 are assumed to be taken with replacement, meaning that after 10 student values are taken, all 10 of those students can be chosen again in subsequent samples.

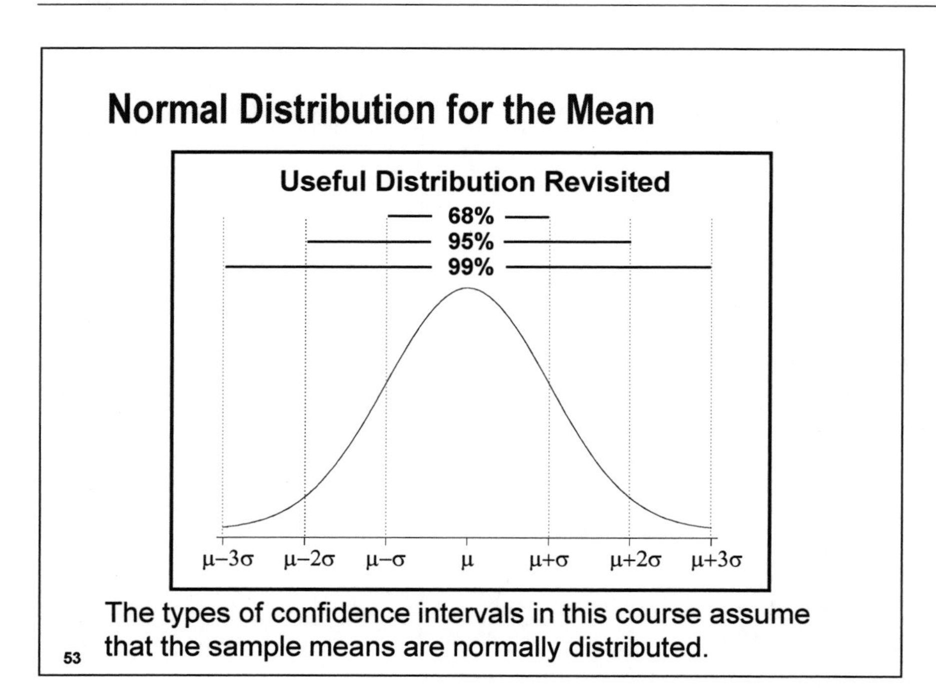


For purposes of finding confidence limits for parameters (such as a mean), you might make assumptions about a theoretical population distribution. You might, for example, assume normality of sample means.

## Standard Error of the Mean

A statistic that measures the variability of your estimate is the *standard error of the mean*.

It differs from the sample standard deviation because

- the sample standard deviation is a measure of the variability of data
- the standard error of the mean is a measure of the variability of sample means.
  - Standard error of the mean= $\frac{s}{\sqrt{n}} = s_{\bar{x}}$

54

The standard error of the mean is computed as follows:

$$s_{\bar{x}} = \frac{s}{\sqrt{n}}$$

where

$s$ is the sample standard deviation.

$n$ is the sample size.

The standard error of the mean for the variable **SATScore** is $147.058447/\sqrt{80}$, or approximately 16.44. This is a measure of how much variability of sample means there is around the population mean. The smaller the standard error, the more precise your sample estimate is.

You can improve the precision of an estimate by increasing the sample size.

## Confidence Intervals

**95% Confidence**

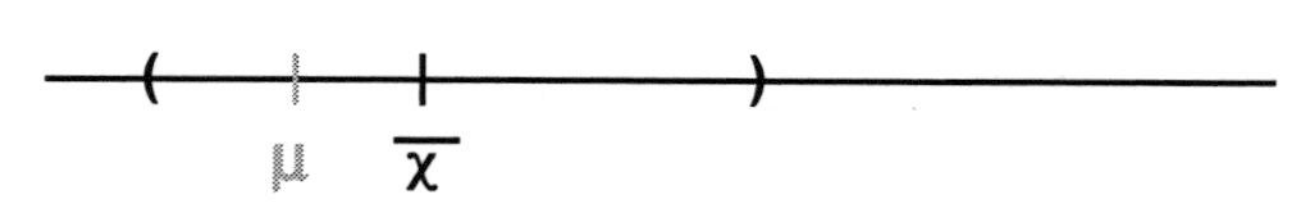


- A 95% confidence interval represents a range of values within which you are 95% certain that the true population mean exists.
  - One interpretation is that if 100 different samples were drawn from the same population and 100 intervals were calculated, approximately 95 of them would contain the population mean.

55

A *confidence interval*

- is a range of values that you believe to contain the population parameter of interest
- is defined by an upper and lower bound around a sample statistic.

To construct a confidence interval, a significance level must be chosen.

A 95% confidence interval is commonly used to assess the variability of the sample mean. In the test score example, you interpret a 95% confidence interval by stating that you are 95% confident that the interval contains the mean SAT test score for your population.

Do you want to be as confident as possible?

- Yes, but if you increase the confidence level, the width of your interval increases.
- As the width of the interval increases, it becomes less useful.

## Confidence Interval for the Mean

$$\bar{x} \pm t \cdot s_{\bar{x}} \quad \text{or} \quad (\bar{x} - t \cdot s_{\bar{x}},\ \bar{x} + t \cdot s_{\bar{x}})$$

where

$\bar{x}$ is the sample mean.

$t$ is the $t$ value corresponding to the confidence level and $n$-1 degrees of freedom, where $n$ is the sample size.

$s_{\bar{x}}$ is the standard error of the mean.

$$s_{\bar{x}} = \frac{s}{\sqrt{n}}$$

56

Student's $t$ distribution arises when you make inferences about a population mean and (as in nearly all practical statistical work) the population standard deviation (and therefore, standard error) is unknown and must be estimated from the data. It is approximately normal as the sample size grows larger. The $t$ in the equation above refers to the number of standard deviation (or standard error) units away from the mean required to get a desired confidence in a confidence interval. That value varies not only with the confidence that you choose, but also with the sample size. For 95% confidence, that $t$ value is usually approximately 2, because, as you have seen, two standard errors below to two standard errors above a mean gives you approximately 95% of the area under a normal distribution curve.

**Details**

In any normal distribution of sample means with parameters $\mu$ and $\sigma$, over samples of size $n$, the probability is 0.95 for the following:

$$-1.96\sigma_{\mu} \leq \bar{x} - \mu \leq 1.96\sigma_{\mu}$$

This is the basis-of-confidence intervals for the mean. If you rearrange the terms above the probability is 0.95 for as shown below:

$$\bar{x} - 1.96\sigma_{\mu} \leq \mu \leq \bar{x} + 1.96\sigma_{\mu}$$

When the value of $\sigma$ is unknown, one of the family of Student's $t$ distributions is used in place of 1.96 (a value that comes from the normal (z) distribution). The value of 1.96 is replaced by a $t$-value determined by the desired confidence and the degrees of freedom. When the sample size is larger, the $t$-value is closer to 1.96. Then also you must replace the known $\sigma_{\mu}$ with the estimated standard error, $s_{\bar{x}}$:

$$\bar{x} - t * s_{\bar{x}} \leq \mu \leq \bar{x} + t * s_{\bar{x}}$$

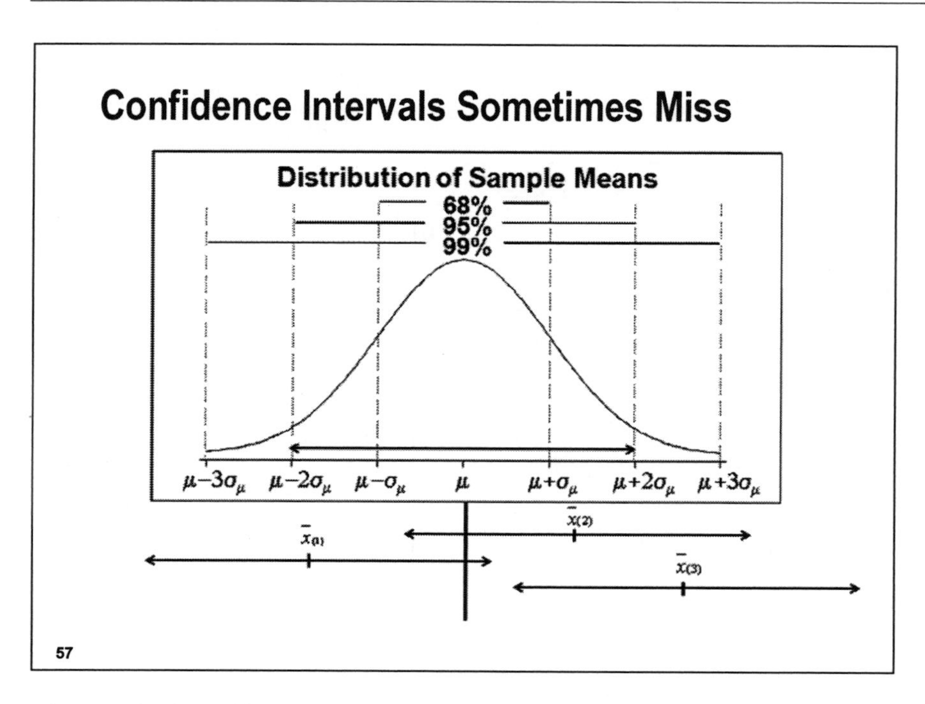


The graph above is the distribution of sample means. You typically take only one sample from that distribution, but in this picture you see that three researchers each took a sample from the same population. Each sample had a different mean. The standard errors are all approximately the same and approximately the same as the population standard error.

The double-headed arrows around each of the means (for researcher 1, 2, and 3) measure approximately two standard errors to each side of the sample mean. (The *t* value is approximately 2 for these researchers.) The sample means for researcher 1 and 2 fell within two standard errors from the (unknown) population mean, by good luck. Actually, 95% of all researchers should have equivalent "luck." Researcher number 3 was in the unlucky 5%. He did his work as well and rigorously and then blissfully reported his sample mean and confidence interval. Because his sample mean was more than two standard errors from the (unknown) population mean, his confidence interval did not extend far enough to include that true mean.

If the confidence interval is faithfully calculated using the formula shown earlier and assumptions are met, 95% of the time they include the true mean. Unfortunately, there is no way to know whether yours is in the 95% group or the 5% group.

The observed value of *t* (the number of standard errors your observed mean is away from a hypothesized mean) is related to a specific probability, known in statistics as a *p*-value.

## Normality and the Central Limit Theorem

To satisfy the assumption of normality, you can do one of the following:

- Verify that the population distribution is approximately normal.
- Apply the ***central limit theorem***.
  - The central limit theorem states that the distribution of sample means is approximately normal, regardless of the population distribution's shape, if the sample size is large enough.
  - "Large enough" is usually about 30 observations. It is more if the data are heavily skewed, and fewer if the data are symmetric.

58

To apply the central limit theorem, the standard rule of thumb with a relatively symmetric population is that your sample size should be at least 30. For skewed populations, the sample size should be greater. The central limit theorem applies even if you have no reason to believe that the population distribution is normal.

Because the sample size for the test scores example is 80 and the random sample implies that the population is relatively symmetric, you can apply the central limit theorem and satisfy the assumption of normality for the confidence intervals of the sample mean.

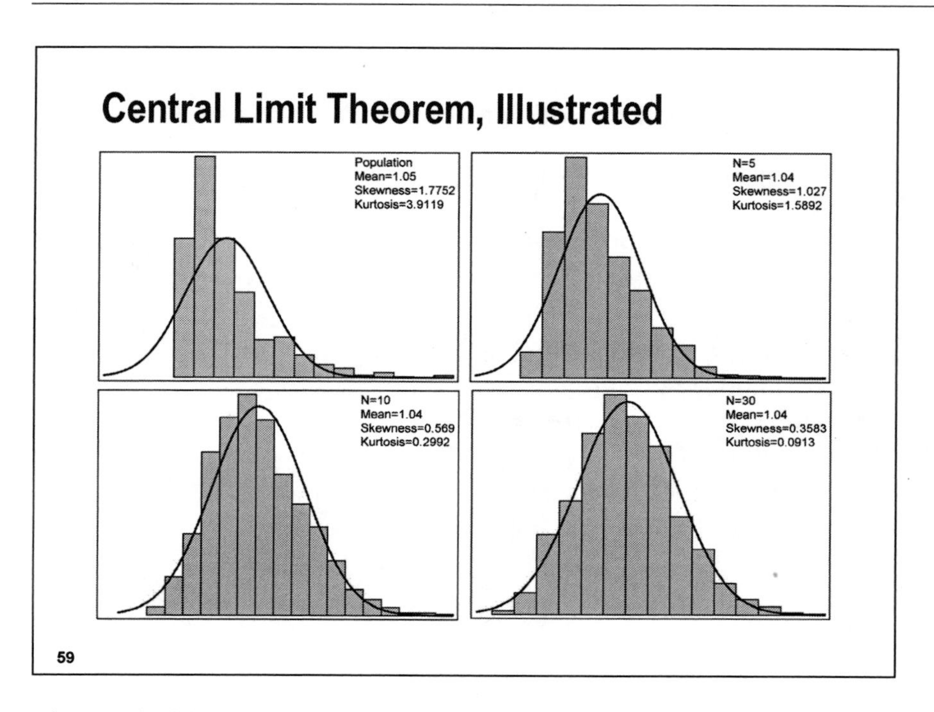


The graphs illustrate the tendency of a distribution of sample means to approach normality as the sample size increases.

The first chart is a histogram of data values drawn from an exponential distribution. The remaining charts are histograms of the sample means for samples of different sizes drawn from the same exponential distribution.

1. Data from an exponential distribution
2. 1000 samples of size 5
3. 1000 samples of size 10
4. 1000 samples of size 30

For the sample size of 30, the distribution is approximately bell-shaped and symmetric, even though the sample data are highly skewed. The number 30 is not a magic number, but a common rule of thumb.

## Confidence Intervals

Example: Use the MEANS procedure to generate a 95% confidence interval for the mean of **SATScore** in the **sasuser.testscores** data set.

```
/*st101d03.sas*/
proc means data=sasuser.testscores maxdec=2
           n mean std stderr clm;
   var SATScore;
   title '95% Confidence Interval for SAT';
run;
```

Selected PROC MEANS statement options:

CLM requests confidence limits for the mean.

STDERR requests the standard error of the mean.

The output is shown below.

| Analysis Variable : SATScore | | | | | |
|---|---|---|---|---|---|
| N | Mean | Std Dev | Std Error | Lower 95% CL for Mean | Upper 95% CL for Mean |
| 80 | 1190.63 | 147.06 | 16.44 | 1157.90 | 1223.35 |

In the test score example, you are 95% confident that the population mean is contained in the interval 1157.90 and 1223.35. Because the interval between the upper and lower limits is small from a practical point of view, you can conclude that the sample mean is a fairly precise estimate of the population mean.

How do you increase the precision of your estimate using the same confidence level? If you increase your sample size, you reduce the standard error of the sample mean and therefore reduce the width of your confidence interval. Thus, your estimate is more precise.

You can use the ALPHA= option in the PROC MEANS statement to construct confidence intervals with a different confidence level. Choose (1.00-Confidence/100) as your ALPHA level. By default, ALPHA=0.05 (1.00 – 95/100).

## Exercises

**3. Producing Confidence Intervals**

Generate the 95% confidence interval for the mean of **BodyTemp** in the **sasuser.NormTemp** data set.

**a.** Is the assumption of normality met to produce a confidence interval for this data?

**b.** What are the bounds of the confidence interval?

### 1.03 Multiple Answer Poll

The distribution of sample means is approximately normal if which of the following are true?

a. The population is normal.
b. The sample size is "large enough."
c. The sample standard deviation is small.

64

# 1.4 Hypothesis Testing

## Objectives

- Define some common terminology related to hypothesis testing.
- Perform hypothesis testing using the UNIVARIATE and TTEST procedures.

67

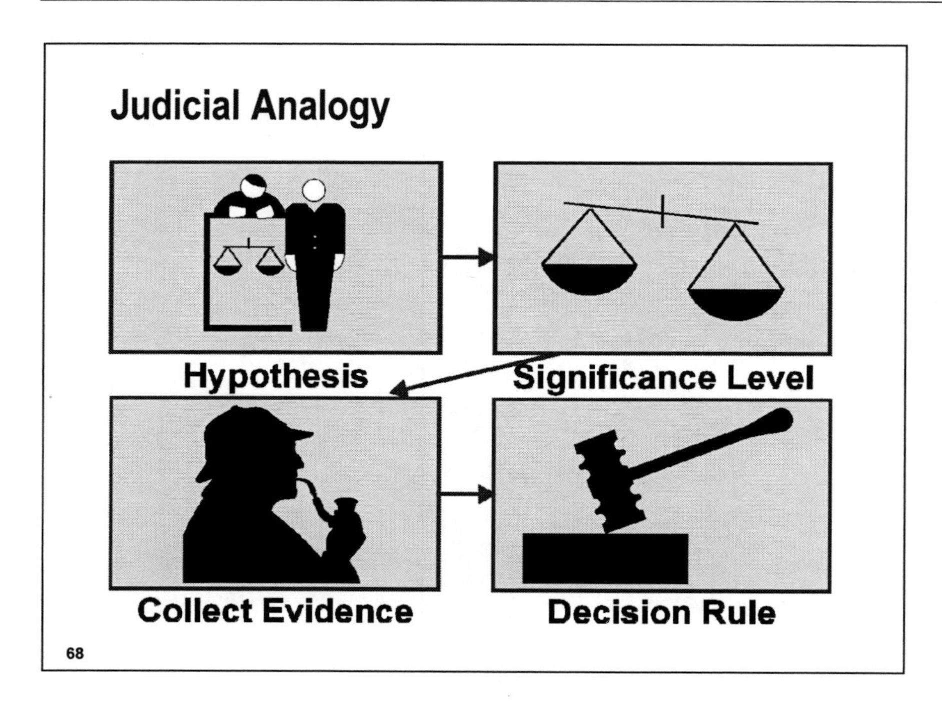


In a criminal court, you put defendants on trial because you suspect they are guilty of a crime. But how does the trial proceed?

First, the two sides need to be determined. In order to relate this to statistical hypothesis testing, name these two sides the null and alternative hypotheses. In criminal court, there exists a presumption of innocence and the defense attorney presents that side. This can be called the *null hypothesis* for a criminal court case. The *alternative hypothesis* is typically your initial research hypothesis (the defendant is guilty). The prosecuting attorney (or the statistical researcher) argues that the presumption of innocence is wrong. The alternative is the logical opposite of the null hypothesis. You generally start with the assumption that the null hypothesis is true, even if your research aims are to disprove the null.

Select a *significance level* as the amount of evidence needed to convict. In a criminal court, the evidence must prove guilt "beyond a reasonable doubt." In a civil court, the plaintiff must prove his or her case by the "preponderance of the evidence." In either case, the burden of proof is specified before the trial.

Collect evidence. More accurately, present the collected evidence to the judge and jury.

Use a *decision rule* to make a judgment. If the evidence contradicting the null hypothesis is

- sufficiently strong to meet the burden of proof (significance level), then reject the null hypothesis.
- not strong enough to meet the burden of proof, then fail to reject the null hypothesis. Be aware that failing to prove guilt does not mean that the defendant is ***proven*** innocent. It could mean that the prosecuting attorney did not build a strong enough case to meet the burden of proof.

Statistical hypothesis testing follows this same basic path.

## Coin Example

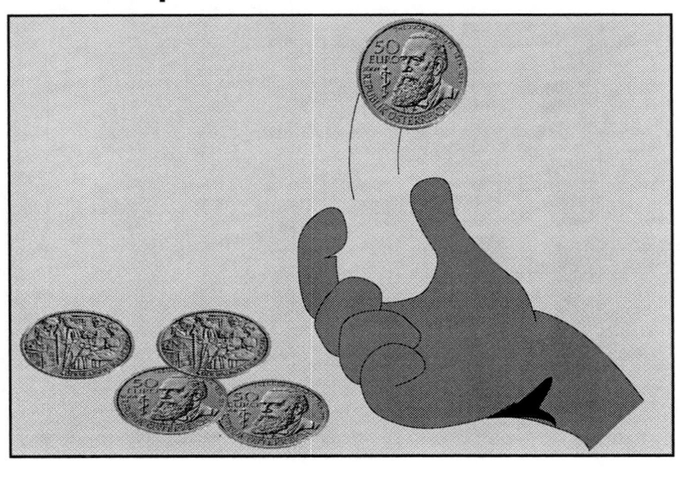

69

Suppose you want to know whether a coin is fair. You cannot flip it forever, so you decide to take a sample. Flip it five times and count the number of heads and tails.

## 1.04 Poll

If you have a fair coin and flip it 100 times, is it possible for it to land on heads 100 times?

- ❍ Yes
- ❍ No

71

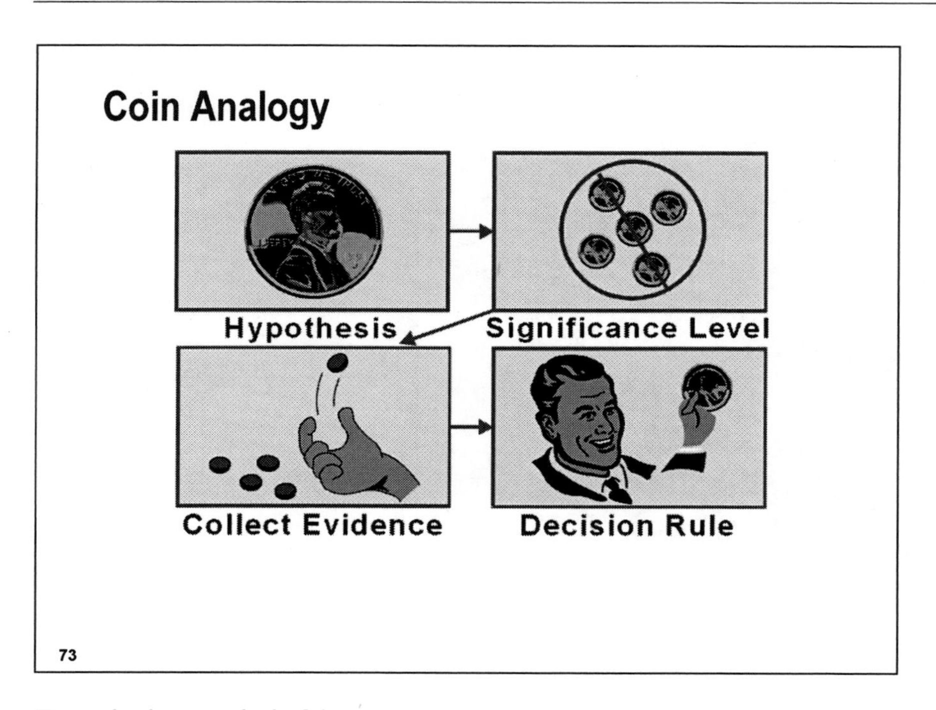


Test whether a coin is fair.

1. You suspect that the coin is ***not*** fair, but recall the legal example and begin by assuming that the coin is fair. In other words, you assume that the null hypothesis is true.
2. You select a significance level. If you observe five heads in a row or five tails in a row, you conclude that the coin is not fair. Otherwise, you decide that there is not enough evidence to show that the coin is not fair.
3. In order to collect evidence, you flip the coin five times and count the number of heads and tails.
4. You evaluate the data using your decision rule and make a decision that there is
   - enough evidence to reject the assumption that the coin is fair
   - not enough evidence to reject the assumption that the coin is fair.

## Types of Errors

You used a decision rule to make a decision, but was the decision correct?

| DECISION \ ACTUAL | $H_0$ Is True | $H_0$ Is False |
|---|---|---|
| Fail to Reject Null | Correct | Type II Error |
| Reject Null | Type I Error | Correct |

74

Recall that you start by assuming that the coin is fair.

The probability of a Type I error, often denoted α, is the probability that you reject the null hypothesis when it is true. It is also called the *significance level* of a test.

- In the legal example, it is the probability that you conclude that the person is guilty when he or she is innocent.
- In the coin example, it is the probability that you conclude that the coin is not fair when it is fair.

The probability of a Type II error, often denoted β, is the probability that you fail to reject the null hypothesis when it is false.

- In the legal example, it is the probability that you fail to find the person guilty when he or she is guilty.
- In the coin example, it is the probability that you fail to find that the coin is not fair when it is not fair.

The *power* of a statistical test is equal to 1–β, where β is the Type II error rate. This is the probability that you correctly reject the null hypothesis, given some assumed values of the true population mean and standard deviation in the population and the sample size.

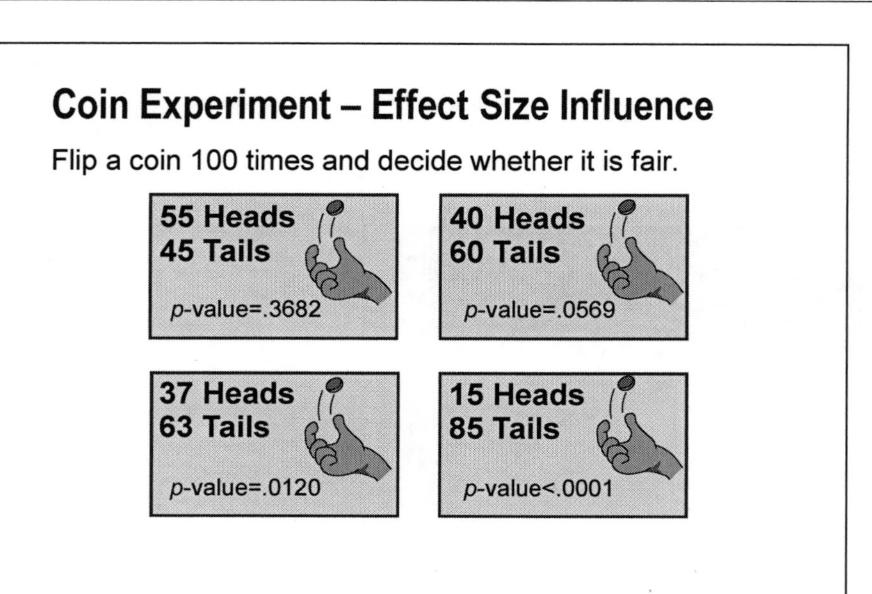


The *effect size* refers to the magnitude of the difference in sampled population from the null hypothesis. In this example, the null hypothesis of a fair coin suggests 50% heads and 50% tails. If the true coin flipped were actually weighted to give 55% heads, the effect size would be 5%.

If you flip a coin 100 times and count the number of heads, you do not doubt that the coin is fair if you observe exactly 50 heads. However, you might be

- somewhat skeptical that the coin is fair if you observe 40 or 60 heads
- even more skeptical that the coin is fair if you observe 37 or 63 heads
- highly skeptical that the coin is fair if you observe 15 or 85 heads.

In this situation, as the difference between the number of heads and tails increases, you have more evidence that the coin is not fair.

A *p-value* measures the probability of observing a value as extreme or more extreme than the one observed, simply by chance, given that the null hypothesis is true. For example, if your null hypothesis is that the coin is fair and you observe 40 heads (60 tails), the *p*-value is the probability of observing a difference in the number of heads and tails of 20 or more from a fair coin tossed 100 times.

A large *p*-value means that you would often see a test statistic value this large in experiments with a fair coin. A small *p*-value means that you would rarely see differences this large from a fair coin. In the latter situation, you have evidence that the coin is not fair, because if the null hypothesis were true, a random sample selected from it would not likely have the observed statistic values.

Flip a coin and get 40% heads and decide whether it is fair.

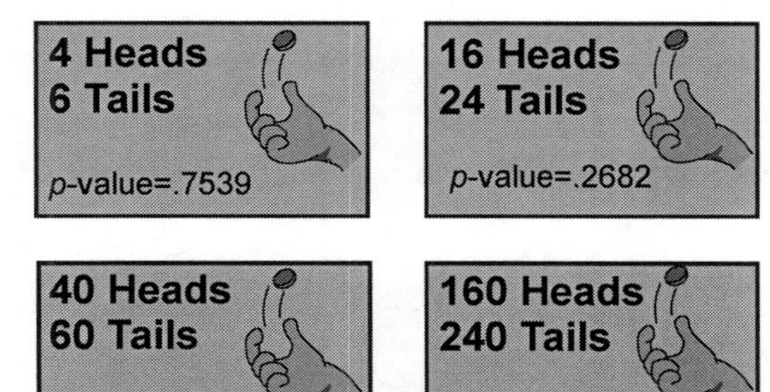


76

A *p*-value is not only affected by the effect size. It is also affected by the sample size (number of coin flips, *k*).

For a fair coin, you would expect 50% of *k* flips to be heads. In this example, in each case, the observed proportion of heads from *k* flips was 0.4. This value is different from the 0.5 you would expect under $H_0$. The evidence is stronger, when the number of trials (*k*) on which the proportion is based increases. As you saw in the section about confidence intervals, the variability around a mean estimate is smaller, when the sample size is larger. For larger sample sizes, you can measure means more precisely. Therefore, 40% of the heads out of 400 flips would make you more certain that this was not a chance difference from 50% than would 40% out of 10 flips. The smaller *p*-values reflect this confidence. The *p*-value here assesses the probability that this difference from 50% occurred purely by chance.

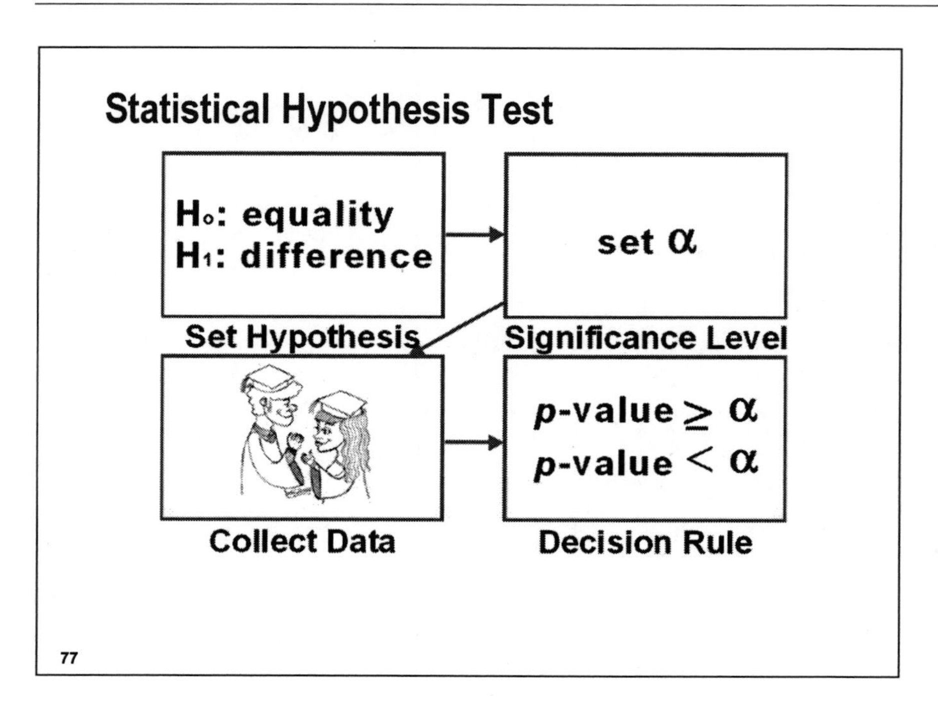


In statistics, the following rules apply:

1. The null hypothesis, denoted $H_0$, is your initial assumption and is usually one of equality or no relationship. For the test score example, $H_0$ is that the mean combined Math and Verbal SAT score is 1200. The alternative hypothesis, $H_1$, is the logical opposite of the null, namely that the combined Math and Verbal SAT score is ***not*** 1200.
2. The significance level is usually denoted by $\alpha$, the Type I error rate.
3. The strength of the evidence is measured by a $p$-value.
4. The decision rule is
   - fail to reject the null hypothesis if the $p$-value is greater than or equal to $\alpha$
   - reject the null hypothesis if the $p$-value is less than $\alpha$.

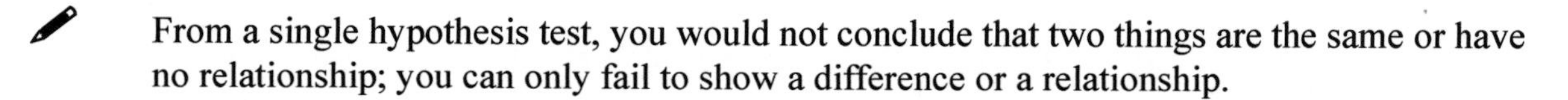

From a single hypothesis test, you would not conclude that two things are the same or have no relationship; you can only fail to show a difference or a relationship.

## Comparing $\alpha$ and the *p*-Value

In general, you do one of the following:

- reject the null hypothesis if *p*-value$<\alpha$
- fail to reject the null hypothesis if *p*-value$\geq\alpha$.

78

It is important to clarify the following:

- The value of $\alpha$, the probability of Type I error, is specified by the experimenter before collecting data.
- The *p*-value is calculated from the collected data.

In most statistical hypothesis tests, you compare $\alpha$ and the associated *p*-value to make a decision.

Remember that $\alpha$ is set before data collection based on the circumstances of the experiment. The level of $\alpha$ is chosen based on the cost of making a Type I error. It is also a function of your knowledge of the data and theoretical considerations.

For the test score example, $\alpha$ was set to 0.05, based on the consequences of making a Type I error (the error of concluding that the mean SAT combined score is not 1200 when it really is 1200). If making a Type I error is especially egregious, you might consider choosing a lower significance level when planning your analysis.

## 1.05 Multiple Choice Poll

Which of the following affects alpha?

a. The *p*-value of the test
b. The sample size
c. The number of Type I errors
d. All of the above
e. Answers a and b only
f. None of the above

80

## Performing a Hypothesis Test

To test the null hypothesis $H_0$: $\mu=\mu_0$, SAS software calculates the *Student's t* statistic value:

$$t = \frac{(\overline{x} - \mu_0)}{s_{\overline{x}}}$$

For the test score example:

$$t=\frac{(1190.625-1200)}{16.4416}=-0.5702$$

The null hypothesis is rejected when the calculated value is more extreme (either positive or negative) than would be expected by chance if $H_0$ were true.

82

For the test score example, $\mu_0$ is the hypothesized value of 1200, $\overline{x}$ is the sample mean SAT score of students selected from the school district, and $s_{\overline{x}}$ is the standard error of the mean.

- This statistic measures how far $\overline{x}$ is from the hypothesized mean.
- To reject a test with this statistic, the *t* statistic should be much higher or lower than 0 and have a small corresponding *p*-value.
- The results of this test are valid if the distribution of sample means is normally distributed.

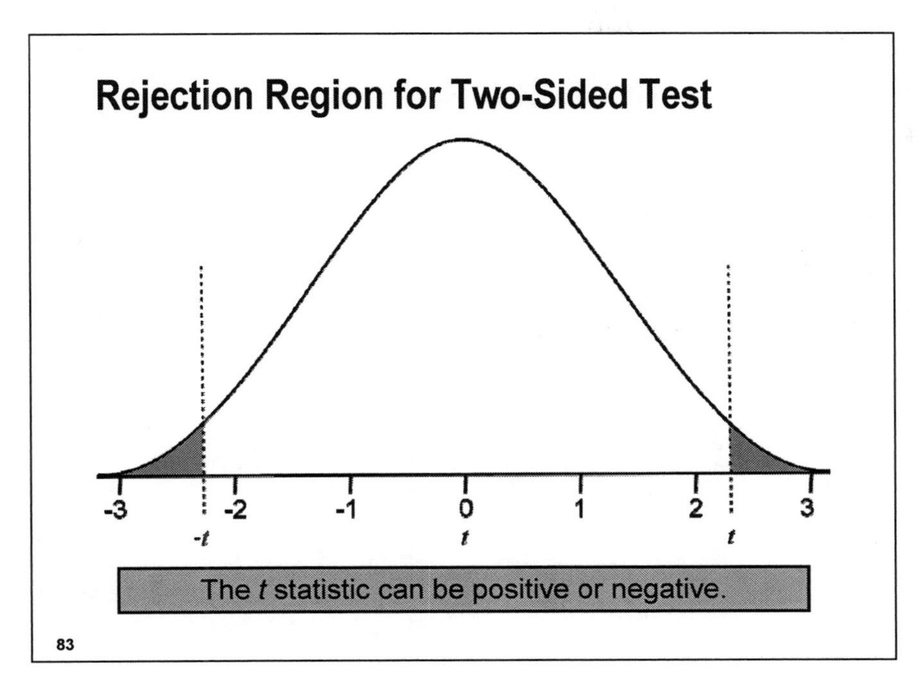


For a two-sided test of a hypothesis, the rejection region is contained in both tails of the *t* distribution. If the *t* statistic falls in the rejection region (in the shaded region in the graph above), then you reject the null hypothesis. Otherwise, you fail to reject the null hypothesis.

The area in each of the tails corresponds to $\alpha/2$ or 2.5%. The sum of the areas under the tails is 5%, which is alpha.

The alpha and *t*-distribution mentioned here are the same as those in the section about confidence intervals. In fact, there is a direct relationship. The rejection region based on $\alpha$ begins at the point where the $(1.00-\alpha)\%$ confidence interval no longer includes the true value of $\mu_0$.

## The TTEST Procedure

General form of the TTEST procedure:

```
PROC TTEST DATA=SAS-data-set;
      CLASS variable;
      PAIRED variables;
      VAR variables;
RUN;
```

84

The TTEST procedure performs *t* tests and computes confidence limits for one sample, paired observations, two independent samples, and the AB/BA crossover design. With ODS Statistical Graphics, PROC TTEST can also be used to produce histograms, Quantile-Quantile plots, box plots, and confidence limit plots.

Selected TTEST procedure statements:

| | |
|---|---|
| CLASS | specifies the two-level variable for the analysis. Only one variable is allowed in the CLASS statement. If no CLASS statement is included, a one-sample *t* test is performed. |
| PAIRED *PairLists*; | specifies the *PairLists* to identify the variables to be compared in paired comparisons. You can use one or more PairLists. |
| VAR | specifies *numeric* response variables for the analysis. If the VAR statement is not specified, PROC TTEST analyzes all numeric variables in the input data set that are not listed in a CLASS (or BY) statement. |

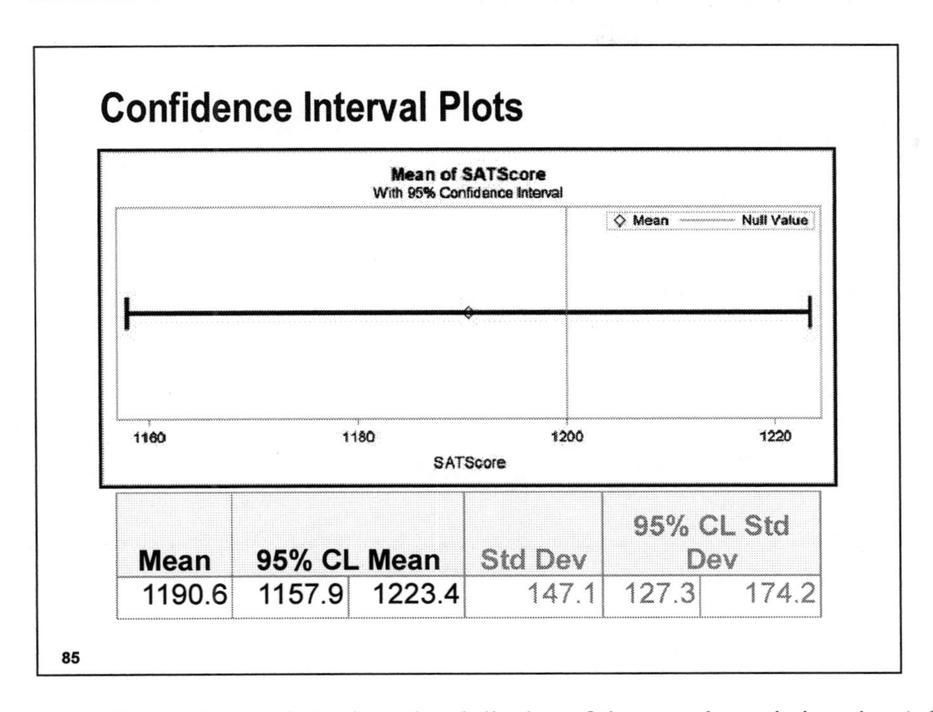


| Mean | 95% CL Mean | | Std Dev | 95% CL Std Dev | |
|---|---|---|---|---|---|
| 1190.6 | 1157.9 | 1223.4 | 147.1 | 127.3 | 174.2 |

A *confidence interval plot* is a visual display of the sample statistic value (of the mean, in this case) and the confidence interval calculated from the data. If there is a null hypothesized value for the parameter, it can be drawn on the plot as a reference line. In this way, the statistical significance of a test can be visually assessed. If the (1.00-$\alpha$)% confidence interval does not include the null hypothesis value, then that implies that the null hypothesis can be rejected at the $\alpha$ significance level. If the confidence interval includes the null hypothesis value, then that implies that the null hypothesis cannot be rejected at that significance level.

## Hypothesis Testing

Example: Use the MU0= option in the UNIVARIATE procedure to test the hypothesis that the mean of SAT Math+Verbal score is equal to 1200.

```
/*st101d04.sas*/  /*Part A*/
ods graphics off;
proc univariate data=sasuser.testscores mu0=1200;
   var SATScore;
   title 'Testing Whether the Mean of SAT Scores = 1200';
run;
ods graphics on;
```

Selected PROC UNIVARIATE statement option:

MU0= specifies the value of the mean or location parameter in the null hypothesis for tests of location.

Partial PROC UNIVARIATE Output

| Tests for Location: Mu0=1200 | | | | |
|---|---|---|---|---|
| **Test** | **Statistic** | | **p Value** | |
| **Student's t** | **t** | -0.5702 | **Pr > \|t\|** | 0.5702 |
| **Sign** | **M** | -5 | **Pr >= \|M\|** | 0.3019 |
| **Signed Rank** | **S** | -207 | **Pr >= \|S\|** | 0.2866 |

The *t* statistic and *p*-value are labeled Student's t and Pr > |t|, respectively.

- The *t* statistic value is -0.5702 and the *p*-value is .5702.
- Therefore, you cannot reject the null hypothesis at the 0.05 level. Thus, even though the mean of the student scores in this sample (1190.625) is slightly lower than the magnet school goal of 1200, there is not enough evidence to reject the hypothesis that the population mean of all magnet school students in the district is equal to 1200.

The Sign and Signed Rank tests are known as *nonparametric tests for location.* If the normality assumption cannot be met, then these tests can be used to test slightly modified tests about the central location of the population.

Use the H0= option in the TTEST procedure to test the hypothesis that the mean of the SAT Math+Verbal score is equal to 1200.

```
/*st101d04.sas*/  /*Part B*/
proc ttest data=sasuser.testscores h0=1200
           plots(shownull)=interval;
   var SATScore;
   title 'Testing Whether the Mean of SAT Scores = 1200 '
         'Using PROC TTEST';
run;
```

Selected PROC TTEST statement options:

| | |
|---|---|
| H0= | specifies the value of the mean or location parameter in the null hypothesis for tests of location (H0=0 by default). |
| PLOTS(SHOWNULL)=INTERVAL | includes a plot of confidence intervals of the mean. SHOWNULL places a vertical reference line at the mean value of the null hypothesis. |

PROC TTEST Output

| N | Mean | Std Dev | Std Err | Minimum | Maximum |
|---|---|---|---|---|---|
| 80 | 1190.6 | 147.1 | 16.4416 | 890.0 | 1600.0 |

Summary statistics are reported. These are the same values that were obtained using both PROC MEANS and PROC UNIVARIATE.

| Mean | 95% CL Mean | | Std Dev | 95% CL Std Dev | |
|---|---|---|---|---|---|
| 1190.6 | 1157.9 | 1223.4 | 147.1 | 127.3 | 174.2 |

The confidence interval around the sample mean and sample standard deviation are reported. Notice that the 95% confidence interval around the mean includes the null hypothesis value of 1200. This implies a lack of statistical significance at the $\alpha=0.05$ significance level.

| DF | t Value | Pr > \|t\| |
|---|---|---|
| 79 | -0.57 | 0.5702 |

The *p*-value is 0.5702, which is the same as was calculated using PROC UNIVARIATE. As the confidence interval information suggested, this value is not statistically significant at the $\alpha=0.05$ significance level.

Two default plots are produced along with the confidence interval plot that was requested in the code.

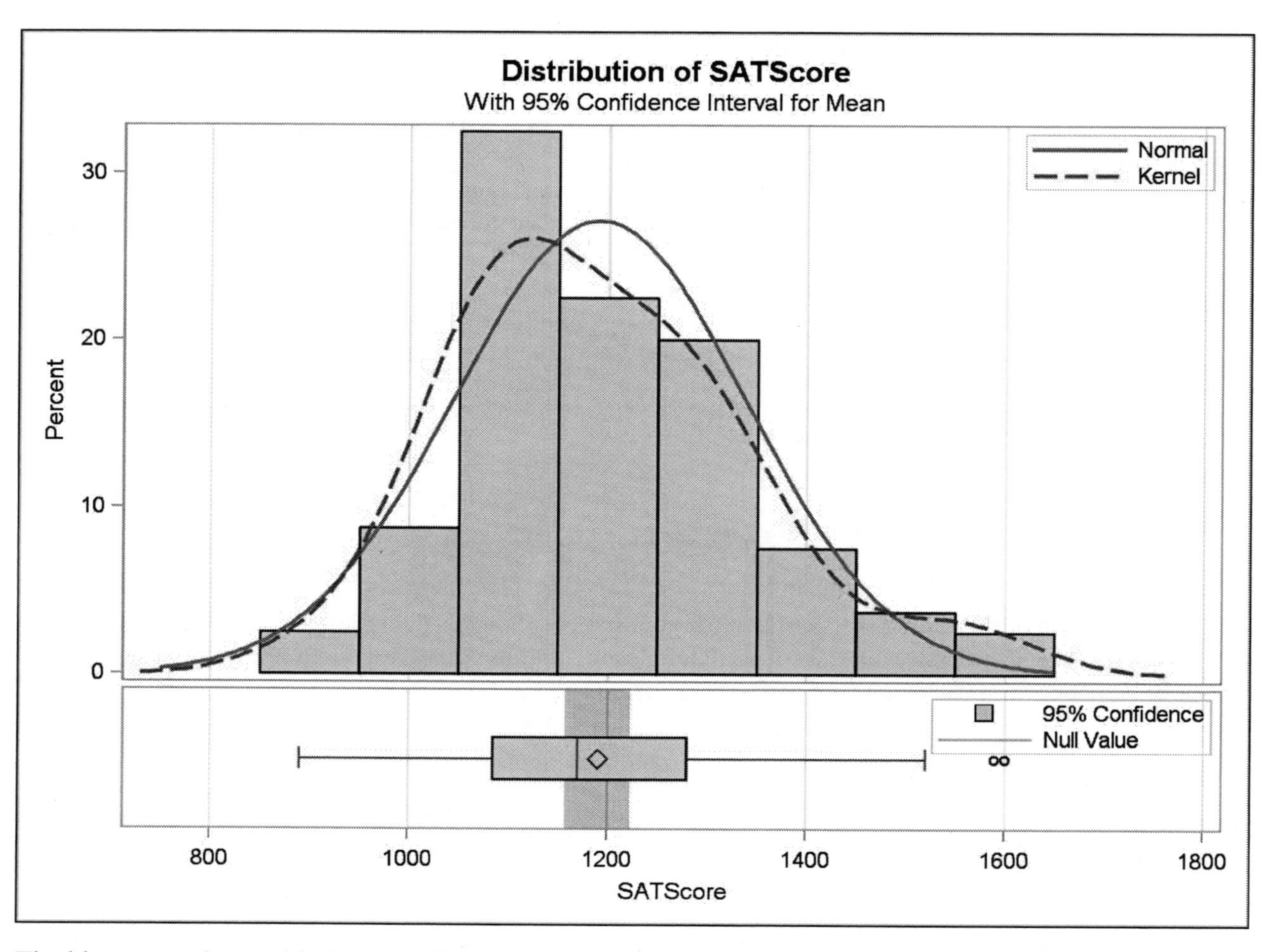


The histogram along with the normal and kernel density curves are produced on one plot, along with a horizontal box plot with a shaded confidence interval for the mean included.

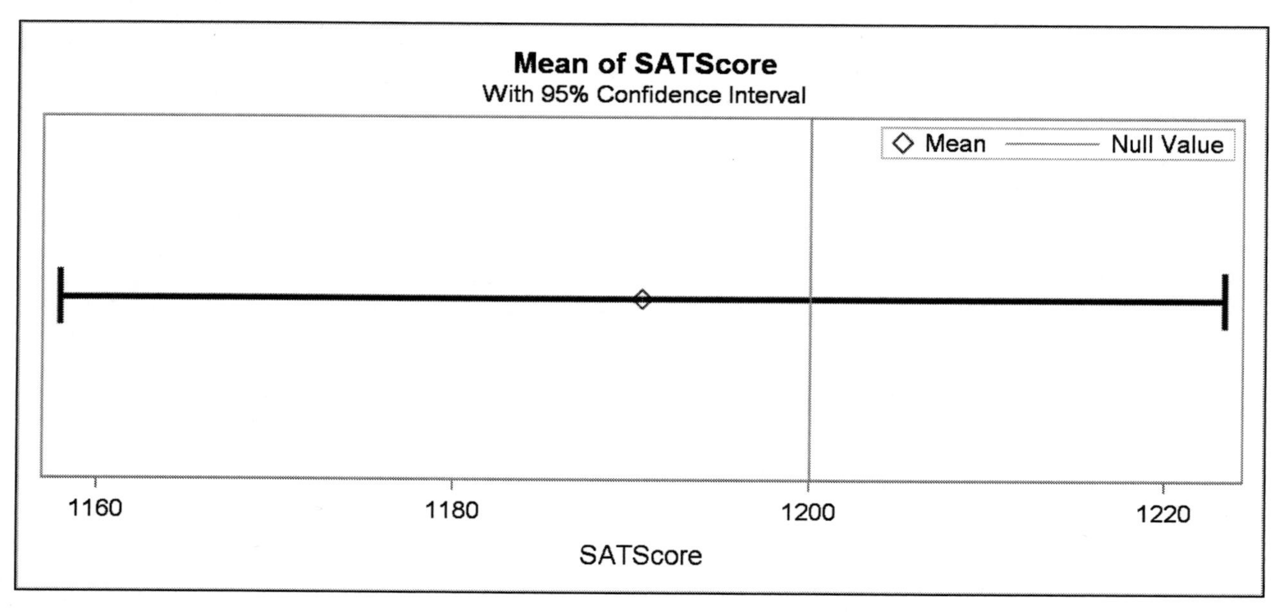


The confidence interval plot gives a visual display of the confidence interval table from above.

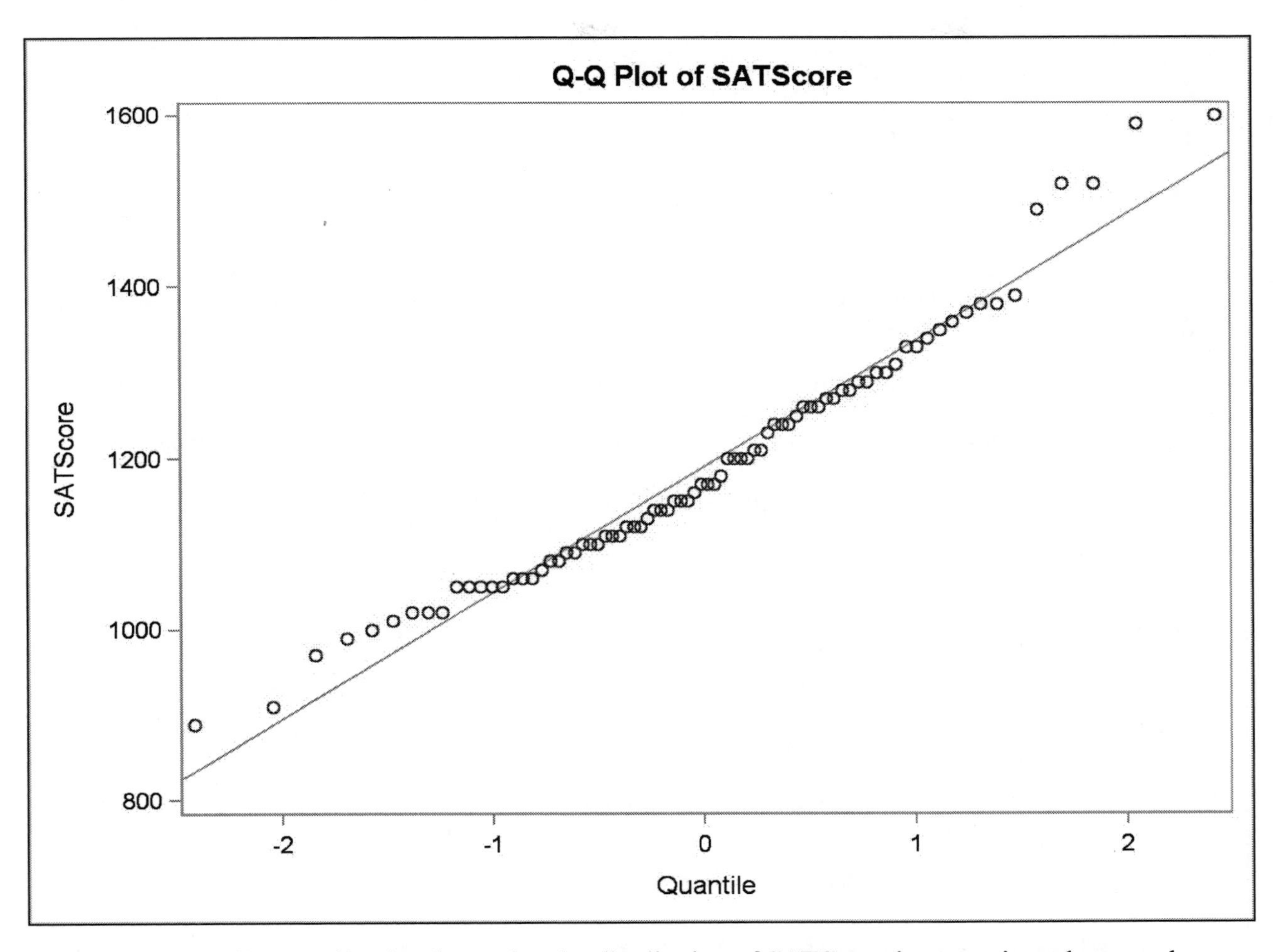


The normal quantile-quantile plot shows that the distribution of **SATScore** is approximately normal in this sample.

## Exercises

**4. Performing a One-Sample *t* Test**

Perform a one-sample *t* test to determine whether the mean of body temperatures (the variable **BodyTemp** in **sasuser.NormTemp**) is truly 98.6.

**a.** What is the value of the *t* statistic and the corresponding *p*-value?

**b.** Produce a confidence interval plot of **BodyTemp** with the value 98.6 used as a reference.

**c.** Do you reject or fail to reject the null hypothesis at the 0.05 level that the average temperature is 98.6 degrees?

### 1.06 Multiple Choice Poll

A 95% confidence interval for SAT scores is (1157.90, 1223.35). From this, what can you conclude, at alpha=0.05?

a. The true average SAT score is significantly different from 1200.
b. The true average SAT score is not significantly different from 1200.
c. The true average SAT score is less than 1200.
d. None of the above – You cannot determine statistical significance from confidence intervals.

90

# 1.5 Solutions

## Solutions to Exercises

1. **Calculating Basic Statistics in PROC MEANS**

```
/*st101s01.sas*/  /*Parts a and b*/
proc means data=sasuser.NormTemp
           maxdec=2
           n mean std q1 q3 qrange;
   var BodyTemp;
   title 'Selected Descriptive Statistics for Body Temp';
run;
```

PROC MEANS Output

| Analysis Variable : BodyTemp | | | | | |
|---|---|---|---|---|---|
| N | Mean | Std Dev | Lower Quartile | Upper Quartile | Quartile Range |
| 130 | 98.25 | 0.73 | 97.80 | 98.70 | 0.90 |

**a.** What is the overall mean and standard deviation of body temperature in the sample?

**The overall mean is 98.25.**

**b.** What is the interquartile range of body temperature?

**The interquartile range is 0.90 (98.70 – 97.80).**

**c.** Do the mean values seem to differ between men and women?

```
/*st101s01.sas*/  /*Part c*/
proc means data=sasuser.NormTemp
           maxdec=2
           n mean std q1 q3 qrange;
   var BodyTemp;
   class Gender;
   title 'Selected Descriptive Statistics for Body Temp';
run;
```

| Analysis Variable : BodyTemp | | | | | | | |
|---|---|---|---|---|---|---|---|
| Gender | N Obs | N | Mean | Std Dev | Lower Quartile | Upper Quartile | Quartile Range |
| Female | 65 | 65 | 98.39 | 0.74 | 98.00 | 98.80 | 0.80 |
| Male | 65 | 65 | 98.10 | 0.70 | 97.60 | 98.60 | 1.00 |

**The values differ somewhat.**

## 2. Producing Descriptive Statistics

Use the **sasuser.NormTemp** data set to answer the following:

**a.** What are the minimum, the maximum, the mean, and the standard deviation for **BodyTemp**? Does the variable appear to be normally distributed?

```
/*st101s02.sas*/  /*Part a*/
proc univariate data=sasuser.NormTemp noprint;
   var BodyTemp;
   histogram BodyTemp / normal(mu=est sigma=est noprint) kernel;
   inset min max skewness kurtosis / position=ne;
   probplot BodyTemp / normal(mu=est sigma=est);
   inset min max skewness kurtosis;
   title 'Descriptive Statistics Using PROC UNIVARIATE';
run;
```

The NOPRINT option in both the PROC UNIVARIATE and HISTOGRAM statements suppresses the printing of the tabular output. Because the statistics are being reported in the insets of the plots, they are not needed in the output tables.

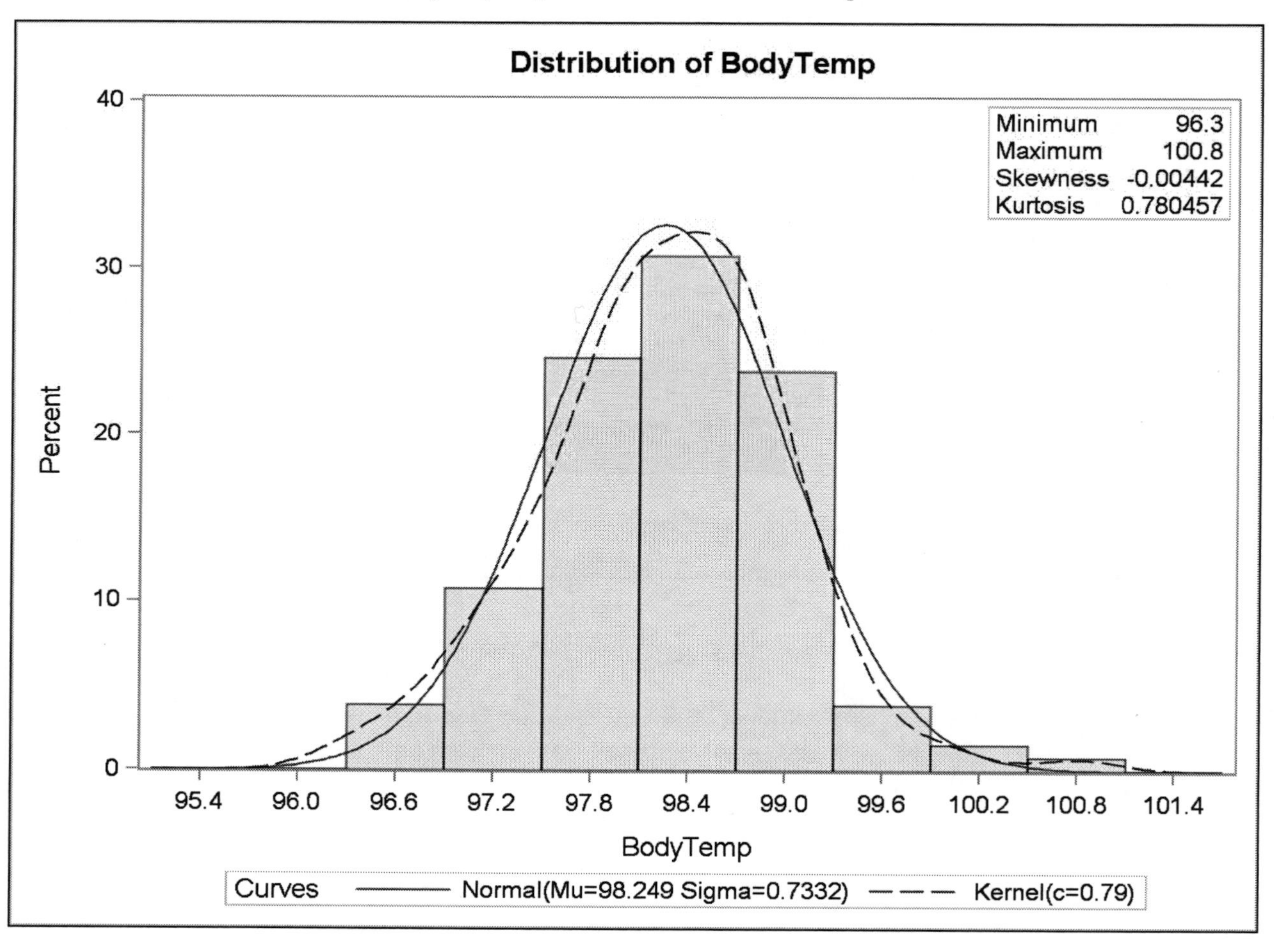

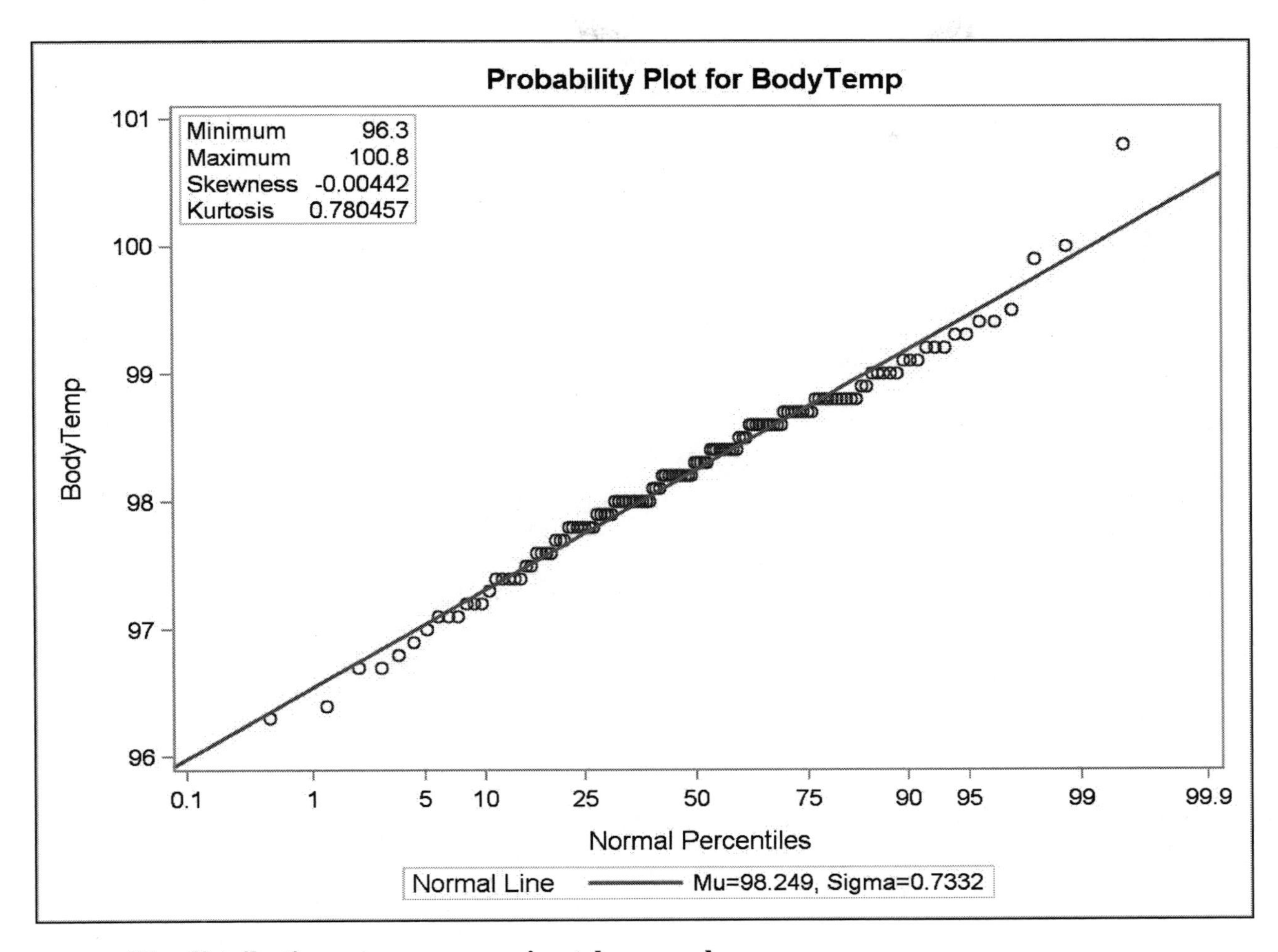


**The distribution appears approximately normal.**

b. Create box plots for **BodyTemp**. Use **ID** to identify outliers. Display a reference line at 98.6 degrees. Does the average body temperature seem to be 98.6 degrees?

```
/*st101s02.sas*/  /*Part b*/
proc sgplot data=sasuser.NormTemp;
   vbox BodyTemp / datalabel=ID;
   format ID 3.;
   refline 98.6 / axis=y label;
   title "Box-and-whisker Plots of Body Temp";
run;
```

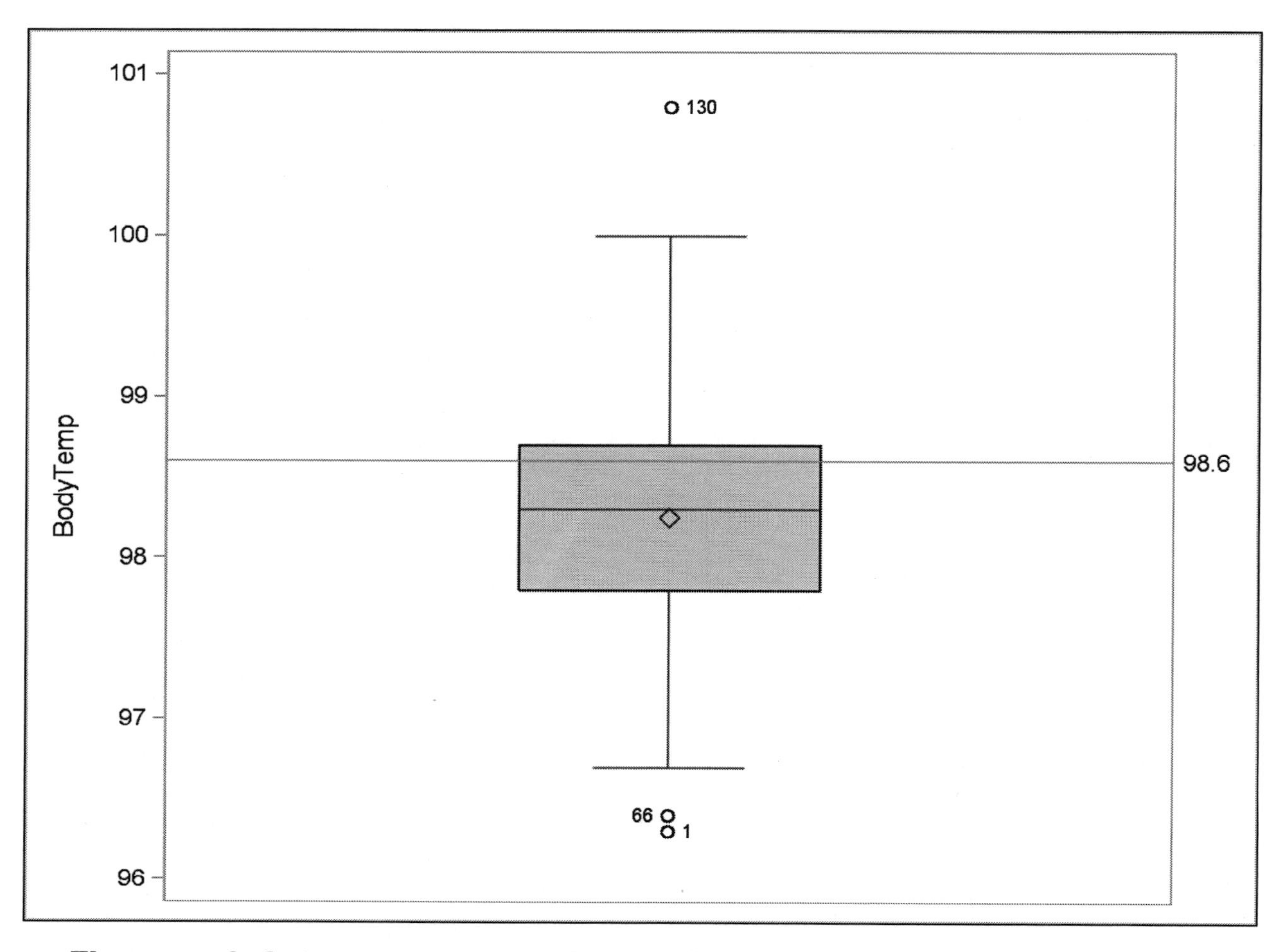


**The average body temperature seems to be somewhat less than 98.6 degrees, as was seen in the tabular output.**

3. **Producing Confidence Intervals**

Generate the 95% confidence interval for the mean of **BodyTemp** in the **sasuser.NormTemp** data set.

```
/*st101s03.sas*/
proc means data=sasuser.NormTemp maxdec=2
           n mean std stderr clm;
   var BodyTemp;
   title '95% Confidence Interval for Body Temp';
run;
```

| Analysis Variable : BodyTemp | | | | | |
|---|---|---|---|---|---|
| N | Mean | Std Dev | Std Error | Lower 95% CL for Mean | Upper 95% CL for Mean |
| 130 | 98.25 | 0.73 | 0.06 | 98.12 | 98.38 |

**a.** Is the assumption of normality met to produce a confidence interval for this data?

**Yes. Because the sample size is large enough and because the data values seemed to be normally distributed, the normality assumption seems to hold.**

**b.** What are the bounds of the confidence interval?

**The 95% confidence interval is 98.12 to 98.38 degrees Fahrenheit.**

4. **Performing a One-Sample *t* Test**

Perform a one-sample *t* test to determine whether the mean of body temperatures (the variable **BodyTemp** in **sasuser.NormTemp**) is truly 98.6.

```
/*st101s04.sas*/  /*PROC UNIVARIATE*/
proc univariate data=sasuser.NormTemp mu0=98.6;
   var BodyTemp;
   title 'Testing Whether the Mean Body Temperature = 98.6 ';
         'Using PROC UNIVARIATE';
run;
```

Partial Output

| Tests for Location: Mu0=98.6 | | | | |
|---|---|---|---|---|
| Test | Statistic | | p Value | |
| Student's t | t | -5.45482 | Pr > \|t\| | <.0001 |
| Sign | M | -21 | Pr >= \|M\| | 0.0002 |
| Signed Rank | S | -1963 | Pr >= \|S\| | <.0001 |

```
/*st101s04.sas*/  /*PROC TTEST*/
proc ttest data=sasuser.NormTemp h0=98.6
           plots(shownull)=interval;
   var BodyTemp;
   title 'Testing Whether the Mean Body Temperature = 98.6 '
         'Using PROC TTEST';
run;
```

Partial Output

| DF | t Value | Pr > \|t\| |
|---|---|---|
| 129 | -5.45 | <.0001 |

**a.** What is the value of the *t* statistic and the corresponding *p*-value?

**They are -5.45 and <.0001, respectively.**

**b.** Produce a confidence interval plot of **BodyTemp** with the value 98.6 used as a reference.

| N | Mean | Std Dev | Std Err | Minimum | Maximum |
|---|---|---|---|---|---|
| 130 | 98.2492 | 0.7332 | 0.0643 | 96.3000 | 100.8 |

| Mean | 95% CL Mean | | Std Dev | 95% CL Std Dev | |
|---|---|---|---|---|---|
| 98.2492 | 98.1220 | 98.3765 | 0.7332 | 0.6536 | 0.8350 |

| DF | t Value | Pr > \|t\| |
|---|---|---|
| 129 | -5.45 | <.0001 |

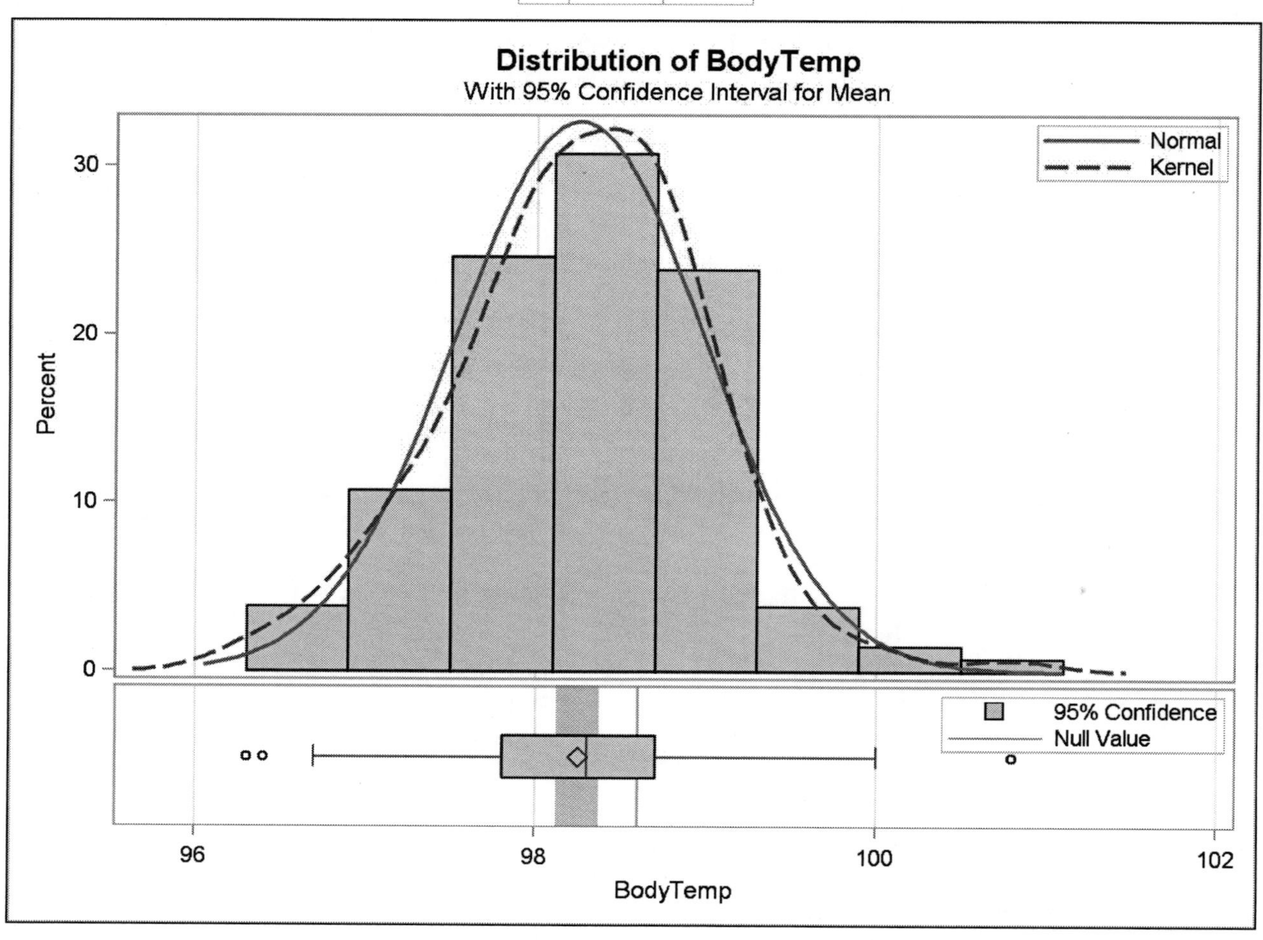


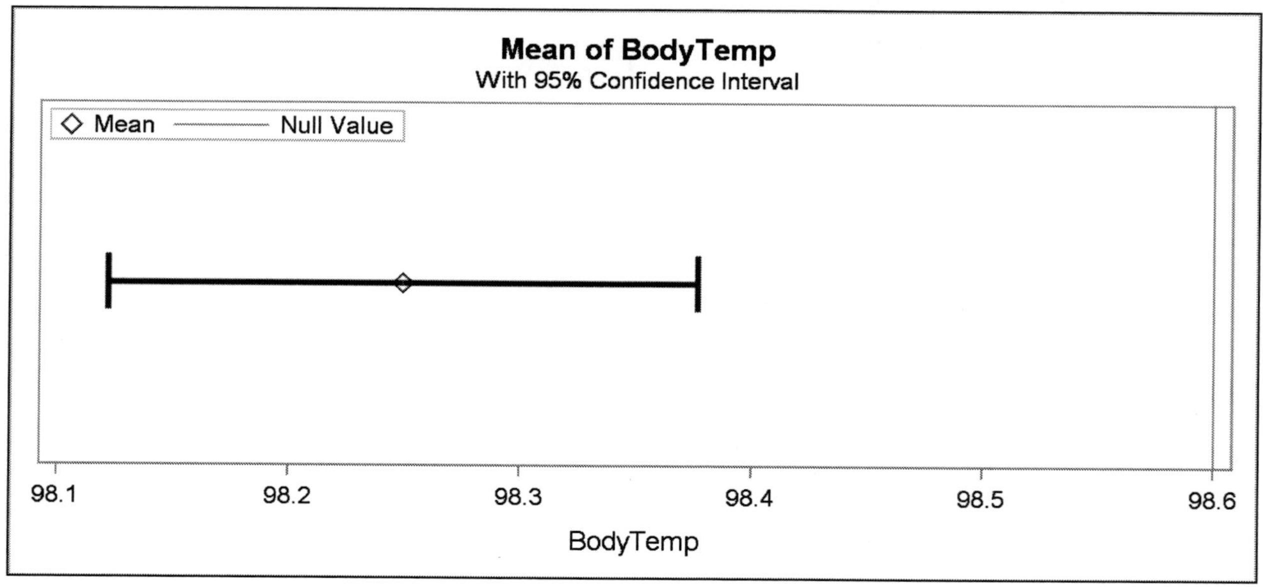

c. Do you reject or fail to reject the null hypothesis at the 0.05 level that the average temperature is 98.6 degrees?

**Because the *p*-value is less than the stated alpha level of 0.05, you do reject the null hypothesis. The confidence limit plot can be used to reach the same conclusion. The 95% confidence interval does not contain the value 98.6. Therefore, you can reject the null hypothesis that the true population mean body temperature is 98.6 degrees Fahrenheit.**

## Solutions to Student Activities (Polls/Quizzes)

### 1.01 Multiple Answer Poll – Correct Answers

A sample from a population should be which of the following?

a. Random
(b.) Representative
c. Normal

15

### 1.02 Multiple Choice Poll – Correct Answers

In the **NormTemp** data set, the distribution of **BodyTemp** seemed to be which of the following?

(a.) Close to normal
b. Left skewed
c. Right skewed
d. Having high positive kurtosis
e. Having high negative kurtosis

47

## 1.03 Multiple Answer Poll – Correct Answers

The distribution of sample means is approximately normal if which of the following are true?

(a.) The population is normal.
(b.) The sample size is "large enough."
c. The sample standard deviation is small.

65

## 1.04 Poll – Correct Answer

If you have a fair coin and flip it 100 times, is it possible for it to land on heads 100 times?

(❍) Yes
❍ No

72

## 1.05 Multiple Choice Poll – Correct Answer

Which of the following affects alpha?

a. The *p*-value of the test
b. The sample size
c. The number of Type I errors
d. All of the above
e. Answers a and b only
(f.) None of the above

81

## 1.06 Multiple Choice Poll – Correct Answer

A 95% confidence interval for SAT scores is (1157.90, 1223.35). From this, what can you conclude, at alpha=0.05?

a. The true average SAT score is significantly different from 1200.
(b.) The true average SAT score is not significantly different from 1200.
c. The true average SAT score is less than 1200.
d. None of the above – You cannot determine statistical significance from confidence intervals.

91

# Chapter 2 Analysis of Variance (ANOVA)

# 2.1 Two-Sample *t* Tests in the TTEST Procedure

## Objectives

- Use the TTEST procedure to analyze the differences between two population means.
- Verify the assumptions of a two-sample *t* test.

3

## Test Score Data Set, Revisited

| Gender | SATScore | IDNumber |
|---|---|---|
| Male | 1170 | 61469897 |
| Female | 1090 | 33081197 |
| Male | 1240 | 68137597 |
| Female | 1000 | 37070397 |
| Male | 1210 | 64608797 |
| Female | 970 | 60714297 |
| Male | 1020 | 16907997 |
| Female | 1490 | 9589297 |
| Male | 1200 | 93891897 |
| Female | 1260 | 5859397 |
| ... | ... | ... |

4

Recall the study in the previous chapter by students in Ms. Chao's statistics class. The Board of Education set a goal of having their graduating class scoring, on average, 1200 on the SAT. The students then investigated whether the school district met its goal by drawing a sample of 80 students at random. The conclusion was that it was reasonable to assume that the mean of all magnet students was, in fact, 1200. However, when they planned the project, an argument arose between the boys and the girls about whether boys or girls scored higher. Therefore, they also collected information about gender to test for differences.

## Assumptions

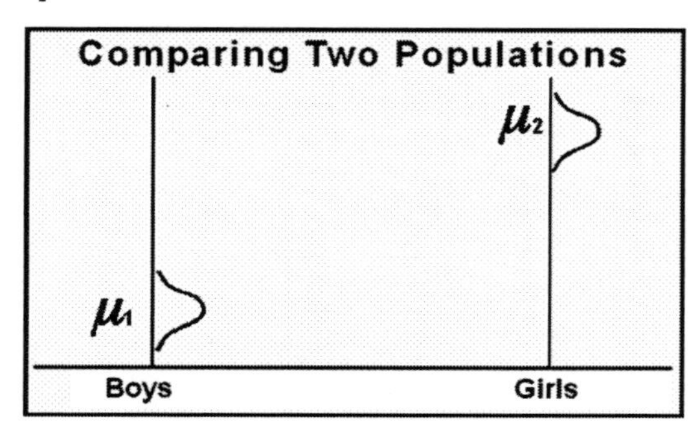


- independent observations
- normally distributed data for each group
- equal variances for each group

5

Before you start the analysis, examine the data to verify that the statistical assumptions are valid.

The assumption of independent observations means that no observations provide any information about any other observation that you collect. For example, measurements are not repeated on the same subject. This assumption can be verified during the design stage.

The assumption of normality can be relaxed if the data are approximately normally distributed or if enough data are collected. This assumption can be verified by examining plots of the data.

There are several tests for equal variances. If this assumption is not valid, an approximate *t* test can be performed.

If these assumptions are ***not*** valid and no adjustments are made, the probability of drawing incorrect conclusions from the analysis could increase.

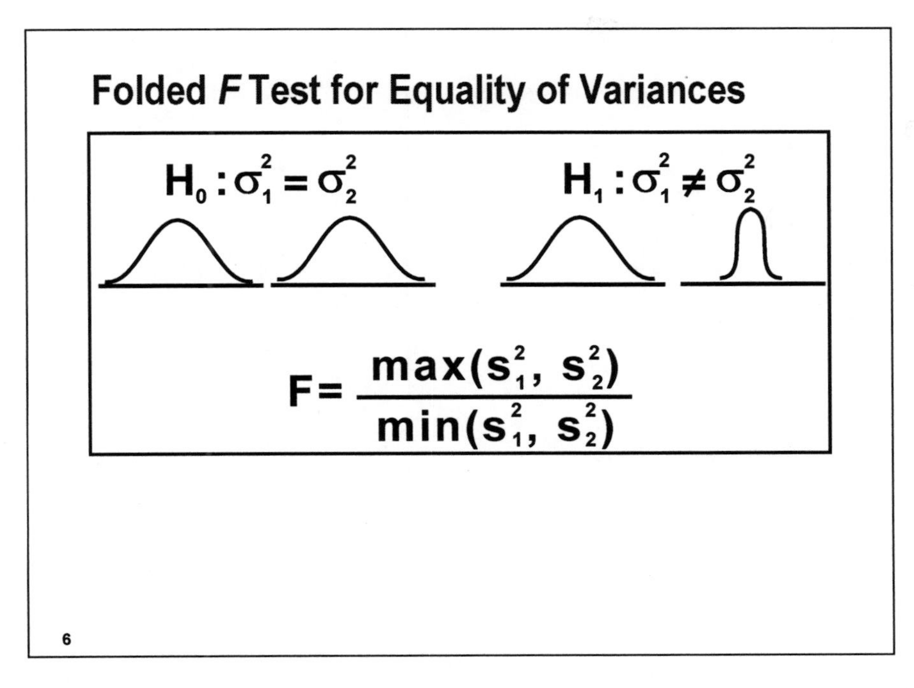


To evaluate the assumption of equal variances in each group, you can use the Folded *F* test for equality of variances. The null hypothesis for this test is that the variances are equal. The *F* value is calculated as a ratio of the greater of the two variances divided by the lesser of the two. Thus, if the null hypothesis is true, *F* tends to be close to 1.0 and the *p*-value for *F* is statistically nonsignificant ($p>0.05$).

This test is valid ***only*** for independent samples from normal distributions. Normality is required even for large sample sizes.

If your data are not normally distributed, you can look at plots to determine whether the variances are approximately equal.

If you reject the null hypothesis, it is recommended that you use the unequal variance *t* test in the PROC TTEST output for testing the equality of group means.

## The TTEST Procedure

General form of the TTEST procedure:

```
PROC TTEST DATA=SAS-data-set;
      CLASS variable;
      VAR variables;
      PAIRED variable1*variable2;
RUN;
```

7

Selected TTEST procedure statements:

CLASS — specifies the two-level variable for the analysis. Only one variable is allowed in the CLASS statement.

VAR — specifies numeric response variables for the analysis. If the VAR statement is not specified, PROC TTEST analyzes all numeric variables in the input data set that are not listed in a CLASS (or BY) statement.

PAIRED — specifies pairs of numeric response variables from which difference scores (**variable1-variable2**) are calculated. A one-sample *t* test is then performed on the difference scores.

- If the CLASS statement and PAIRED statement are omitted, PROC TTEST performs a one-sample *t* test.
- When the CLASS statement is present, a two-sample test is performed.
- When a PAIRED statement is present instead, a paired *t* test is performed.

## Equal Variance *t* Test and *p*-Values

***t* Tests for Equal Means:** $H_0: \mu_1 - \mu_2 = 0$

**Equal Variance *t* Test (Pooled):**

T = 7.4017 DF = 6.0 Prob > |T| = 0.0003 ❷

**Unequal Variance *t* Test (Satterthwaite):**

T = 7.4017 DF = 5.8 Prob > |T| = 0.0004

***F* Test for Equal Variances:** $H_0: \sigma_{12} = \sigma_{22}$

**Equality of Variances Test (Folded F):**

F' = 1.51 DF = (3,3) Prob > F' = 0.7446 ❶

8

❶ Check the assumption of equal variances and then use the appropriate test for equal means. Because the *p*-value of the test *F* statistic is 0.7446, there is not enough evidence to reject the null hypothesis of equal variances.

❷ Therefore, use the equal variance *t*-test line in the output to test whether the means of the two populations are equal.

The null hypothesis that the group means are equal is rejected at the 0.05 level. You conclude that there is a difference between the means of the groups.

The equality of variances *F* test is found at the bottom of the PROC TTEST output.

## Unequal Variance *t* Test and *p*-Values

***t* Tests for Equal Means:** $H_0$: $\mu_1 - \mu_2 = 0$

**Equal Variance *t* Test (Pooled):**

T = -1.7835 DF = 13.0 Prob > |T| = 0.0979

**Unequal Variance *t* Test (Satterthwaite):**

T = -2.4518 DF = 11.1 Prob > |T| = 0.0320 ❷

***F* Test for Equal Variances:** $H_0$: $\sigma_{12} = \sigma_{22}$

**Equality of Variances Test (Folded F):**

F' = 15.28 DF = (9,4) Prob > F' = 0.0185 ❶

9

❶ Again, check the assumption of equal variances and then use the appropriate test for equal means. Because the *p*-value of the test *F* statistic is less than alpha=0.05, there is enough evidence to reject the null hypothesis of equal variances.

❷ Therefore, use the unequal variance *t*-test line in the output to test whether the means of the two populations are equal.

The null hypothesis that the group means are equal is rejected at the 0.05 level.

If you choose the equal variance *t* test, you would ***not*** reject the null hypothesis at the 0.05 level. This shows the importance of choosing the appropriate *t* test.

# Two-Sample *t* Test

```
/*st102d01.sas*/
proc ttest data=sasuser.TestScores plots(shownull)=interval;
   class Gender;
   var SATScore;
   title "Two-Sample t-test Comparing Girls to Boys";
run;
```

First, it is advisable to verify the assumptions of *t* tests. There is an assumption of normality of the distribution of each group. This assumption can be verified with a quick check of the Summary panel and Q-Q plot.

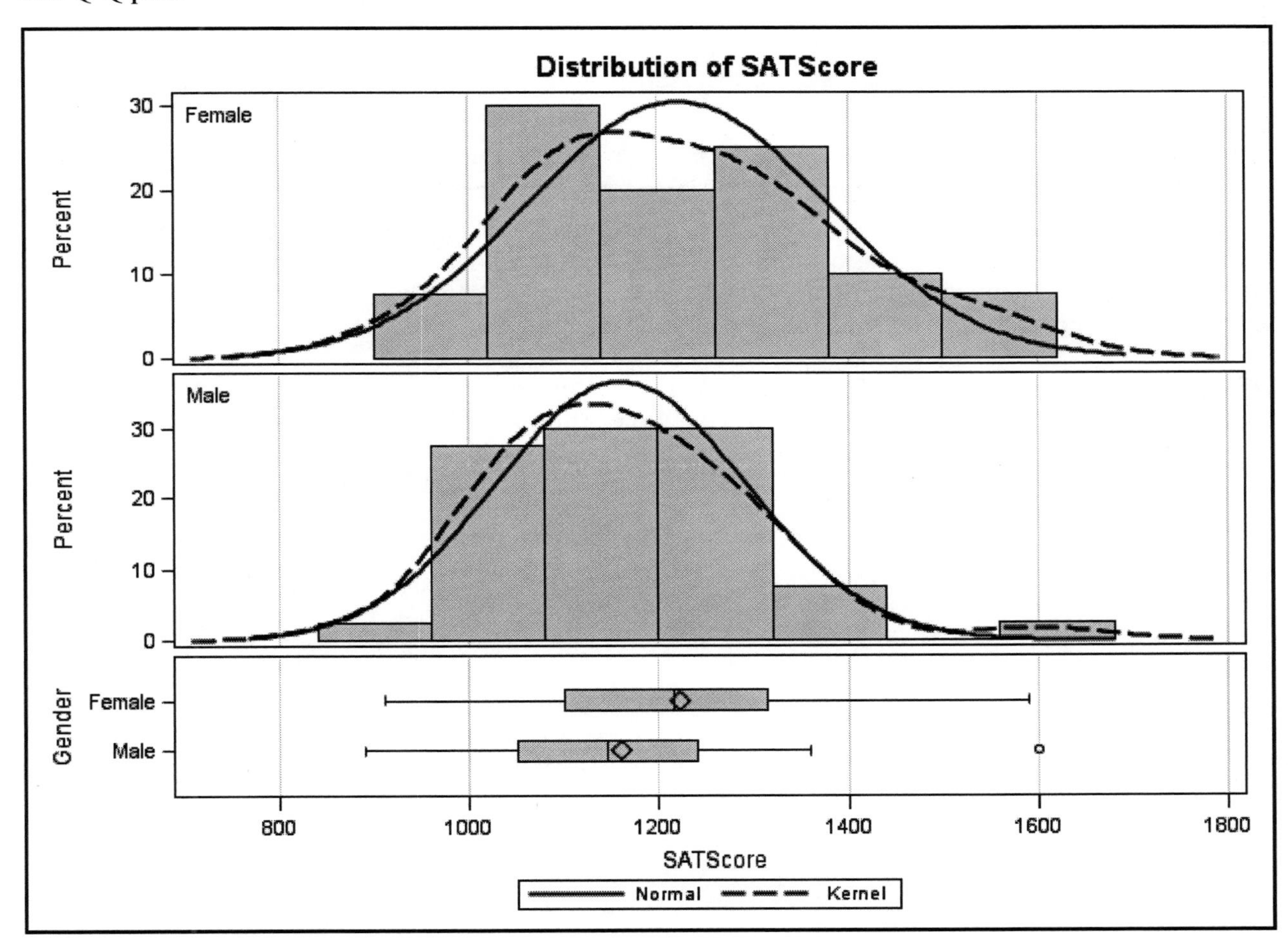

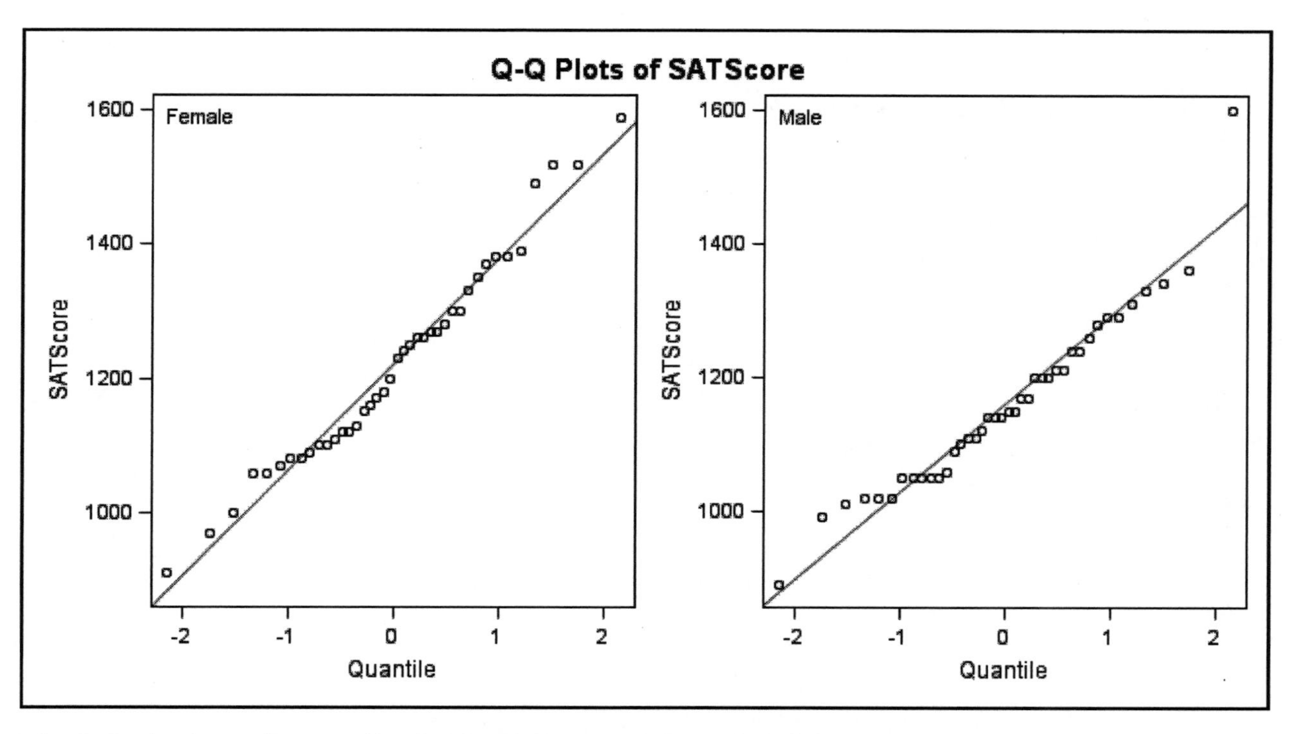


The Q-Q plot (quantile-quantile plot) is similar to the Normal Probability plot that you saw earlier. The X-axis for this plot is scaled as quantiles, rather than probabilities. For each group it seems that the data approximate a normal distribution. There seems to be one potential outlier, a male scoring a perfect 1600 on the SAT, when no other male scored greater than 1400.

If assumptions are not met, you can do an equivalent nonparametric test, which does not make distributional assumptions. PROC NPAR1WAY is one procedure for performing this type of test. It is described in an appendix.

The statistical tables for the TTEST procedure are displayed below.

| | Gender | N | Mean | Std Dev | Std Err | Minimum | Maximum |
|---|---|---|---|---|---|---|---|
| ❶ | Female | 40 | 1221.0 | 157.4 | 24.8864 | 910.0 | 1590.0 |
| | Male | 40 | 1160.3 | 130.9 | 20.7008 | 890.0 | 1600.0 |
| | Diff (1-2) | | 60.7500 | 144.8 | 32.3706 | | |

| | Gender | Method | Mean | 95% CL Mean | | Std Dev | 95% CL Std Dev | |
|---|---|---|---|---|---|---|---|---|
| | Female | | 1221.0 | 1170.7 | 1271.3 | 157.4 | 128.9 | 202.1 |
| | Male | | 1160.3 | 1118.4 | 1202.1 | 130.9 | 107.2 | 168.1 |
| ❸ | Diff (1-2) | Pooled | 60.7500 | -3.6950 | 125.2 | 144.8 | 125.2 | 171.7 |
| | Diff (1-2) | Satterthwaite | 60.7500 | -3.7286 | 125.2 | | | |

| | Method | Variances | DF | t Value | Pr > \|t\| |
|---|---|---|---|---|---|
| ❸ | Pooled | Equal | 78 | 1.88 | 0.0643 |
| | Satterthwaite | Unequal | 75.497 | 1.88 | 0.0644 |

| | Equality of Variances | | | | |
|---|---|---|---|---|---|
| | Method | Num DF | Den DF | F Value | Pr > F |
| ❷ | Folded F | 39 | 39 | 1.45 | 0.2545 |

❶ In the Statistics table, examine the descriptive statistics for each group and their differences.

❷ Look at the Equality of Variances table that appears at the bottom of the output. The *F* test for equal variances has a *p*-value of 0.2545. Because this value is greater than the alpha level of 0.05, do not reject the null hypothesis of equal variances (This is equivalent to saying that there is insufficient evidence to indicate that the variances are not equal.)

❸ Based on the *F* test for equal variances, you then look in the T-Tests table at the *t* test for the hypothesis of equal means. Using the equal variance (Pooled) *t* test, you do not reject the null hypothesis that the group means are equal. The mean difference between boys and girls is 60.75. However, because the *p*-value is greater than 0.05 (Pr>|t|=0.0643), you conclude that there is no significant difference in the average SAT score between boys and girls.

✎ The confidence interval for the mean difference (-3.6950, 125.2) includes 0. This implies that you cannot say with 95% confidence that the difference between boys and girls is ***not*** zero. Therefore, it also implies that the *p*-value is greater than 0.05.

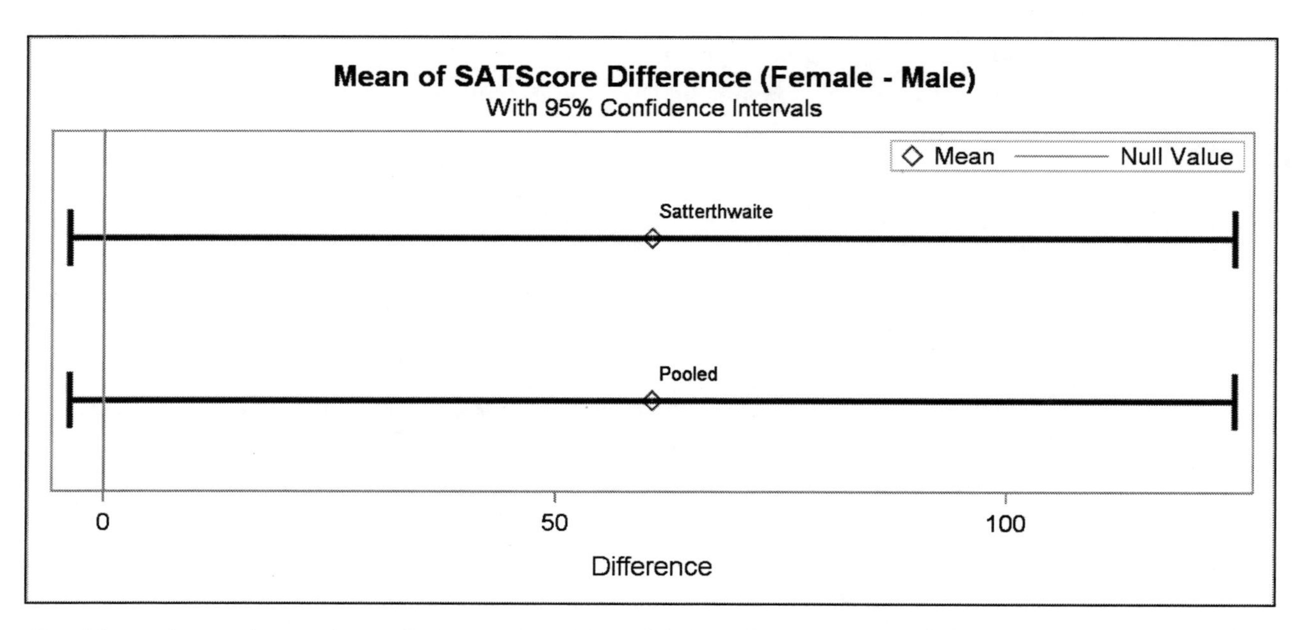


Confidence intervals are shown in the output object titled Difference Interval Plot. Because the variances here are so similar between males and females, the Pooled and Satterthwaite intervals (and *p*-values) are very similar. The lower bound of the Pooled interval extends past zero.

A good argument can be made that the point estimate for the difference between males and females is big from a practical standpoint. If the sample were a bit larger, that same difference might be significant because the pooled standard error would be smaller. However, such a sample needs to be drawn to confirm this hypothesis.

## Exercises

1. **Using PROC TTEST for Comparing Groups**

   Elli Sagerman, a Masters of Education candidate in German Education at the University of North Carolina at Chapel Hill in 2000, collected data for a study. She looked at the effectiveness of a new type of foreign language teaching technique on grammar skills. She selected 30 students to receive tutoring; 15 received the new type of training during the tutorials and 15 received standard tutoring. Two students moved away from the district before completing the study. Scores on a standardized German grammar test were recorded immediately before the 12-week tutorials and then again 12 weeks later at the end of the trial. Sagerman wanted to see the effect of the new technique on grammar skills. The data are in the **SASUSER.GERMAN** data set.

   | | |
   |---|---|
   | **Change** | Change in grammar test scores |
   | **Group** | The assigned treatment, coded **Treatment** and **Control** |

   Analyze the data using PROC TTEST. Assess whether the treatment group improved more than the control group.

   **a.** Do the two groups appear to be approximately normally distributed?

   **b.** Do the two groups have approximately equal variances?

   **c.** Does the new teaching technique seem to result in significantly different change scores compared with the standard technique?

### 2.01 Multiple Answer Poll

How do you tell PROC TTEST that you want to do a two-sample *t* test?

a. SAMPLE=2 option
b. CLASS statement
c. GROUPS=2 option
d. PAIRED statement

12

# 2.2 One-Way ANOVA

## Objectives

- Use the GLM procedure to analyze the differences between population means.
- Verify the assumptions of analysis of variance.

17

## Overview of Statistical Models

| Type of Response \ Type of Predictors | Categorical | Continuous | Continuous and Categorical |
|---|---|---|---|
| **Continuous** | **Analysis of Variance (ANOVA)** | Ordinary Least Squares (OLS) Regression | Analysis of Covariance (ANCOVA) |
| Categorical | Contingency Table Analysis or Logistic Regression | Logistic Regression | Logistic Regression |

18

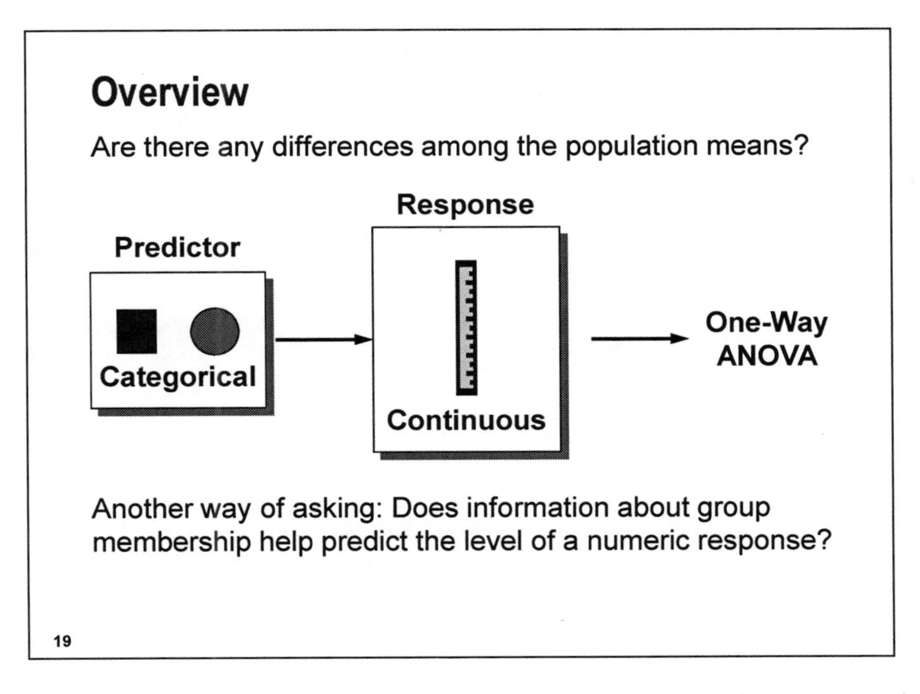


*Analysis of variance* (ANOVA) is a statistical technique used to compare the means of two or more groups of observations or treatments. For this type of problem, you have the following:

- a continuous dependent variable, or *response* variable
- a discrete independent variable, also called a *predictor* or *explanatory* variable.

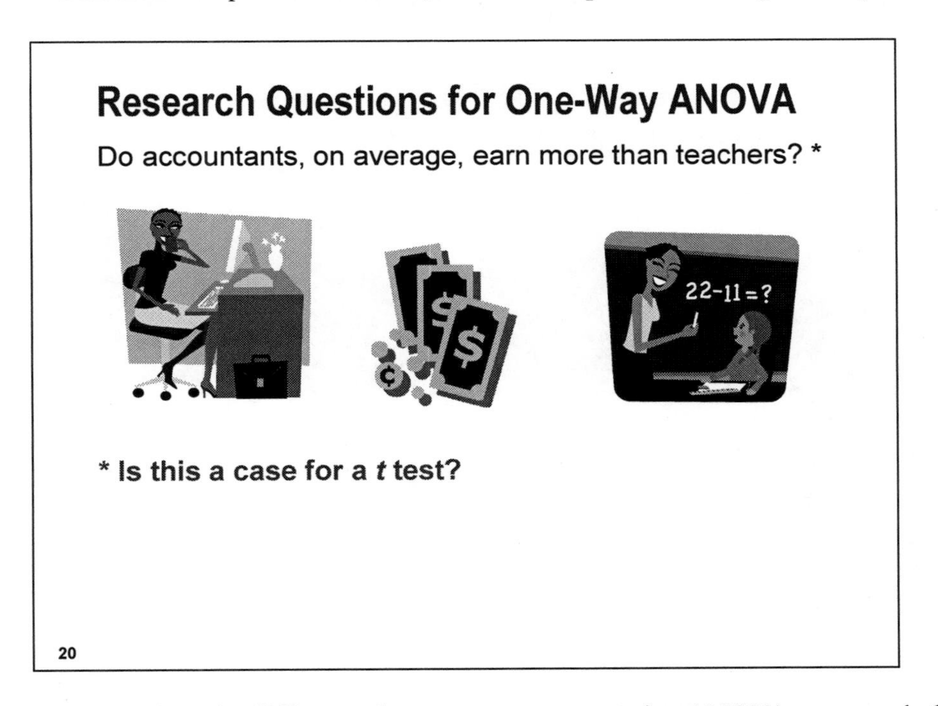


If you analyze the difference between two means using ANOVA, you reach the same conclusions as you reach using a pooled, two-group *t* test. Performing a two-group mean comparison in PROC GLM gives you access to different graphical and assessment tools than performing the same comparison in PROC TTEST.

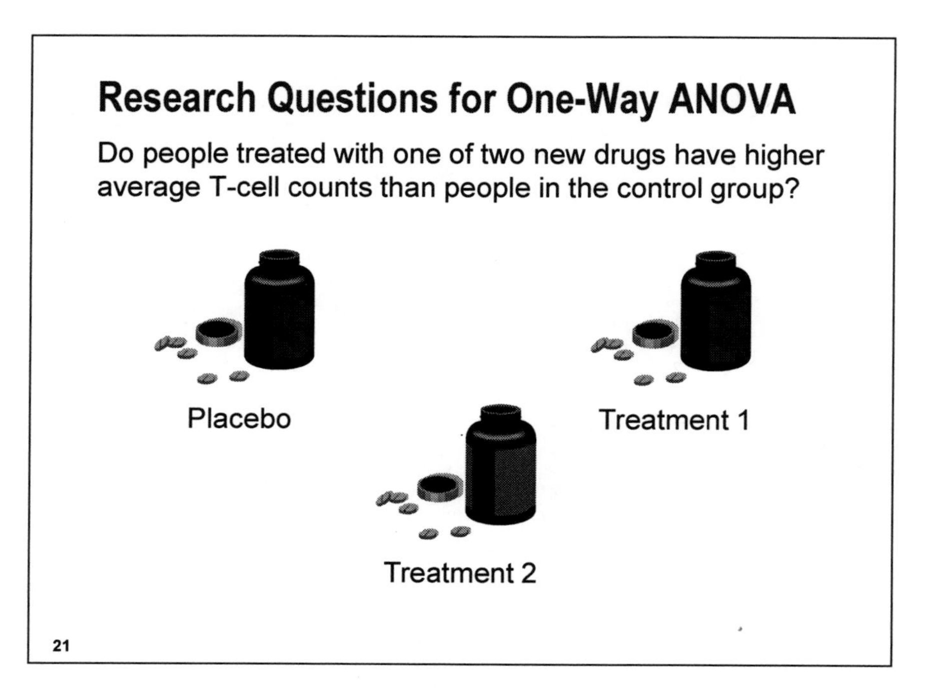


When there are three or more levels for the grouping variable, a simple approach is to run a series of *t* tests between all the pairs of levels. For example, you might be interested in T-cell counts in patients taking three medications (including one placebo). You could simply run a *t* test for each pair of medications. A more powerful approach is to analyze all the data simultaneously. The mathematical model is called a *one-way analysis of variance* (ANOVA), and the test statistic is the *F* ratio, rather than the Student's *t* value.

## Research Questions for One-Way ANOVA

Do people spend different amounts depending on which type of credit card they have?

22

## Research Questions for One-Way ANOVA

Does the type of fertilizer used affect the average weight of garlic grown at the Montana Gourmet Garlic Ranch?

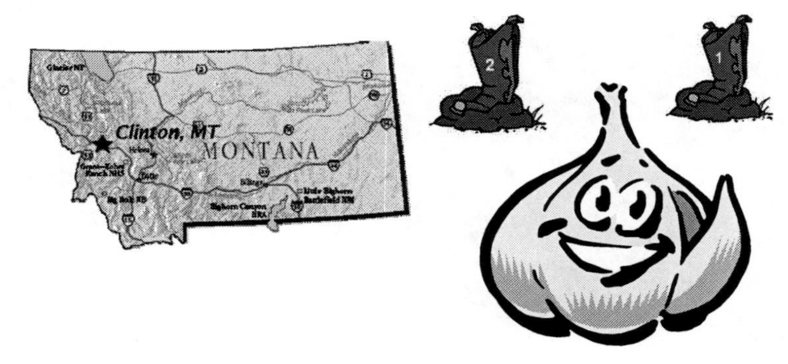


23

Example: Montana Gourmet Garlic is a company that grows garlic using organic methods. It specializes in hardneck varieties. Knowing a little about experimental methods, the owners design an experiment to test whether growth of the garlic is affected by the type of fertilizer used. They limit the experimentation to a Rocambole variety named Spanish Roja, and test three organic fertilizers and one chemical fertilizer (as a control). They blind themselves to the fertilizer by using containers with numbers 1 through 4. (In other words, they design the experiment in such a way that they do not know which fertilizer is in which container.) One acre of farmland is set aside for the experiment. It is divided into 32 beds. They randomly assign fertilizers to beds. At harvest, they calculate the average weight of garlic bulbs in each of the beds. The data are in the **sasuser.MGGarlic** data set.

These are the variables in the data set:

| | |
|---|---|
| **Fertilizer** | The type of fertilizer used (1 through 4) |
| **BulbWt** | The average garlic bulb weight (in pounds) in the bed |
| **Cloves** | The average number of cloves on each bulb |
| **BedID** | A randomly assigned bed identification number |

## Descriptive Statistics across Groups

Example: Print the data in the **sasuser.MGGarlic** data set and create descriptive statistics.

```
/*st102d02.sas*/  /*Part A*/
proc print data=sasuser.MGGarlic (obs=10);
   title 'Partial Listing of Garlic Data';
run;
```

Part of the data is shown below.

| Obs | Fertilizer | BulbWt | Cloves | BedID |
|---|---|---|---|---|
| 1 | 4 | 0.20901 | 11.5062 | 30402 |
| 2 | 3 | 0.25792 | 12.2550 | 23423 |
| 3 | 2 | 0.21588 | 12.0982 | 20696 |
| 4 | 4 | 0.24754 | 12.9199 | 25412 |
| 5 | 1 | 0.24402 | 12.5793 | 10575 |
| 6 | 3 | 0.20150 | 10.6891 | 21466 |
| 7 | 1 | 0.20891 | 11.5416 | 14749 |
| 8 | 4 | 0.15173 | 14.0173 | 25342 |
| 9 | 2 | 0.24114 | 9.9072 | 20383 |
| 10 | 3 | 0.23350 | 11.2130 | 23306 |

Next, look at the fertilizer groups separately.

```
/*st102d02.sas*/  /*Part B*/
proc means data=sasuser.MGGarlic printalltypes maxdec=3;
   var BulbWt;
   class Fertilizer;
   title 'Descriptive Statistics of Garlic Weight';
run;

/*st102d02.sas*/  /*Part C*/
proc sgplot data=sasuser.MGGarlic;
   vbox BulbWt / category=Fertilizer datalabel=BedID;
   format BedID 5.;
   title "Box and Whisker Plots of Garlic Weight";
run;
```

Selected PROC MEANS statement option:

PRINTALLTYPES displays all requested combinations of class variables (all _TYPE_ values) in the printed or displayed output.

Selected PROC MEANS statement:

CLASS variable(s) specifies the variables whose values define the subgroup combinations for the analysis. Class variables are numeric or character and can have continuous values, but they typically have a few discrete values that define levels of the variable. You do not have to sort the data by class variables.

Selected SGPLOT VBOX statement option:

CATEGORY= produces separate box plots for each level of the variable listed.

| Analysis Variable : BulbWt | | | | | |
|---|---|---|---|---|---|
| N Obs | N | Mean | Std Dev | Minimum | Maximum |
| 32 | 32 | 0.219 | 0.029 | 0.152 | 0.278 |

| Analysis Variable : BulbWt | | | | | | |
|---|---|---|---|---|---|---|
| Fertilizer | N Obs | N | Mean | Std Dev | Minimum | Maximum |
| 1 | 9 | 9 | 0.225 | 0.025 | 0.188 | 0.254 |
| 2 | 8 | 8 | 0.209 | 0.026 | 0.159 | 0.241 |
| 3 | 11 | 11 | 0.230 | 0.026 | 0.189 | 0.278 |
| 4 | 4 | 4 | 0.196 | 0.041 | 0.152 | 0.248 |

The design is not *balanced*. In other words, the groups are not equally sized.

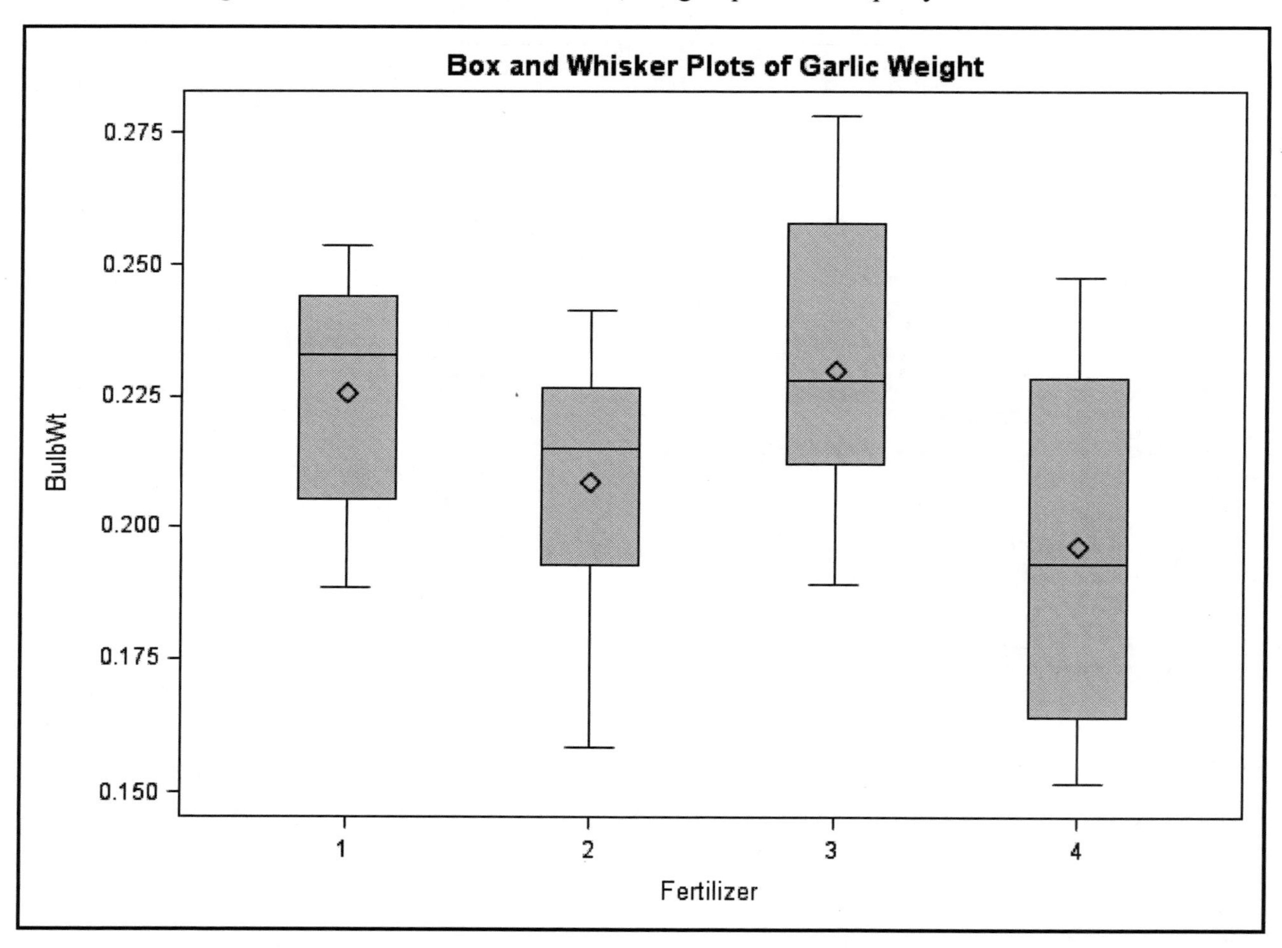


Caution should be exercised when viewing the box plots since there are few observations per group, increasing variability.

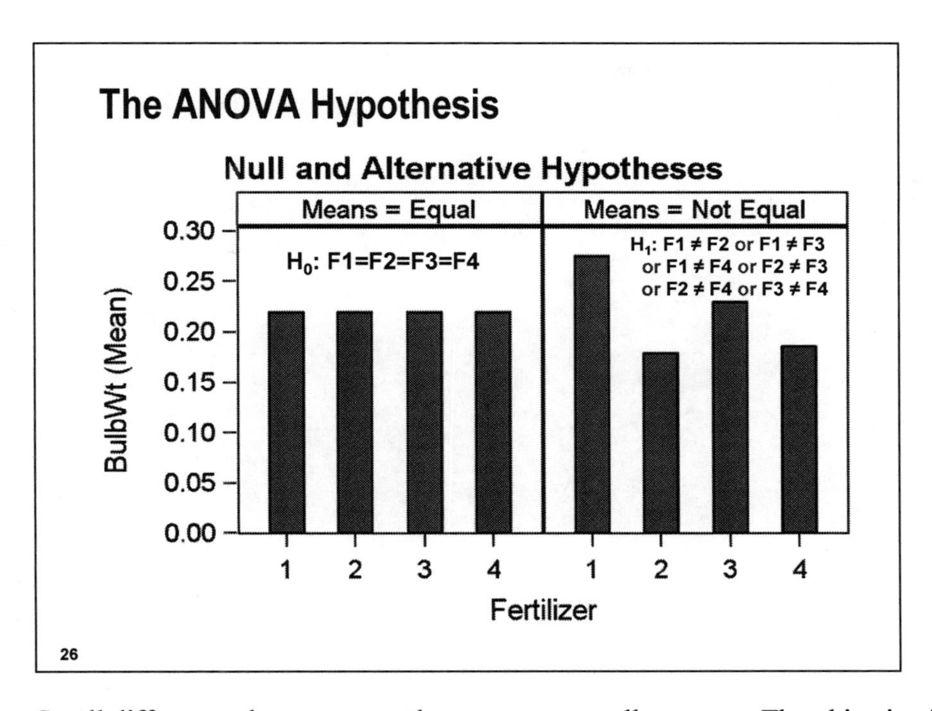


Small differences between sample means are usually present. The objective is to determine whether these differences are statistically significant. In other words, is the difference more than what might be expected to occur by chance?

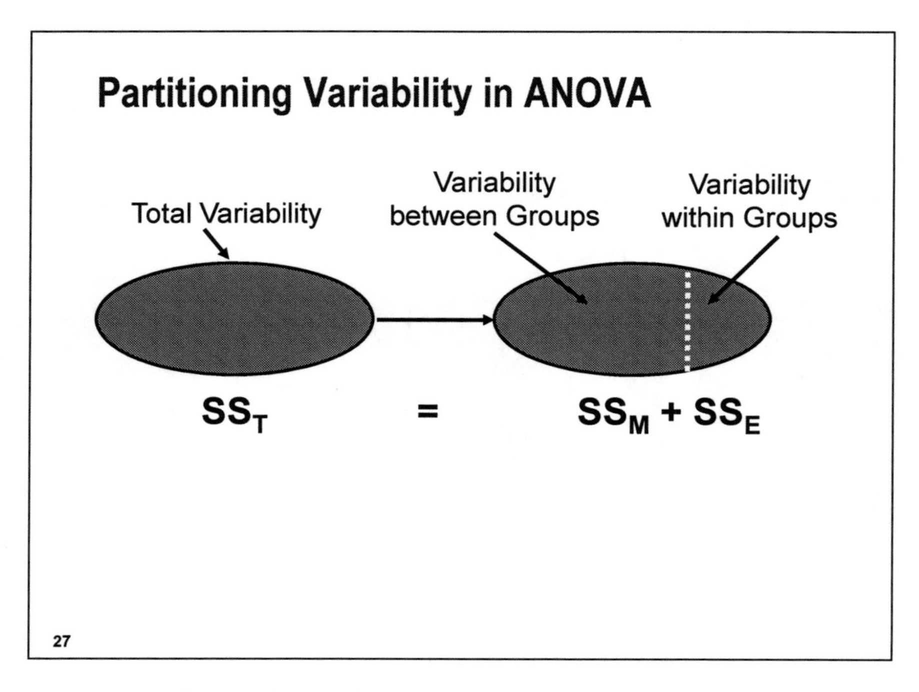


In ANOVA, the Total Variation (as measured by the corrected total sum of squares) is partitioned into two components, the Between Group Variation (displayed in the ANOVA table as the Model Sum of Squares) and the Within Group Variation (displayed as the Error Sum of Squares). As its name implies, ANalysis Of VAriance analyzes, or breaks apart, the variance of the dependent variable to determine whether the between-group variation is a significant portion of the total variation. ANOVA compares the portion of variation in the response variable attributable to the grouping variable to the portion of variability that is unexplained. The test statistic, the *F* Ratio, is only a ratio of the model variance to the error variance. The calculations are shown below.

**Total Variation** the ***overall*** variability in the response variable. It is calculated as the sum of the squared differences between each observed value and the overall mean, $\sum\sum\left(Y_{ij}-\overline{\overline{Y}}\right)^2$. This measure is also referred to as the *Total Sum of Squares* ($SS_T$).

**Between Group Variation** the variability explained by the independent variable and therefore represented by the between treatment sums of squares. It is calculated as the weighted (by group size) sum of the squared differences between the mean for each group and the overall mean, $\sum n_i\left(\overline{Y}_i-\overline{\overline{Y}}\right)^2$. This measure is also referred to as the *Model Sum of Squares* ($SS_M$).

**Within Group Variation** the variability not explained by the model. It is also referred to as *within treatment variability* or *residual sum of squares*. It is calculated as the sum of the squared differences between each observed value and the mean for its group, $\sum\sum\left(Y_{ij}-\overline{Y}_i\right)^2$. This measure is also referred to as the *Error Sum of Squares* ($SS_E$).

$SS_T=SS_M+SS_E$, meaning that the model sum of squares and the error sum of squares sums to the total sum of squares.

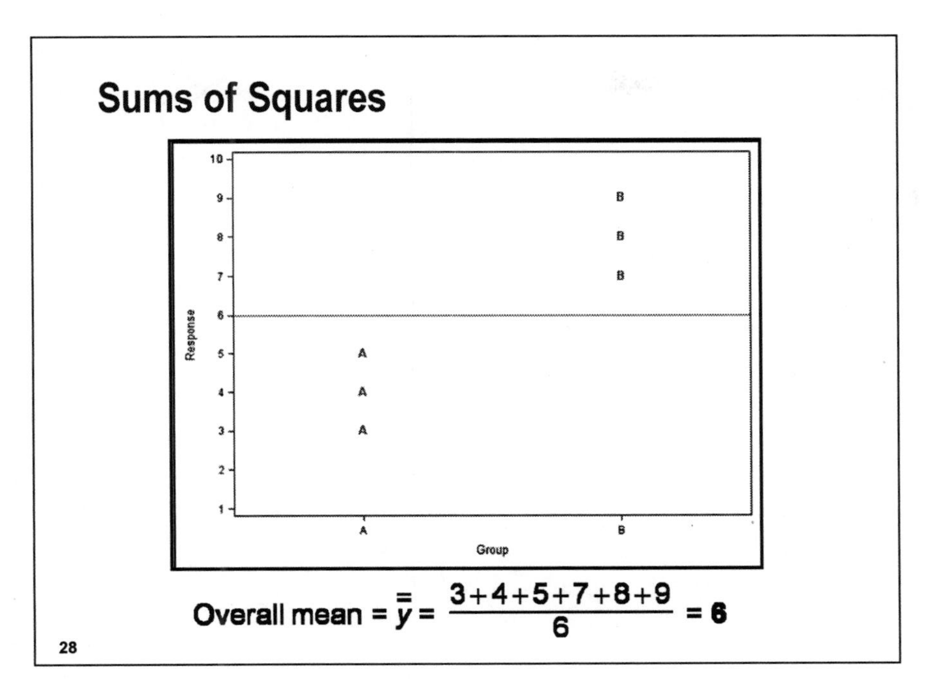


A simple example of the various sums of squares is shown in this set of slides. First, the overall mean of all data values is calculated.

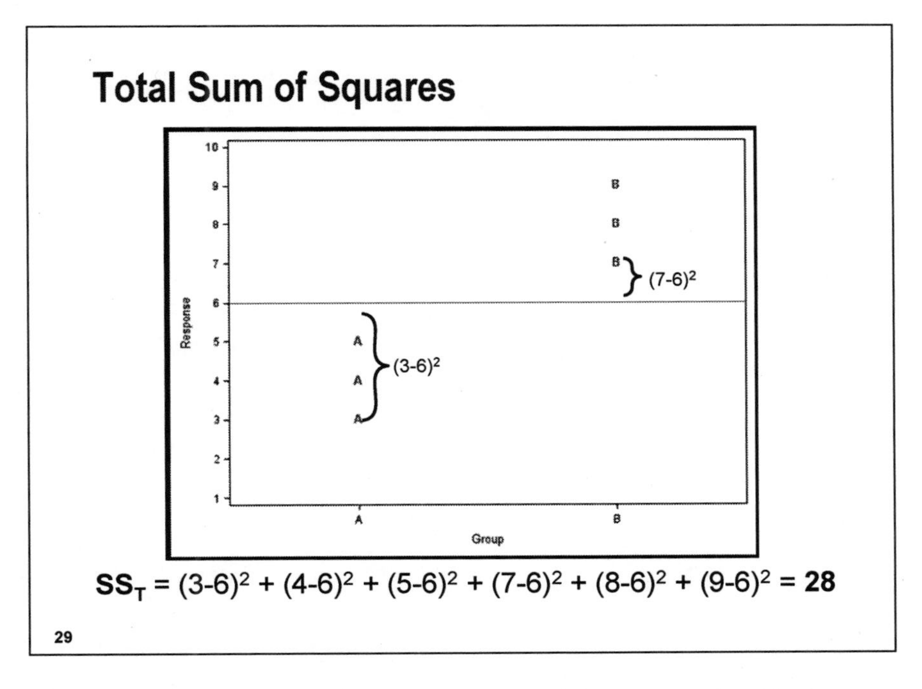


The total sum of squares, $SS_T$, is a measure of the total variability in a response variable. It is calculated by summing the squared distances from each point to the overall mean. Because it is correcting for the mean, this sum is sometimes called the *corrected total sum of squares*.

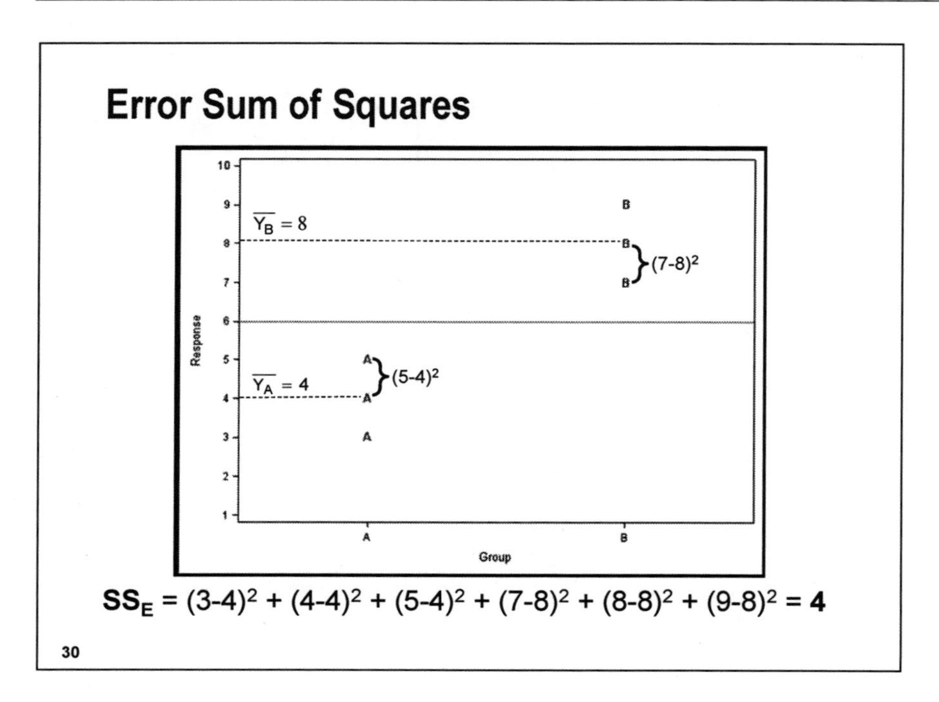


The error sum of squares, $SS_E$, measures the random variability ***within*** groups; it is the sum of the squared deviations between observations in each group and that group's mean. This is often referred to as the *unexplained variation* or *within-group variation.*

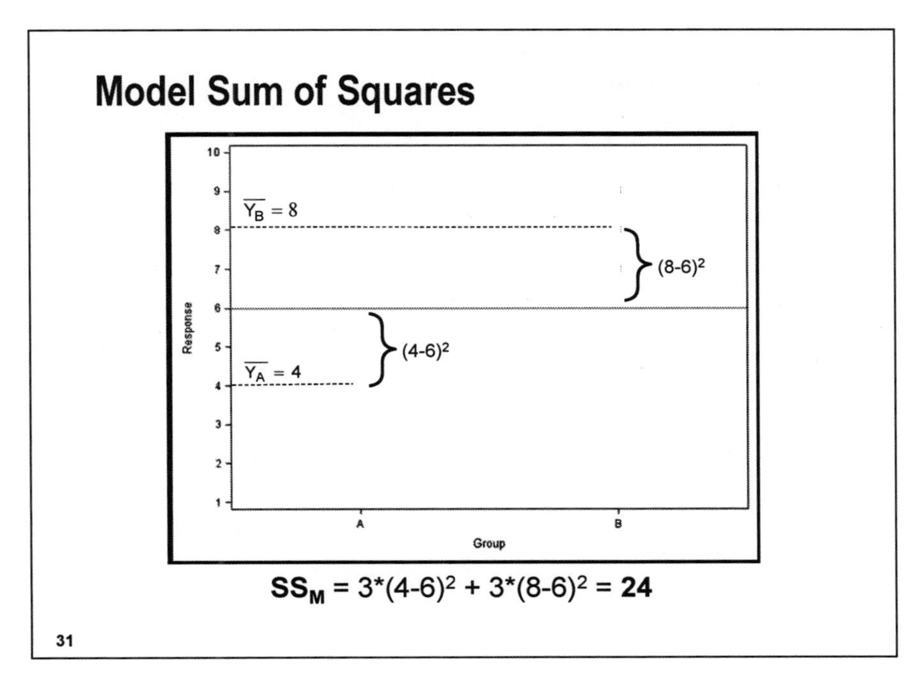


The model sum of squares, $SS_M$, measures the variability ***between*** groups; it is the sum of the squared deviations between each group mean and the overall mean, weighted by the number of observations in each group. This is often referred to as the *explained variation*. The model sum of squares can also be calculated by subtracting the error sum of squares from the total sum of squares: $SS_M = SS_T - SS_E$.

In this example, the model explains approximately 85.7%, $((SS_M / SS_T)*100)\%$, of the variability in the response. The other 14.3% represents unexplained variability, or process variation. In other words, the variability due to differences between the groups (the explained variability) makes up a larger proportion of the total variability than the random error within the groups (the unexplained variability).

The total sum of squares ($SS_T$) refers to the ***overall*** variability in the response variable. The $SS_T$ is computed under the null hypothesis (that the group means are all the same). The error sum of squares ($SS_E$) refers to the variability ***within*** the treatments not explained by the independent variable. The $SS_E$ is computed under the alternative hypothesis (that the model includes nonzero effects). The model sum of squares ($SS_M$) refers to the variability ***between*** the treatments explained by the independent variable.

The basic measures of variation under the two hypotheses are transformed into a ratio of the model and the error variances that has a known distribution (a sample statistic, the $F$ ratio) under the null hypothesis that all group means are equal. The $F$ ratio can be used to compute a $p$-value.

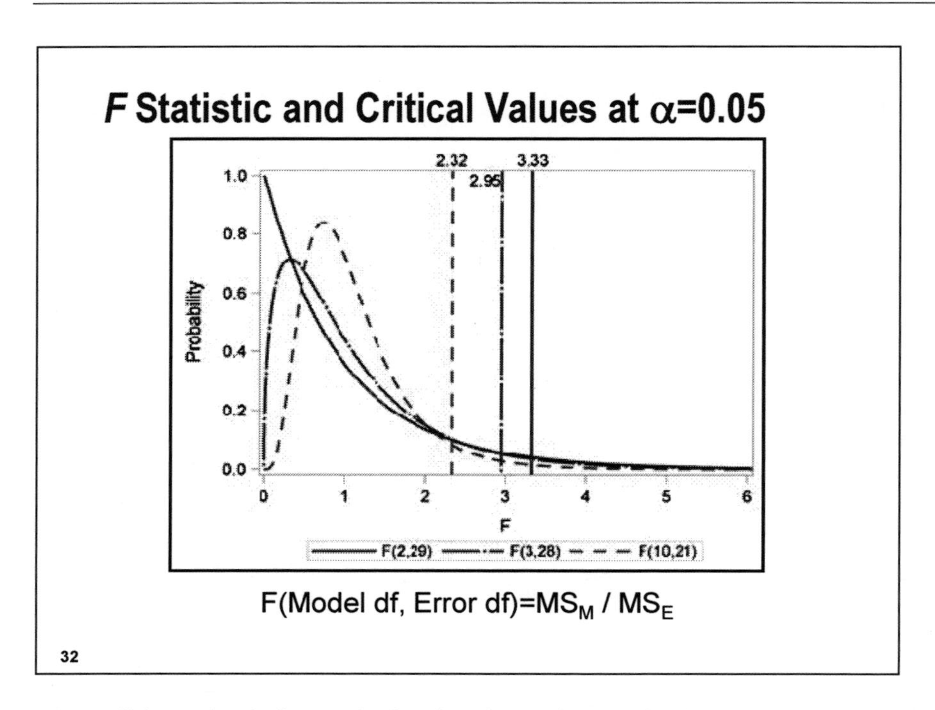


The null hypothesis for analysis of variance is tested using an *F* statistic. The *F* statistic is calculated as the ratio of the Between Group Variance to the Within Group Variance. In the output of PROC GLM, these values are shown as the Model Mean Square and the Error Mean Square. The mean square values are calculated as the sum of square value divided by the degrees of freedom.

In general, *degrees of freedom* (DF) can be thought of as the number of independent pieces of information.

- Model DF is the number of treatments minus 1.
- Corrected total DF is the sample size minus 1.
- Error DF is the sample size minus the number of treatments (or the difference between the corrected total DF and the Model DF.

*Mean squares* are calculated by taking sums of squares and dividing by the corresponding degrees of freedom. They can be thought of as variances.

- Mean square error (MSE) is an estimate of $\sigma^2$, the constant variance assumed for all treatments.
- If $\mu_i=\mu_j$, for all $i \neq j$, then the mean square for the model (MSM) is also an estimate of $\sigma^2$.
- If $\mu_i \neq \mu_j$, for any $i \neq j$, then MSM estimates $\sigma^2$ plus a positive constant.
- $F = \dfrac{MSM}{MSE} = \dfrac{SS_M / df_M}{SS_E / df_E}$.
- The *p*-value for the test is then calculated from the F distribution with appropriate degrees of freedom.

*Variance* is the traditional measure of precision. *Mean square error (MSE)* is the traditional measure of accuracy used by statisticians. MSE is equal to variance plus bias-squared. Because the sample mean $(\bar{x})$ is an unbiased estimate of the population mean ($\mu$), bias=0 and MSE measures the variance.

## Coefficient of Determination

$$R^2 = SS_M / SS_T$$

"Proportion of variance accounted for by the model"

33

The *coefficient of determination*, $R^2$, is a measure of the proportion of variability explained by the independent variables in the analysis. This statistic is calculated as $R^2 = \frac{SS_M}{SS_T}$

The value of $R^2$ is between 0 and 1. The value is

- close to 0 if the independent variables do not explain much variability in the data
- close to 1 if the independent variables explain a relatively large proportion of variability in the data.

Although values of $R^2$ closer to 1 are preferred, judging the magnitude of $R^2$ depends on the context of the problem.

The *coefficient of variation* (denoted Coeff Var) expresses the root MSE (the estimate of the standard deviation for all treatments) as a percent of the mean. It is a unitless measure that is useful in comparing the variability of two sets of data with different units of measure.

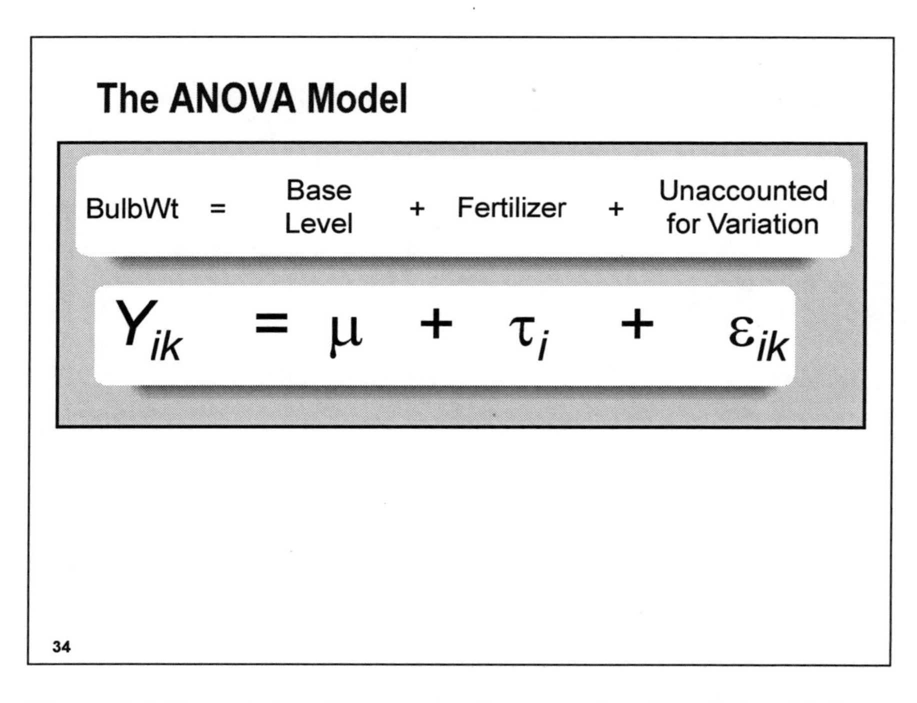


The model, $Y_{ik}=\mu+\tau_i+\varepsilon_{ik}$, is one way of representing the relationship between the dependent and independent variables in ANOVA.

$Y_{ik}$ the $k^{th}$ value of the response variable for the $i^{th}$ treatment.

$\mu$ the overall population mean of the response, for example, garlic bulb weight.

$\tau_i$ the difference between the population mean of the $i^{th}$ treatment and the overall mean, $\mu$. This is referred to as the *effect* of treatment *i*.

$\varepsilon_{ik}$ the difference between the observed value of the $k^{th}$ observation in the $i^{th}$ group and the mean of the $i^{th}$ group. This is called the *error term*.

PROC GLM uses a parameterization of categorical variables in its CLASS statement that will not directly estimate the values of the parameters in the model shown. The correct parameter estimates can be obtained by adding the SOLUTION option in the MODEL statement in PROC GLM and then using simple algebra. Parameter estimates and standard errors can also be obtained using ESTIMATE statements. These issues are discussed in depth in the Statistics 2: ANOVA and Regression course and in the SAS documentation.

The researchers are interested only in these four specific fertilizers. In some applications this would be considered a *fixed effect*. If the fertilizers used were a sample of many that can be used, the sampling variability of fertilizers would need to be taken into account in the model. In that case, the fertilizer variable would be treated as a *random effect*. (Random effects are not discussed in this course.)

## The GLM Procedure

General form of the GLM procedure:

```
PROC GLM DATA=SAS-data-set PLOTS=options;
      CLASS variables;
      MODEL dependents=independents </ options>;
      MEANS effects </ options>;
      LSMEANS effects </ options>;
      OUTPUT OUT=SAS-data-set keyword=variable...;
RUN;
QUIT;
```

35

Selected GLM procedure statements:

CLASS specifies classification variables for the analysis.

MODEL specifies dependent and independent variables for the analysis.

MEANS computes unadjusted means of the dependent variable for each value of the specified effect.

LSMEANS produces adjusted means for the outcome variable, broken out by the variable specified and adjusting for any other explanatory variables included in the MODEL statement.

OUTPUT specifies an output data set that contains all variables from the input data set and variables that represent statistics from the analysis.

PROC GLM supports RUN-group processing, which means the procedure stays active until a PROC, DATA, or QUIT statement is encountered. This enables you to submit additional statements followed by another RUN statement without resubmitting the PROC statement.

## Assumptions for ANOVA

- Observations are independent.
- Errors are normally distributed.
- All groups have equal error variances.

36

The validity of the *p*-values depends on the data meeting the assumptions for ANOVA. Therefore, it is good practice to verify those assumptions in the process of performing the analysis of group differences.

- Independence implies that the $\varepsilon_{ij}$ occurrences in the theoretical model are uncorrelated.
- The errors are assumed to be normally distributed for every group or treatment.
- Approximately equal error variances are assumed across treatments.

## Assessing ANOVA Assumptions

- Good data collection designs help ensure the independence assumption.
- Diagnostic plots from PROC GLM can be used to verify the assumption that the error is approximately normally distributed.
- PROC GLM produces a test of equal variances with the HOVTEST option in the MEANS statement. H0 for this hypothesis test is that the variances are equal for all populations.

37

## Predicted and Residual Values

The predicted value in ANOVA is the *group mean*.

A *residual* is the difference between the observed value of the response and the predicted value of the response variable.

| Observation | Fertilizer | Observed | Predicted | Residual |
|---|---|---|---|---|
| 1 | 4 | 0.20901000 | 0.19635250 | 0.01265750 |
| 2 | 3 | 0.25792000 | 0.22982091 | 0.02809909 |
| 3 | 2 | 0.21588000 | 0.20856500 | 0.00731500 |
| 4 | 4 | 0.24754000 | 0.19635250 | 0.05118750 |
| 5 | 1 | 0.24402000 | 0.22540667 | 0.01861333 |

38

The residuals from the ANOVA are calculated as the actual values minus the predicted values (the group means in ANOVA). Diagnostic plots (including normal quantile-quantile plots of the residuals) can be used to assess the normality assumption. With a reasonably sized sample and approximately equal groups (balanced design), only severe departures from normality are considered a problem. Residual values sum to 0 in ANOVA.

In ANOVA with more than one predictor variable, the HOVTEST option is unavailable. In those circumstances, you can plot the residuals against their predicted values to visually assess whether the variability is constant across groups.

## 2.02 Multiple Choice Poll

If you have 20 observations in your ANOVA and you calculate the residuals, to which of the following would they sum?

a. -20
b. 0
c. 20
d. 400
e. Unable to tell from the information given

40

## 2.03 Multiple Choice Poll

If you have 20 observations in your ANOVA and you calculate the squared residuals, to which of the following would they sum?

a. -20
b. 0
c. 20
d. 400
e. Unable to tell from the information given

42

# The GLM Procedure

```
/*st102d03.sas*/  /*Part A*/
proc glm data=sasuser.MGGarlic;
   class Fertilizer;
   model BulbWt=Fertilizer;
   title 'Testing for Equality of Means with PROC GLM';
run;
quit;
```

Turn your attention to the first two tables of the output. The first table specifies the number of levels and the values of the class variable.

| Class Level Information | | |
|---|---|---|
| **Class** | **Levels** | **Values** |
| **Fertilizer** | 4 | 1 2 3 4 |

The second table shows both the number of observations read and the number of observations used. These values are the same because there are no missing values in for any variable in the model. If any row has ***missing data*** for a predictor or response variable, that row is ***dropped*** from the analysis.

| | |
|---|---|
| **Number of Observations Read** | 32 |
| **Number of Observations Used** | 32 |

The second part of the output contains all of the information that is needed to test the equality of the treatment means. It is divided into three parts:

- the analysis of variance table
- descriptive information
- information about the effect of the independent variable in the model

Look at each of these parts separately.

| Source | DF | Sum of Squares | Mean Square | F Value | Pr > F |
|---|---|---|---|---|---|
| **Model** | 3 | 0.00457996 | 0.00152665 | 1.96 | 0.1432 |
| **Error** | 28 | 0.02183054 | 0.00077966 | | |
| **Corrected Total** | 31 | 0.02641050 | | | |

The $F$ statistic and corresponding $p$-value are reported in the Analysis of Variance table. Because the reported $p$-value (0.1432) is greater than 0.05, you do not reject the null hypothesis of no difference between the means.

| R-Square | Coeff Var | Root MSE | BulbWt Mean |
|---|---|---|---|
| 0.173414 | 12.74520 | 0.027922 | 0.219082 |

The **BulbWt** Mean is the mean of all of the data values in the variable **BulbWt** without regard to **Fertilizer**.

As discussed previously, the $R^2$ value is often interpreted as the "proportion of variance accounted for by the model." Therefore, you might say that in this model, **Fertilizer** explains about 17% of the variability of **BulbWt**.

| Source | DF | Type I SS | Mean Square | F Value | Pr > F |
|---|---|---|---|---|---|
| Fertilizer | 3 | 0.00457996 | 0.00152665 | 1.96 | 0.1432 |

| Source | DF | Type III SS | Mean Square | F Value | Pr > F |
|---|---|---|---|---|---|
| Fertilizer | 3 | 0.00457996 | 0.00152665 | 1.96 | 0.1432 |

For a one-way analysis of variance (only one classification variable), the information about the independent variable in the model is an exact duplicate of the model line of the analysis of variance table.

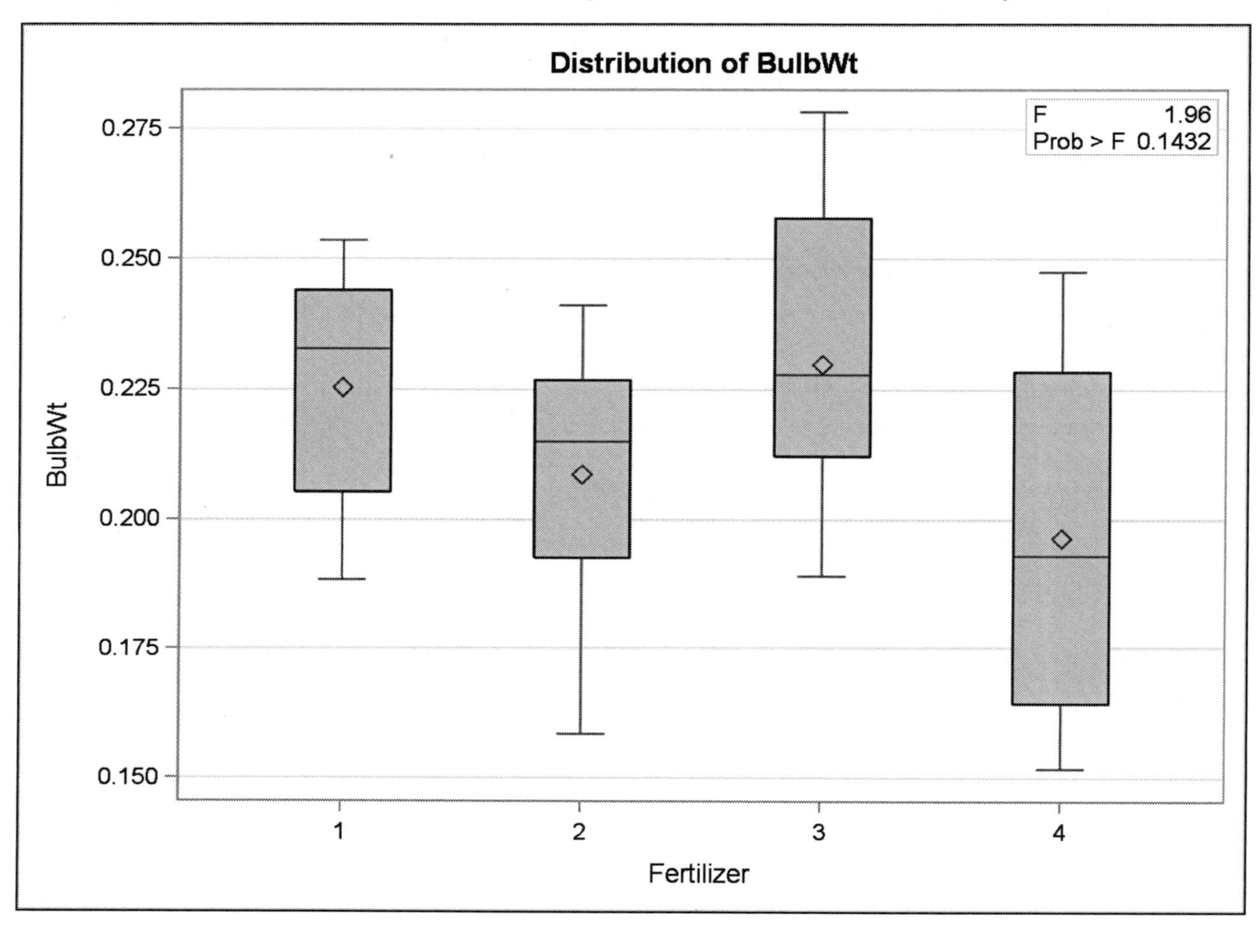


The default plot created with this code is a box plot.

It is good practice to check the validity of your ANOVA assumptions. The next part of the program is dedicated to verifying those statistical assumptions for inference tests.

```
/*st102d03.sas*/  /*Part B*/
proc glm data=sasuser.MGGarlic plots(only)=diagnostics;
   class Fertilizer;
   model BulbWt=Fertilizer;
   means Fertilizer / hovtest;
   title 'Testing for Equality of Means with PROC GLM';
run;
quit;
```

Selected MEANS statement option:

HOVTEST performs Levene's test for homogeneity (equality) of variances. The null hypothesis for this test is that the variances are equal. Levene's test is the default.

Selected PLOTS option:

DIAGNOSTICS produces a panel display of diagnostic plots for linear models.

The UNPACK option can be used in order to separate the individual plots in the panel display.

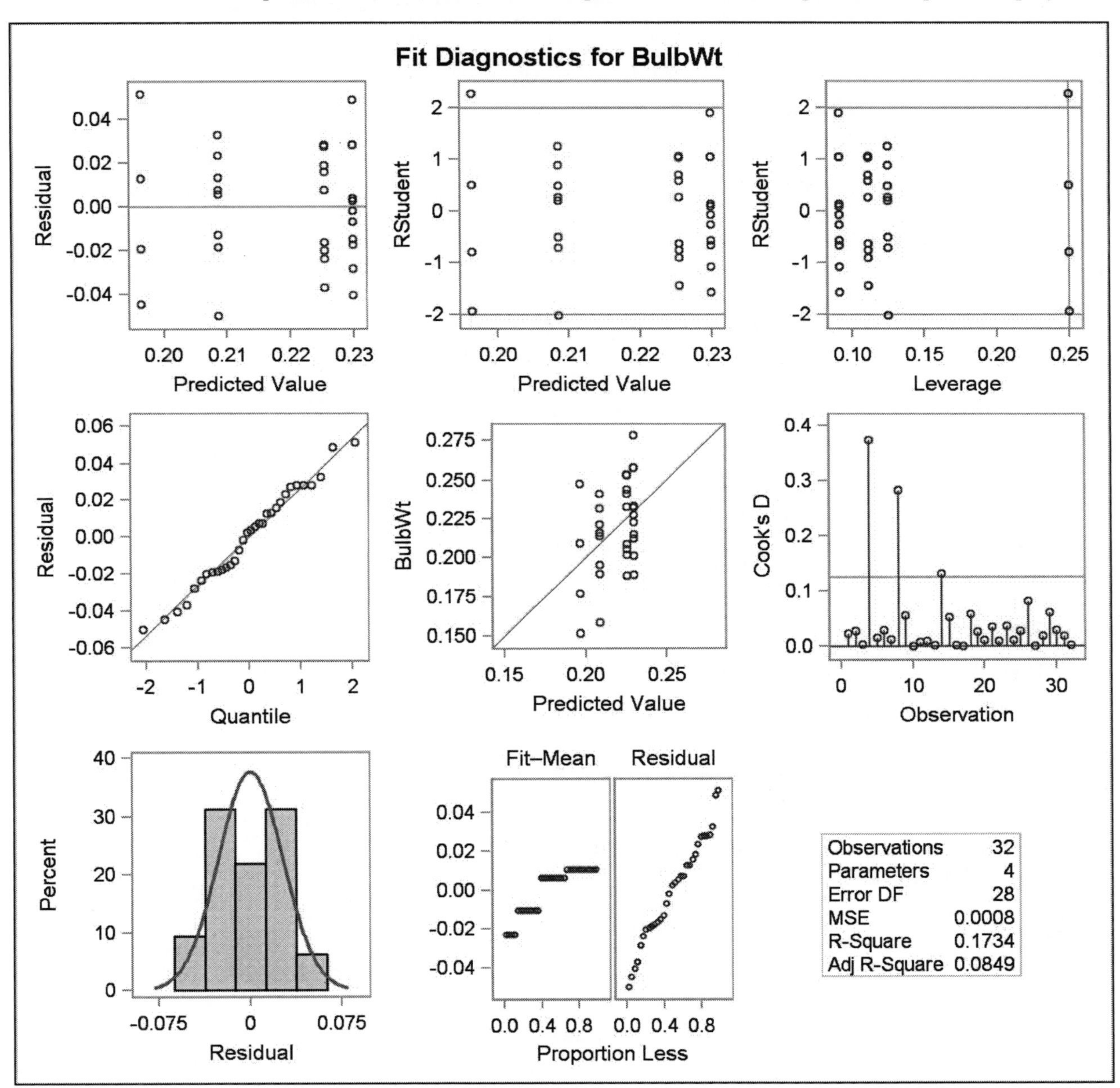


The panel in the upper left corner shows a plot of the residuals versus the fitted values from the ANOVA model. Essentially, you are looking for a random scatter within each group. Any patterns or trends in this plot can indicate model misspecification.

To check the normality assumption, open the residual histogram and Q-Q plot, which are at the bottom left and middle left, respectively.

The histogram has no unique peak and it has short tails. However, it is approximately symmetric.

The data values in the quantile-quantile plot stay close to the diagonal reference line and give strong support to the assumption of normally distributed errors.

Near the end of the tabular output, you can check the assumption of equal variances.

**Levene's Test for Homogeneity of BulbWt Variance**
**ANOVA of Squared Deviations from Group Means**

| Source | DF | Sum of Squares | Mean Square | F Value | Pr > F |
|---|---|---|---|---|---|
| Fertilizer | 3 | 1.716E-6 | 5.719E-7 | 0.98 | 0.4173 |
| Error | 28 | 0.000016 | 5.849E-7 | | |

The output above is the result of the HOVTEST option in the MEANS statement. Levene's test for homogeneity of variances is the default. The null hypothesis is that the variances are equal over all **Fertilizer** groups. The *p*-value of 0.4173 is not smaller than your alpha level of 0.05 and therefore you do not reject the null hypothesis. One of your assumptions is met.

At this point, if you determined that the variances were not equal, you could add the WELCH option to the MEANS statement. This requests Welch's (1951) variance-weighted one-way ANOVA. This alternative to the usual ANOVA is robust to the assumption of equal variances. This is similar to the unequal variance *t* test for two populations. See the appendix for more information.

## Analysis Plan for ANOVA – Summary

Null Hypothesis: All means are equal.

Alternative Hypothesis: At least one mean is different.

1. Produce descriptive statistics.
2. Verify assumptions.
   - Independence
   - Errors are normally distributed.
   - Error variances are equal for all groups.
3. Examine the *p*-value in the ANOVA table. If the *p*-value is less than alpha, reject the null hypothesis.

45

## Exercises

**2. Analyzing Data in a Completely Randomized Design**

Consider an experiment to study four types of advertising: local newspaper ads, local radio ads, in-store salespeople, and in-store displays. The country is divided into 144 locations, and 36 locations are randomly assigned to each type of advertising. The level of sales is measured for each region in thousands of dollars. You want to see whether the average sales are significantly different for various types of advertising. The **sasuser.ads** data set contains data for these variables:

**Ad** type of advertising

**Sales** level of sales in thousands of dollars

**a.** Examine the data. Use the MEANS and SGPLOT procedures. What information can you obtain from looking at the data?

**b.** Test the hypothesis that the means are equal. Be sure to check that the assumptions of the analysis method that you choose are met. What conclusions can you reach at this point in your analysis?

# 2.3 ANOVA with Data from a Randomized Block Design

## Objectives

- Recognize the difference between a completely randomized design and a randomized block design.
- Differentiate between observed data and designed experiments.
- Use the GLM procedure to analyze data from a randomized block design.

49

## Observational or Retrospective Studies

- Groups can be naturally occurring.
  - for example, gender and ethnicity
- Random assignment might be unethical or untenable.
  - for example, smoking or credit risk groups
- Often you look at what already happened (retrospective) instead of following through to the future (prospective).
- You have little control over other factors contributing to the outcome measure.

50

In the original study, the Montana Gourmet Garlic growers randomly assigned their treatments (fertilizer) to plants in each of their Spanish Roja beds. They did this as an afterthought before they realized that they were going to do a statistical analysis. In fact, this could reasonably be thought of as a retrospective study. When you analyze the differences between naturally occurring groups, you are not actually manipulating a treatment. There is no true independent variable.

Many public health and business analyses are retrospective studies. The data values are observed as they occur, not affected by an experimental design. Often this is the best you can do. For example, you cannot ethically randomly assign people to smoking and nonsmoking groups.

## Controlled Experiments

- Random assignment might be desirable to eliminate selection bias.
- You often want to look at the outcome measure prospectively.
- You can manipulate the factors of interest and can more reasonably claim causation.
- You can design your experiment to control for other factors contributing to the outcome measure.

51

Given the negative results of the fertilizer study from 2006, the garlic growers planned a prospective study in 2007. They decided they needed to try more rigorously to control the influences on the growth of garlic.

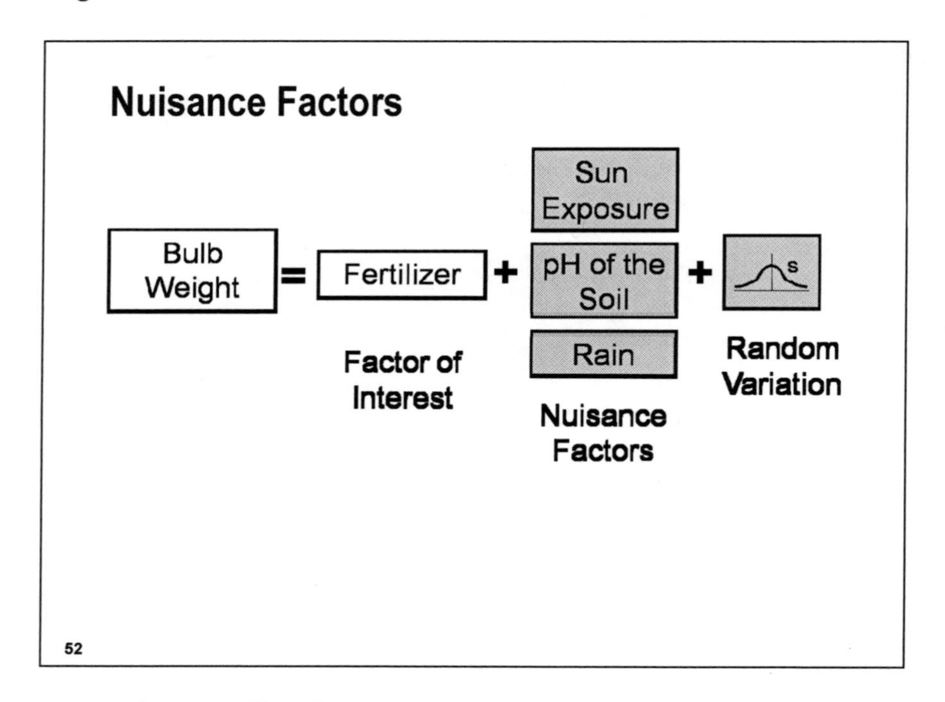


Factors that can affect the outcome but are not of interest in the experiment are called *nuisance factors*. The variation due to nuisance factors becomes part of the random variation.

## 2.04 Multiple Choice Poll

Which part of the ANOVA tables contains the variation due to nuisance factors?

a. Sum of Squares Model
b. Sum of Squares Error
c. Degrees of Freedom

54

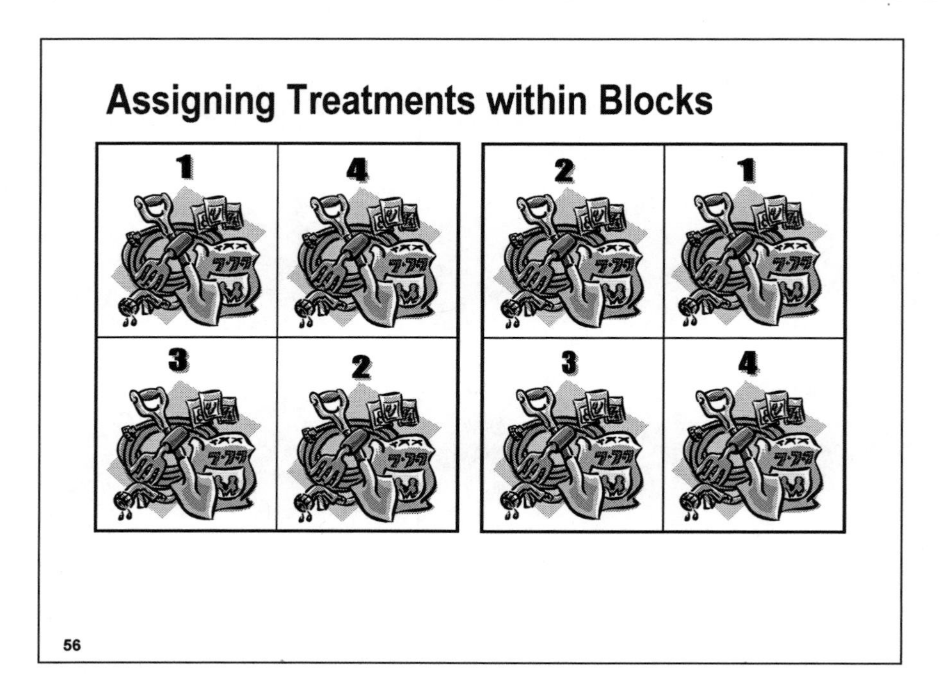


A discussion with a statistician helped the farmers identify other determinants of garlic bulb weight. The statistician suggested that, although they could not actually apply those factors randomly (they could not change the weather or the soil pH or composition or sun exposure), they could control for those factors by blocking. He suggested that whatever the effects of those external influences are, the magnitudes of those nuisance factors should be approximately the same within sectors of the farm land. Therefore, instead of randomizing the **Fertilizer** treatment across all 32 beds, he suggested they only randomize the application of the four **Fertilizer** treatments within each of the eight sectors.

An experimental design such as this is often referred to as a *randomized block design*. In this case, **Sector** is the block. The blocking variable **Sector** is included in the model, but you are not interested in its effect, only in controlling the nuisance factor effects explained by it. By including **Sector** in the model, you could potentially account for many nuisance factors.

Blocking is a logical grouping of experimental units. In this study, applying all four fertilizers to the same sector makes sense from a practical point of view. There might be a great disparity in the presence of nuisance factors across sectors, but you can be reasonably confident that the nuisance factor influence is fairly even within sectors.

Blocking is a restriction on randomization and therefore must be taken into account in data analysis.

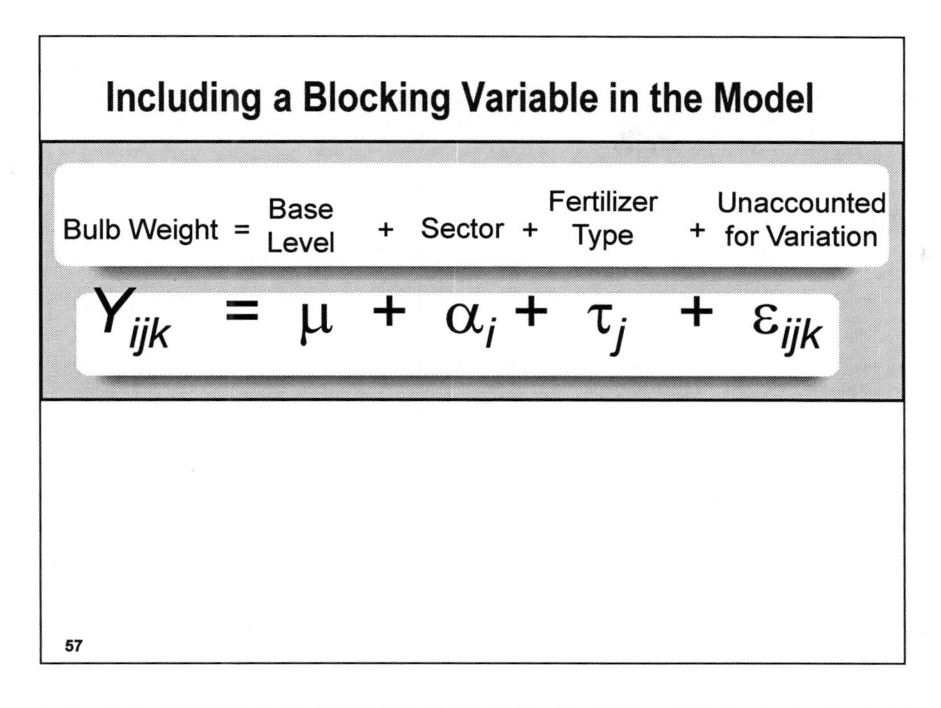


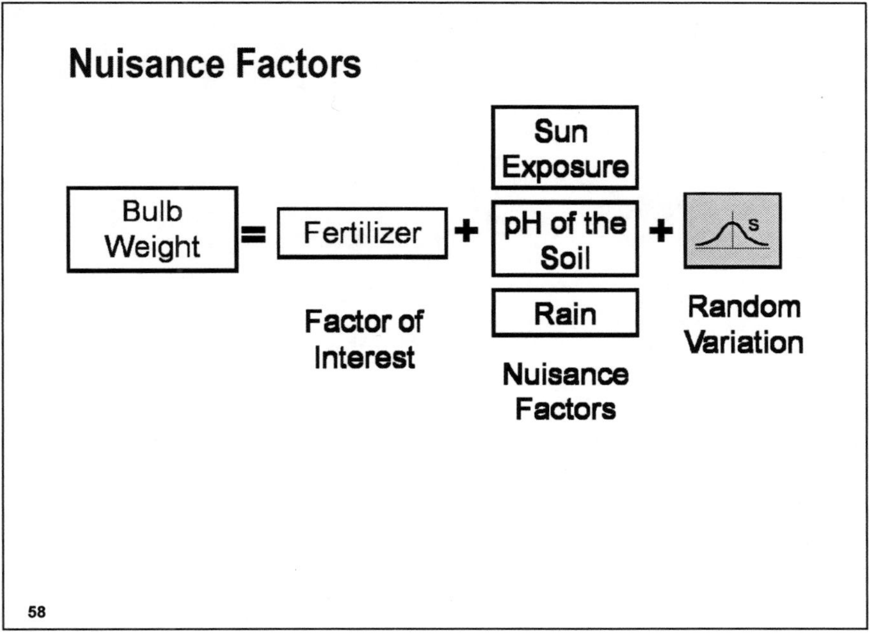


Because **Sector** is included in the ANOVA model, any effect caused by the nuisance factors that are common within a sector are accounted for in the Model Sum of Squares and not the Error Sum of Squares, as was the case in the previous study. Removing significant effects from the Error Sum of Squares tends to give more power to the test of the effect of interest (in this case, **Fertilizer**). That is because the MSE, the denominator of the *F* statistic, tends to be reduced, increasing the *F* value and thereby decreasing the *p*-value.

## 2.05 Multiple Choice Poll

In a block design, which part of the ANOVA table contains the variation due to the nuisance factor?

a. Sum of Squares Model
b. Sum of Squares Error
c. Degrees of Freedom

60

## Including a Blocking Variable in the Model

Additional assumptions are as follows:

- Treatments are randomly assigned within each block.
- The effects of the treatment factor are constant across the levels of the blocking variable.

In the garlic example, the design is balanced, which means that there is the same number of garlic samples for every **Fertilizer/Sector** combination.

62

Typically, when the effects of the treatment factor are not constant across the levels of the other variable, then this condition is called *interaction*. However, when a randomized block design is used, it is assumed that the effects are the same within each block. In other words, it is assumed that there are no interactions with the block variable.

In most randomized block designs, the blocking variable is treated as a *random effect*. Treating an effect as random changes how standard errors are calculated and can give different answers from treating it as a fixed effect (as in the example).

In this example, you have the same number of garlic samples for every **Fertilizer/Sector** combination. This is a balanced design. When treatment groups are compared to each other (in other words, not to 0 or some other specified value), the results from treating the block as a fixed or random effect are exactly the same.

A model that includes both random and fixed effects is called a *mixed model* and can be analyzed with the MIXED procedure. The Mixed Models Analyses Using SAS® class focuses on analyzing mixed models. The Statistics 2: ANOVA and Regression class has more detail about how to analyze unbalanced designs and data that do not meet ANOVA assumptions.

For more information about mixed models in SAS, you can also consult the SAS online documentation or the SAS Books by Users book *SAS® System for Mixed Models*, which also goes into detail about the statistical assumptions for mixed models.

## ANOVA with Blocking

```
/*st102d04.sas*/
proc glm data=sasuser.MGGarlic_Block plots(only)=diagnostics;
   class Fertilizer Sector;
   model BulbWt=Fertilizer Sector;
   title 'ANOVA for Randomized Block Design';
run;
quit;
```

Selected PLOTS() option:

(ONLY) requests that only the requested plots be produced and no default plots.

The blocking variable must be in the model and it must be listed in the CLASS statement.

A check of the normality assumption using the Q-Q plot follows.

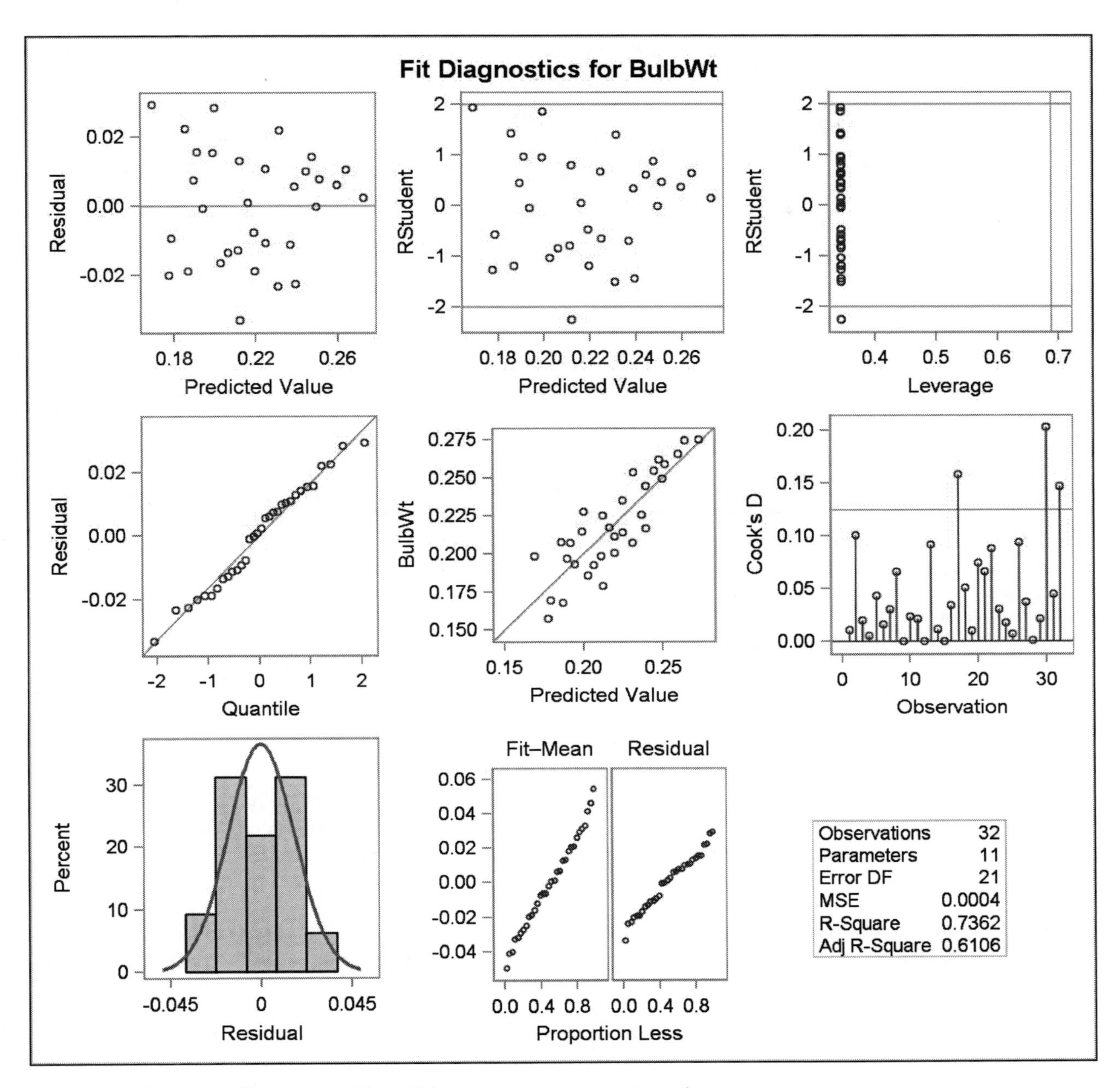


No severe departure from normality of the error terms seem to exist.

Validation of the equal variances assumption for models with more than one independent variable is beyond the scope of this text. This topic is discussed in the Statistics 2: ANOVA and Regression class.

| Class Level Information | | |
|---|---|---|
| **Class** | **Levels** | **Values** |
| **Fertilizer** | 4 | 1 2 3 4 |
| **Sector** | 8 | 1 2 3 4 5 6 7 8 |

The Class Level Information table reflects the addition of the eight-level **Sector** variable.

| Number of Observations Read | 32 |
|---|---|
| Number of Observations Used | 32 |

| Source | DF | Sum of Squares | Mean Square | F Value | Pr > F |
|---|---|---|---|---|---|
| Model | 10 | 0.02307263 | 0.00230726 | 5.86 | 0.0003 |
| Error | 21 | 0.00826745 | 0.00039369 | | |
| Corrected Total | 31 | 0.03134008 | | | |

| R-Square | Coeff Var | Root MSE | BulbWt Mean |
|---|---|---|---|
| 0.736202 | 9.085064 | 0.019842 | 0.218398 |

| Source | DF | Type I SS | Mean Square | F Value | Pr > F |
|---|---|---|---|---|---|
| Fertilizer | 3 | 0.00508630 | 0.00169543 | 4.31 | 0.0162 |
| Sector | 7 | 0.01798632 | 0.00256947 | 6.53 | 0.0004 |

| Source | DF | Type III SS | Mean Square | F Value | Pr > F |
|---|---|---|---|---|---|
| Fertilizer | 3 | 0.00508630 | 0.00169543 | 4.31 | 0.0162 |
| Sector | 7 | 0.01798632 | 0.00256947 | 6.53 | 0.0004 |

The overall $F$ test ($F(10,21)=5.86$, $p=0.0003$) indicates that there are significant differences between the means of the garlic bulb weights across fertilizers or blocks (sectors). However, because there is more than one term in the model, you cannot tell whether the differences are due to differences among the fertilizers or differences across sectors. In order to make that determination, you must look at the subsequent tests for each factor.

What have you gained by including **Sector** in the model? If you compare the estimate of the experimental error variance (MSE), you note this is smaller compared to the data and model that included **Fertilizer** only (0.00039369 versus 0.00077966). Depending on the magnitude of the difference, this could affect the comparisons between the treatment means by finding more significant differences than the **Fertilizer**-only model, given the same sample sizes.

Also notice that the R square for this model is much greater than that in the previous model (0.736 versus 0.173). To some degree, this is a function of having more model degrees of freedom, but it is unlikely this is the only reason for this magnitude of difference.

Most important to the Montana Gourmet Garlic farmers is that the effect of **Fertilizer** in this model is now significant ($F=4.31$, $p=0.0162$). The Type III SS test is at the bottom of the output tests for differences due to each variable, controlling for (or "adjusting for") the other variable.

The Type I SS test is *sequential*. In other words, the test for each variable only adjusts for the variables above it. In this case, because the design is completely balanced, the Type I and Type III tests would be exactly the same. In general that would not be true.

In determining the usefulness of having a blocking variable (**Sector**) included in the model, you can consider the $F$ value for the blocking variable. Some statisticians suggest that if this ratio is greater than 1, then the blocking factor is useful. If the ratio is less than 1, then adding the variable is detrimental to the analysis. If you find that including the blocking factor is detrimental to the analysis, then you can exclude it from future studies, but it ***must*** be included in all ANOVA models calculated with the sample that you already collected. This is because blocking places a restriction on the random assignment of units to treatments, and modeling the data without the blocking variable treats the data as if that restriction did not exist.

## Exercises

### 3. Analyzing Data in a Randomized Block Design

When you design the advertising experiment in the first question, you are concerned that there is variability caused by the area of the country. You are not particularly interested in what differences are caused by **Area**, but you are interested in isolating the variability due to this factor. The **sasuser.ads1** data set contains data for the following variables:

| | |
|---|---|
| **Ad** | type of advertising |
| **Area** | area of the country |
| **Sales** | level of sales in thousands of dollars |

Test the hypothesis that the means are equal. Include all of the variables in your MODEL statement.

**a.** What can you conclude from your analysis?

**b.** Was adding the blocking variable **Area** into the design and analysis detrimental to the test of **Ad**?

## 2.06 Multiple Answer Poll

If the blocking variable **Area** had a very small *F* value, what would be a valid next step? Select all that apply.

a. Remove it from the MODEL statement and rerun the analysis.
b. Test an interaction term.
c. Report the *F* value and plan a new study.

67

## My Groups Are Different. What Next?

- The *p*-value for **Fertilizer** indicates you should reject the $H_0$ that all groups are the same.
- From which pairs of fertilizers, are garlic bulb weights different from one another?
- Should you go back and do several *t* tests?

70

The garlic researchers know that not all fertilizers are created equal, but which one is the best?

# 2.4 ANOVA Post Hoc Tests

## Objectives

- Perform pairwise comparisons among groups after finding a significant effect of an independent variable in ANOVA.
- Demonstrate graphical features in PROC GLM for performing post hoc tests.
- Interpret a diffogram.
- Interpret a control plot.

72

## 2.07 Multiple Choice Poll

With a fair coin, your probability of getting heads on one flip is 0.5. If you flip a coin once and got heads, what is the probability of getting heads on the second try?

a. 0.50
b. 0.25
c. 0.00
d. 1.00
e. 0.75

74

## 2.08 Multiple Choice Poll

With a fair coin, your probability of getting heads on one flip is 0.5. If you flip a coin twice, what is the probability of getting ***at least*** one head out of two?

a. 0.50

b. 0.25

c. 0.00

d. 1.00

e. 0.75

76

## Multiple Comparison Methods

| Comparisonwise Error Rate ($\alpha$=0.05) | Number of Comparisons | Experimentwise Error Rate ($\alpha$=0.05) |
|---|---|---|
| .05 | 1 | .05 |
| .05 | 3 | .14 |
| .05 | 6 | .26 |
| .05 | 10 | .40 |

EER $\leq 1 - (1 - \alpha)^{nc}$ where *nc*=number of comparisons

78

When you control the comparisonwise error rate (CER), you fix the level of alpha for a single comparison, without taking into consideration all the pairwise comparisons that you are making.

The experimentwise error rate (EER) uses an alpha that takes into consideration all the pairwise comparisons that you are making. Presuming no differences exist, the chance that you falsely conclude that ***at least one*** difference exists is much higher when you consider all possible comparisons.

If you want to make sure that the error rate is 0.05 for the entire set of comparisons, use a method that controls the experimentwise error rate at 0.05.

There is some disagreement among statisticians about the need to control the experimentwise error rate.

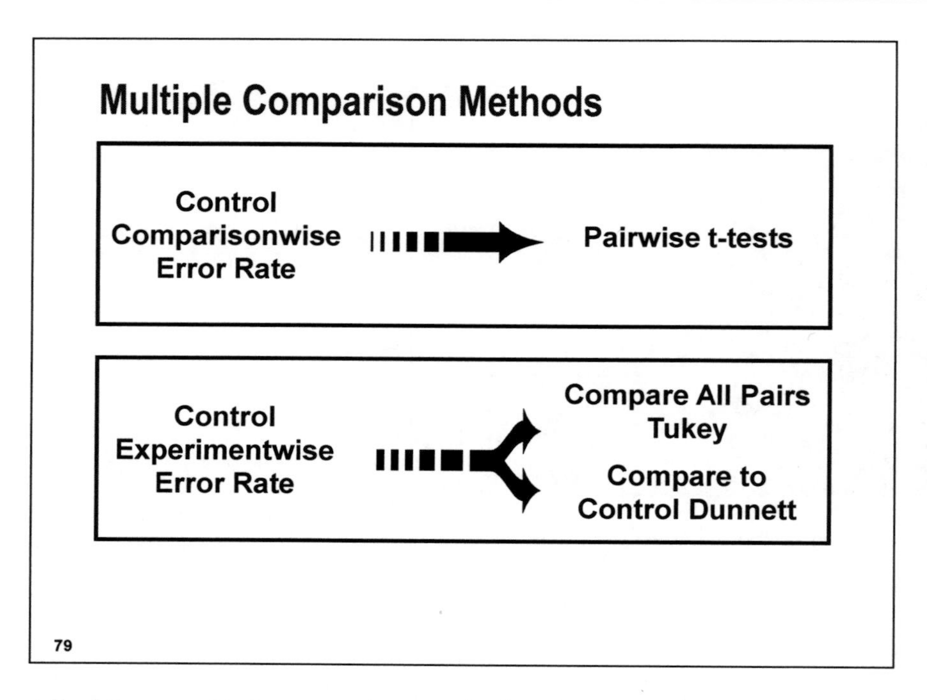


All of these multiple comparison methods are requested with options in the LSMEANS statement of PROC GLM.

In order to call for the statistical hypothesis tests for group differences and ODS Statistical Graphics to support them, turn on ODS Graphics and then:

- For Comparisonwise Control LSMEANS / PDIFF=ALL ADJUST=T
- For Experimentwise Control LSMEANS / PDIFF=ALL ADJUST=TUKEY or PDIFF=CONTROL('*control level*') ADJUST=DUNNETT

Many other available options control the experimentwise error rate. For information about these options, see the SAS documentation.

One-tailed tests against a control level can be requested using the CONTROLL (lower tail) or CONTROLU (upper tail) options in the LSMEANS statement.

## Tukey's Multiple Comparison Method

This method is appropriate when you consider pairwise comparisons only.

The experimentwise error rate is

- equal to alpha when ***all*** pairwise comparisons are considered
- less than alpha when ***fewer*** than all pairwise comparisons are considered.

80

A pairwise comparison examines the difference between two treatment means. "All pairwise comparisons" means all possible combinations of two treatment means.

Tukey's multiple comparison adjustment is based on conducting all pairwise comparisons and guarantees that the Type I experimentwise error rate is equal to alpha for this situation. If you choose to do fewer than all pairwise comparisons, then this method is more conservative.

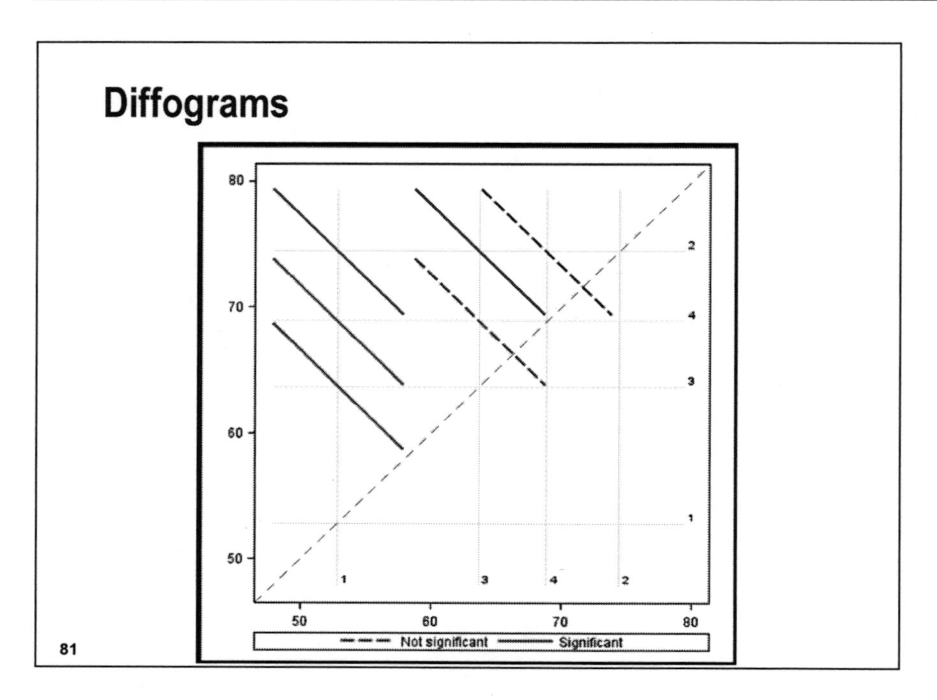


A *diffogram* can be used to quickly tell whether two group means are statistically significant. The point estimates for the differences between pairs of group means can be found at the intersections of the vertical and horizontal lines drawn at group mean values. The downward-sloping diagonal lines show the confidence intervals for the differences. The upward-sloping line is a reference line showing where the group means would be equal. Intersection of the downward-sloping diagonal line for a pair with the upward-sloping, broken gray diagonal line implies that the confidence interval includes zero and that the mean difference between the two groups is not statistically significant. In that case, the diagonal line for the pair will be broken. If the confidence interval does not include zero, then the diagonal line for the pair will be solid. With ODS statistical graphics, these plots are automatically generated when you use the PDIFF=ALL option in the LSMEANS statement.

## Special Case of Comparing to a Control

Comparing to a control is appropriate when there is a natural reference group, such as a placebo group in a drug trial.

- Experimentwise error rate is no greater than the stated alpha.
- Comparing to a control takes into account the correlations among tests.
- One-sided hypothesis tests against a control group can be performed.
- Control comparison computes and tests *k*-1 groupwise differences, where *k* is the number of levels of the CLASS variable.
- An example is the Dunnett method.

82

Dunnett's method is recommended when there is a true control group. When appropriate (when a natural control category exists, against which all other categories are compared) it is more powerful than methods that control for all possible comparisons. In order to do a one-sided test, use the option PDIFF=CONTROLL (for lower-tail tests when the alternative hypothesis states that a group's mean is less than the control group's mean) or PDIFF=CONTROLU (for upper-tail tests when the alternative hypothesis states that a group's mean is greater than the control group's mean).

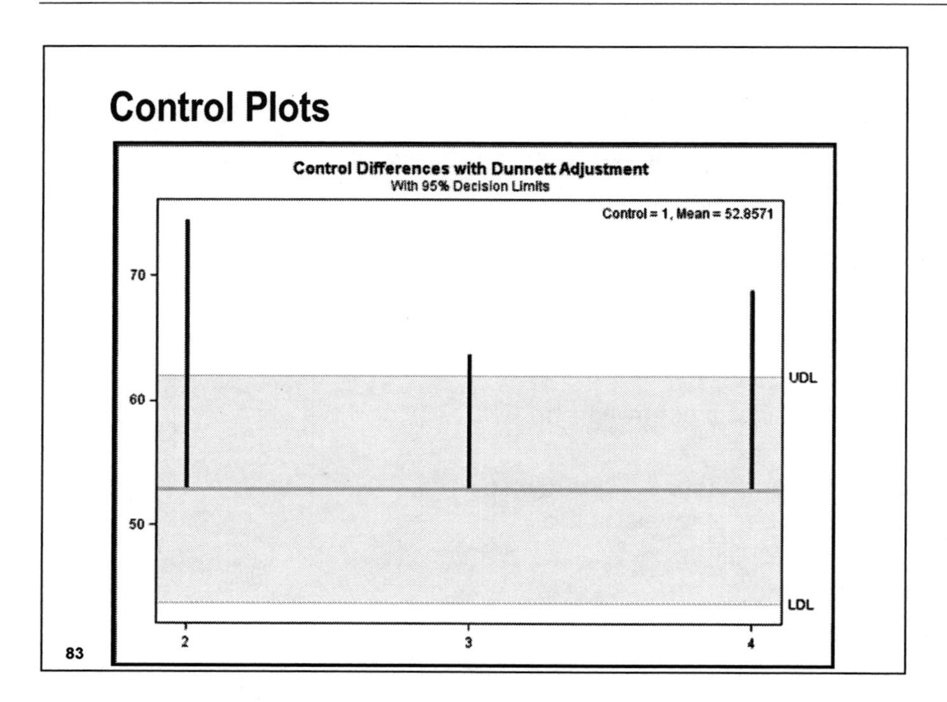


LS-mean control plots are produced only when you specify PDIFF=CONTROL or ADJUST=DUNNETT in the LSMEANS statement, and in this case they are produced by default. The value of the control is shown as a horizontal line. The shaded area is bounded by the UDL and LDL (Upper Decision Limit and Lower Decision Limit). If the vertical line extends past the shaded area, that means that the group represented by that line is significantly different from the control group.

## Post Hoc Pairwise Comparisons

Example: Use the LSMEANS statement in PROC GLM to produce comparison information about the means of the treatments.

```
/*st102d05.sas*/
proc glm data=sasuser.MGGarlic_Block
         plots(only)=(controlplot diffplot(center));
   class Fertilizer Sector;
   model BulbWt=Fertilizer Sector;
   lsmeans Fertilizer / pdiff=all adjust=tukey;
   lsmeans Fertilizer / pdiff=control('4') adjust=dunnett;
   lsmeans Fertilizer / pdiff=all adjust=t;
   title 'Garlic Data: Multiple Comparisons';
run;
quit;
```

Multiple LSMEANS statements are permitted, although typically only one type of multiple comparison method would be used for each LSMEANS effect. Three different methods are shown for illustration here. For this analysis, the garlic growers were unblinded to the fertilizers and number 4 is the chemical fertilizer. They might conceivably use Dunnett comparisons if they were only interested in knowing whether any of the organic fertilizers created differently sized bulbs compared with the chemical fertilizer.

Selected PLOTS= options:

CONTROLPLOT
: requests a display in which least squares means are compared against a reference level. LS-mean control plots are produced only when you specify PDIFF=CONTROL or ADJUST=DUNNETT in the LSMEANS statement, and in this case they are produced by default.

DIFFPLOT
: modifies the diffogram produced by an LSMEANS statement with the PDIFF=ALL option (or only PDIFF, because ALL is the default argument). The CENTER option marks the center point for each comparison. This point corresponds to the intersection of two least squares means.

Selected LSMEANS statement options:

PDIFF=
: requests *p*-values for the differences, which is the probability of seeing a difference between two means that is as large as the observed means or larger if the two population means are actually the same. You can request to compare all means using PDIFF=ALL. You can also specify which means to compare. For details, see the documentation for LSMEANS under the GLM procedure.

ADJUST=
: specifies the adjustment method for multiple comparisons. If no adjustment method is specified, the Tukey method is used by default. The T option asks that no adjustment be made for multiple comparisons. The TUKEY option uses Tukey's adjustment method. The DUNNETT option uses Dunnett's method. For a list of available methods, check the documentation for LSMEANS under the GLM procedure.

The MEANS statement can be used for multiple comparisons. However, the results can be misleading if the groups that are specified have different numbers of observations.

The following output is for the Tukey LSMEANS comparisons.

| Fertilizer | BulbWt LSMEAN | LSMEAN Number |
|---|---|---|
| 1 | 0.23625000 | 1 |
| 2 | 0.21115125 | 2 |
| 3 | 0.22330125 | 3 |
| 4 | 0.20288875 | 4 |

**Least Squares Means for effect Fertilizer**
**Pr > |t| for H0: LSMean(i)=LSMean(j)**

**Dependent Variable: BulbWt**

| i/j | 1 | 2 | 3 | 4 |
|---|---|---|---|---|
| 1 | | 0.0840 | 0.5699 | 0.0144 |
| 2 | 0.0840 | | 0.6186 | 0.8383 |
| 3 | 0.5699 | 0.6186 | | 0.1995 |
| 4 | 0.0144 | 0.8383 | 0.1995 | |

The first part of the output shows the means for each group. The second part of the output shows *p*-values from pairwise comparisons of all possible combinations of means. Notice that row 2/column 4 has the same *p*-value as row 4/column 2 because the same two means are compared in each case. Both are displayed as a convenience to the user. Notice also that row 1/column 1, row 2/column 2, and so on, are blank, because it does not make any sense to compare a mean to itself.

The only significant pairwise difference is between fertilizer 1 and fertilizer 4 (*p*-value=0.0144).

The Least Square Means are shown graphically in the mean plot. The Tukey-adjusted differences among the LSMEANS are shown in the diffogram.

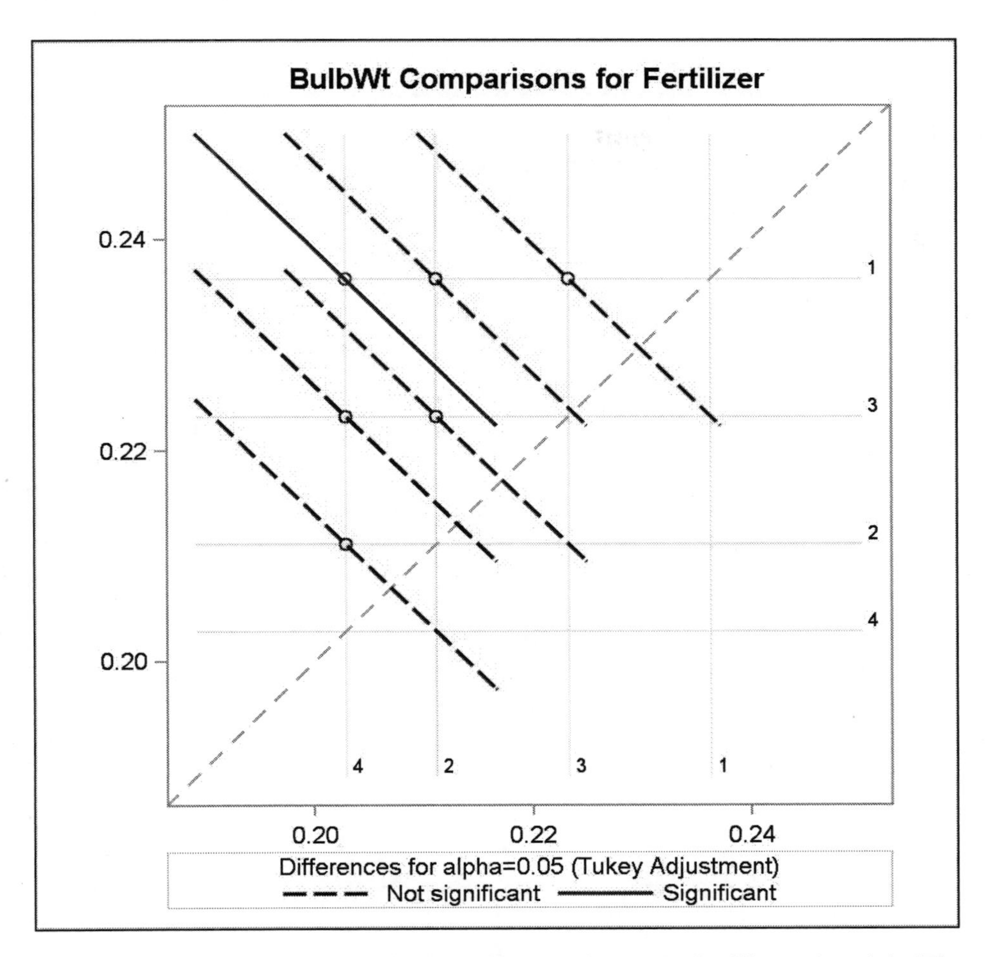


The solid line shows the significant difference between fertilizers 1 and 4. (The confidence limit for the difference does not cross the diagonal equivalence line.)

The following output is for the Dunnett LSMEANS comparisons:

| Fertilizer | BulbWt LSMEAN | H0:LSMean=Control Pr > \|t\| |
|---|---|---|
| 1 | 0.23625000 | 0.0080 |
| 2 | 0.21115125 | 0.7435 |
| 3 | 0.22330125 | 0.1274 |
| 4 | 0.20288875 | |

In this case, the first three fertilizers are compared to fertilizer 4, the chemical fertilizer. Even though the mean weights of garlic bulbs using any of the three organic methods are all greater than the mean weight of garlic bulbs grown using the chemical fertilizer, only fertilizer 1 can be said to be statistically significantly better.

The Control plot is below:

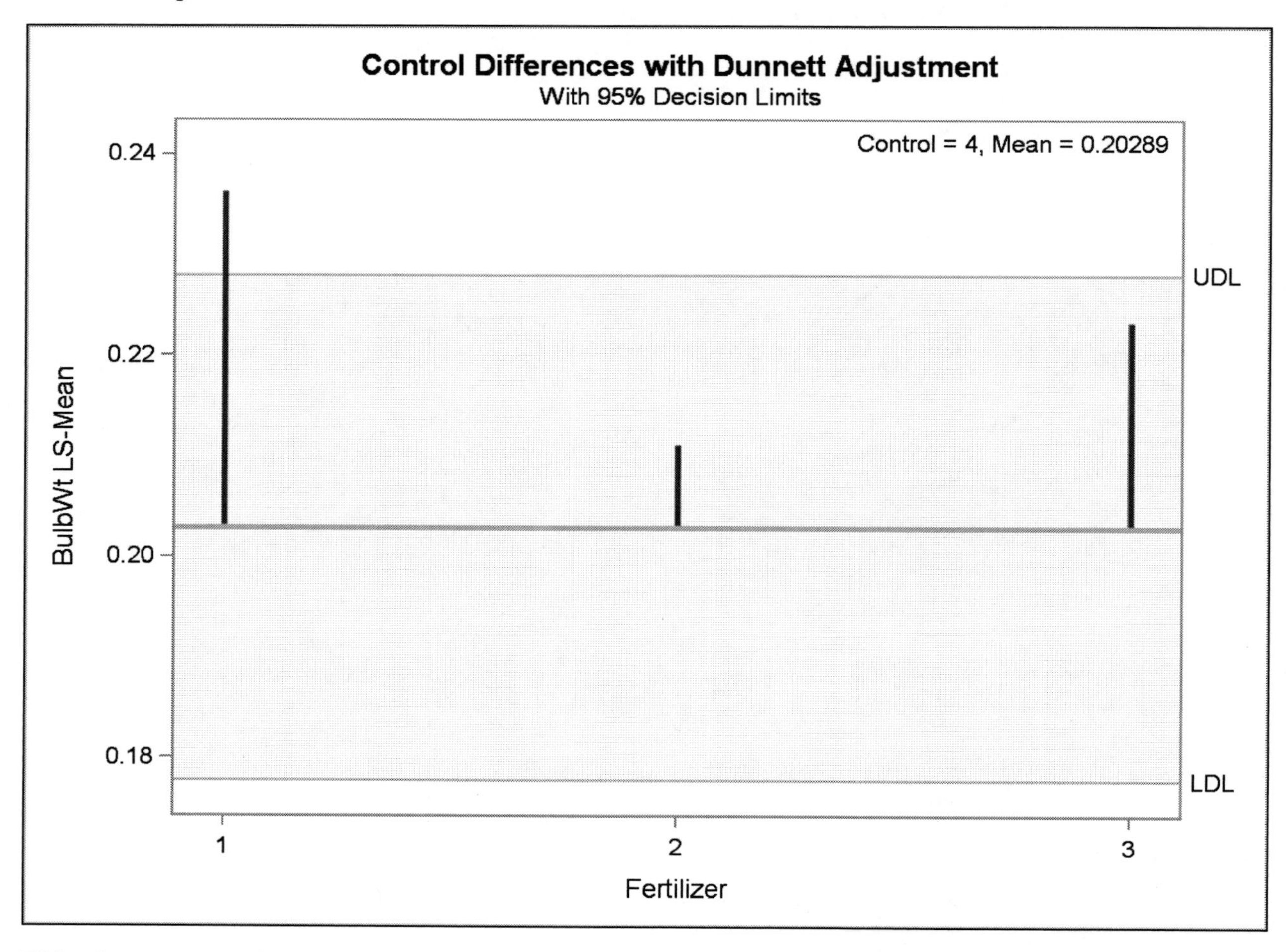


This plot corresponds to the tables that were summarized. The horizontal line is drawn at the least squared mean for group 4, which is 0.20289. The three other means are represented by the tops of the vertical lines extending from the horizontal control line. The only line that extended beyond the shaded area of nonsignificance is the line for fertilizer 1. That shows graphically that the mean bulb weight for fertilizer 1 is significantly different from the mean bulb weight for fertilizer 4.

Finally, for comparison, the *t* tests are shown, which do not adjust for multiple comparisons and are therefore more liberal than tests that do control for experimentwise error:

| Fertilizer | BulbWt LSMEAN | LSMEAN Number |
|---|---|---|
| 1 | 0.23625000 | 1 |
| 2 | 0.21115125 | 2 |
| 3 | 0.22330125 | 3 |
| 4 | 0.20288875 | 4 |

| Least Squares Means for effect Fertilizer<br>Pr > \|t\| for H0: LSMean(i)=LSMean(j)<br><br>Dependent Variable: BulbWt | | | | |
|---|---|---|---|---|
| i/j | 1 | 2 | 3 | 4 |
| 1 | | 0.0195 | 0.2059 | 0.0029 |
| 2 | 0.0195 | | 0.2342 | 0.4143 |
| 3 | 0.2059 | 0.2342 | | 0.0523 |
| 4 | 0.0029 | 0.4143 | 0.0523 | |

The *p*-values in this table are all smaller than those in the Tukey table. In fact, using this method shows one additional significant pairwise difference. Fertilizer 1 is significantly different from fertilizer 2 (*p*=0.0195). The comparison between 3 and 4 is nearly significant at alpha=0.05 (*p*=0.0523).

The diffogram shows the additional significant difference:

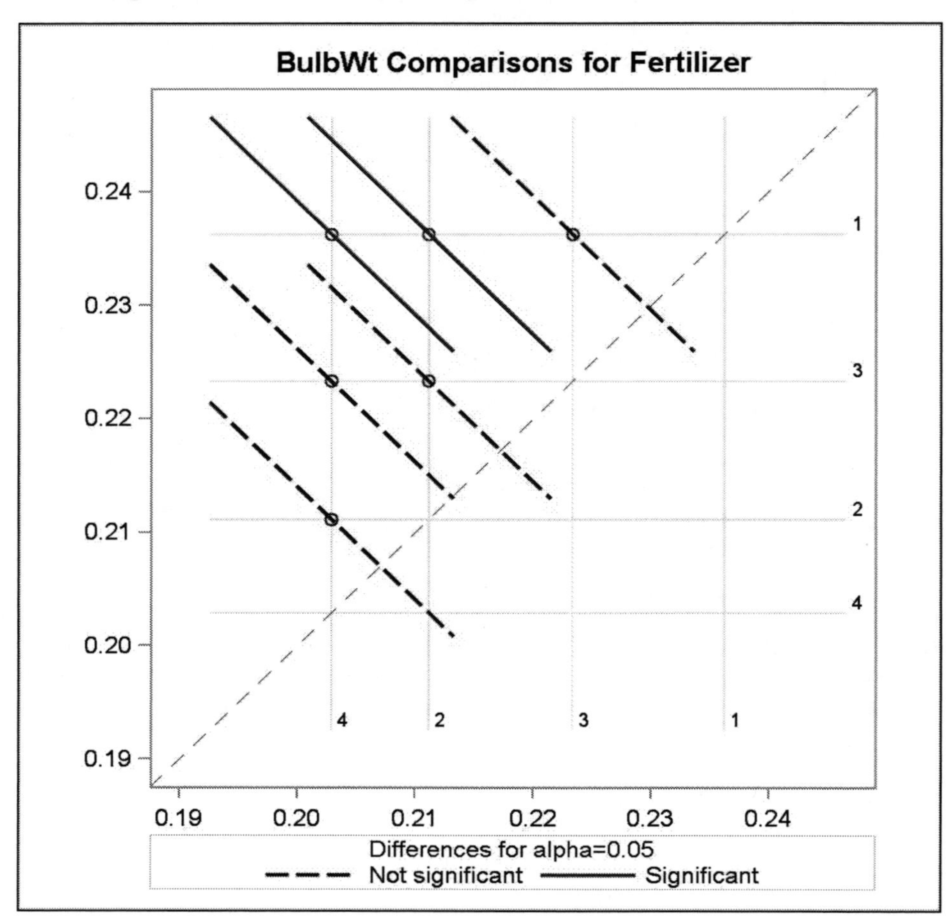

# Exercises

**4. Post Hoc Pairwise Comparisons**

Consider again the analysis of the **sasuser.Ads1** data set. There was a statistically significant difference among means for sales for the different types of advertising. Perform a post hoc test to look at the individual differences among means for the advertising campaigns.

**a.** Conduct pairwise comparisons with an experimentwise error rate of $\alpha=0.05$. (Use the Tukey adjustment.) Which types of advertising are significantly different?

**b.** Use **display** (case sensitive) as the control group and do a Dunnett comparison of all other advertising methods to see whether those methods resulted in significantly different amounts of sales compared with display ads in stores.

# 2.5 Two-Way ANOVA with Interactions

## Objectives

- Fit a two-way ANOVA model.
- Detect interactions between factors.
- Analyze the treatments when there is a significant interaction.

88

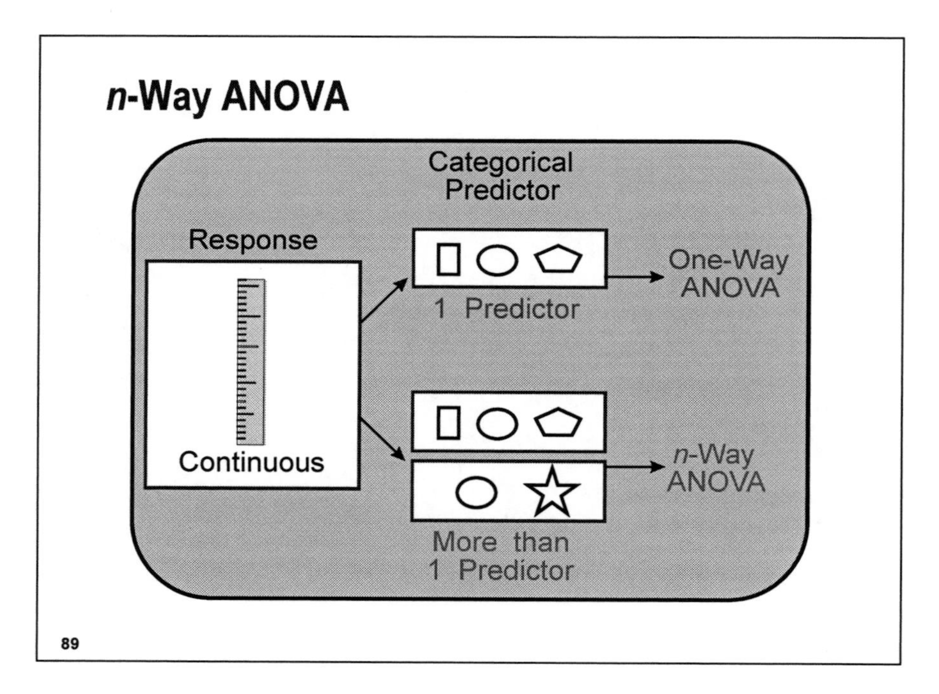


In the previous section, you considered the case where you had one categorical predictor and a blocking variable. In this section, consider a case with two categorical predictors. In general, any time you have more than one categorical predictor variable and a continuous response variable, it is called *n*-way ANOVA. The *n* can be replaced with the number of categorical predictor variables.

The analysis for a randomized block design is actually a special type of *n*-way ANOVA.

## Drug Example

The purpose of the study is to look at the effect of a new prescription drug on blood pressure.

90

Example: Data were collected in an effort to determine whether different dose levels of a given drug have an effect on blood pressure for people with one of three types of heart disease. The data are in the **sasuser.Drug** data set.

The data set contains the following variables:

**DrugDose** dosage level of drug (1, 2, 3, 4), corresponding to (Placebo, 50 mg, 100 mg, 200 mg)

**Disease** heart disease category

**BloodP** change in diastolic blood pressure after 2 weeks treatment

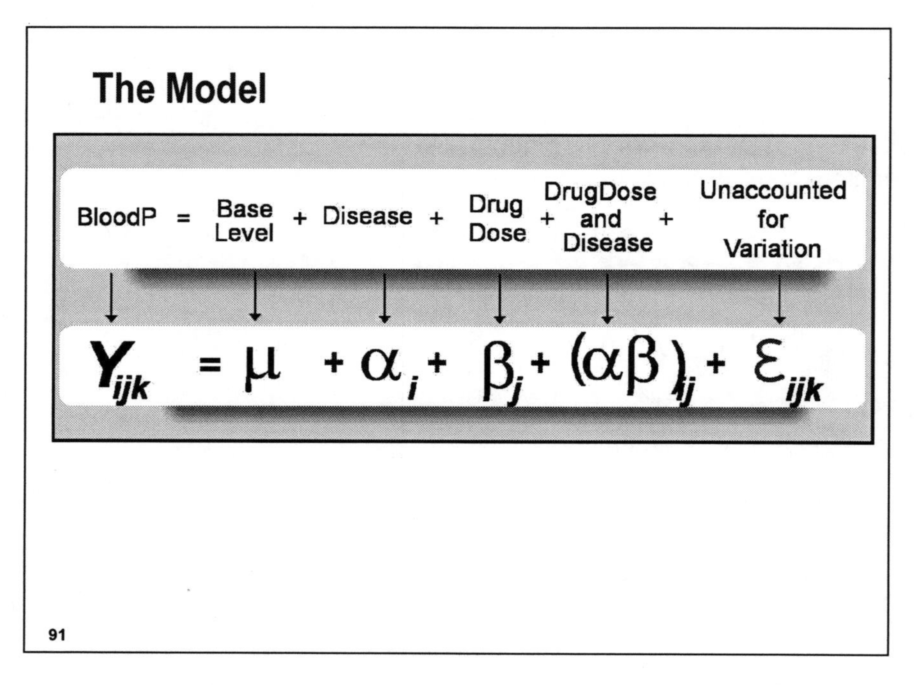


$Y_{ijk}$ the observed **BloodP** for each subject

$\mu$ the overall base level of the response, **BloodP**

$\alpha_i$ the effect of the $i^{th}$ **Disease**

$\beta_j$ the effect of the $j^{th}$ **DrugDose**

$(\alpha\beta)_{ij}$ the effect of the interaction between the $i^{th}$ **Disease** and the $j^{th}$ **DrugDose**

$\varepsilon_{ijk}$ error term, or residual

In the model, the following is assumed:

- Observations are independent.
- Error terms are normally distributed for each treatment.
- Variances are equal across treatments.

Verifying ANOVA assumptions with more than two variables is discussed in the Statistics 2: ANOVA and Regression class.

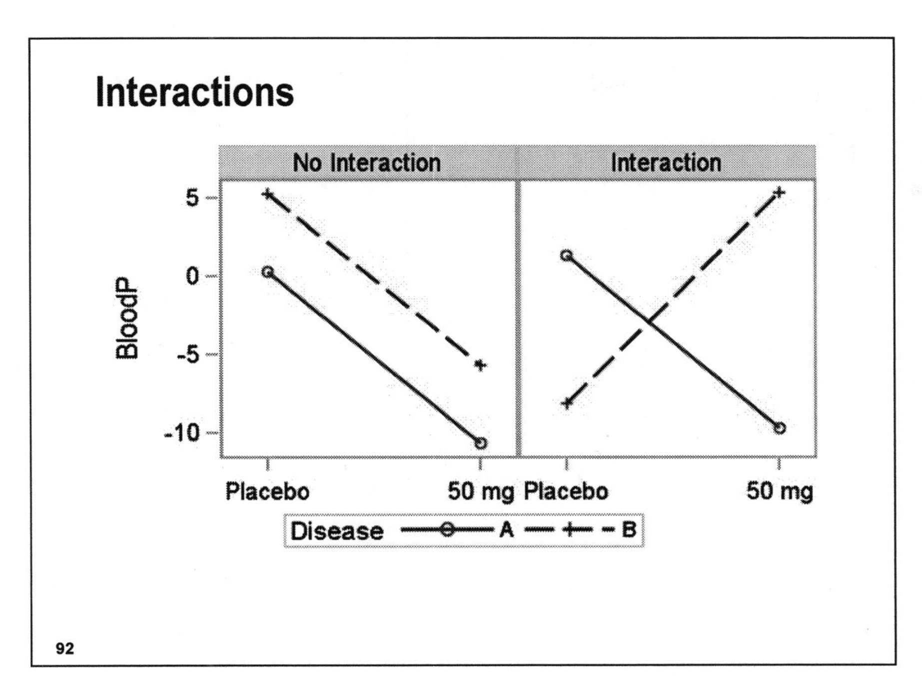


An interaction occurs when the differences between group means on one variable change at different levels of another variable.

The average blood pressure change over different doses was plotted in mean plots and then connected for disease A and B.

In the left plot above, different types of disease show the same change across different levels of dose.

In the right plot, however, as the dose increases, average blood pressure ***decreases*** for those with disease A, but ***increases*** for those with disease B. This indicates an interaction between the variables **DrugDose** and **Disease**.

When you analyze an *n*-way ANOVA with interactions, you should first look at any tests for interaction among factors.

If there is no interaction between the factors, the tests for the individual factor effects can be interpreted as true effects of that factor.

If an interaction exists between any factors, the tests for the individual factor effects might be misleading, due to masking of the effects by the interaction. This is especially true for unbalanced data.

In the previous section, you used a blocking variable and a categorical predictor as effects in the model. It is generally assumed that blocks do not interact with other factors. In this section, neither independent variable is a blocking variable. An interaction between the two can be hypothesized and tested.

## Nonsignificant Interaction

Analyze the main effects with the interaction in the model.

$$Y_{ijk} = \mu + \alpha_i + \beta_j + (\alpha\beta)_{ij} + \varepsilon_{ijk}$$

...or...

Delete the interaction from the model, and then analyze the main effects.

$$Y_{ijk} = \mu + \alpha_i + \beta_j + \varepsilon_{ijk}$$

93

When the interaction is not statistically significant, the main effects can be analyzed with the model as originally written. This is generally the method used when analyzing designed experiments.

However, even when analyzing designed experiments, some statisticians suggest that if the interaction is nonsignificant, the interaction effect can be deleted from the model and then the main effects are analyzed. This increases the power of the main effects tests.

Neter, Kutner, Wasserman, and Nachtsheim (1996) suggest both guidelines for when to delete the interaction from the model:

- There are fewer than five degrees of freedom for the error.
- The $F$ value for the interaction term is $< 2$.

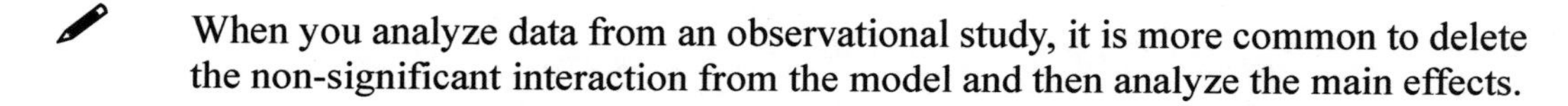

When you analyze data from an observational study, it is more common to delete the non-significant interaction from the model and then analyze the main effects.

## Two-Way ANOVA with Interactions

Before conducting an analysis of variance, you should explore the data.

Presume that the initial data exploration was completed (output not shown here) and that no particular concerns were noted about unusual data values or the distribution of the data. During this exploration, you determine that the sample sizes for all treatments are not equal. The researchers recruited 240 patients (80 per heart disease category), but only 170 were randomized into the trial.

```
/*st102d06.sas*/  /*Part A*/
proc print data=sasuser.drug(obs=10);
   title 'Partial Listing of Drug Data Set';
run;
```

PROC PRINT Output

| Obs | PatientID | DrugDose | Disease | BloodP |
|---|---|---|---|---|
| 1 | 69 | 2 | B | 13 |
| 2 | 162 | 4 | A | -47 |
| 3 | 181 | 1 | B | 12 |
| 4 | 209 | 4 | A | -4 |
| 5 | 308 | 2 | A | 4 |
| 6 | 331 | 4 | C | 37 |
| 7 | 340 | 4 | C | -19 |
| 8 | 350 | 1 | B | -9 |
| 9 | 360 | 2 | B | -17 |
| 10 | 363 | 4 | A | -41 |

Negative values for **BloodP** mean that diastolic blood pressure was reduced, on average, by that amount. Positive values mean that blood pressure was raised, on average.

```
/*st102d06.sas*/  /*Part B*/
proc format;
   value dosefmt 1='Placebo'
                 2='50 mg'
                 3='100 mg'
                 4='200 mg';
run;

proc means data=sasuser.drug
           mean var std nway;
   class Disease DrugDose;
   var BloodP;
   format DrugDose dosefmt.;
   output out=means mean=BloodP_Mean;
   title 'Selected Descriptive Statistics for Drug Data Set';
run;
```

Selected PROC MEANS statement:

OUTPUT This statement creates an output data set that contains values and statistics requested in the statement.

Selected PROC MEANS statement option:

NWAY When you include CLASS variables, NWAY specifies that the output data set contains only statistics for the observations with the highest _TYPE_ and _WAY_ values. NWAY corresponds to the combination of all class variables.

PROC MEANS Output

**Analysis Variable : BloodP**

| Disease | DrugDose | N Obs | Mean | Variance | Std Dev |
|---|---|---|---|---|---|
| A | Placebo | 12 | 1.3333333 | 183.1515152 | 13.5333483 |
| | 50 mg | 16 | -9.6875000 | 356.7625000 | 18.8881577 |
| | 100 mg | 13 | -26.2307692 | 329.0256410 | 18.1390640 |
| | 200 mg | 18 | -22.5555556 | 445.0849673 | 21.0970369 |
| B | Placebo | 15 | -8.1333333 | 285.9809524 | 16.9109714 |
| | 50 mg | 15 | 5.4000000 | 479.1142857 | 21.8886794 |
| | 100 mg | 14 | 24.7857143 | 563.7197802 | 23.7427838 |
| | 200 mg | 13 | 23.2307692 | 556.3589744 | 23.5872630 |
| C | Placebo | 14 | 0.4285714 | 411.8021978 | 20.2929100 |
| | 50 mg | 13 | -4.8461538 | 577.6410256 | 24.0341637 |
| | 100 mg | 14 | -5.1428571 | 195.5164835 | 13.9827209 |
| | 200 mg | 13 | 1.3076923 | 828.5641026 | 28.7847894 |

The mean blood pressure reduction seemed to change at different levels of **DrugDose**. These changes, however, do not seem to follow a consistent pattern across **Disease** categories.

To further explore the numerous treatments, examine the PROC MEANS output graphically.

```
/*st102d06.sas*/  /*Part C*/
proc sgplot data=means;
   series x=DrugDose y=BloodP_Mean / group=Disease markers;
   xaxis integer;
   title 'Plot of Stratified Means in Drug Data Set';
   format DrugDose dosefmt.;
run;
```

The SERIES statement creates a line plot.

Selected SERIES statement option:

MARKERS adds data point markers to the series plot data points.

Selected AXIS statement:

XAXIS INTEGER forces the X-axis to have tick marks only at integer values.

PROC SGPLOT Output

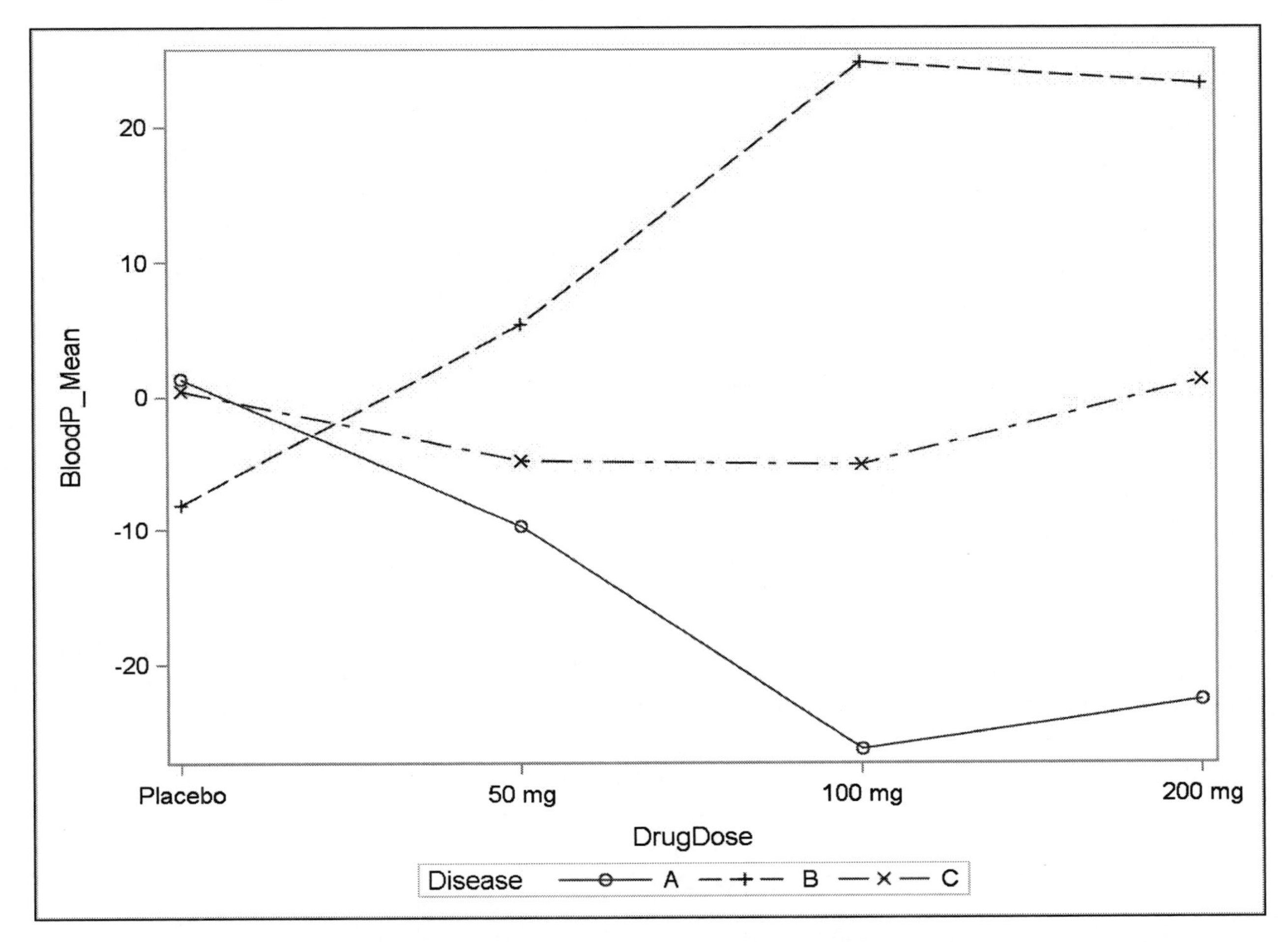


From the graph, the relationship is clearer. For disease type A, blood pressure falls to a greater degree as the drug level increases through 100 mg, and then the change levels off. For disease type B, blood pressure climbs to a greater degree as the drug level increases through 100 mg, and then the change levels off. For disease type C, blood pressure change is relatively unchanged for different drug levels. In fact, the average change score stays close to 0, implying that the drug had neither positive nor negative effects on these patients, regardless of dose. This plot is exploratory, and helps you plan your analysis. Later you see similar plots output directly from PROC GLM.

You can use the GLM procedure to discover whether these differences and their interactions are statistically significant.

```
/*st102d06.sas*/  /*Part D*/
proc glm data=sasuser.drug order=internal;
   class DrugDose Disease;
   model Bloodp=DrugDose Disease DrugDose*Disease;
   title 'Analyze the Effects of DrugDose and Disease';
   title2 'Including Interaction';
   format DrugDose dosefmt.;
run;
quit;
```

Selected PROC GLM option:

ORDER=DATA | FORMATTED | FREQ | INTERNAL

specifies the sorting order for the levels of all classification variables. The ordering is important for the plot in this case.

As seen in the MODEL statement, the interaction term can be added to the model by using a * to separate the two main effects. It does ***not*** need to be created in a DATA step.

PROC GLM Output

| Class Level Information | | |
|---|---|---|
| **Class** | **Levels** | **Values** |
| **DrugDose** | 4 | Placebo 50 mg 100 mg 200 mg |
| **Disease** | 3 | A B C |

| | |
|---|---|
| **Number of Observations Read** | 170 |
| **Number of Observations Used** | 170 |

The next part of the output shows the source table with the $F$ test for the overall model. This tests the null hypothesis that none of the effects in the model is statistically different. In other words, that there are no differences among the 12 group means (one for each **DrugDose*Disease** combination).

| Source | DF | Sum of Squares | Mean Square | F Value | Pr > F |
|---|---|---|---|---|---|
| **Model** | 11 | 36476.8353 | 3316.0759 | 7.66 | <.0001 |
| **Error** | 158 | 68366.4589 | 432.6991 | | |
| **Corrected Total** | 169 | 104843.2941 | | | |

| R-Square | Coeff Var | Root MSE | BloodP Mean |
|---|---|---|---|
| 0.347918 | -906.7286 | 20.80142 | -2.294118 |

The BloodP Mean value indicates that the average blood pressure change over all observations is-2.294118. (the same value as would be obtained using PROC MEANS.) The R square for this model is 0.347918.

The $p$-value is <.0001. Presuming an alpha equal to 0.05, you reject the null hypothesis and conclude that at least one treatment mean is different from one other treatment mean. Which factor(s) explain this difference?

The next part of the output shows tests of the main effects and the interaction.

| Source | DF | Type I SS | Mean Square | F Value | Pr > F |
|---|---|---|---|---|---|
| DrugDose | 3 | 54.03137 | 18.01046 | 0.04 | 0.9886 |
| Disease | 2 | 19276.48690 | 9638.24345 | 22.27 | <.0001 |
| DrugDose*Disease | 6 | 17146.31698 | 2857.71950 | 6.60 | <.0001 |

| Source | DF | Type III SS | Mean Square | F Value | Pr > F |
|---|---|---|---|---|---|
| DrugDose | 3 | 335.73526 | 111.91175 | 0.26 | 0.8551 |
| Disease | 2 | 18742.62386 | 9371.31193 | 21.66 | <.0001 |
| DrugDose*Disease | 6 | 17146.31698 | 2857.71950 | 6.60 | <.0001 |

The Type I SS are *model-order dependent*. Each effect is adjusted only for the preceding effects in the model. They are also known as *sequential sums of squares*. They are useful in cases where the marginal (additional) effect for adding terms in a specific order is important. An example is a test of polynomials, where X, X*X, and X*X*X are in the MODEL statement. Each term is only tested controlling for a lower order term. The TYPE I SS values are additive. They sum to the Model Sum of Squares for the overall model.

The Type III sums of squares are commonly called *partial sums of squares*. The Type III sum of squares for a particular variable is the increase in the model sum of squares due to adding the variable to a model that already contains all the other variables in the model. Type III sums of squares, therefore, do not depend on the order in which the explanatory variables are specified in the model. The Type III SS values are not generally additive (except in a completely balanced design). The values do not necessarily sum to the Model SS.

You will generally interpret and report results based on the Type III SS.

You should consider the test for the interaction first, because if there is an interaction, then by definition this means that the effect of each main effect is different at each level of the other main effect. The *p*-value for **DrugDose*Disease** is <.0001. Presuming an alpha of 0.05, you reject the null hypothesis. You have sufficient evidence to conclude that there is an interaction between the two factors. As shown in the graph, the effect of the level of drug changes for different disease types. With ODS Graphics, you get an interaction plot, as well.

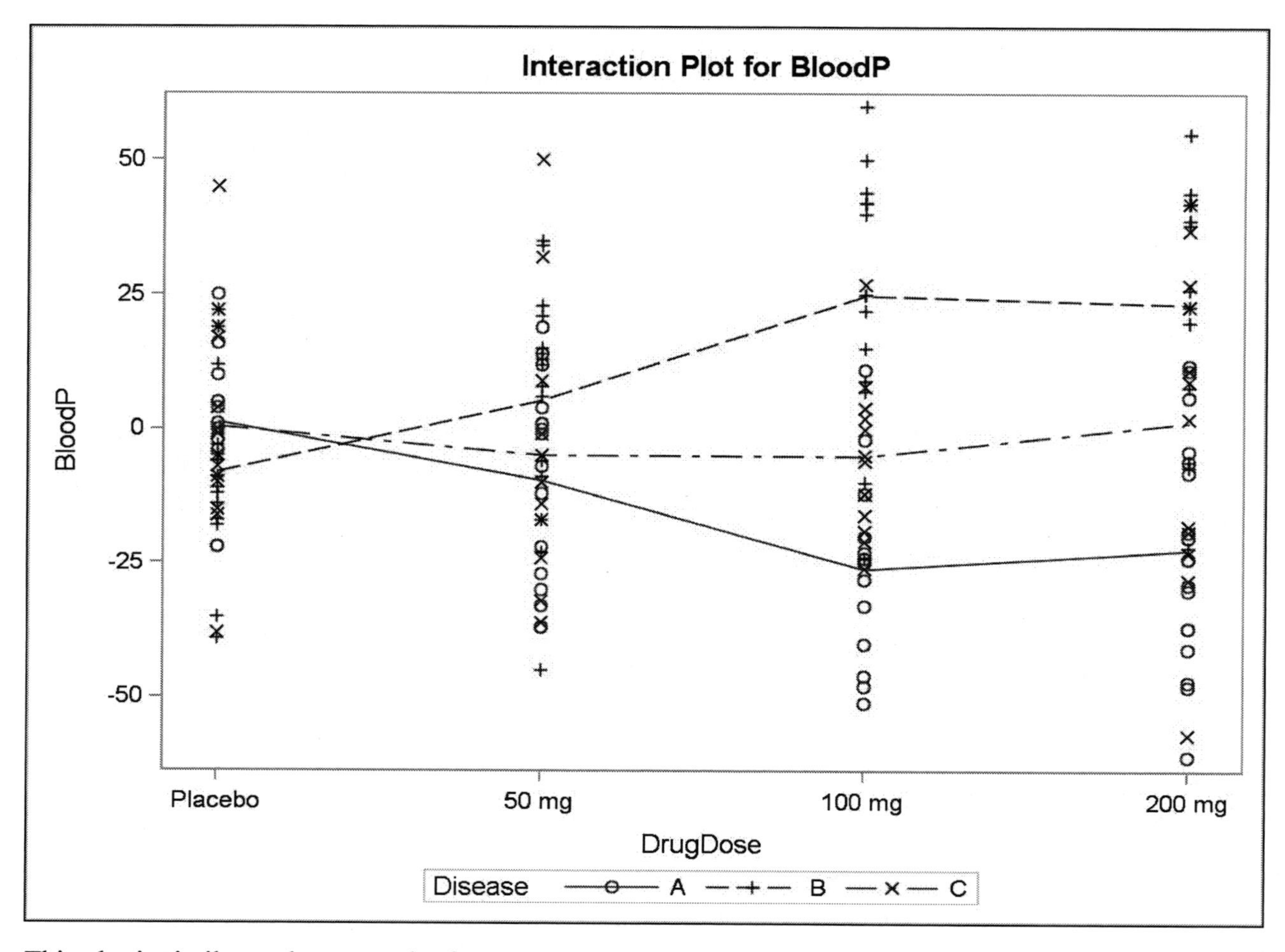


This plot is similar to the mean plot from PROC SGPLOT.

Because of the interaction, you do not know the effect of **DrugDose** at any particular level of **Disease**. The LSMEANS statement can be used to test the effect of **DrugDose** at each level of **Disease**.

```
/*st102d06.sas*/  /*Part E*/
ods graphics off;
ods select LSMeans SlicedANOVA;
proc glm data=sasuser.drug order=internal;
   class DrugDose Disease;
   model Bloodp=DrugDose Disease DrugDose*Disease;
   lsmeans DrugDose*Disease / slice=Disease;
   title 'Analyze the Effects of DrugDose';
   title2 'at Each Level of Disease';
   format DrugDose dosefmt.;
run;
quit;
ods graphics on;
```

Selected ODS statement:

ODS SELECT specifies output objects for ODS destinations. To specify an output object, you need to know which output objects your SAS program produces. The ODS TRACE statement writes to the SAS log a trace record that includes the path, the label, and other information about each output object that your SAS program produces. The SAS documentation for each PROC also lists output object names.

Selected LSMEANS statement option:

SLICE= specifies effects within which to test for differences between interaction LS-mean effects. This can produce what are known as *tests of simple effects* (Winer 1971). For example, suppose that A*B is significant and you want to test for the effect of A within each level of B. The appropriate LSMEANS statement is as follows:

```
lsmeans A*B / slice=B;
```

PROC GLM Output

The first table is a report of the least squared mean for each unique **DrugDose*Disease** combination.

| DrugDose | Disease | BloodP LSMEAN |
|---|---|---|
| Placebo | A | 1.3333333 |
| Placebo | B | -8.1333333 |
| Placebo | C | 0.4285714 |
| 50 mg | A | -9.6875000 |
| 50 mg | B | 5.4000000 |
| 50 mg | C | -4.8461538 |
| 100 mg | A | -26.2307692 |
| 100 mg | B | 24.7857143 |
| 100 mg | C | -5.1428571 |
| 200 mg | A | -22.5555556 |
| 200 mg | B | 23.2307692 |
| 200 mg | C | 1.3076923 |

The second table displays a test of the effect of **DrugDose** at each level of **Disease**.

| DrugDose*Disease Effect Sliced by Disease for BloodP | | | | | |
|---|---|---|---|---|---|
| Disease | DF | Sum of Squares | Mean Square | F Value | Pr > F |
| A | 3 | 6320.126747 | 2106.708916 | 4.87 | 0.0029 |
| B | 3 | 10561 | 3520.222833 | 8.14 | <.0001 |
| C | 3 | 468.099308 | 156.033103 | 0.36 | 0.7815 |

The **DrugDose** effect is significant when used in patients with either disease A or disease B, but not in patients with disease C.

Given all of this information, it seems that you would want to aggressively treat blood pressure in people with disease A with high doses of the drug. For those with disease B (perhaps caused by a traumatic event), treating with the drug at all would be a mistake. For those with disease C, there seems to be no effect on blood pressure.

## Exercises

**5. Performing Two-Way ANOVA**

Consider an experiment to test three different brands of concrete and see whether an additive makes the cement in the concrete stronger. Thirty test plots are poured and the following features are recorded in the **sasuser.concrete** data set:

| | |
|---|---|
| **Strength** | the measured strength of a concrete test plot |
| **Additive** | whether an additive was used in the test plot |
| **Brand** | the brand of concrete being tested |

**a.** Use the MEANS procedure to examine the data. Output the means to a data set and then plot them using the SGPLOT procedure, and put **Strength** on the Y axis, **Additive** on the X axis, and then stratify by **Brand**. What information can you obtain from looking at the data?

**b.** Test the hypothesis that the means are equal, making sure to include an interaction term if the results from PROC SGPLOT indicate that would be advisable. What conclusions can you reach at this point in your analysis?

**c.** Do the appropriate multiple comparisons test for statistically significant effects?

## 2.09 Multiple Answer Poll

A study is conducted to compare the average monthly credit card spending for males versus females. Which statistical method might be used?

a. One-sample *t* test
b. Two-sample *t* test
c. One-way ANOVA
d. Two-way ANOVA

98

# 2.6 Solutions

## Solutions to Exercises

1. **Using PROC TTEST for Comparing Groups**

   Assess whether the treatment group changed the same amount as the control group. Use a two-sided *t* test.

```
/*st102s01.sas*/
proc ttest data=sasuser.German plots(shownull)=interval;
   class Group;
   var Change;
   title "German Grammar Training, Comparing Treatment to Control";
run;
```

   a. Do the two groups appear to be approximately normally distributed?

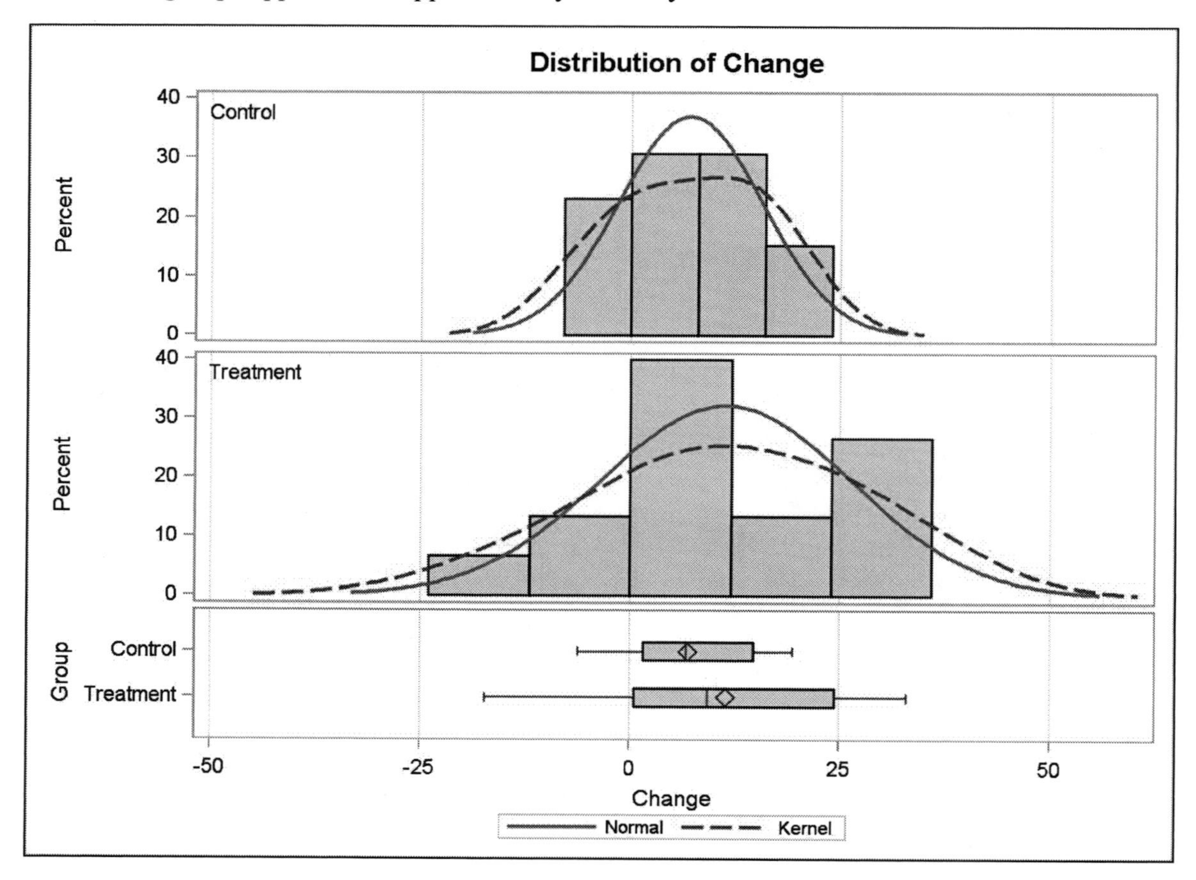

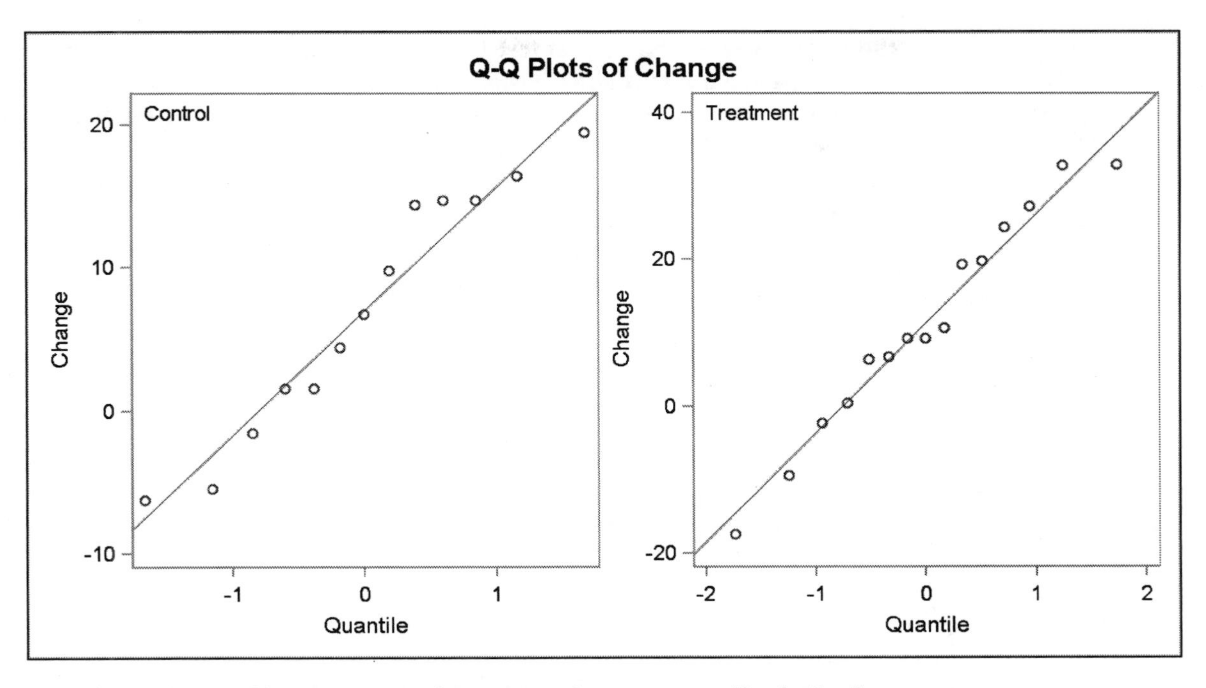


**The plots show evidence supporting approximate normality in both groups.**

b. Do the two groups have approximately equal variances?

From the bottom of the PROC TTEST output:

| Equality of Variances | | | | |
|---|---|---|---|---|
| Method | Num DF | Den DF | F Value | Pr > F |
| Folded F | 14 | 12 | 2.97 | 0.0660 |

**Because the *p*-value for the Equality of Variances test is greater than the alpha level of 0.05, you would not reject the null hypothesis. This conclusion supports the assumption of equal variance (the null hypothesis being tested here).**

c. Does the new teaching technique seem to result in significantly different change scores compared with the standard technique?

| Group | N | Mean | Std Dev | Std Err | Minimum | Maximum |
|---|---|---|---|---|---|---|
| Control | 13 | 6.9677 | 8.6166 | 2.3898 | -6.2400 | 19.4100 |
| Treatment | 15 | 11.3587 | 14.8535 | 3.8352 | -17.3300 | 32.9200 |
| Diff (1-2) | | -4.3910 | 12.3720 | 4.6882 | | |

| Group | Method | Mean | 95% CL Mean | | Std Dev | 95% CL Std Dev | |
|---|---|---|---|---|---|---|---|
| Control | | 6.9677 | 1.7607 | 12.1747 | 8.6166 | 6.1789 | 14.2238 |
| Treatment | | 11.3587 | 3.1331 | 19.5843 | 14.8535 | 10.8747 | 23.4255 |
| Diff (1-2) | Pooled | -4.3910 | -14.0276 | 5.2457 | 12.3720 | 9.7432 | 16.9550 |
| Diff (1-2) | Satterthwaite | -4.3910 | -13.7401 | 4.9581 | | | |

| Method | Variances | DF | t Value | Pr > \|t\| |
|---|---|---|---|---|
| Pooled | Equal | 26 | -0.94 | 0.3576 |
| Satterthwaite | Unequal | 22.947 | -0.97 | 0.3413 |

**The *p*-value for the Pooled (Equal Variance) test for the difference between the two means shows that the two groups are not statistically significantly different. Therefore, there is not strong enough evidence to say conclusively that the new teaching technique is different from the old. The Difference Interval plot displays these conclusions graphically.**

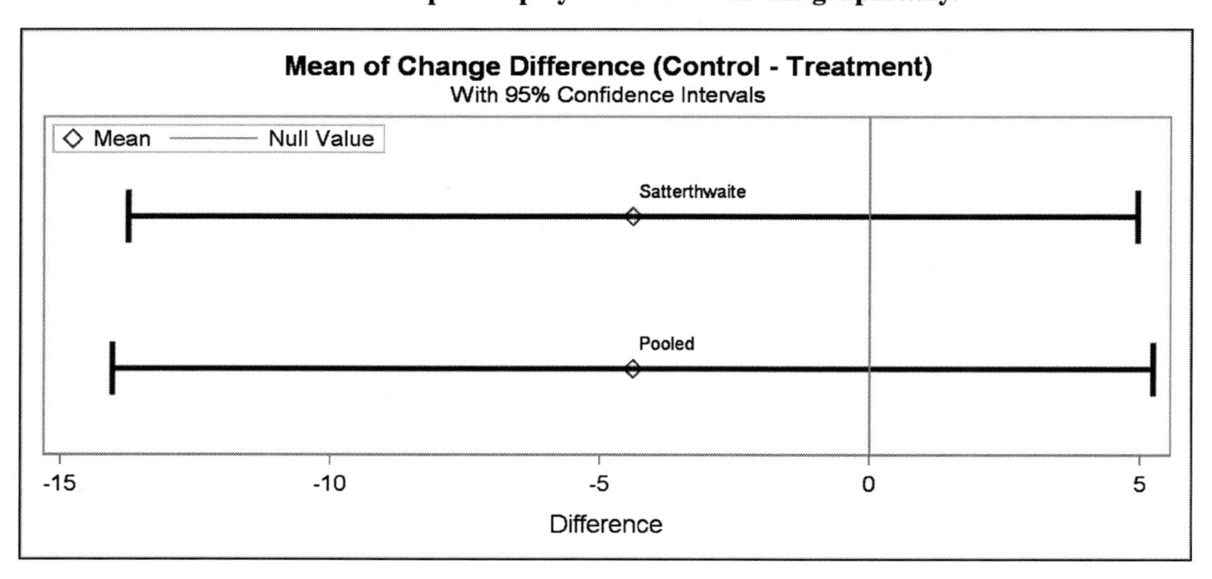


**The confidence interval includes the value zero, indicating a lack of statistical significance of the mean difference.**

2. **Analyzing Data in a Completely Randomized Design**

   **a.** Examine the data. Use the MEANS (using the SKEWNESS and KURTOSIS options in the PROC MEANS statement) and SGPLOT procedures. What information can you obtain from looking at the data?

```
/*st102s02.sas*/  /*Part A*/
proc means data=sasuser.Ads printalltypes n mean std skewness
   kurtosis;
   var Sales;
   class Ad;
   title 'Descriptive Statistics of Sales by Ad Type';
run;

proc sgplot data=sasuser.Ads;
   vbox Sales / category=Ad datalabel=Sales;
   title "Box and Whisker Plots of Sales by Ad Type";
run;
```

| Analysis Variable : Sales | | | | | |
|---|---|---|---|---|---|
| N Obs | N | Mean | Std Dev | Skewness | Kurtosis |
| 144 | 144 | 66.8194444 | 13.5278282 | -0.2547089 | -0.1295813 |

| Analysis Variable : Sales | | | | | | |
|---|---|---|---|---|---|---|
| Ad | N Obs | N | Mean | Std Dev | Skewness | Kurtosis |
| display | 36 | 36 | 56.5555556 | 11.6188134 | 0.3456470 | 0.0256814 |
| paper | 36 | 36 | 73.2222222 | 9.7339204 | -0.0474705 | -0.5475341 |
| people | 36 | 36 | 66.6111111 | 13.4976776 | -0.5998808 | -0.2130516 |
| radio | 36 | 36 | 70.8888889 | 12.9676031 | -0.2172278 | 1.6565242 |

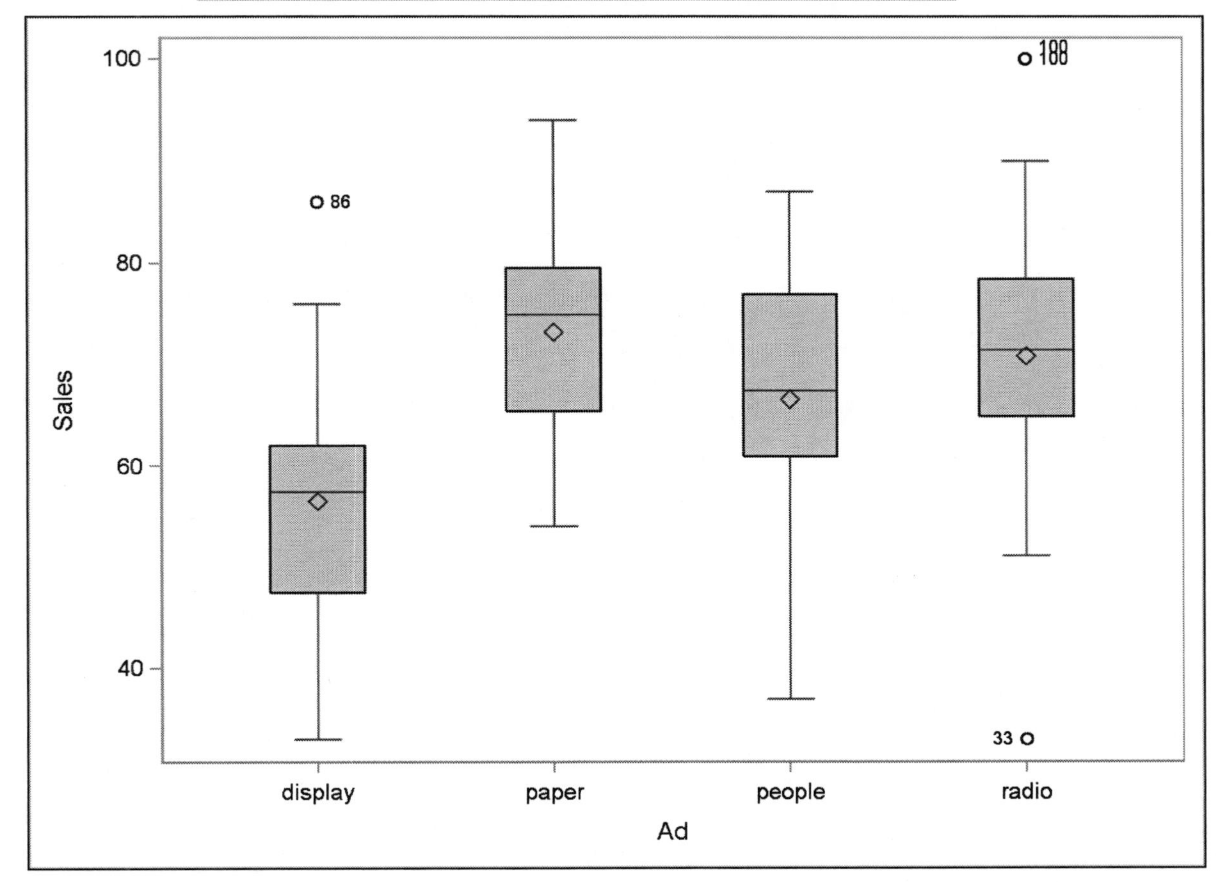


**It appears that the in-store display mean is lower than the others. The value display has a positive outlier, and radio has outliers in both directions.**

**b.** Test the hypothesis that the means are equal. Be sure to check that the assumptions of the analysis method that you choose are met. What conclusions can you reach at this point in your analysis?

```
/*st102s02.sas*/  /*Part B*/
proc glm data=sasuser.Ads plots=diagnostics;
   class Ad;
   model Sales=Ad;
   means Ad / hovtest;
   title 'Testing for Equality of Ad Type on Sales';
run;
quit;
```

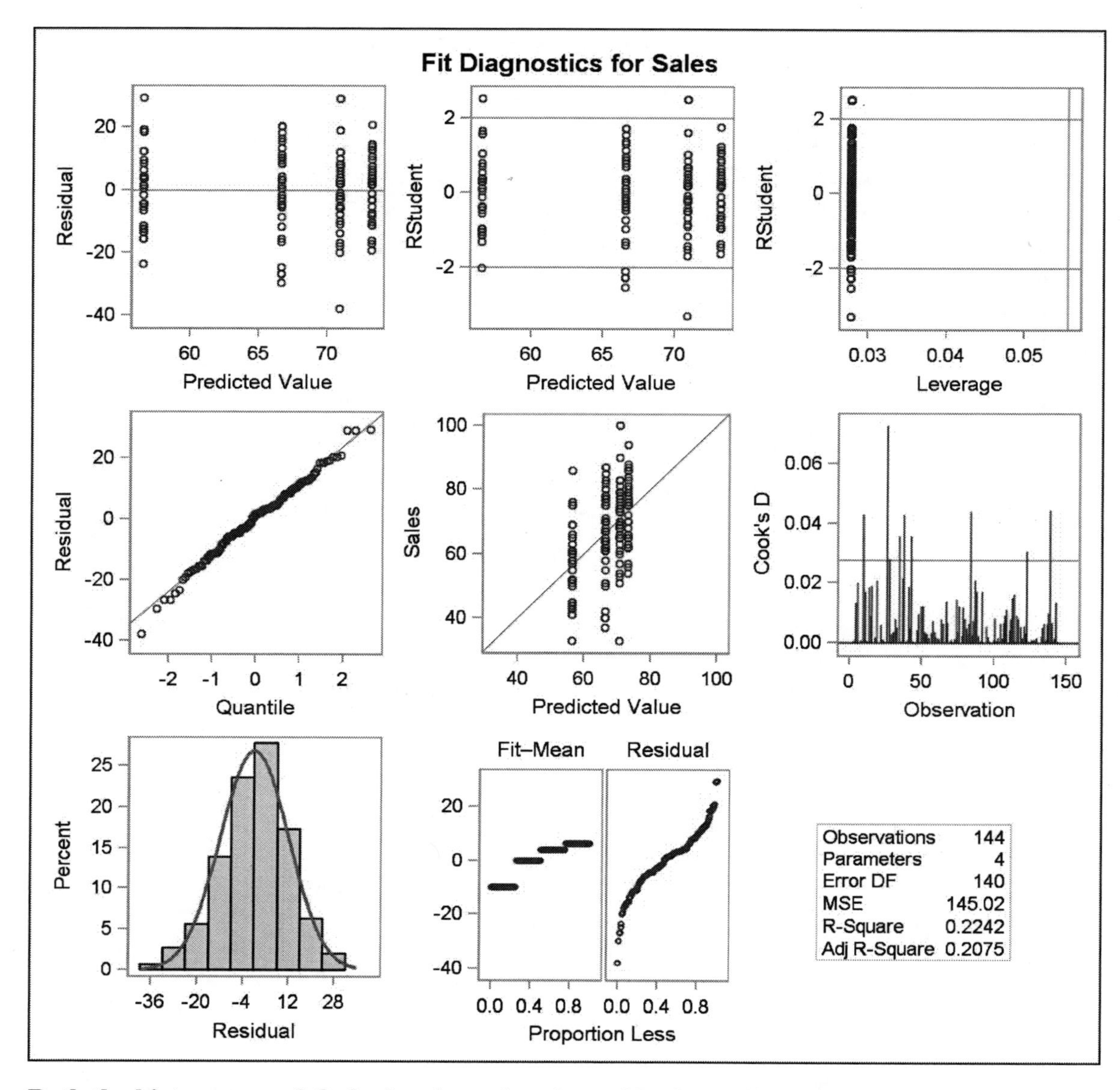


**Both the histogram and Q-Q plot show that the residuals seem normally distributed (one assumption for ANOVA).**

| Levene's Test for Homogeneity of Sales Variance ANOVA of Squared Deviations from Group Means | | | | | |
|---|---|---|---|---|---|
| Source | DF | Sum of Squares | Mean Square | F Value | Pr > F |
| Ad | 3 | 154637 | 51545.6 | 1.10 | 0.3532 |
| Error | 140 | 6586668 | 47047.6 | | |

**The Levene's Test for Homogeneity of Variance shows a *p*-value greater than alpha. Therefore, do not reject the hypothesis of homogeneity of variances (equal variances across Ad types). This assumption for ANOVA is met.**

| Class Level Information | | |
|---|---|---|
| Class | Levels | Values |
| Ad | 4 | display paper people radio |

| Number of Observations Read | 144 |
|---|---|
| Number of Observations Used | 144 |

| Source | DF | Sum of Squares | Mean Square | F Value | Pr > F |
|---|---|---|---|---|---|
| Model | 3 | 5866.08333 | 1955.36111 | 13.48 | <.0001 |
| Error | 140 | 20303.22222 | 145.02302 | | |
| Corrected Total | 143 | 26169.30556 | | | |

| R-Square | Coeff Var | Root MSE | Sales Mean |
|---|---|---|---|
| 0.224159 | 18.02252 | 12.04255 | 66.81944 |

| Source | DF | Type I SS | Mean Square | F Value | Pr > F |
|---|---|---|---|---|---|
| Ad | 3 | 5866.083333 | 1955.361111 | 13.48 | <.0001 |

| Source | DF | Type III SS | Mean Square | F Value | Pr > F |
|---|---|---|---|---|---|
| Ad | 3 | 5866.083333 | 1955.361111 | 13.48 | <.0001 |

**The overall *F* value from the analysis of variance table is associated with a *p*-value less than or equal to .0001. Presuming that all assumptions of the model are valid, you know that at least one treatment mean is different from one other treatment mean. At this point, you do not know which means are significantly different.**

3. **Analyzing Data in a Randomized Block Design**

   Test the hypothesis that the means are equal. Include all of the variables in your MODEL statement.

```
/*st102s03.sas*/
proc glm data=sasuser.Ads1 plots(only)=diagnostics;
   class Ad Area;
   model Sales=Ad Area;
   title 'ANOVA for Randomized Block Design';
run;
quit;
```

Partial PROC GLM Output

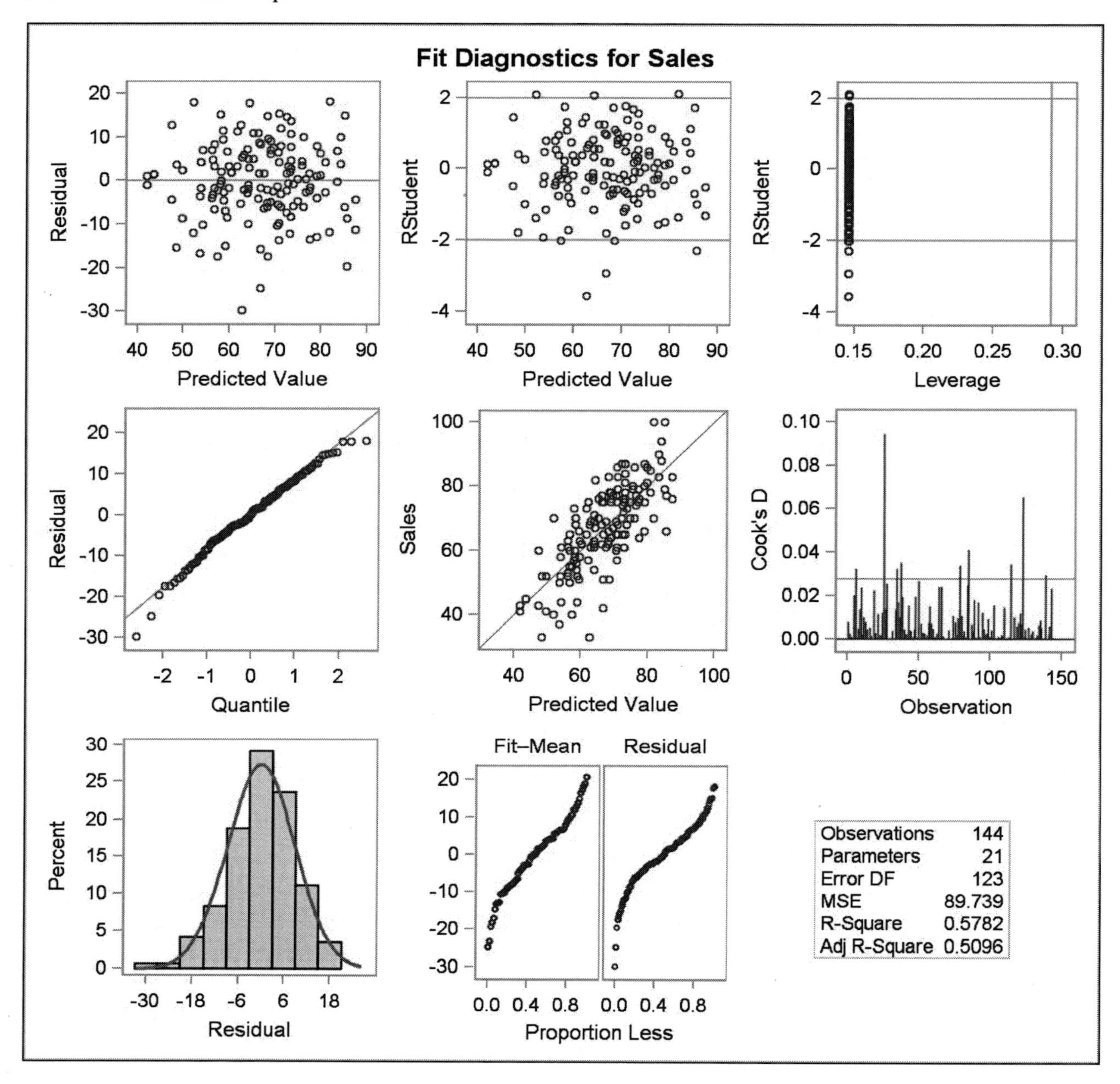

The Q-Q plot of residuals indicates that the normality assumption for ANOVA is met.

| Class Level Information | | |
|---|---|---|
| **Class** | **Levels** | **Values** |
| **Ad** | 4 | display paper people radio |
| **Area** | 18 | 1 2 3 4 5 6 7 8 9 10 11 12 13 14 15 16 17 18 |

| | |
|---|---|
| **Number of Observations Read** | 144 |
| **Number of Observations Used** | 144 |

| Source | DF | Sum of Squares | Mean Square | F Value | Pr > F |
|---|---|---|---|---|---|
| **Model** | 20 | 15131.38889 | 756.56944 | 8.43 | <.0001 |
| **Error** | 123 | 11037.91667 | 89.73916 | | |
| **Corrected Total** | 143 | 26169.30556 | | | |

The ANOVA table shows that there is some difference in mean sales level across Ad types or across geographic areas (or both).

| R-Square | Coeff Var | Root MSE | Sales Mean |
|---|---|---|---|
| 0.578211 | 14.17712 | 9.473076 | 66.81944 |

| Source | DF | Type I SS | Mean Square | F Value | Pr > F |
|---|---|---|---|---|---|
| **Ad** | 3 | 5866.083333 | 1955.361111 | 21.79 | <.0001 |
| **Area** | 17 | 9265.305556 | 545.017974 | 6.07 | <.0001 |

| Source | DF | Type III SS | Mean Square | F Value | Pr > F |
|---|---|---|---|---|---|
| **Ad** | 3 | 5866.083333 | 1955.361111 | 21.79 | <.0001 |
| **Area** | 17 | 9265.305556 | 545.017974 | 6.07 | <.0001 |

**a.** What can you conclude from your analysis?

**The *p*-value for Ad (<.0001) indicates that there was some difference in sales among the advertising campaign types, when controlling for Area.**

**b.** Was adding the blocking factor **Area** into the design and analysis detrimental to the test of **Ad**?

**The large (statistically significant) *F* value for Area gives evidence that area of the country was a useful factor to block on. It was definitely not detrimental.**

**4. Post Hoc Pairwise Comparisons**

**a.** Conduct pairwise comparisons with an experimentwise error rate of $\alpha$=0.05. (Use the Tukey adjustment.) Which types of advertising are significantly different?

```
/*st102s04.sas*/  /*Part A*/
proc glm data=sasuser.Ads1 plots(only)=diffplot(center);
   class Ad Area;
   model Sales=Ad Area;
   lsmeans Ad / pdiff=all adjust=tukey;
   title 'Tukey Pairwise Differences for Ad Types on Sales';
run;
quit;
```

Partial Output

| Ad | Sales LSMEAN | LSMEAN Number |
|---|---|---|
| display | 56.5555556 | 1 |
| paper | 73.2222222 | 2 |
| people | 66.6111111 | 3 |
| radio | 70.8888889 | 4 |

| Least Squares Means for effect Ad<br>Pr > \|t\| for H0: LSMean(i)=LSMean(j)<br><br>Dependent Variable: Sales | | | | |
|---|---|---|---|---|
| i/j | 1 | 2 | 3 | 4 |
| 1 | | <.0001 | <.0001 | <.0001 |
| 2 | <.0001 | | 0.0190 | 0.7233 |
| 3 | <.0001 | 0.0190 | | 0.2268 |
| 4 | <.0001 | 0.7233 | 0.2268 | |

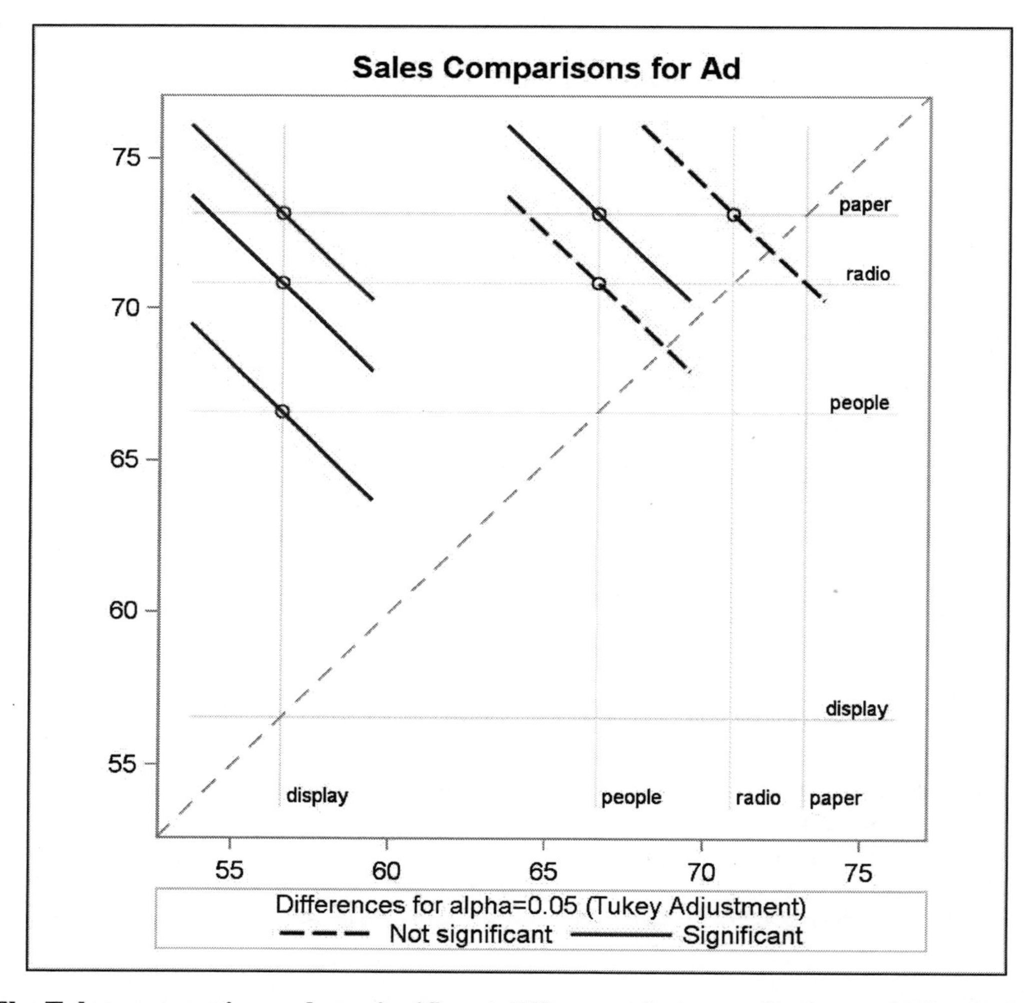


**The Tukey comparisons show significant differences between display and all other types of advertising and between paper and people (*p*=0.0190).**

**b.** Use **display** (case sensitive) as the control group and do a Dunnett comparison of all other advertising methods to see whether those methods resulted in significantly different amounts of sales compared with display ads in stores.

```
/*st102s04.sas*/  /*Part B*/
proc glm data=sasuser.Ads1 plots(only)=controlplot;
   class Ad Area;
   model Sales=Ad Area;
   lsmeans Ad / pdiff=control('display') adjust=dunnett;
   title 'Dunnett Pairwise Differences for Ad Types on Sales';
run;
quit;
```

| | | H0:LSMean=Control |
|---|---|---|
| Ad | Sales LSMEAN | Pr > \|t\| |
| display | 56.5555556 | |
| paper | 73.2222222 | <.0001 |
| people | 66.6111111 | <.0001 |
| radio | 70.8888889 | <.0001 |

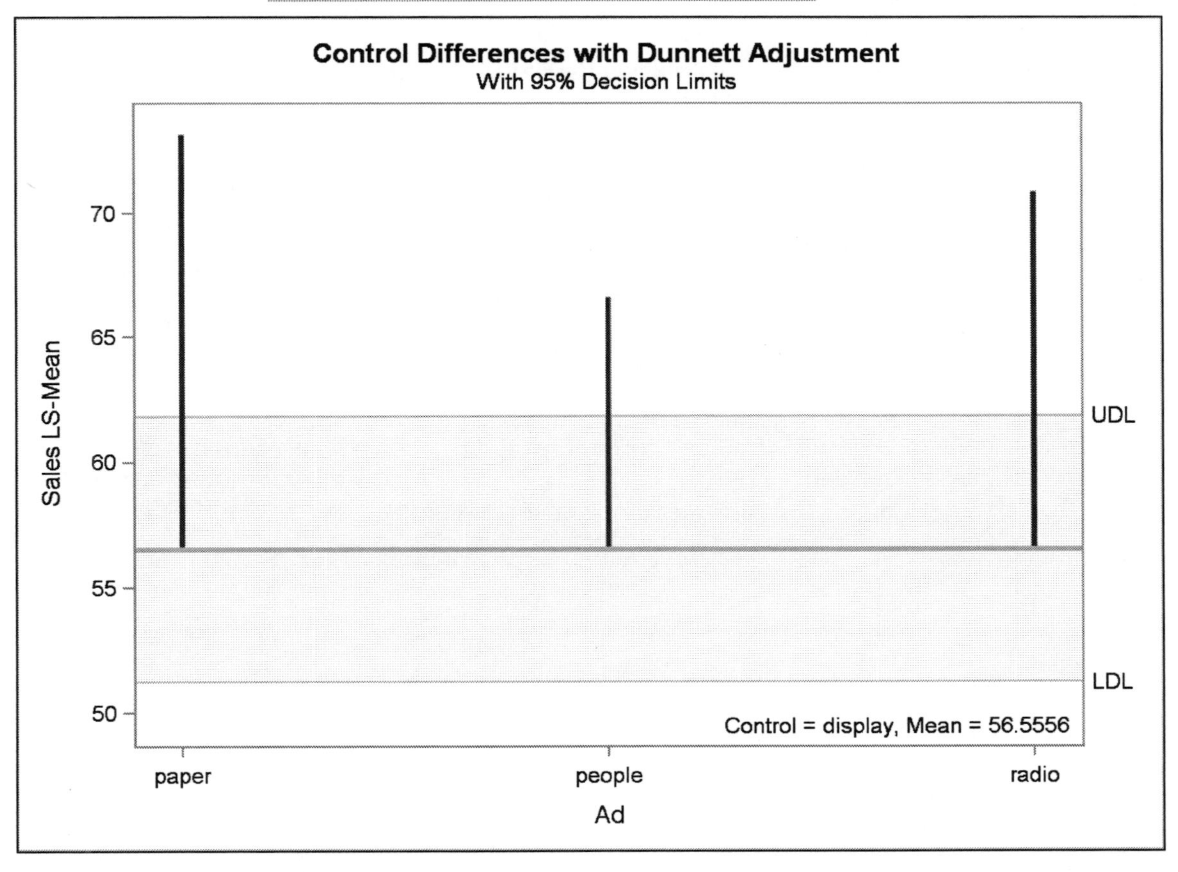


**All other advertising campaigns resulted in significantly different (higher, in this case) average sales than display.**

## 5. Performing Two-Way ANOVA

a. Use the MEANS procedure to examine the data. Output the means to a data set and then plot them using the SGPLOT procedure, and put **Strength** on the Y axis, **Additive** on the X axis, and then stratify by **Brand**. What information can you obtain from looking at the data?

```
/*st102s05.sas*/  /*Part A*/
proc means data=sasuser.concrete
           mean var std nway;
   class Brand Additive;
   var Strength;
   output out=means mean=Strength_Mean;
   title 'Selected Descriptive Statistics for Concrete Data Set';
run;

proc sgplot data=means;
   series x=Additive y=Strength_Mean / group=Brand markers;
   xaxis integer;
   title 'Plot of Stratified Means in Concrete Data Set';
run;
```

**Analysis Variable : Strength**

| Brand | Additive | N Obs | Mean | Variance | Std Dev |
|---|---|---|---|---|---|
| Consolidated | reinforced | 5 | 25.8000000 | 5.6300000 | 2.3727621 |
| | standard | 5 | 22.6000000 | 2.3450000 | 1.5313393 |
| EZ Mix | reinforced | 5 | 27.2600000 | 3.8430000 | 1.9603571 |
| | standard | 5 | 24.4000000 | 14.2350000 | 3.7729299 |
| Graystone | reinforced | 5 | 30.6600000 | 1.7930000 | 1.3390295 |
| | standard | 5 | 25.2800000 | 9.8920000 | 3.1451550 |

```
/*Alternative code to generate same plot but not using the MEANS procedure.*/
proc sgplot data=sasuser.concrete;
  vline Additive / group=Brand stat=mean response=Strength;
run;
```

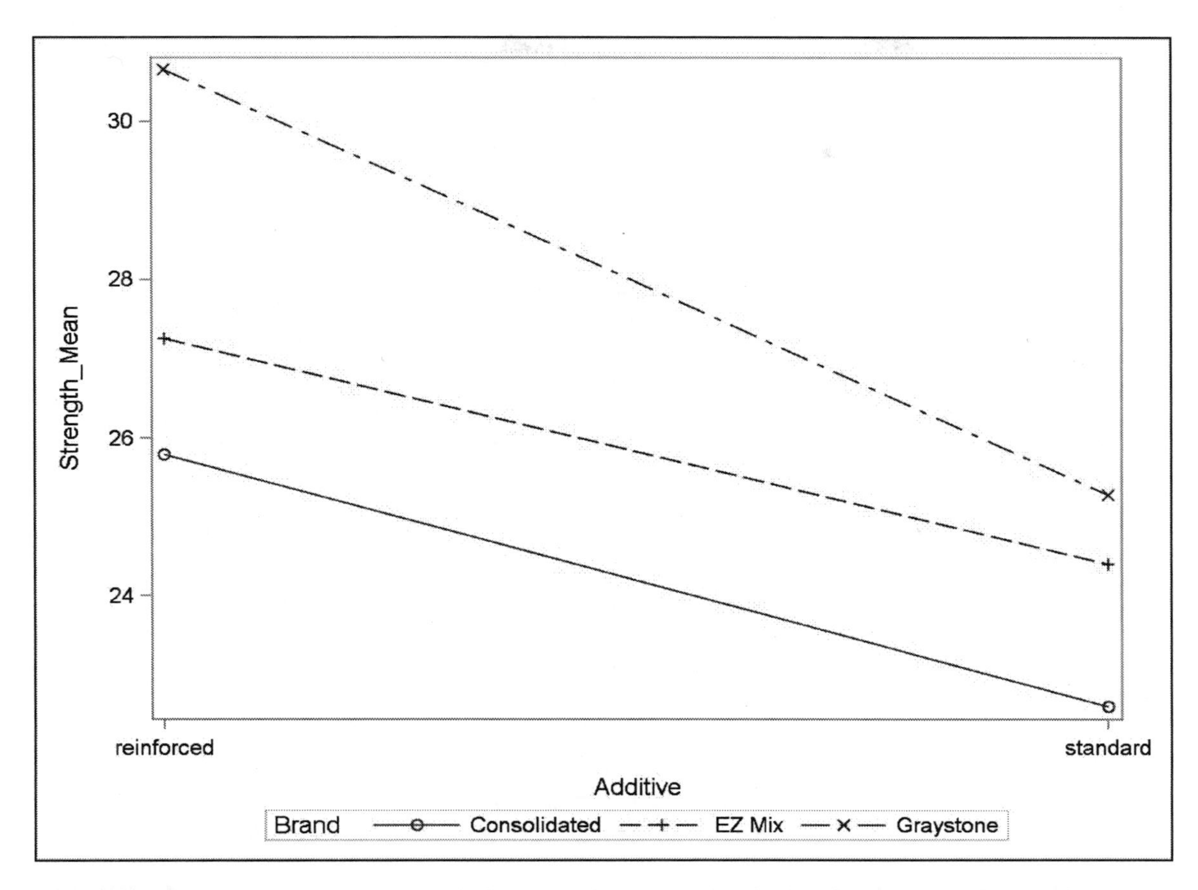


**The difference between means (reinforced minus standard) for Consolidated is 3.20; the mean difference for EZ Mix is 2.86; and for Graystone, the difference is approximately 5.38. It appears that the difference between concretes using standard and reinforced cements differs by brand. In other words, it appears that there is an interaction between Additive and Brand. That means that an interaction term in the ANOVA model would be appropriate to assess statistical significance of the interaction.**

**b.** Test the hypothesis that the means are equal, making sure to include an interaction term if the results from PROC SGPLOT indicate that would be advisable. What conclusions can you reach at this point in your analysis?

```
/*st102s05.sas*/  /*Part B*/
proc glm data=sasuser.concrete;
   class Additive Brand;
   model Strength=Additive Brand Additive*Brand;
   title 'Analyze the Effects of Additive and Brand';
   title2 'on Concrete Strength';
run;
quit;
```

| Class Level Information | | |
|---|---|---|
| Class | Levels | Values |
| Additive | 2 | reinforced standard |
| Brand | 3 | Consolidated EZ Mix Graystone |

| | |
|---|---|
| Number of Observations Read | 30 |
| Number of Observations Used | 30 |

| Source | DF | Sum of Squares | Mean Square | F Value | Pr > F |
|---|---|---|---|---|---|
| Model | 5 | 189.9080000 | 37.9816000 | 6.04 | 0.0009 |
| Error | 24 | 150.9520000 | 6.2896667 | | |
| Corrected Total | 29 | 340.8600000 | | | |

| R-Square | Coeff Var | Root MSE | Strength Mean |
|---|---|---|---|
| 0.557144 | 9.645849 | 2.507921 | 26.00000 |

| Source | DF | Type I SS | Mean Square | F Value | Pr > F |
|---|---|---|---|---|---|
| Additive | 1 | 109.0613333 | 109.0613333 | 17.34 | 0.0003 |
| Brand | 2 | 71.4980000 | 35.7490000 | 5.68 | 0.0095 |
| Additive*Brand | 2 | 9.3486667 | 4.6743333 | 0.74 | 0.4862 |

| Source | DF | Type III SS | Mean Square | F Value | Pr > F |
|---|---|---|---|---|---|
| Additive | 1 | 109.0613333 | 109.0613333 | 17.34 | 0.0003 |
| Brand | 2 | 71.4980000 | 35.7490000 | 5.68 | 0.0095 |
| Additive*Brand | 2 | 9.3486667 | 4.6743333 | 0.74 | 0.4862 |

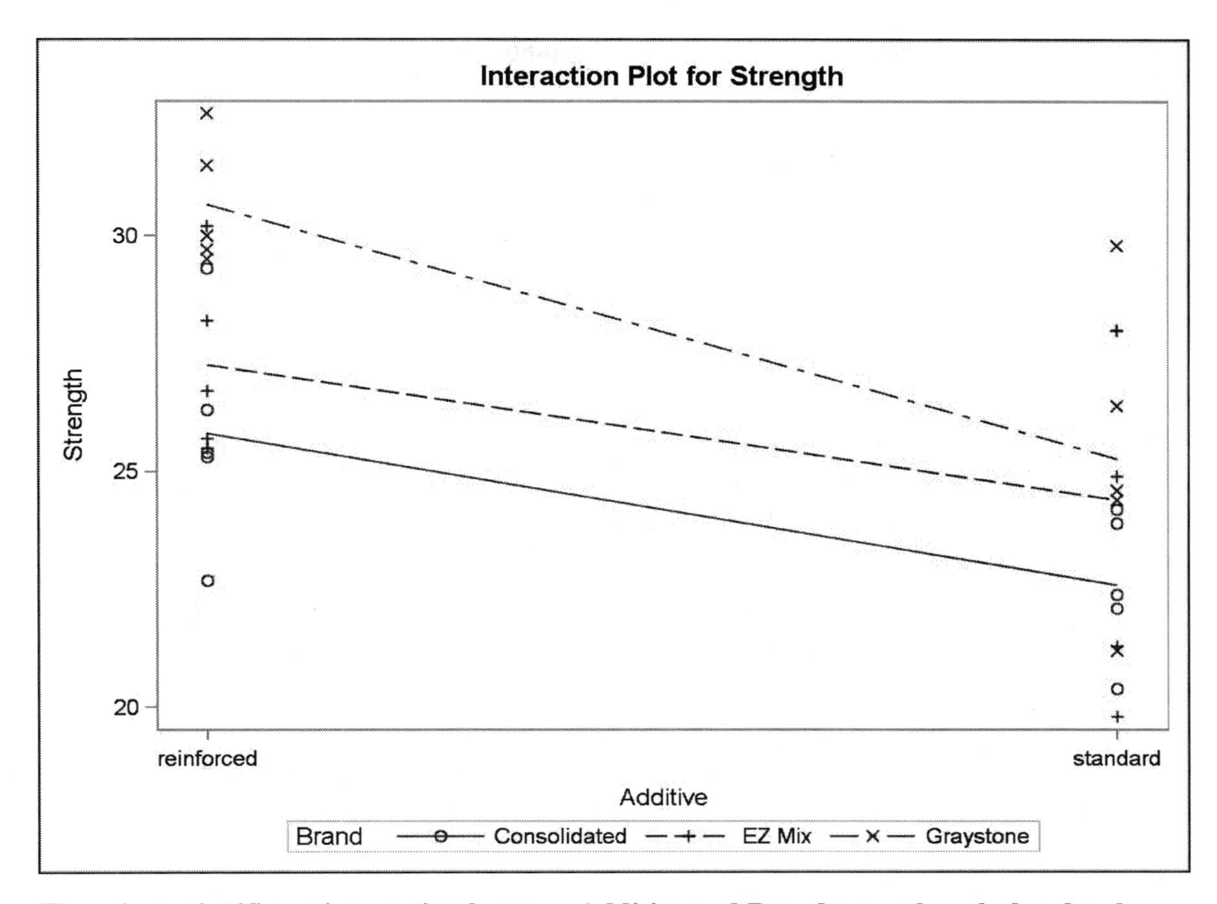


**There is no significant interaction between Additive and Brand, even though the plot shows slightly different slopes among the three brands of concrete. At this point, you can choose to remove the interaction term from the model and, if still significant, conclude that there is a difference in additive types.**

c. Do the appropriate multiple comparisons test for statistically significant effects?

**Because the interaction was not significant, in many cases the interaction term can be removed from the model. A multiple comparisons option in the LSMEANS statement is unnecessary because there are only two levels of the Additive variable. Therefore, the *p*-value for Additive will also be the *p*-value for the comparison between group means for standard and reinforced.**

```
/*st102s05.sas*/  /*Part C*/
ods graphics off;
proc glm data=sasuser.concrete;
   class Additive Brand;
   model Strength=Additive Brand;
   lsmeans Additive;
   title 'Analyze the Effects of Additive and Brand';
   title2 'on Concrete Strength without Interaction';
run;
quit;
ods graphics on;
```

| Class Level Information | | |
|---|---|---|
| Class | Levels | Values |
| Additive | 2 | reinforced standard |
| Brand | 3 | Consolidated EZ Mix Graystone |

| | |
|---|---|
| Number of Observations Read | 30 |
| Number of Observations Used | 30 |

| Source | DF | Sum of Squares | Mean Square | F Value | Pr > F |
|---|---|---|---|---|---|
| Model | 3 | 180.5593333 | 60.1864444 | 9.76 | 0.0002 |
| Error | 26 | 160.3006667 | 6.1654103 | | |
| Corrected Total | 29 | 340.8600000 | | | |

| R-Square | Coeff Var | Root MSE | Strength Mean |
|---|---|---|---|
| 0.529717 | 9.550094 | 2.483024 | 26.00000 |

| Source | DF | Type I SS | Mean Square | F Value | Pr > F |
|---|---|---|---|---|---|
| Additive | 1 | 109.0613333 | 109.0613333 | 17.69 | 0.0003 |
| Brand | 2 | 71.4980000 | 35.7490000 | 5.80 | 0.0083 |

| Source | DF | Type III SS | Mean Square | F Value | Pr > F |
|---|---|---|---|---|---|
| Additive | 1 | 109.0613333 | 109.0613333 | 17.69 | 0.0003 |
| Brand | 2 | 71.4980000 | 35.7490000 | 5.80 | 0.0083 |

**The test for Additive is still significant. There is a difference between standard and reinforced. The estimate of the two least squared means is found in the results for LS Means.**

| Additive | Strength LSMEAN |
|---|---|
| reinforced | 27.9066667 |
| standard | 24.0933333 |

**Reinforced additive in cement in the concrete seems to add more strength than a standard additive does. The mean difference is about 3.8.**

## Solutions to Student Activities (Polls/Quizzes)

### 2.01 Multiple Answer Poll – Correct Answer

How do you tell PROC TTEST that you want to do a two-sample *t* test?

a. SAMPLE=2 option
b. CLASS statement
c. GROUPS=2 option
d. PAIRED statement

13

### 2.02 Multiple Choice Poll – Correct Answer

If you have 20 observations in your ANOVA and you calculate the residuals, to which of the following would they sum?

a. -20
b. 0
c. 20
d. 400
e. Unable to tell from the information given

41

## 2.03 Multiple Choice Poll – Correct Answer

If you have 20 observations in your ANOVA and you calculate the squared residuals, to which of the following would they sum?

a. -20
b. 0
c. 20
d. 400
(e.) Unable to tell from the information given

43

## 2.04 Multiple Choice Poll – Correct Answer

Which part of the ANOVA tables contains the variation due to nuisance factors?

a. Sum of Squares Model
(b.) Sum of Squares Error
c. Degrees of Freedom

55

## 2.05 Multiple Choice Poll – Correct Answer

In a block design, which part of the ANOVA table contains the variation due to the nuisance factor?

a. Sum of Squares Model (circled)
b. Sum of Squares Error
c. Degrees of Freedom

61

## 2.06 Multiple Answer Poll – Correct Answer

If the blocking variable **Area** had a very small *F* value, what would be a valid next step? Select all that apply.

a. Remove it from the MODEL statement and rerun the analysis.
b. Test an interaction term.
c. Report the *F* value and plan a new study. (circled)

68

## 2.07 Multiple Choice Poll – Correct Answer

With a fair coin, your probability of getting heads on one flip is 0.5. If you flip a coin once and got heads, what is the probability of getting heads on the second try?

a. 0.50
b. 0.25
c. 0.00
d. 1.00
e. 0.75

75

## 2.08 Multiple Choice Poll – Correct Answer

With a fair coin, your probability of getting heads on one flip is 0.5. If you flip a coin twice, what is the probability of getting ***at least*** one head out of two?

a. 0.50
b. 0.25
c. 0.00
d. 1.00
e. 0.75

77

## 2.09 Multiple Answer Poll – Correct Answers

A study is conducted to compare the average monthly credit card spending for males versus females. Which statistical method might be used?

a. One-sample *t* test
b. Two-sample *t* test
c. One-way ANOVA
d. Two-way ANOVA

99

# Chapter 3 Regression

# 3.1 Exploratory Data Analysis

## Objectives

- Use a scatter plot to examine the relationship between two continuous variables.
- Use correlation statistics to quantify the degree of association between two continuous variables.
- Describe potential misuses of the correlation coefficient.
- Use the CORR procedure to obtain Pearson correlation coefficients.

3

## Overview of Statistical Models

| Type of Predictors / Type of Response | Categorical | Continuous | Continuous and Categorical |
|---|---|---|---|
| **Continuous** | Analysis of Variance (ANOVA) | Ordinary Least Squares (OLS) Regression | Analysis of Covariance (ANCOVA) |
| **Categorical** | Contingency Table Analysis or Logistic Regression | Logistic Regression | Logistic Regression |

4

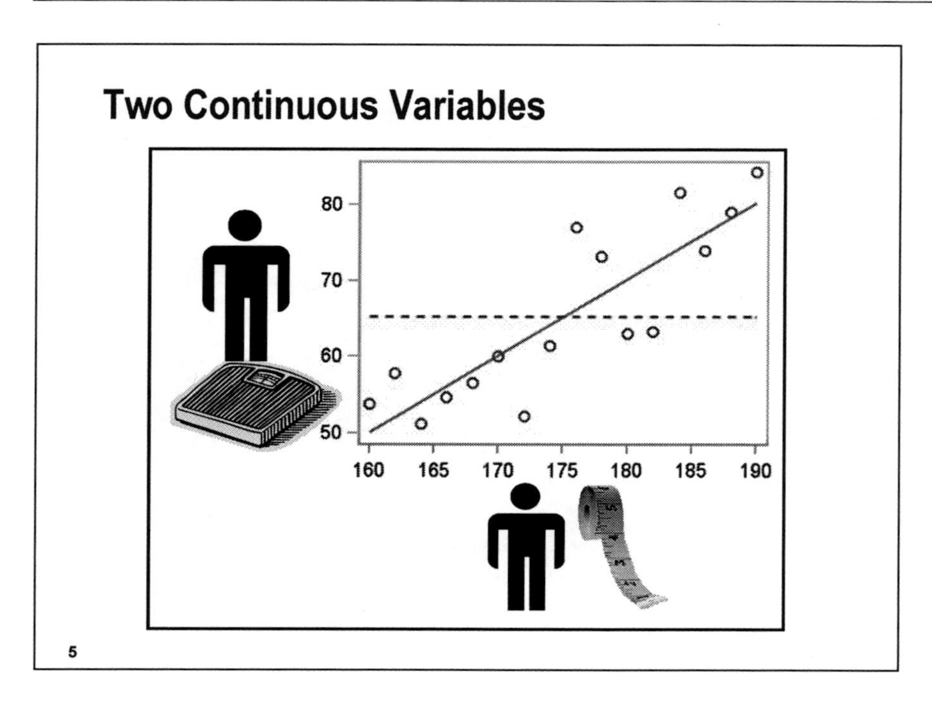


In the previous chapter, you learned that when you have a discrete predictor variable and a continuous outcome variable you use ANOVA to analyze your data. In this section, you have two continuous variables.

You use correlation analysis to examine and describe the relationship between two continuous variables. However, before you use correlation analysis, it is important to view the relationship between two continuous variables using a scatter plot.

Example: A random sample of high school students is selected to determine the relationship between a person's height and weight. Height and weight are measured on a numeric scale. They have a large, potentially infinite number of possible values, rather than a few categories such as short, medium, and tall. Therefore, these variables are considered to be continuous.

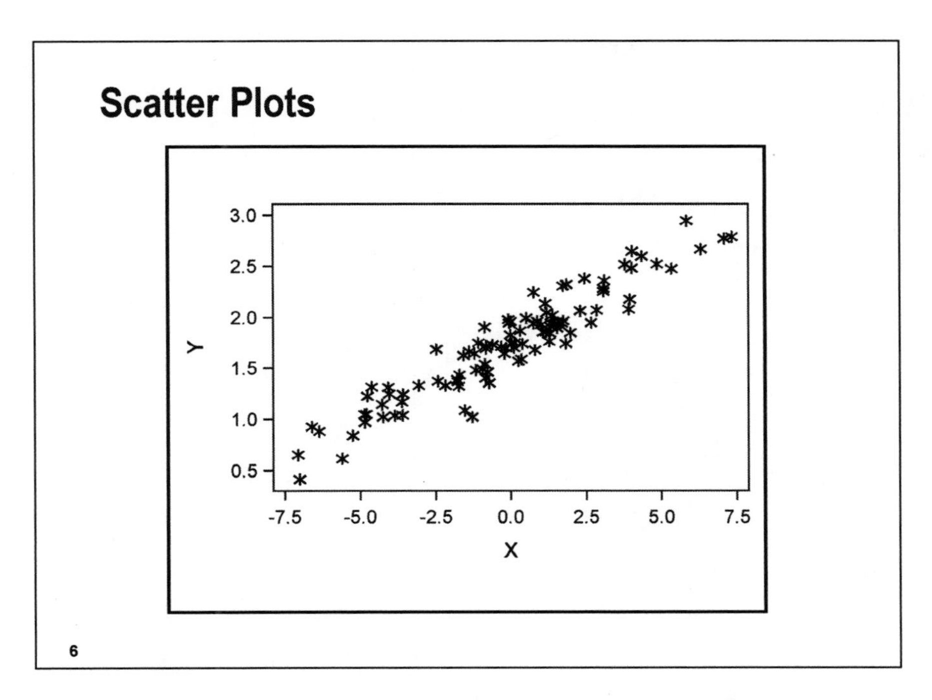


*Scatter plots* are two-dimensional graphs produced by plotting one variable against another within a set of coordinate axes. The coordinates of each point correspond to the values of the two variables.

Scatter plots are useful to accomplish the following:

- explore the relationships between two variables
- locate outlying or unusual values
- identify possible trends
- identify a basic range of Y and X values
- communicate data analysis results

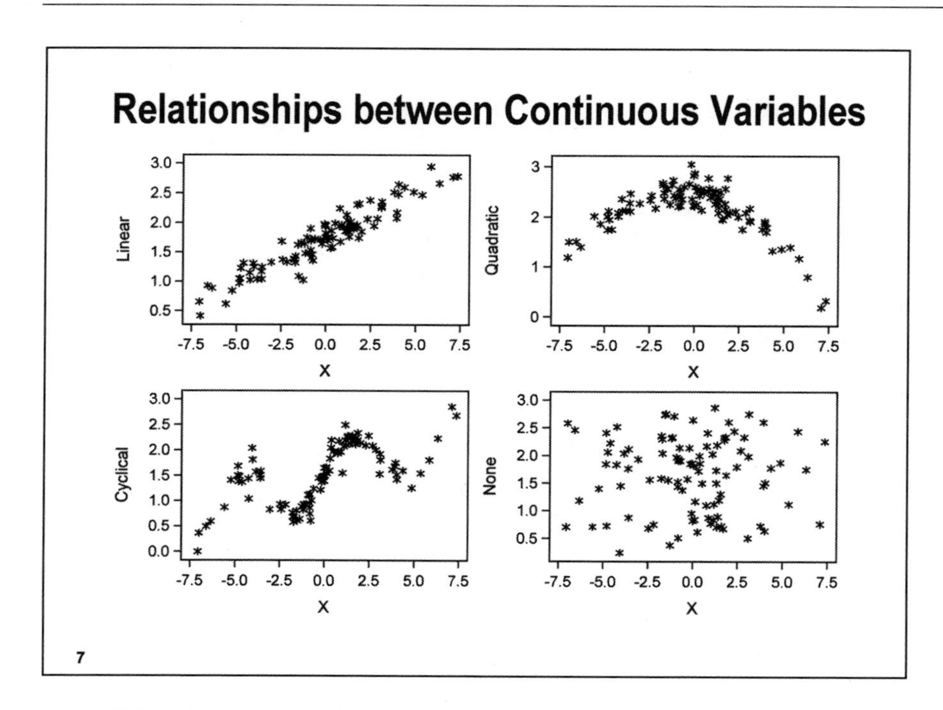


Describing the relationship between two continuous variables is an important first step in any statistical analysis. The scatter plot is the most important tool that you have in describing these relationships. The diagrams above illustrate some possible relationships.

1. A straight line describes the relationship.
2. Curvature is present in the relationship.
3. There could be a cyclical pattern in the relationship. You might see this when the predictor is time.
4. There is no clear relationship between the variables.

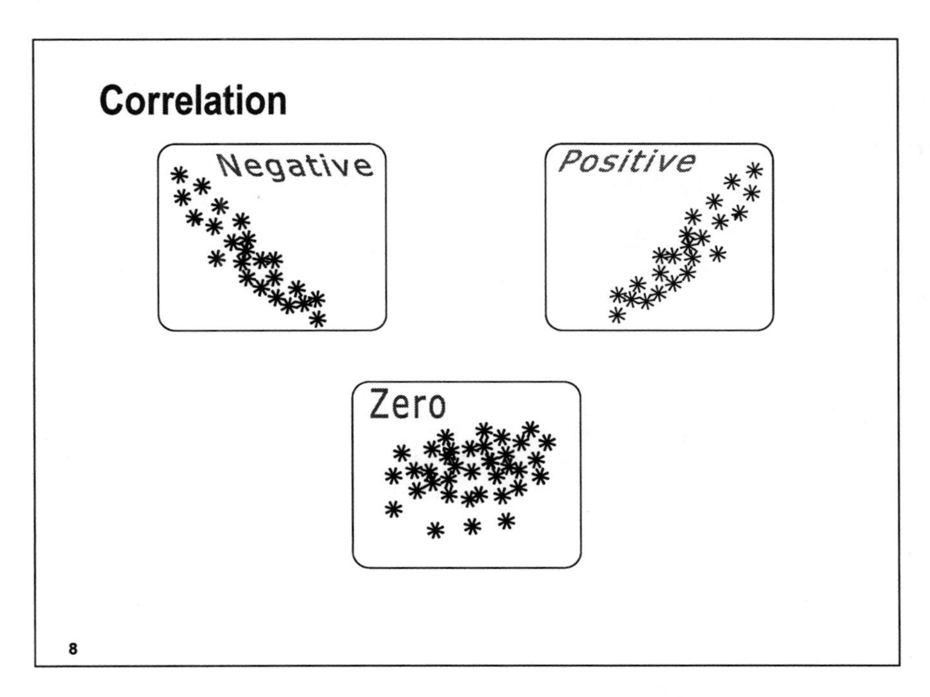


As you examine the scatter plot, you can also quantify the relationship between two variables with correlation statistics. Two variables are correlated if there is a ***linear*** association between them. If not, the variables are uncorrelated.

You can classify correlated variables according to the type of correlation:

| | |
|---|---|
| Positive | One variable tends to increase in value as the other variable increases in value. |
| Negative | One variable tends to decrease in value as the other variable increases in value. |
| Zero | No linear relationship exists between the two variables (uncorrelated). |

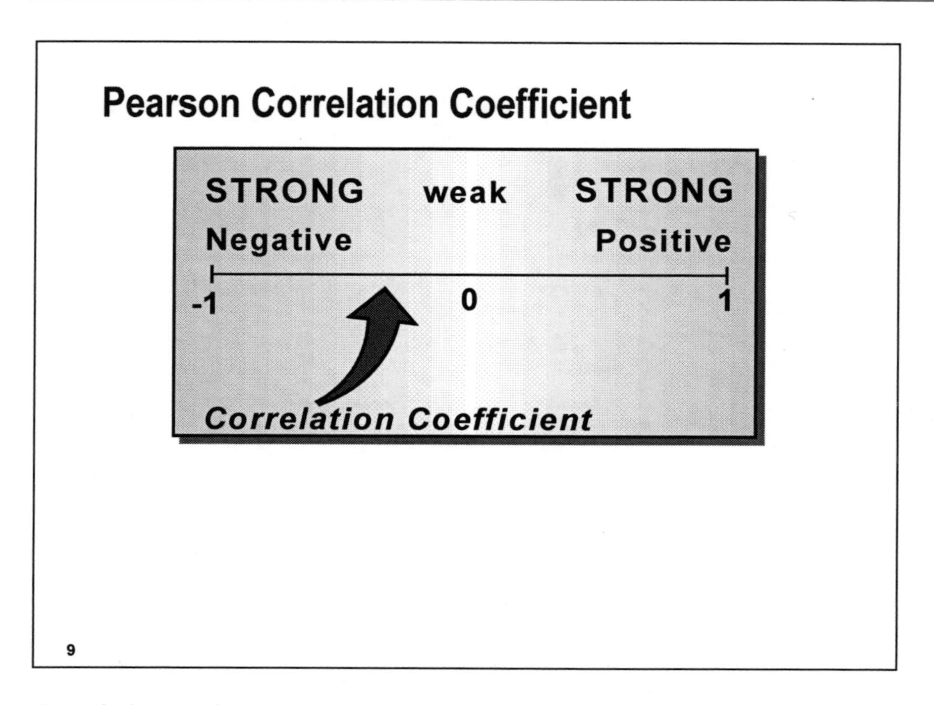


Correlation statistics measure the degree of linear association between two variables. A common correlation statistic used for continuous variables is the Pearson correlation coefficient. Values of correlation statistics are as follows:

- between −1 and 1
- closer to either extreme if there is a high degree of linear association between the two variables
- close to 0 if there is no linear association between the two variables
- greater than 0 if there is a positive linear association
- less than 0 if there is a negative linear association

## Hypothesis Test for a Correlation

- The parameter representing correlation is $\rho$.
- $\rho$ is estimated by the sample statistic *r*.
- $H_0$: $\rho=0$
- Rejecting $H_0$ indicates only great confidence that $\rho$ is not exactly zero.
- A *p*-value does not measure the magnitude of the association.
- Sample size affects the *p*-value.

10

The null hypothesis for a test of a correlation coefficient is $\rho=0$. Rejecting the null hypothesis only means that you can be confident that the true population correlation is not 0. Small *p*-values can occur (as with many statistics) because of very large sample sizes. Even a correlation coefficient of 0.01 can be statistically significant with a large enough sample size. Therefore, it is important to also look at the value of *r* itself to see whether it is meaningfully large.

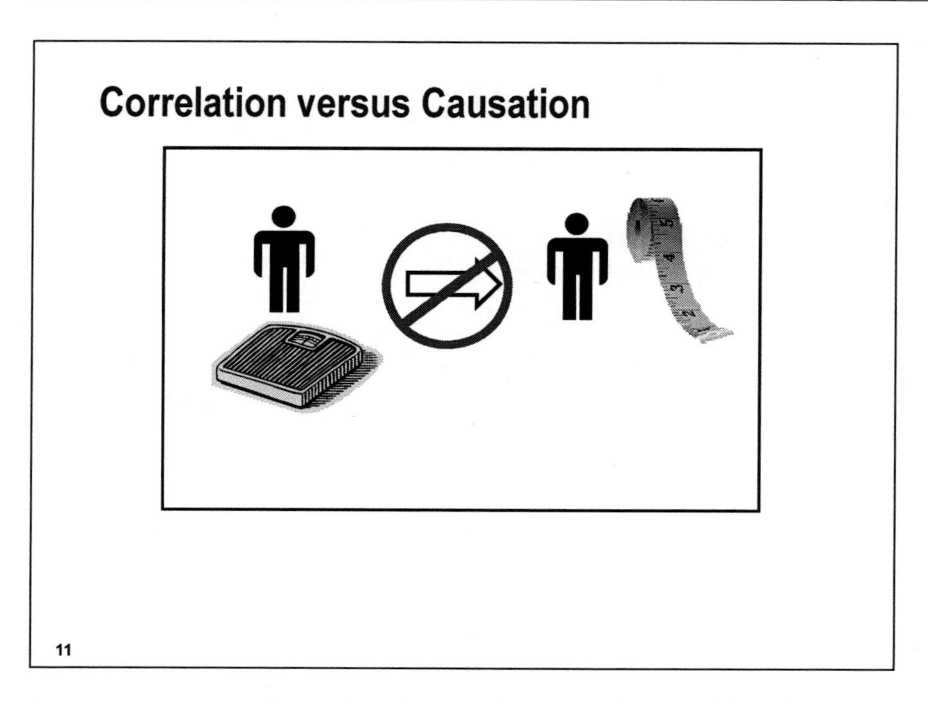


Common errors can be made when you interpret the correlation between variables. One example of this is using correlation coefficients to conclude a cause-and-effect relationship.

- A strong correlation between two variables does not mean change in one variable causes the other variable to change, or vice versa.
- Sample correlation coefficients can be large because of chance or because both variables are affected by other variables.
- "Correlation does not imply causation."

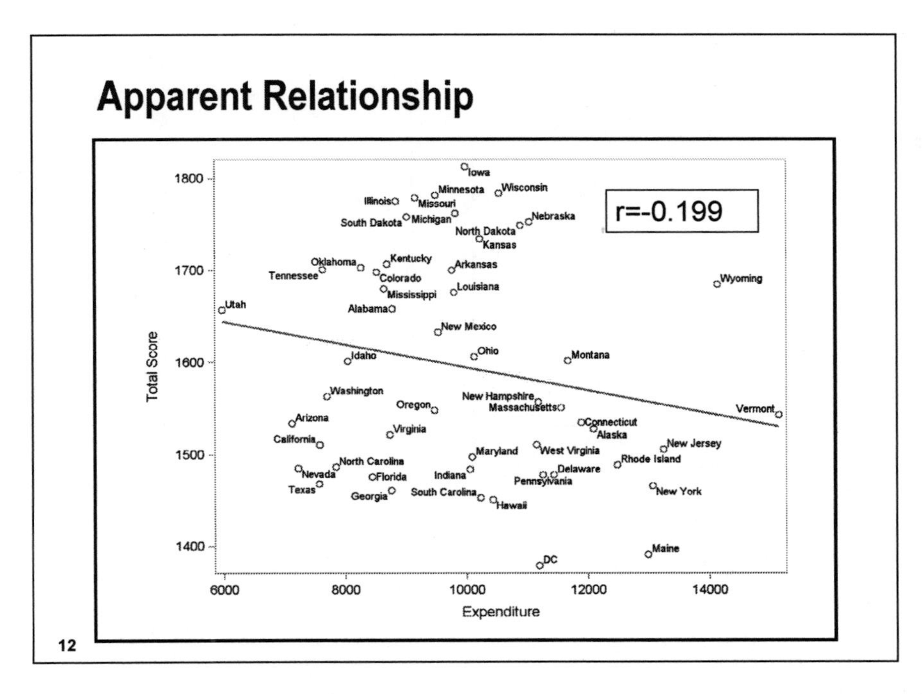


An example of reaching errant conclusions comes from U.S. Department of Education data from the Scholastic Aptitude Test (SAT) from 2005. The scatter plot above shows each state's average total SAT score versus the average state expenditure in U.S. dollars per public school student. The correlation between the two variables is –0.199. Looking at the plot and at this statistic, you might argue (and many argued) that more state spending does little or might even hurt student performance.

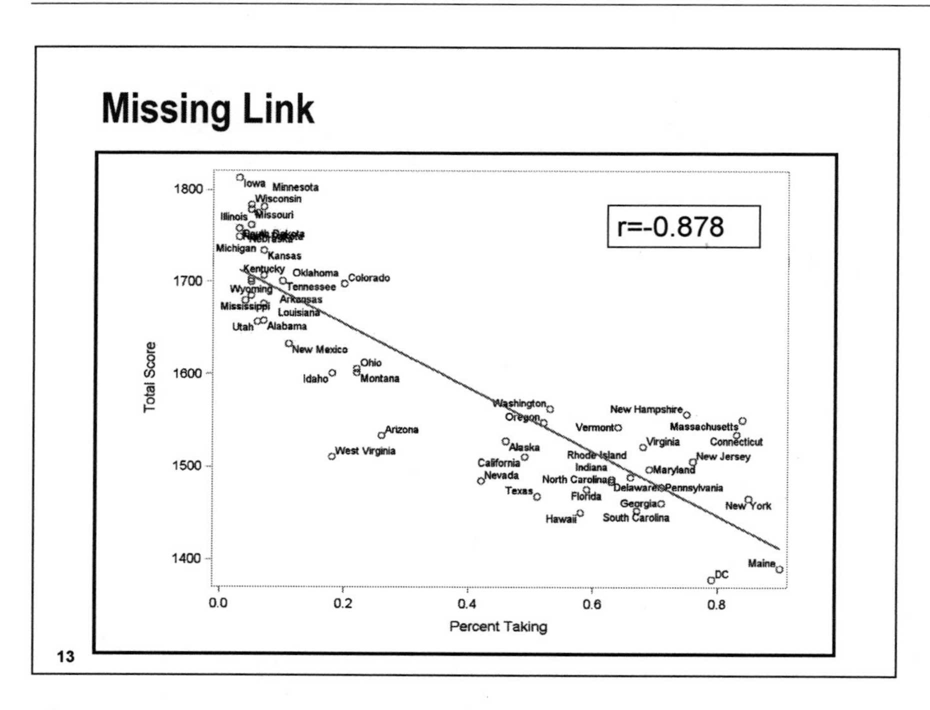


The 2005 report did not take into account the differences among the states in the percentage of students taking the SAT. There are many reasons for the varying participation rates. Some states have lower participation because their students primarily take the rival ACT standardized test. Others have rules requiring even non-college-bound students to take the test. In low participating states, often only the highest performing students choose to take the SAT. Another reported table shows the relationship between participation rate (percent taking the SAT) and average SAT total score. The correlation is –0.878, indicating that states with lower participation rates tend to have higher average scores.

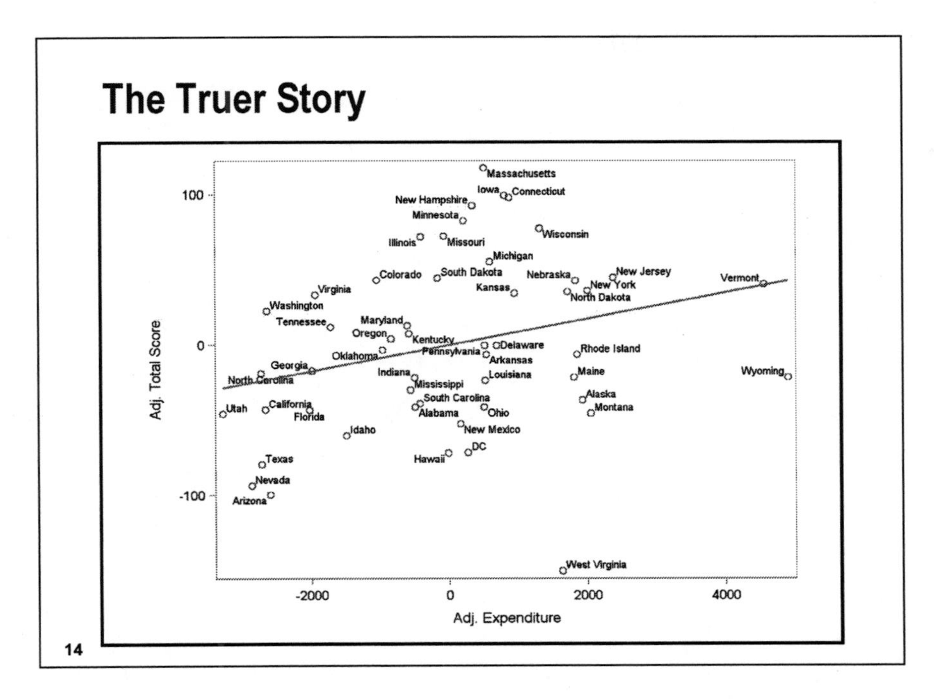


If you adjust for differences in participation rates, the conclusions about the effect of expenditures might change. In this case, there seems to be a slight positive linear relationship between expenditures and average total score on the SAT when you first adjust for participation rates. (These types of adjustments are described in greater detail in the sections about multiple regression.)

Simple correlations often do not tell the whole story.

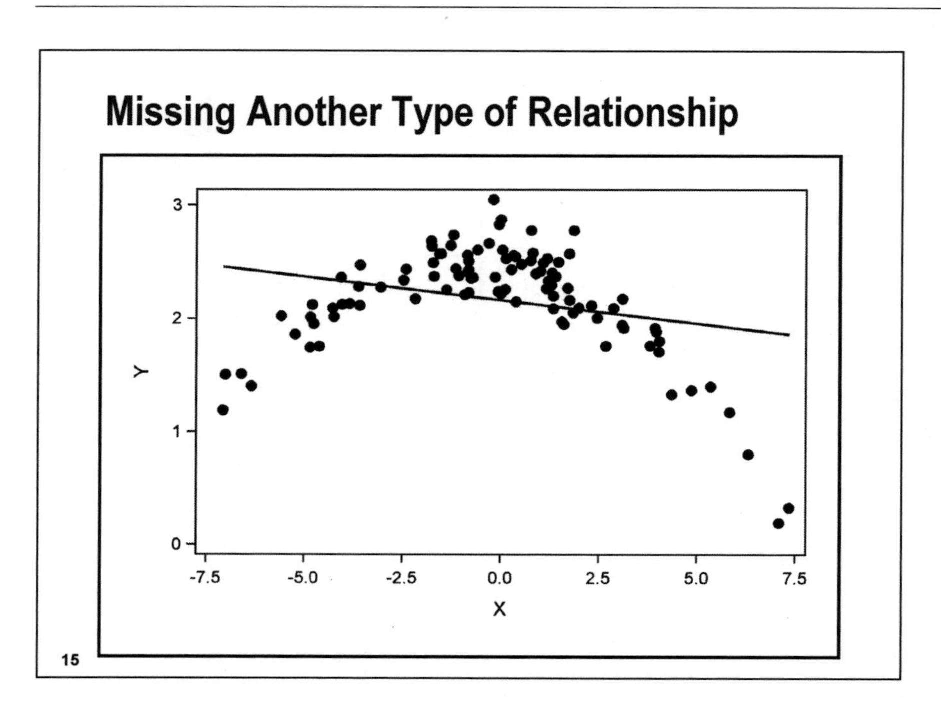


In the scatter plot, the variables have a fairly low Pearson correlation coefficient. Why?

- Pearson correlation coefficients measure linear relationships.
- A Pearson correlation coefficient close to 0 indicates that there is not a strong linear relationship between two variables.
- A Pearson correlation coefficient close to 0 does not mean that there is no relationship of any kind between the two variables.

In this example, there is a curvilinear relationship between the two variables.

## Extreme Data Values

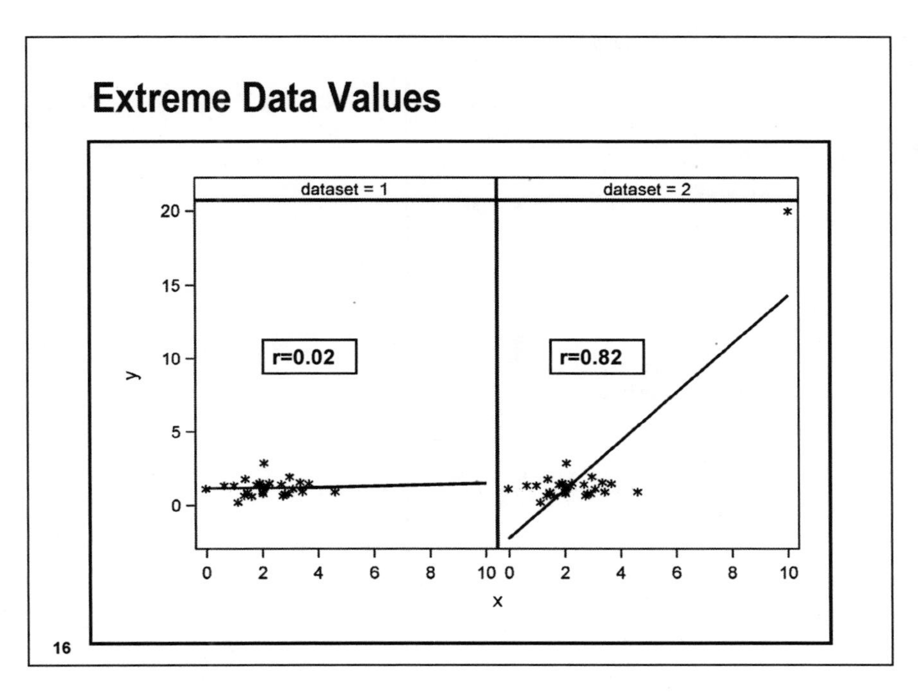


Correlation coefficients are highly affected by a few extreme values on either variable's range. The scatter plots show that the degree of linear relationship is mainly determined by one point. If you include the unusual point in the data set, the correlation is close to 1. If you do not include it, the correlation is close to 0.

In this situation, follow these steps:

1. Investigate the unusual data point to make sure it is valid.
2. If the data point is valid, collect more data between the unusual data point and the group of data points to see whether a linear relationship unfolds.
3. Try to replicate the unusual data point by collecting data at a fixed value of *x* (in this case, $x$=10). This determines whether the data point is unusual.
4. Compute two correlation coefficients, one with the unusual data point and one without it. This shows how influential the unusual data point is in the analysis. In this case, it is greatly influential.

## The CORR Procedure

General form of the CORR procedure:

```
PROC CORR DATA=SAS-data-set <options>;
      VAR variables;
      WITH variables;
      ID variables;
RUN;
```

17

You can use the CORR procedure to produce correlation statistics and scatter plots for your data. By default, PROC CORR produces Pearson correlation statistics and corresponding *p*-values.

Selected CORR procedure statements:

VAR specifies variables for which to produce correlations. If a WITH statement is not specified, correlations are produced for each pair of variables in the VAR statement. If the WITH statement is specified, the VAR statement specifies the column variables in the correlation matrix.

WITH produces correlations for each variable in the VAR statement with all variables in the WITH statement. The WITH statement specifies the row variables in the correlation matrix.

ID specifies one or more additional tip variables to identify observations in scatter plots and scatter plot matrices.

## The CORR Procedure

- Scatter plots and scatter plot matrices are available through ODS Graphics.
- The ID statement enables you to specify additional variables to identify observations in scatter plots and scatter plot matrices.

18

Exploratory analysis in preparation for multiple regression often involves looking at bivariate scatter plots and correlations between each of the predictor variables and the response variable. It is not suggested that exclusion or inclusion decisions be made on the basis of these analyses. The purpose is to explore the shape of the relationships (because linear regression assumes a linear shape to the relationship) and to screen for outliers. You also want to check for multivariate outliers when you test your multiple regression models later.

PROC CORR provides bivariate correlation tables. These tables are accompanied by ODS Statistical Graphics. An ID statement in the procedure helps identify outliers in the plots.

## PROC CORR PLOTS OPTION: Syntax and Selected Sub-Options

- **PLOTS <(ONLY)> <= (*plot-request* < *plot-request* >) >**
  - **ALL**
  - **MATRIX** <( *matrix-options* )>
  - **SCATTER** <( *scatter-options* )>
  - **HIST | HISTOGRAM**
  - **NVAR=ALL |** *n*
  - **ELLIPSE=PREDICTION | CONFIDENCE | NONE**

19

Selected PLOTS= sub-options:

| | |
|---|---|
| MATRIX <( *matrix-options* )> | requests a scatter plot matrix for variables. |
| SCATTER <( *scatter-options* )> | requests scatter plots for pairs of variables. When a scatter plot or a scatter plot matrix is requested, the Pearson correlations are also displayed. |

The available *matrix-options* are as follows:

| | |
|---|---|
| HIST \| HISTOGRAM | displays histograms of variables in the VAR list in the scatter plot matrix. |
| NVAR=ALL \| *n* | specifies the maximum number of variables in the VAR list to be displayed in the scatter plot matrix. By default, NVAR=5. |
| ELLIPSE= | requests prediction ellipses for new observations (ELLIPSE=PREDICTION), confidence ellipses for the mean (ELLIPSE=CONFIDENCE), or no ellipses (ELLIPSE=NONE) to be created in the scatter plots. By default, ELLIPSE=PREDICTION. |

In exercise physiology, an objective measure of aerobic fitness is how efficiently the body can absorb and use oxygen (oxygen consumption). Subjects participated in a predetermined exercise run of 1.5 miles. Measurements of oxygen consumption as well as several other continuous measurements such as age, pulse, and weight were recorded. The researchers are interested in determining whether any of these other variables can help predict oxygen consumption. These data are found in Rawlings (1998) but certain values of **Maximum_Pulse** and **Run_Pulse** were changed for illustration. **Name**, **Gender**, and **Performance** were also modified for illustration.

The **sasuser.fitness** data set contains the following variables:

| | |
|---|---|
| **Name** | name of the member |
| **Gender** | gender of the member |
| **RunTime** | time to run 1.5 miles (in minutes) |
| **Age** | age of the member (in years) |
| **Weight** | weight of the member (in kilograms) |
| **Oxygen_Consumption** | a measure of the ability to use oxygen in the blood stream |
| **Run_Pulse** | pulse rate at the end of the run |
| **Rest_Pulse** | resting pulse rate |
| **Maximum_Pulse** | maximum pulse rate during the run |
| **Performance** | a measure of overall fitness |

## Data Exploration, Correlations, and Scatter Plots

Examine the relationships between **Oxygen_Consumption** and the continuous predictor variables in the data set. Use the CORR procedure.

```
/*st103d01.sas*/  /*Part A*/
ods graphics / reset=all imagemap;
proc corr data=sasuser.fitness rank
          plots(only)=scatter(nvar=all ellipse=none);
   var RunTime Age Weight Run_Pulse
       Rest_Pulse Maximum_Pulse Performance;
   with Oxygen_Consumption;
   id name;
   title "Correlations and Scatter Plots with Oxygen_Consumption";
run;
```

IMAGEMAP=ON in the ODS GRAPHICS statement enables tooltips to be used in HTML output. Tooltips are also functional in SAS Report output when you use SAS Enterprise Guide, starting with Version 4.3. Tooltips enable the user to identify data points by moving the cursor over observations in a plot. In PROC CORR, the variables used in the tooltips are the X axis and Y axis variables, the observation number, and any variable in the ID statement.

Selected PROC CORR statement options:

| | |
|---|---|
| RANK | orders the correlations from highest to lowest in absolute value. |
| PLOTS | creates scatter plots and scatter plot matrices using ODS GRAPHICS. |

Selected PROC CORR statement:

| | |
|---|---|
| ID | when used in HTML output with IMAGEMAP, adds the listed variables to the information available with tooltips. |

Suboptions for the PLOTS option:

| | |
|---|---|
| SCATTER | generates scatter plots for pairs of variables. |

Suboptions for the SCATTER sub-option:

| | |
|---|---|
| NVAR=<*k*> | specifies the maximum number of variables in the VAR list to be displayed in the matrix plot. If NVAR=ALL is specified, then all variables in the VAR list (up to a limit of 10) are displayed. |
| ELLIPSE=NONE | suppresses the drawing of confidence ellipses on scatter plots. |

The tabular output from PROC CORR is shown below. By default, the analysis generates a table of univariate statistics for the analysis variables and then a table of correlations and *p*-values.

PROC CORR Output

| 1 With Variables: | Oxygen_Consumption |
|---|---|
| 7 Variables: | RunTime Age Weight Run_Pulse Rest_Pulse Maximum_Pulse Performance |

| Simple Statistics | | | | | | |
|---|---|---|---|---|---|---|
| **Variable** | **N** | **Mean** | **Std Dev** | **Sum** | **Minimum** | **Maximum** |
| **Oxygen_Consumption** | 31 | 47.37581 | 5.32777 | 1469 | 37.39000 | 60.06000 |
| **RunTime** | 31 | 10.58613 | 1.38741 | 328.17000 | 8.17000 | 14.03000 |
| **Age** | 31 | 47.67742 | 5.26236 | 1478 | 38.00000 | 57.00000 |
| **Weight** | 31 | 77.44452 | 8.32857 | 2401 | 59.08000 | 91.63000 |
| **Run_Pulse** | 31 | 169.64516 | 10.25199 | 5259 | 146.00000 | 186.00000 |
| **Rest_Pulse** | 31 | 53.45161 | 7.61944 | 1657 | 40.00000 | 70.00000 |
| **Maximum_Pulse** | 31 | 173.77419 | 9.16410 | 5387 | 155.00000 | 192.00000 |
| **Performance** | 31 | 56.64516 | 18.32584 | 1756 | 20.00000 | 94.00000 |

| Pearson Correlation Coefficients, N = 31<br>Prob > \|r\| under H0: Rho=0 | | | | | | | |
|---|---|---|---|---|---|---|---|
| **Oxygen_Consumption** | RunTime<br>-0.86219<br><.0001 | Performance<br>0.77890<br><.0001 | Rest_Pulse<br>-0.39935<br>0.0260 | Run_Pulse<br>-0.39808<br>0.0266 | Age<br>-0.31162<br>0.0879 | Maximum_Pulse<br>-0.23677<br>0.1997 | Weight<br>-0.16289<br>0.3813 |

The correlation coefficient between **Oxygen_Consumption** and **RunTime** is -0.86219. The *p*-value is small, which indicates that the population correlation coefficient (Rho) is likely different from 0. The second largest correlation coefficient, in absolute value, is **Performance**, at 0.77890.

Scatter plots associated with these correlations are shown below.

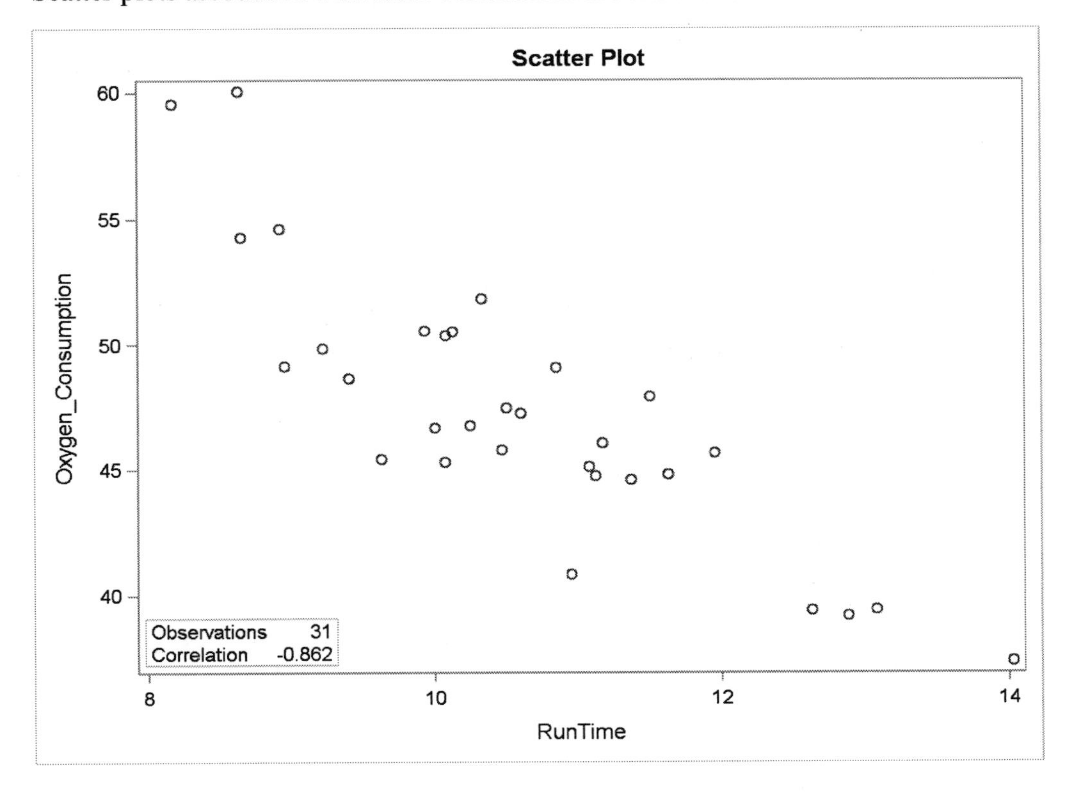

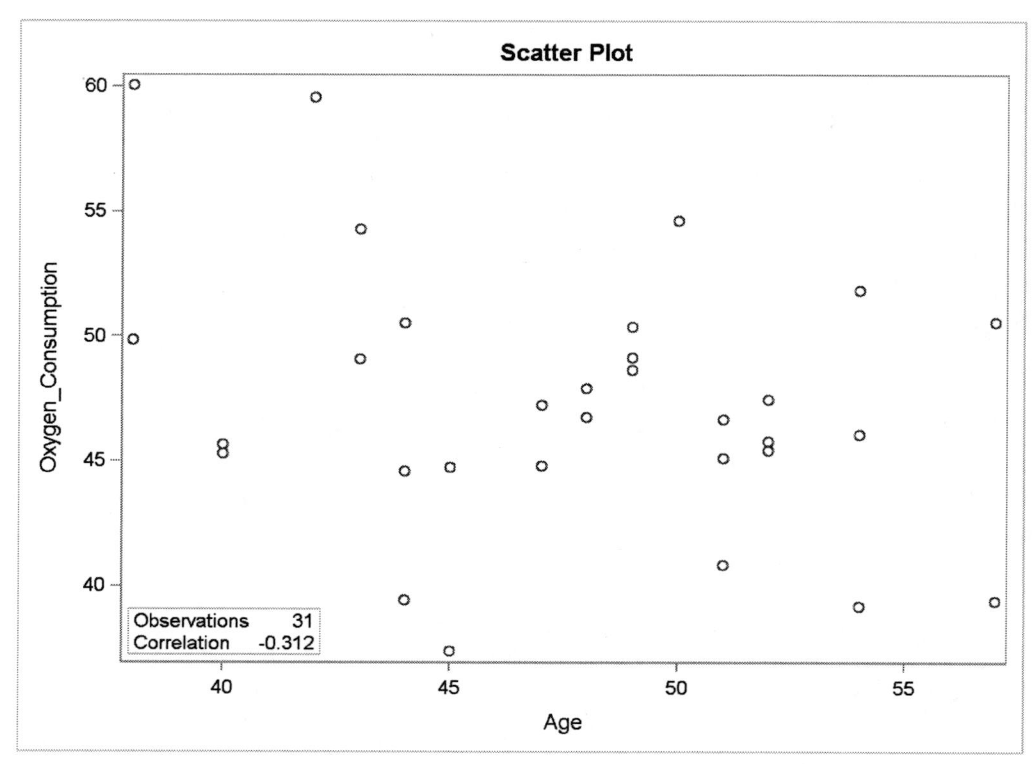
Scatter Plot
Oxygen_Consumption
60
55
50
45
40
Observations 31
Correlation -0.312
40
45
50
55
Age

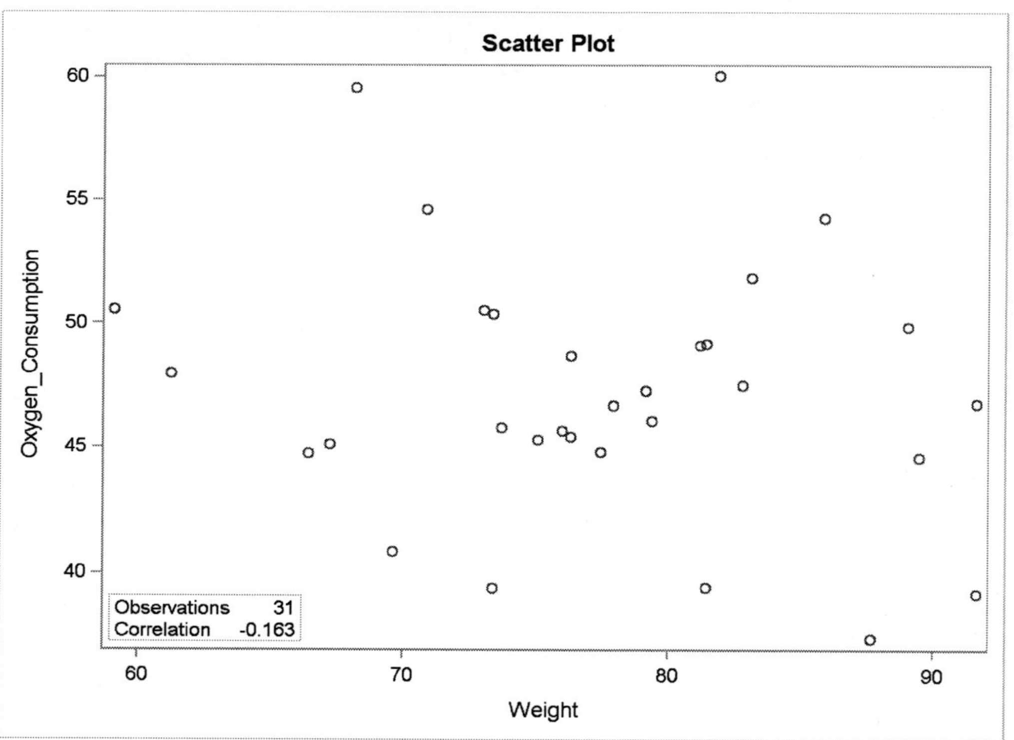
Scatter Plot
Oxygen_Consumption
60
55
50
45
40
Observations 31
Correlation -0.163
60
70
80
90
Weight

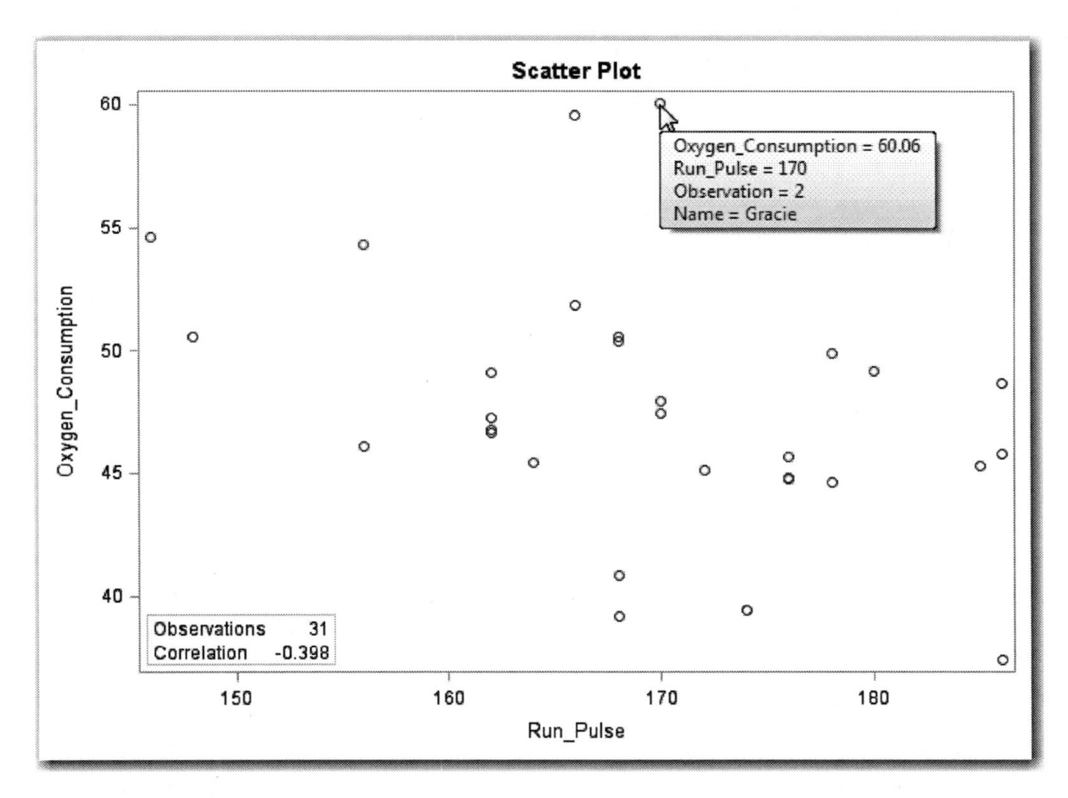


If you want to explore an observation further, you can move the cursor over the observation and information is displayed in a floating box. You can only do this in an HTML file with IMAGEMAP turned on. The coordinate values, observation number, and ID variable values are displayed.

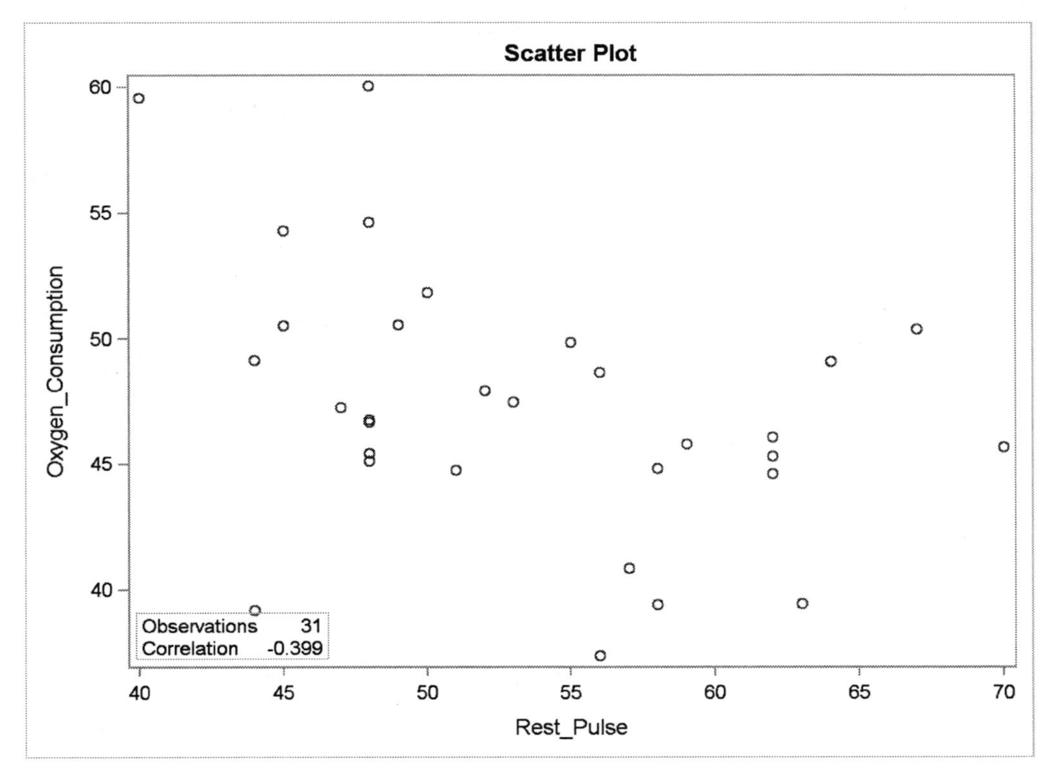

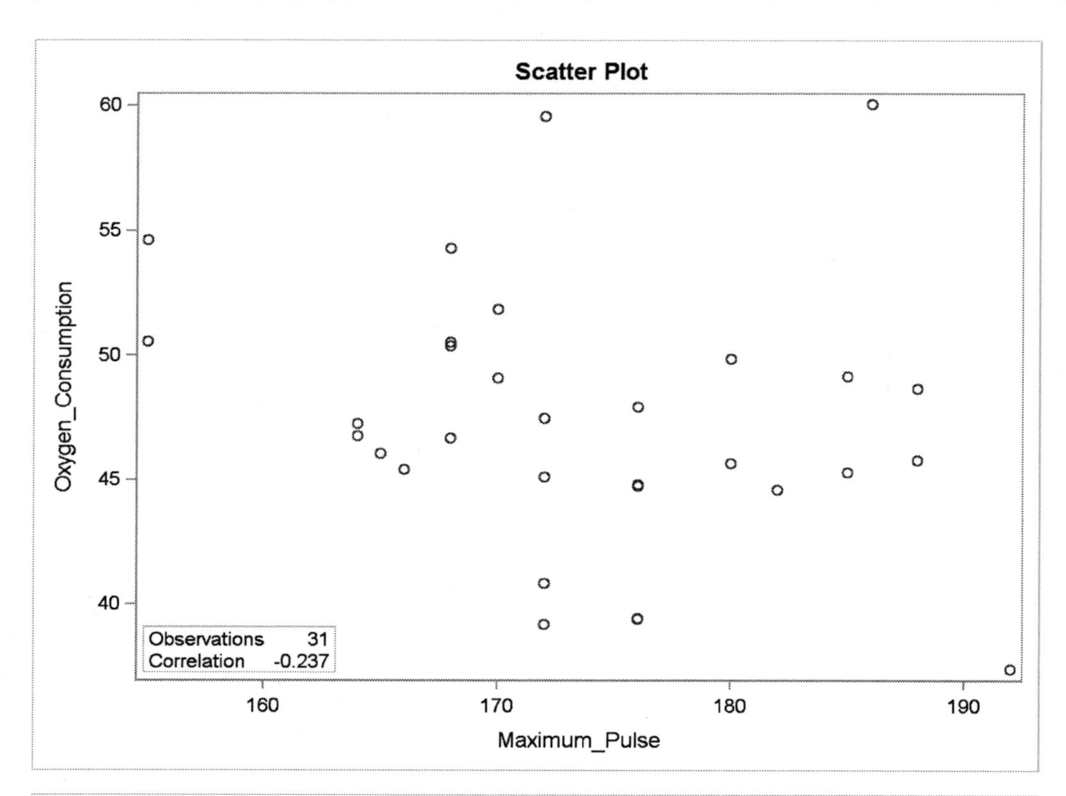


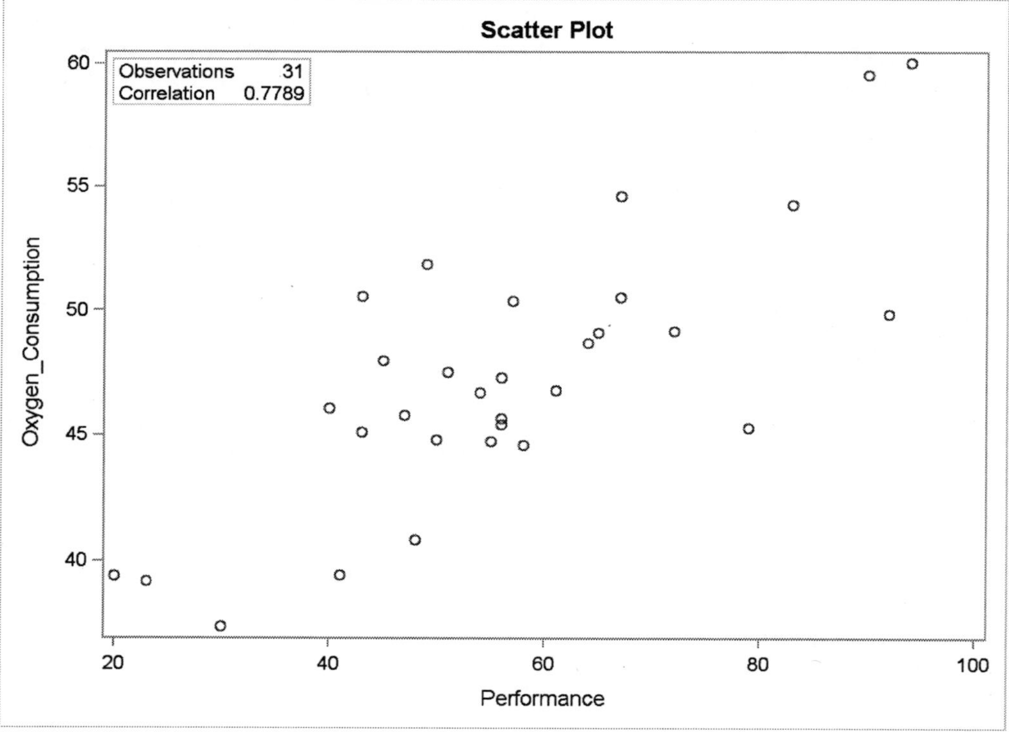


The correlation and scatter plot analyses indicate that several variables might be good predictors for **Oxygen_Consumption**.

When you prepare to conduct a regression analysis, it is always good practice to examine the correlations among the potential predictor variables. PROC CORR can be used to generate a matrix of correlation coefficients. To ensure that the imagemap feature used in the previous demonstration is deactivated, we will include a RESET=ALL option in the ODS statement.

```
/*st103d01.sas*/  /*Part B*/
ods graphics / reset=all;
proc corr data=sasuser.fitness nosimple
          plots=matrix(nvar=all histogram);
   var RunTime Age Weight Run_Pulse
       Rest_Pulse Maximum_Pulse Performance;
   title "Correlations and Scatter Plot Matrix of Fitness Predictors";
run;
```

Selected PROC CORR statement option:

NOSIMPLE suppresses printing simple descriptive statistics for each variable.

PROC CORR Output

| **7 Variables:** | RunTime | Age | Weight | Run_Pulse | Rest_Pulse | Maximum_Pulse | Performance |
|---|---|---|---|---|---|---|---|

**Pearson Correlation Coefficients, N = 31**
**Prob > |r| under H0: Rho=0**

| | RunTime | Age | Weight | Run_Pulse | Rest_Pulse | Maximum_Pulse | Performance |
|---|---|---|---|---|---|---|---|
| **RunTime** | 1.00000 | 0.19523<br>0.2926 | 0.14351<br>0.4412 | 0.31365<br>0.0858 | 0.45038<br>0.0110 | 0.22610<br>0.2213 | -0.82049<br><.0001 |
| **Age** | 0.19523<br>0.2926 | 1.00000 | -0.24050<br>0.1925 | -0.31607<br>0.0832 | -0.15087<br>0.4178 | -0.41490<br>0.0203 | -0.71257<br><.0001 |
| **Weight** | 0.14351<br>0.4412 | -0.24050<br>0.1925 | 1.00000 | 0.18152<br>0.3284 | 0.04397<br>0.8143 | 0.24938<br>0.1761 | 0.08974<br>0.6312 |
| **Run_Pulse** | 0.31365<br>0.0858 | -0.31607<br>0.0832 | 0.18152<br>0.3284 | 1.00000 | 0.35246<br>0.0518 | 0.92975<br><.0001 | -0.02943<br>0.8751 |
| **Rest_Pulse** | 0.45038<br>0.0110 | -0.15087<br>0.4178 | 0.04397<br>0.8143 | 0.35246<br>0.0518 | 1.00000 | 0.30512<br>0.0951 | -0.22560<br>0.2224 |
| **Maximum_Pulse** | 0.22610<br>0.2213 | -0.41490<br>0.0203 | 0.24938<br>0.1761 | 0.92975<br><.0001 | 0.30512<br>0.0951 | 1.00000 | 0.09002<br>0.6301 |
| **Performance** | -0.82049<br><.0001 | -0.71257<br><.0001 | 0.08974<br>0.6312 | -0.02943<br>0.8751 | -0.22560<br>0.2224 | 0.09002<br>0.6301 | 1.00000 |

There are strong correlations between **Run_Pulse** and **Maximum_Pulse** (0.92975) and between **RunTime** and **Performance** (-0.82049). These associations are seen in more detail in the matrix of scatter plots.

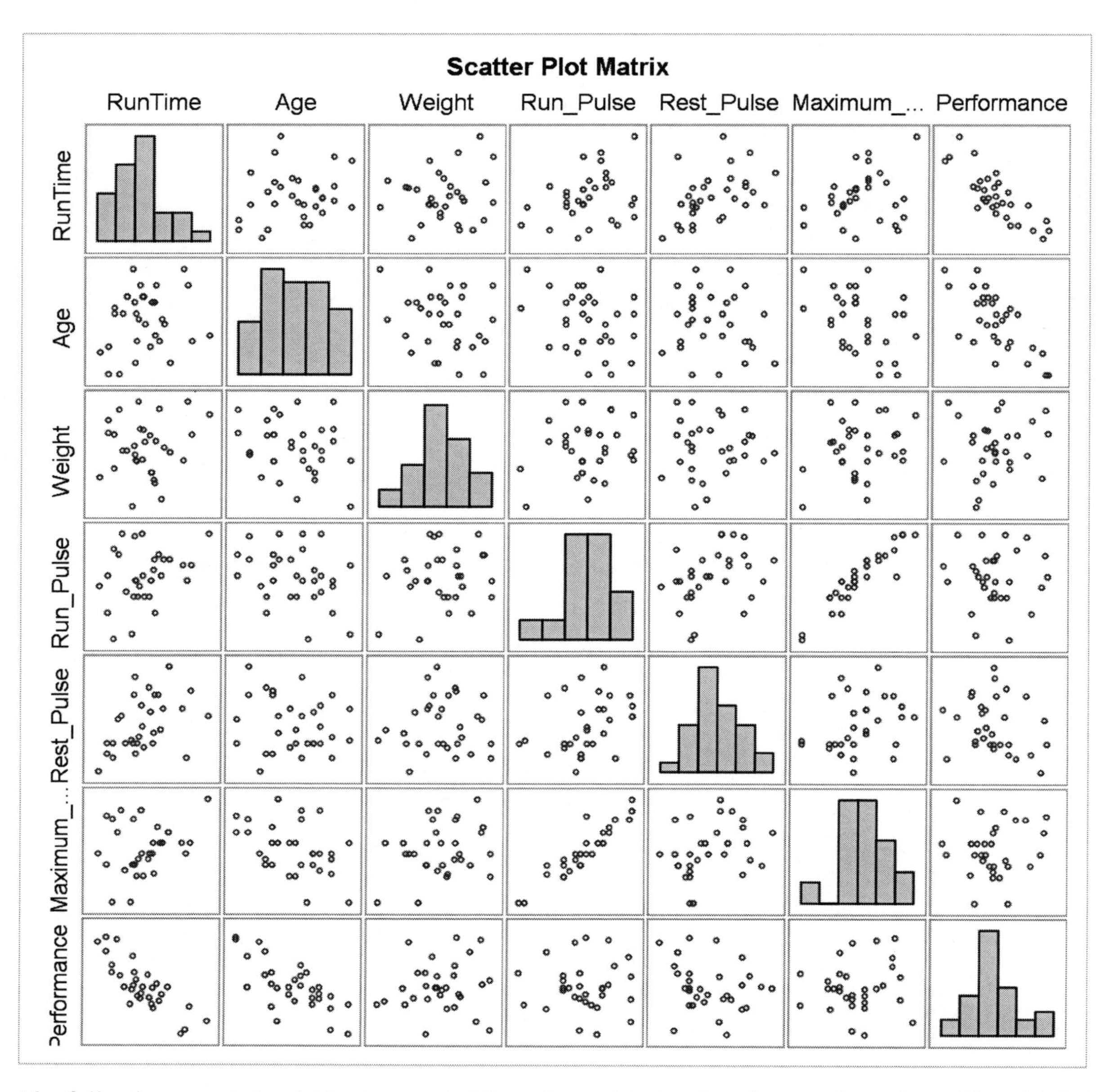


The following correlation table was created from the matrix by choosing small $p$-values. The table is in descending order, based on the absolute value of the correlation. It provides a summary of the correlation analysis of the independent variables.

| Row Variable | Column Variable | Pearson's r | Prob > \|r\| |
|---|---|---|---|
| Run_Pulse | Maximum_Pulse | 0.92975 | <.0001 |
| RunTime | Performance | -0.82049 | <.0001 |
| Performance | Age | -0.71257 | <.0001 |
| RunTime | Rest_Pulse | 0.45038 | 0.0110 |
| Age | Maximum_Pulse | -0.41490 | 0.0203 |
| Run_Pulse | Rest_Pulse | 0.35246 | 0.0518 |

# Exercises

**1. Describing the Relationship between Continuous Variables**

Percentage of body fat, age, weight, height, and 10 body circumference measurements (for example, abdomen) were recorded for 252 men by Dr. Roger W. Johnson of Calvin College in Minnesota. The data are in the **sasuser.BodyFat2** data set. Body fat, one measure of health, was accurately estimated by an underwater weighing technique. There are two measures of percentage body fat in this data set. The following variables are in the data set:

| | |
|---|---|
| **Case** | Case Number |
| **PctBodyFat1** | Percent body fat using Brozek's equation, 457/Density - 414.2 |
| **PctBodyFat2** | Percent body fat using Siri's equation, 495/Density - 450 |
| **Density** | Density (gm/cm^3) |
| **Age** | Age (yrs) |
| **Weight** | Weight (lbs) |
| **Height** | Height (inches) |
| **Adioposity** | Adiposity index=Weight/Height^2 (kg/m^2) |
| **FatFreeWt** | Fat Free Weight=(1-fraction of body fat)*Weight, using Brozek's formula (lbs) |
| **Neck** | Neck circumference (cm) |
| **Chest** | Chest circumference (cm) |
| **Abdomen** | Abdomen circumference (cm) "at the umbilicus and level with the iliac crest" |
| **Hip** | Hip circumference (cm) |
| **Thigh** | Thigh circumference (cm) |
| **Knee** | Knee circumference (cm) |
| **Ankle** | Ankle circumference (cm) |
| **Biceps** | Extended biceps circumference (cm) |
| **Forearm** | Forearm circumference (cm) |
| **Wrist** | Wrist circumference (cm) "distal to the styloid processes" |

**a.** Generate scatter plots and correlations for the VAR variables **Age**, **Weight**, **Height**, and the circumference measures versus the WITH variable, **PctBodyFat2**.

Important! ODS Graphics in PROC CORR limits you to 10 VAR variables at a time, so for this exercise, look at the relationships with **Age**, **Weight**, and **Height** separately from the circumference variables (**Neck Chest Abdomen Hip Thigh Knee Ankle Biceps Forearm Wrist**).

This limitation exists only on the graphics obtained from ODS. The correlation table will display all variables in the VAR statement by default.

1) Can straight lines adequately describe the relationships?

2) Are there any outliers that you should investigate?

3) What variable has the highest correlation with **PctBodyFat2**?

   a) What is the *p*-value for the coefficient?

   b) Is the correlation statistically significant at the 0.05 level?

**b.** Generate correlations among all of the variables in the previously mentioned variables minus **PctBodyFat2**. Are there any notable relationships?

## 3.01 Multiple Choice Poll

The correlation between tuition and rate of graduation at U.S. colleges is 0.55. What does this mean?

a. The way to increase graduation rates at your college is to raise tuition.

b. Increasing graduation rates is expensive, causing tuition to rise.

c. Students who are richer tend to graduate more often than poorer students.

d. None of the above.

25

# 3.2 Simple Linear Regression

## Objectives

- Explain the concepts of simple linear regression.
- Fit a simple linear regression using the REG procedure.
- Produce predicted values and confidence intervals.

28

## Overview

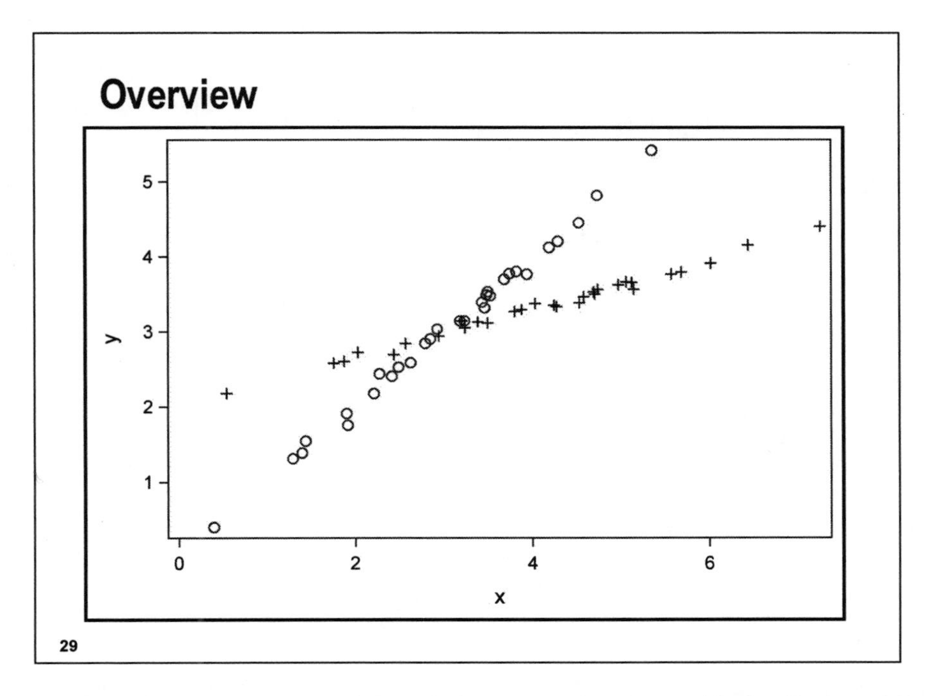


29

In the last section, you used correlation analysis to quantify the linear relationships between continuous response variables. Two pairs of variables can have the same correlation, but very different linear relationships. In this section, you use simple linear regression to define the linear relationship between a response variable and a predictor variable.

- The *response variable* is the variable of primary interest.
- The *predictor variable* is used to explain the variability in the response variable.

## Simple Linear Regression Analysis

The objectives of simple linear regression are as follows:

- assess the significance of the predictor variable in explaining the variability or behavior of the response variable
- predict the values of the response variable given the values of the predictor variable

30

In simple linear regression, the values of the predictor variable are assumed to be fixed. Thus, you try to explain the variability of the response variable given the values of the predictor variable.

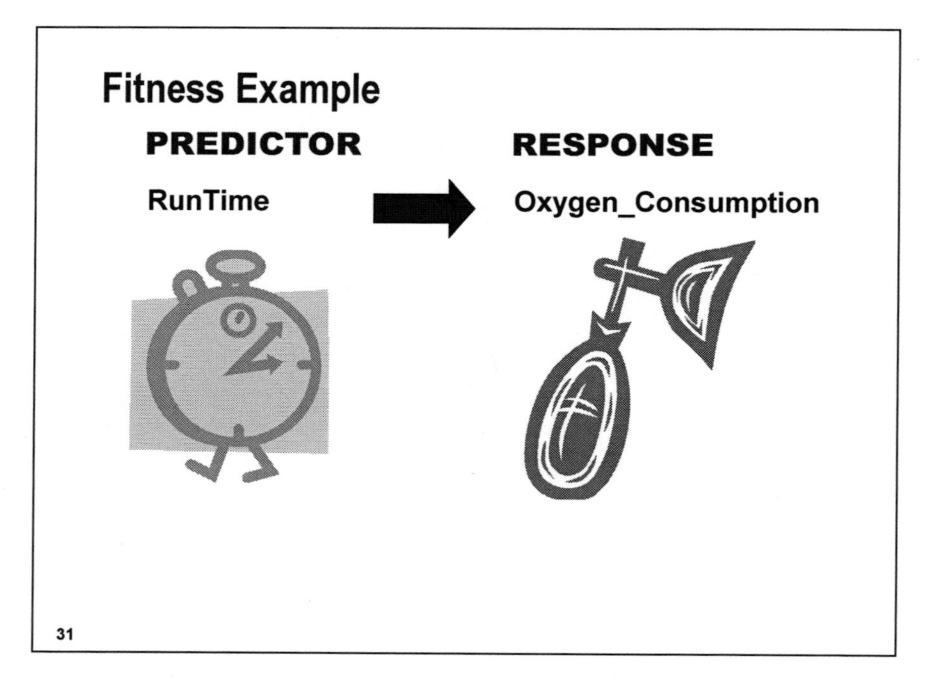


The analyst noted that the running time measure has the highest correlation with the oxygen consumption capacity of the club members. Consequently, she wants to further explore the relationship between **Oxygen_Consumption** and **RunTime**.

She decides to run a simple linear regression of **Oxygen_Consumption** versus **RunTime**.

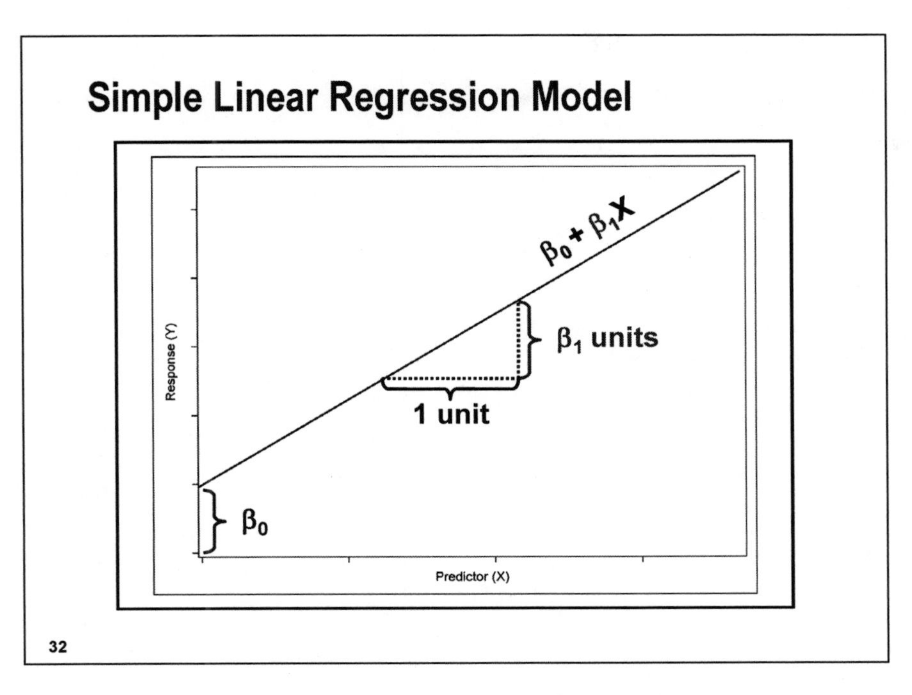


The relationship between the response variable and the predictor variable can be characterized by the equation $y_i=\beta_0+\beta_1 x_i+\varepsilon_i$, $i=1, \ldots, n$

where

| | |
|---|---|
| $y_i$ | is the response variable. |
| $x_i$ | is the predictor variable. |
| $\beta_0$ | is the intercept parameter, which corresponds to the value of the response variable when the predictor is 0. |
| $\beta_1$ | is the slope parameter, which corresponds to the magnitude of change in the response variable given a one unit change in the predictor variable. |
| $\varepsilon_I$ | is the error term representing deviations of $y_i$ about $\beta_0 + \beta_1 x_i$. |

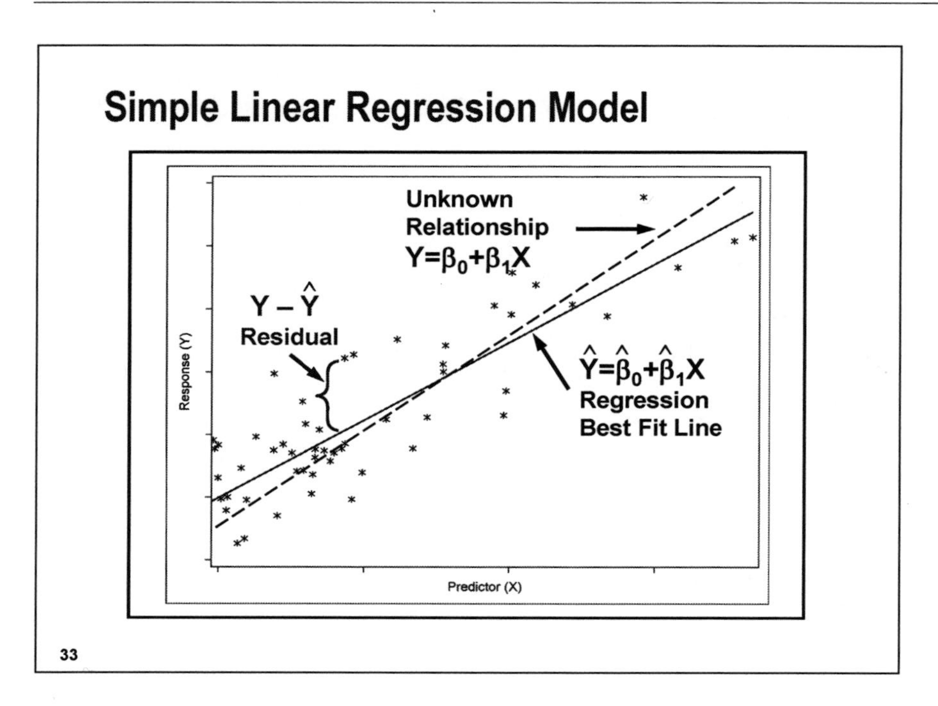


Because your goal in simple linear regression is usually to characterize the relationship between the response and predictor variables in your population, you begin with a sample of data. From this sample, you estimate the unknown population parameters ($\beta_0$, $\beta_1$) that define the assumed relationship between your response and predictor variables.

Estimates of the unknown population parameters $\beta_0$ and $\beta_1$ are obtained by the *method of least squares.* This method provides the estimates by determining the line that minimizes the sum of the squared vertical distances between the observations and the fitted line. In other words, the fitted or regression line is as close as possible to all the data points.

The method of least squares produces parameter estimates with certain optimum properties. If the assumptions of simple linear regression are valid, the least squares estimates are unbiased estimates of the population parameters and have minimum variance (efficiency). The least squares estimators are often called BLUE (Best Linear Unbiased Estimators). The term *best* is used because of the minimum variance property.

Because of these optimum properties, the method of least squares is used by many data analysts to investigate the relationship between continuous predictor and response variables.

With a large and representative sample, the fitted regression line should be a good approximation of the relationship between the response and predictor variables in the population. The estimated parameters obtained using the method of least squares should be good approximations of the true population parameters.

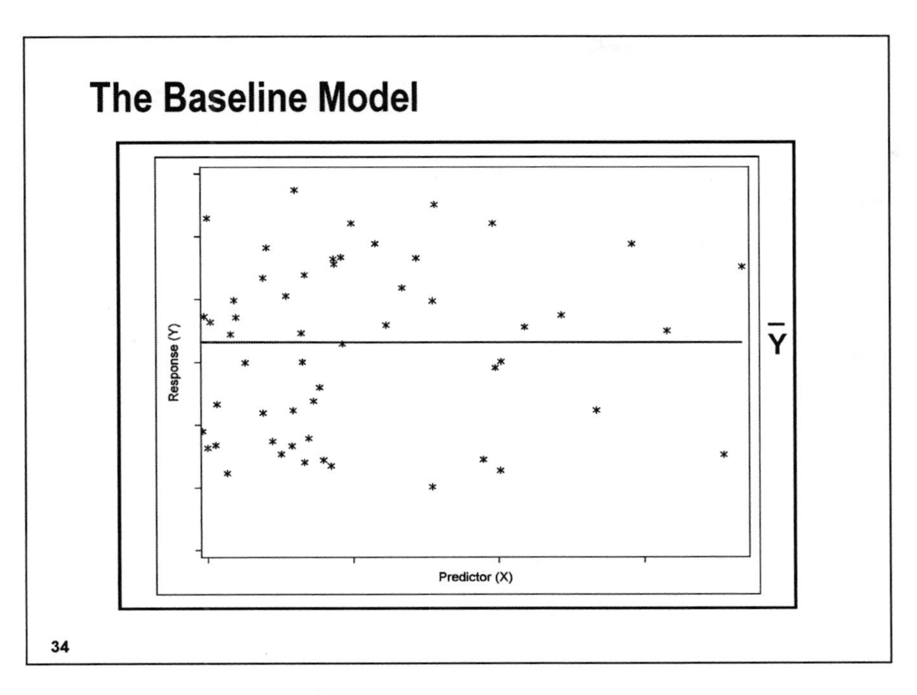


To determine whether the predictor variable explains a significant amount of variability in the response variable, the simple linear regression model is compared to the baseline model. The fitted regression line in a baseline model is a horizontal line across all values of the predictor variable. The slope of the regression line is 0 and the intercept is the sample mean of the response variable, ($\overline{Y}$).

In a baseline model, there is no association between the response variable and the predictor variable. Therefore, knowing the value of the predictor variable does not improve predictions of the response over simply using the unconditional mean (the mean calculated disregarding the predictor variables) of the response variable.

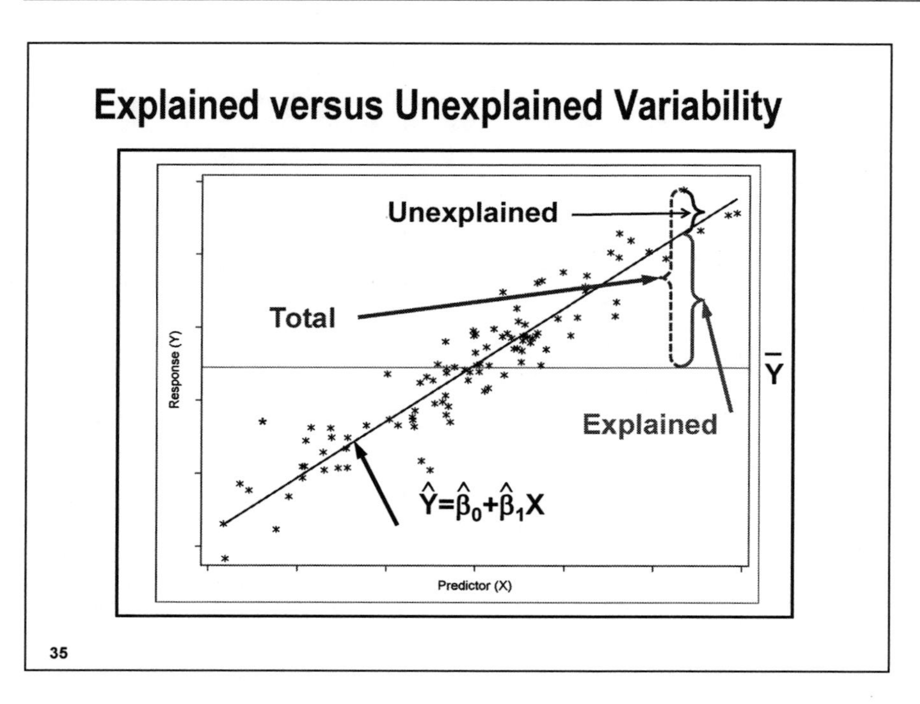


To determine whether a simple linear regression model is better than the baseline model, compare the explained variability to the unexplained variability.

Explained variability is related to the difference between the regression line and the mean of the response variable. The model sum of squares (SSM) is the amount of variability explained by your model. The model sum of squares is equal to $\sum(\hat{Y}_i - \bar{Y})^2$.

Unexplained variability is related to the difference between the observed values and the regression line. The error sum of squares (SSE) is the amount of variability unexplained by your model. The error sum of squares is equal to $\sum(Y_i - \hat{Y}_i)^2$.

Total variability is related to the difference between the observed values and the mean of the response variable. The corrected total sum of squares is the sum of the explained and unexplained variability. The corrected total sum of squares is equal to $\sum(Y_i - \bar{Y})^2$.

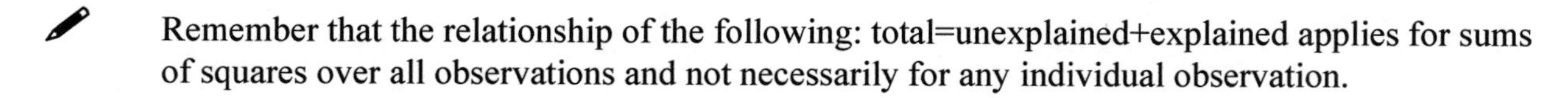

Remember that the relationship of the following: total=unexplained+explained applies for sums of squares over all observations and not necessarily for any individual observation.

## Model Hypothesis Test

**Null Hypothesis:**

- The simple linear regression model does ***not*** fit the data better than the baseline model.
- $\beta_1=0$

**Alternative Hypothesis:**

- The simple linear regression model does fit the data better than the baseline model.
- $\beta_1 \neq 0$

36

If the estimated simple linear regression model does ***not*** fit the data better than the baseline model, you fail to reject the null hypothesis. Thus, you do ***not*** have enough evidence to say that the slope of the regression line in the population differs from zero.

If the estimated simple linear regression model ***does*** fit the data better than the baseline model, you reject the null hypothesis. Thus, you ***do*** have enough evidence to say that the slope of the regression line in the population differs from zero and that the predictor variable explains a significant amount of variability in the response variable.

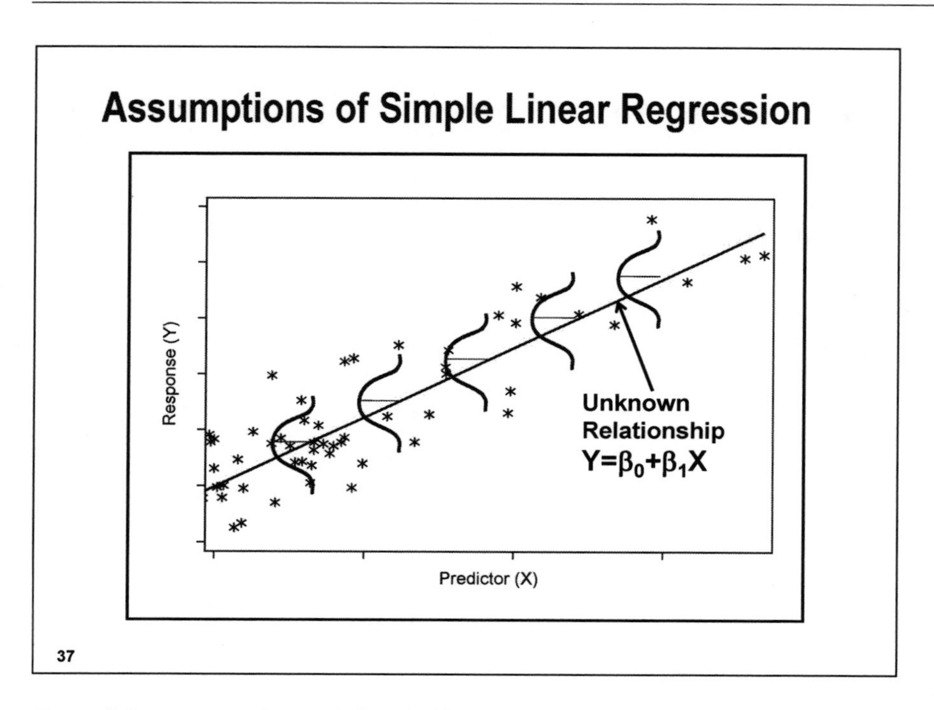


One of the assumptions of simple linear regression is that the mean of the response variable is linearly related to the value of the predictor variable. In other words, a straight line connects the means of the response variable at each value of the predictor variable.

The other assumptions are the same as the assumptions for ANOVA, that is, the error is normally distributed and has constant variance across the range of the predictor variable, and observations are independent.

 The verification of these assumptions is discussed in a later chapter.

## The REG Procedure

General form of the REG procedure:

```
PROC REG DATA=SAS-data-set <options>;
     MODEL dependent(s)=regressor(s) </ options>;
RUN;
QUIT;
```

38

The REG procedure enables you to fit regression models to your data.

Selected REG procedure statement:

MODEL specifies the response and predictor variables. The variables must be numeric.

PROC REG supports RUN-group processing, which means that the procedure stays active until a PROC, DATA, or QUIT statement is encountered. This enables you to submit additional statements followed by another RUN statement without resubmitting the PROC statement.

## Performing Simple Linear Regression

Example: Because there is an apparent linear relationship between **Oxygen_Consumption** and **RunTime**, perform a simple linear regression analysis with **Oxygen_Consumption** as the response variable.

```
/*st103d02.sas*/
proc reg data=sasuser.fitness;
   model Oxygen_Consumption=RunTime;
   title 'Predicting Oxygen_Consumption from RunTime';
run;
quit;
```

PROC REG Output

| Number of Observations Read | 31 |
|---|---|
| Number of Observations Used | 31 |

The Number of Observations Read and the Number of Observations Used are the same, which indicates that no missing values were detected for **Oxygen_Consumption** and **RunTime**.

| Analysis of Variance | | | | | |
|---|---|---|---|---|---|
| Source | DF | Sum of Squares | Mean Square | F Value | Pr > F |
| Model | 1 | 633.01458 | 633.01458 | 84.00 | <.0001 |
| Error | 29 | 218.53997 | 7.53586 | | |
| Corrected Total | 30 | 851.55455 | | | |

The Analysis of Variance (ANOVA) table provides an analysis of the variability observed in the data and the variability explained by the regression line.

The ANOVA table for simple linear regression is divided into six columns:

Source — labels the source of variability.

DF — is the degrees of freedom associated with each source of variability.

Sum of Squares — is the amount of variability associated with each source of variability.

Mean Square — is the ratio of the sum of squares and the degrees of freedom. This value corresponds to the amount of variability associated with each degree of freedom for each source of variation.

F Value — is the ratio of the mean square for the model and the mean square for the error. This ratio compares the variability explained by the regression line to the variability unexplained by the regression line.

Pr>F — is the *p*-value associated with the *F* value.

Each of the column measurements are applied to the following sources of variation:

| | |
|---|---|
| Model | is the variability explained by your model (Between Group). |
| Error | is the variability unexplained by your model (Within Group). |
| Corrected Total | is the total variability in the data (Total). |

The *F* value tests whether the slope of the predictor variable is equal to 0. The *p*-value is small (less than 0.05), so you have enough evidence at the 0.05 significance level to reject the null hypothesis. Thus, you can conclude that the simple linear regression model fits the data better than the baseline model. In other words, **RunTime** explains a significant amount of variability of **Oxygen_Consumption.**

The third part of the output provides summary measures of fit for the model.

| | | | |
|---|---|---|---|
| **Root MSE** | 2.74515 | **R Square** | 0.7434 |
| **Dependent Mean** | 47.37581 | **Adj R Sq** | 0.7345 |
| **Coeff Var** | 5.79442 | | |

Root MSE — The root mean square error is an estimate of the standard deviation of the response variable at each value of the predictor variable. It is the square root of the MSE.

Dependent Mean — The overall mean of the response variable is $\overline{Y}$ .

Coeff Var — The coefficient of variation is the size of the standard deviation relative to the mean. The coefficient of variation is

- calculated as $\left(\frac{RootMSE}{\overline{Y}}\right) * 100$
- a unitless measure, so it can be used to compare data that has different units of measurement or different magnitudes of measurement.

R Square — The coefficient of determination is also referred to as the R-square value. This value is

- between 0 and 1.
- the proportion of variability observed in the data explained by the regression line. In this example, the value is 0.7434, which means that the regression line explains 74% of the total variation in the response values.
- the square of the multiple correlation between Y and the Xs.

The R square is the squared value of the correlation that you saw earlier between **RunTime** and **Oxygen_Consumption** (0.86219). This is no coincidence. For simple regression, the R-square value is the square of the value of the bivariate Pearson correlation coefficient.

Adj R Sq — The adjusted R square is adjusted for the number of parameters in the model. This statistic is useful in multiple regression and is discussed in a later section.

The Parameter Estimates table defines the model for your data.

| Parameter Estimates | | | | | |
|---|---|---|---|---|---|
| Variable | DF | Parameter Estimate | Standard Error | t Value | Pr > \|t\| |
| **Intercept** | 1 | 82.42494 | 3.85582 | 21.38 | <.0001 |
| **RunTime** | 1 | -3.31085 | 0.36124 | -9.17 | <.0001 |

DF — represents the degrees of freedom associated with each term in the model.

Parameter Estimate — is the estimated value of the parameters associated with each term in the model.

Standard Error — is the standard error of each parameter estimate.

t Value — is the *t* statistic, which is calculated by dividing the parameter estimates by their corresponding standard error estimates.

Pr > |t| — is the *p*-value associated with the *t* statistic. It tests whether the parameter associated with each term in the model is different from 0. For this example, the slope for the predictor variable is statistically different from 0. Thus, you can conclude that the predictor variable explains a significant portion of variability in the response variable.

Because the estimate of $\beta_o$=82.42494 and $\beta_1$=–3.31085, the estimated regression equation is given by **Oxygen_Consumption**=82.42494–3.31085*(**RunTime**).

The model indicates that a one-unit greater value for **RunTime** is associated with a 3.31085 lower value for **Oxygen_Consumption**. However, ***extrapolation of the model beyond the range of your predictor variables is inappropriate***. You cannot assume that the relationship maintains in areas that were not sampled from.

The parameter estimates table also shows that the intercept parameter is not equal to 0. However, the test for the intercept parameter only has practical significance when the range of values for the predictor variable includes 0. In this example, the test could not have practical significance because **RunTime**=0 (running at the speed of light) is not inside the range of observed values.

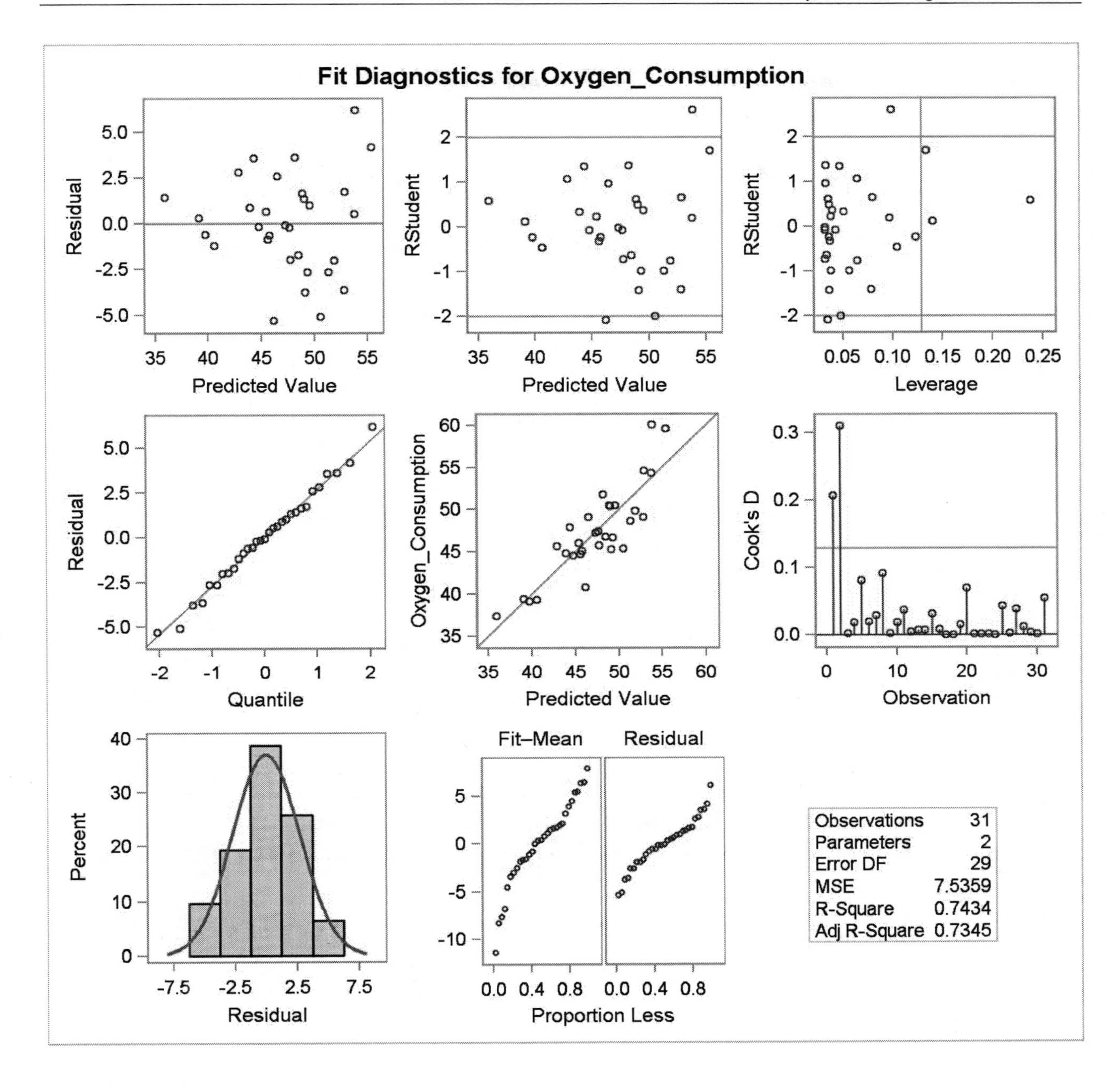
Fit Diagnostics for Oxygen_Consumption
Residual
Predicted Value
RStudent
Leverage
Quantile
Oxygen_Consumption
Cook's D
Observation
Percent
Residual
Fit–Mean
Residual
Proportion Less
Observations 31
Parameters 2
Error DF 29
MSE 7.5359
R-Square 0.7434
Adj R-Square 0.7345

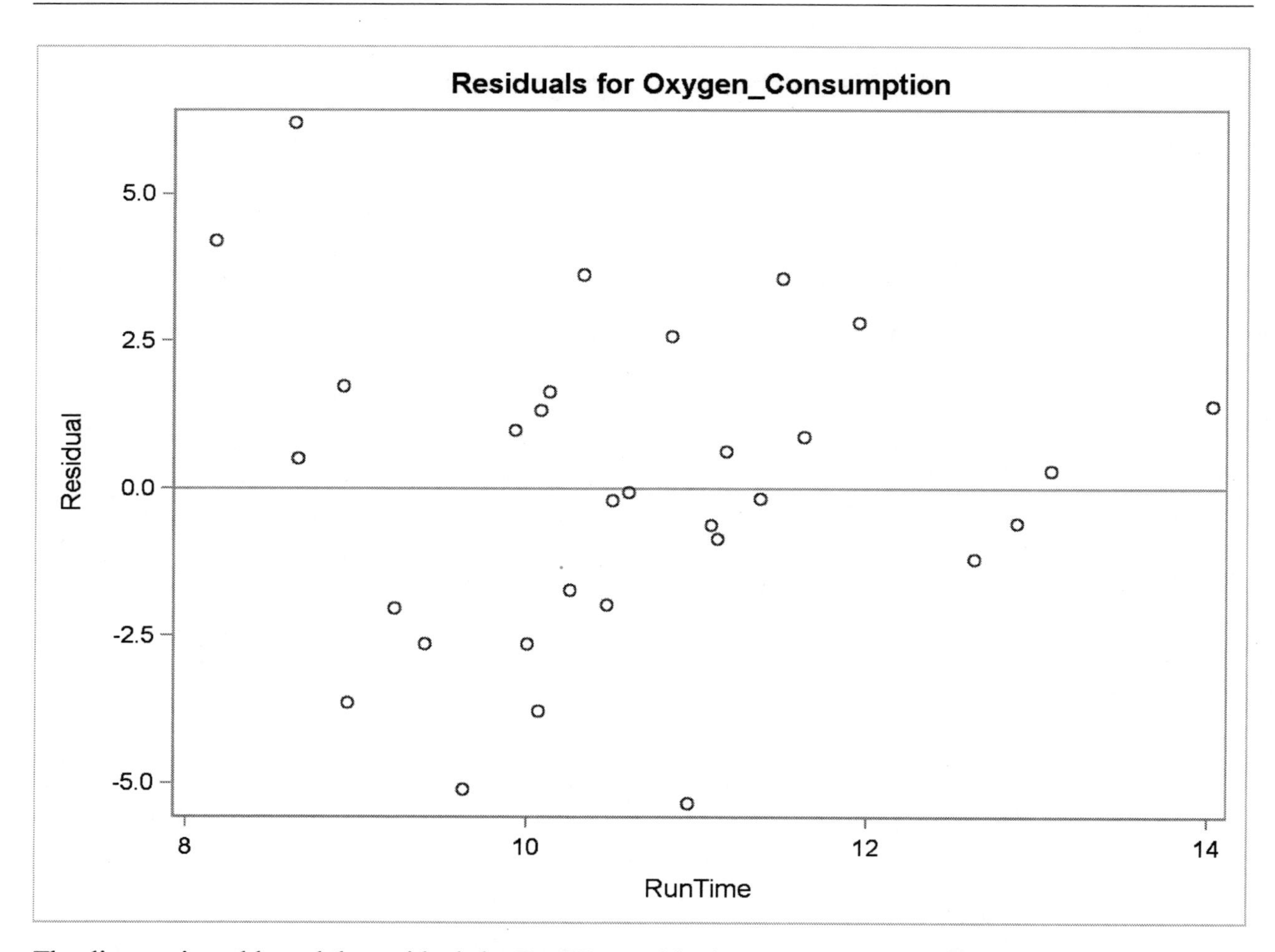


The diagnostics table and the residuals by **RunTime** table show a variety of plots designed to help with an assessment of the data's fulfillment of statistical assumptions and influential outliers. These plots are explored in detail in a later chapter.

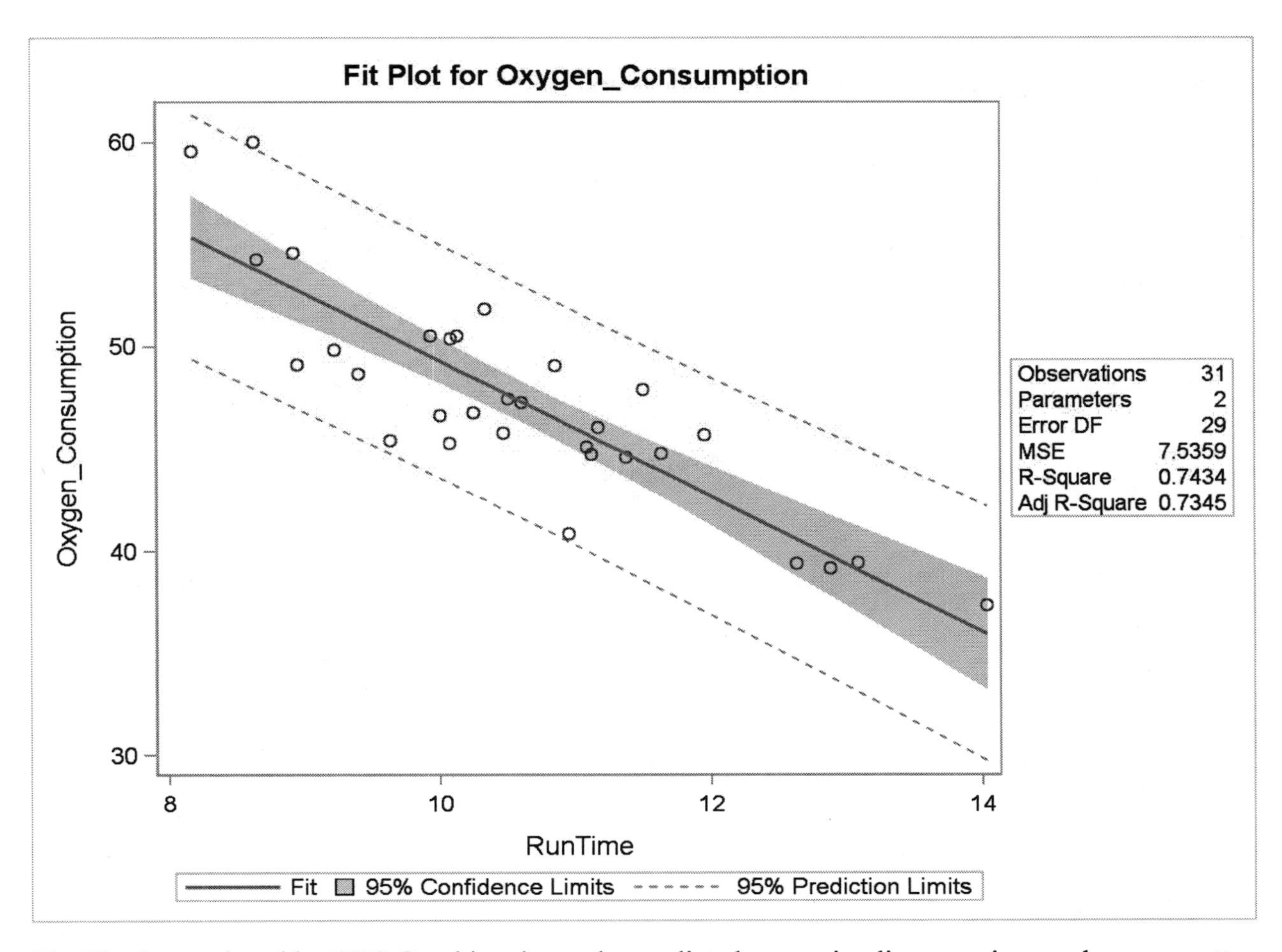


The Fit plot produced by ODS Graphics shows the predicted regression line superimposed over a scatter plot of the data.

To assess the level of precision around the mean estimates of **Oxygen_Consumption**, you can produce ***confidence intervals around the means***. This is represented in the shaded area in the plot.

- A 95% confidence interval for the mean says that you are 95% confident that your interval contains the population mean of Y for a particular X.
- Confidence intervals become wider as you move away from the mean of the independent variable. This reflects the fact that your estimates become more variable as you move away from the means of X and Y.

Suppose that the mean **Oxygen_Consumption** at a fixed value of **RunTime** is not the focus. If you are interested in establishing an inference on a future single observation, you need a ***prediction interval around the individual observations***. This is represented by the area between the broken lines in the plot.

- A 95% prediction interval is one that you are 95% confident contains a new observation.
- Prediction intervals are wider than confidence intervals because single observations have more variability than sample means.

Printed tables for the confidence and prediction intervals at each observed data point can be obtained by adding the CLM and CLI options to the MODEL statement.

## 3.02 Multiple Choice Poll

Run PROC REG with this MODEL statement: `model y=x1;`. If the parameter estimate (slope) of x1 is 0, then the best guess (predicted value) of y when x1=13 is which of the following?

a. 13
b. the mean of y
c. a random number
d. the mean of x1
e. 0

41

## Producing Predicted Values

What is the predicted value for **Oxygen_Consumption** when **RunTime** is **9**, **10**, **11**, **12**, or **13** minutes?

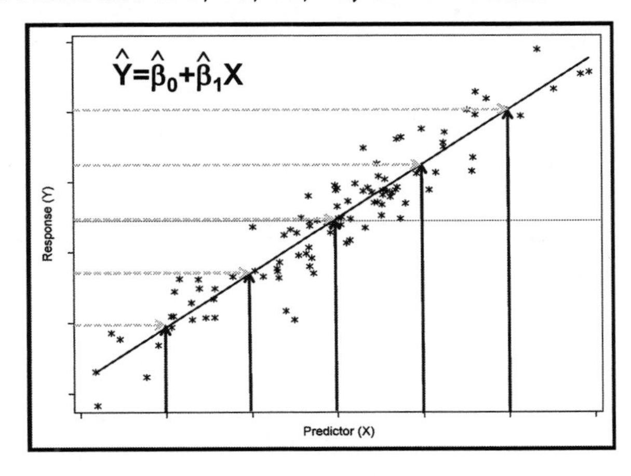


43

One objective in regression analysis is to predict values of the response variable given values of the predictor variables. You can obviously use the estimated regression equation to produce predicted values, but if you want a large number of predictions, this can be cumbersome.

To produce predicted values in PROC REG, follow these steps:

1. Create a data set with the values of the independent variable for which you want to make predictions.
2. Concatenate the data in the step above with the original data set.
3. Fit a simple linear regression model to the new data set and specify the P option in the MODEL statement. Because the observations added in the previous step contain missing values for the response variable, PROC REG does not include these observations when fitting the regression model. However, PROC REG does produce predicted values for these observations.

## The SCORE Procedure

General form of the SCORE procedure:

```
PROC SCORE DATA=SAS-data-set
           <SCORE=SAS-data-set>
           <OUT=SAS-data-set>
           <other options>;
    VAR variables;
RUN;
```

44

The SCORE procedure multiplies values from two SAS data sets, one containing coefficients (for example, factor-scoring coefficients or regression coefficients) and the other containing raw data to be scored using the coefficients from the first data set. The result of this multiplication is a SAS data set that contains linear combinations of the coefficients and the raw data values.

Many statistical procedures output coefficients that PROC SCORE can apply to raw data to produce scores. The new score variable is formed as a linear combination of raw data and scoring coefficients. For each observation in the raw data set, PROC SCORE multiplies the value of a variable in the raw data set by the matching scoring coefficient from the data set of scoring coefficients. This multiplication process is repeated for each variable in the VAR statement. The resulting products are then summed to produce the value of the new score variable. This entire process is repeated for each observation in the raw data set. In other words, PROC SCORE cross multiplies part of one data set with another.

## Producing Predicted Values

Example: Produce predicted values of **Oxygen_Consumption** when **RunTime** is 9, 10, 11, 12, or 13.

Produce predicted values by outputting the parameter estimates from PROC REG into a data set and then scoring the new observations in PROC SCORE. Here is an example program to create the data set containing the observations to be scored.

```
/*st103d03.sas*/
data Need_Predictions;
   input RunTime @@;
   datalines;
9 10 11 12 13
;
run;
```

The regression model is submitted, as usual, but with an OUTEST= option for scoring (predicting the values of) new observations.

The MODEL statement below is preceded by an alphanumeric string followed by a colon (:). This string is the label of the model and is used as the name of the variable containing the predictions from a subsequent run of PROC SCORE.

The default model label is MODEL*n*, where *n* is the ordered value of the $n^{th}$ MODEL statement in one run of PROC REG. That label is eventually used by PROC SCORE to name the variable that contains predicted values for the raw data set (the one to be scored).

```
proc reg data=sasuser.fitness noprint outest=Betas;
   PredOxy: model Oxygen_Consumption=RunTime;
run;
quit;

proc print data=Betas;
   title "OUTEST= Data Set from PROC REG";
run;
```

Selected PROC REG statement option:

OUTEST= outputs parameter estimates and model information to a SAS data set.

| Obs | _MODEL_ | _TYPE_ | _DEPVAR_ | _RMSE_ | Intercept | RunTime | Oxygen_Consumption |
|---|---|---|---|---|---|---|---|
| 1 | PredOxy | PARMS | Oxygen_Consumption | 2.74515 | 82.4249 | -3.31085 | -1 |

Notice the variable **_TYPE_**; its value of that variable is important when you run PROC SCORE.

In the second part of this example, PROC SCORE is used to score a new data set, **Need_Predictions**. For PROC SCORE, the TYPE= specification is PARMS, and the names of the score variables are found in the variable **_MODEL_**, which gets its values from the model label.

```
proc score data=Need_Predictions score=Betas
           out=Scored type=parms;
   var RunTime;
run;

proc print data=Scored;
   title "Scored New Observations";
run;
```

Selected PROC SCORE statement options:

DATA= names the data set with the observations to be scored.

SCORE= names the data set with parameter estimates.

OUT= names the data set to which scored observations are to be written.

TYPE= tells PROC SCORE what type of data the SCORE= data set contains.

| Obs | RunTime | PredOxy |
|---|---|---|
| 1 | 9 | 52.6272 |
| 2 | 10 | 49.3164 |
| 3 | 11 | 46.0055 |
| 4 | 12 | 42.6947 |
| 5 | 13 | 39.3838 |

The predicted value for **Oxygen_Consumption** when **RunTime** is 9 is 52.6272.

Choose only values within or near the range of the predictor variable when you are predicting new values for the response variable. For this example, the values of the variable **RunTime** range from 8.17 to 14.03 minutes. Therefore, it is unwise to predict the value of **Oxygen_Consumption** for a **RunTime** of 18. The reason is that the relationship between the predictor variable and the response variable might be different beyond the range of your data.

## Obtaining Predicted Values Using the P Option in the MODEL Statement (Self-Study)

If the data set used to produce the model is small, then that data set can be concatenated with the data set containing the data to be scored. You can then use the P option in the MODEL statement to produce predicted values.

```
/*st103d03.sas*/  /*Self Study*/
data Need_Predictions;
   input RunTime @@;
   datalines;
9 10 11 12 13
;
run;

data Predict;
   set Need_Predictions
       sasuser.fitness;
run;

ods graphics off;

proc reg data=Predict;
   model Oxygen_Consumption=RunTime / p;
   id RunTime;
   title 'Oxygen_Consumption=RunTime with Predicted Values';
run;
quit;
```

Selected REG procedure statement:

ID specifies a variable to label observations in the output produced by certain MODEL statement options.

Selected MODEL statement option:

P prints the values of the response variable, the predicted values, and the residual values.

PROC REG Output

| | |
|---|---|
| **Number of Observations Read** | 36 |
| **Number of Observations Used** | 31 |
| **Number of Observations with Missing Values** | 5 |

Notice that 36 observations were read; 31 were used and 5 had missing values. The observations in **Need_Predictions** had missing values for **Oxygen_Consumption**, so they were eliminated from the analysis.

| Analysis of Variance | | | | | |
|---|---|---|---|---|---|
| Source | DF | Sum of Squares | Mean Square | F Value | Pr > F |
| Model | 1 | 633.01458 | 633.01458 | 84.00 | <.0001 |
| Error | 29 | 218.53997 | 7.53586 | | |
| Corrected Total | 30 | 851.55455 | | | |

| | | | |
|---|---|---|---|
| Root MSE | 2.74515 | R-Square | 0.7434 |
| Dependent Mean | 47.37581 | Adj R-Sq | 0.7345 |
| Coeff Var | 5.79442 | | |

| Parameter Estimates | | | | | |
|---|---|---|---|---|---|
| Variable | DF | Parameter Estimate | Standard Error | t Value | Pr > \|t\| |
| Intercept | 1 | 82.42494 | 3.85582 | 21.38 | <.0001 |
| RunTime | 1 | -3.31085 | 0.36124 | -9.17 | <.0001 |

The model output is not affected by the extra five observations, because they were not used in any calculations, due to missing values.

Partial Output

| Output Statistics | | | | |
|---|---|---|---|---|
| Obs | RunTime | Dependent Variable | Predicted Value | Residual |
| 1 | 9.00 | . | 52.6272 | . |
| 2 | 10.00 | . | 49.3164 | . |
| 3 | 11.00 | . | 46.0055 | . |
| 4 | 12.00 | . | 42.6947 | . |
| 5 | 13.00 | . | 39.3838 | . |
| 6 | 8.17 | 59.5700 | 55.3753 | 4.1947 |
| 7 | 8.63 | 60.0600 | 53.8523 | 6.2077 |
| 8 | 8.65 | 54.3000 | 53.7860 | 0.5140 |
| 9 | 8.92 | 54.6300 | 52.8921 | 1.7379 |
| 10 | 8.95 | 49.1600 | 52.7928 | -3.6328 |

Because you specified **RunTime** in the ID statement, the values of this variable appear in the first column after **Obs**.

The output shows that the estimated value of **Oxygen_Consumption** is 52.6272 when **RunTime** equals 9. This is identical to the value produced in PROC SCORE.

## Exercises

**2. Fitting a Simple Linear Regression Model**

Use the **sasuser.BodyFat2** data set for this exercise.

**a.** Perform a simple linear regression model with **PctBodyFat2** as the response variable and **Weight** as the predictor.

1) What is the value of the *F* statistic and the associated *p*-value? How would you interpret this with regard to the null hypothesis?

2) Write the predicted regression equation.

3) What is the value of the R-square statistic? How would you interpret this?

**b.** Produce predicted values for **PctBodyFat2** when **Weight** is 125, 150, 175, 200, and 225.

What are the predicted values?

### 3.03 Multiple Choice Poll

What is the predicted value for **PctBodyFat2** when **Weight** is 150?

a. 0.17439
b. 150
c. 14.1067

50

# 3.3 Concepts of Multiple Regression

## Objectives

- Explain the mathematical model for multiple regression.
- Describe the main advantage of multiple regression versus simple linear regression.
- Explain the standard output from the REG procedure.
- Describe common pitfalls of multiple linear regression.

53

## Multiple Linear Regression with Two Variables

Consider the two-variable model

$$Y=\beta_0+\beta_1X_1+\beta_2X_2+\varepsilon$$

where

| | |
|---|---|
| $Y$ | is the dependent variable. |
| $X_1$ and $X_2$ | are the independent or predictor variables. |
| $\varepsilon$ | is the error term. |
| $\beta_0$, $\beta_1$, and $\beta_2$ | are unknown parameters. |

54

In simple linear regression, you can model the relationship between the two variables (two dimensions) with a line (one dimension).

For the two-variable model, you can model the relationship of three variables (three dimensions) with a plane (two dimensions).

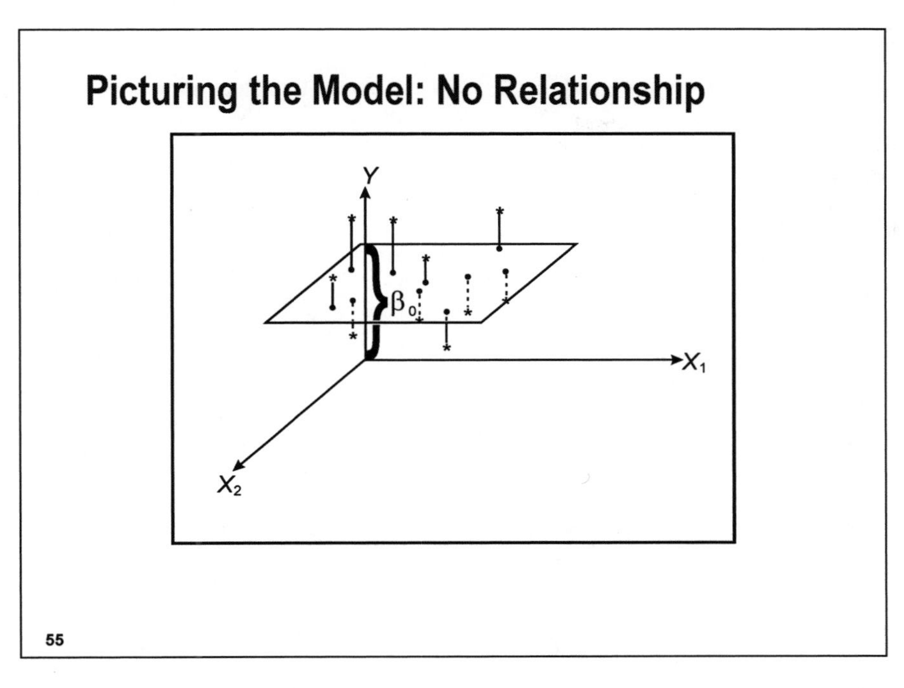


If there is no relationship among Y and $X_1$ and $X_2$, the model is a horizontal plane passing through the point ($Y=\beta_0$, $X_1=0$, $X_2=0$).

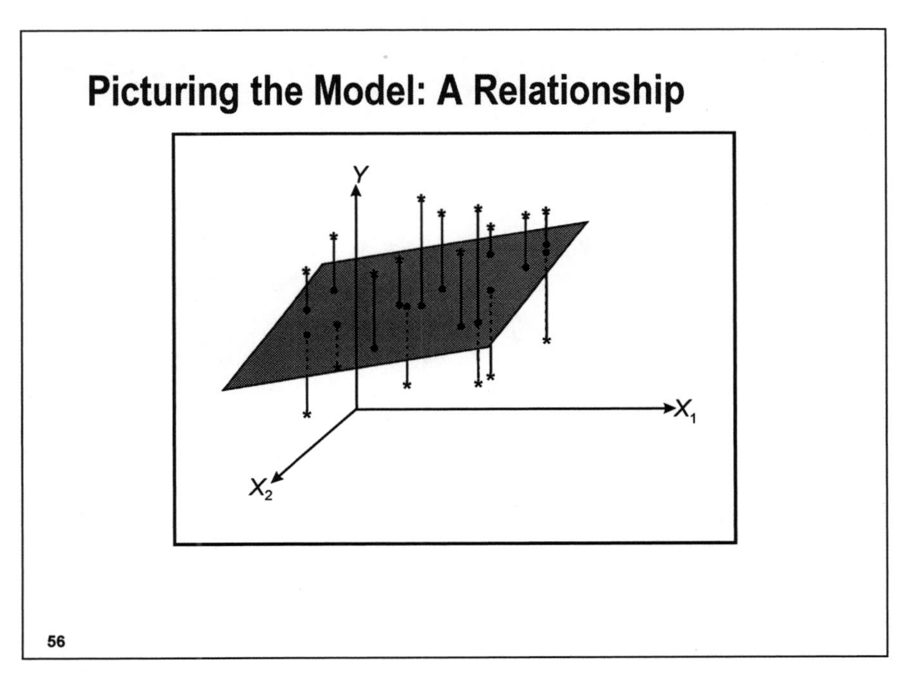


If there is a relationship among Y and $X_1$ and $X_2$, the model is a sloping plane passing through three points:

- ($Y=\beta_0$, $X_1=0$, $X_2=0$)
- ($Y=\beta_0+\beta_1$, $X_1=1$, $X_2=0$)
- ($Y=\beta_0+\beta_2$, $X_1=0$, $X_2=1$)

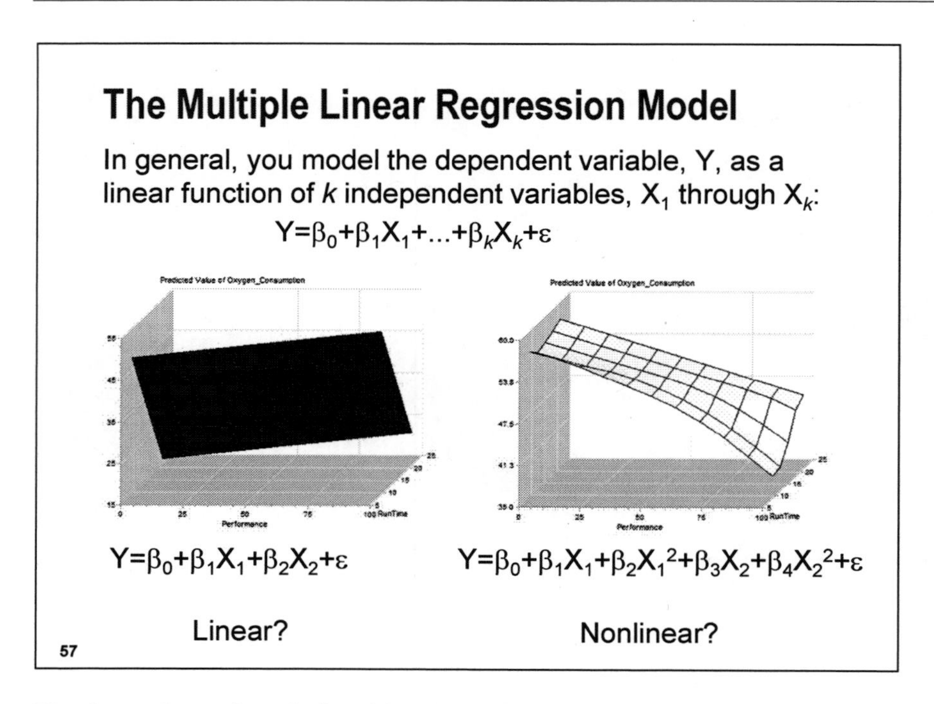


You investigate the relationship among $k$+1 variables ($k$ predictors+1 response) using a $k$-dimensional surface for prediction.

The multiple general linear model is not restricted to modeling only planar relationships. By using higher order terms, such as quadratic or cubic powers of the Xs or cross products of one X with another, surfaces more complex than planes can be modeled.

In the examples, the models are limited to relatively simple surfaces.

The model has $p=k+1$ parameters (the $\beta$s), including the intercept, $\beta_0$.

## Multiple Regression Example

**PREDICTORS** **RESPONSE**

**Performance**

**RunTime**

**Age**  **Oxygen_Consumption**

**Weight**

**Run_Pulse**

**Rest_Pulse**

**Maximum_Pulse**

67

## Model Hypothesis Test

**Null Hypothesis:**

- The regression model does ***not*** fit the data better than the baseline model.
- $\beta_1=\beta_2=\ldots=\beta_k=0$

**Alternative Hypothesis:**

- The regression model does fit the data better than the baseline model.
- Not all $\beta_i$s equal zero.

58

If the estimated linear regression model does ***not*** fit the data better than the baseline model, you fail to reject the null hypothesis. Thus, you do ***not*** have enough evidence to say that all of the slopes of the regression in the population differ from zero. The predictor variables do not explain a significant amount of variability in the response variable.

If the estimated linear regression model ***does*** fit the data better than the baseline model, you reject the null hypothesis. Thus, you ***do*** have enough evidence to say that at least one slope of the regression in the population differs from zero. At least one predictor variable explains a significant amount of variability in the response variable.

## 3.04 Multiple Choice Poll

Which statistic in the ANOVA table is used to test the overall model hypotheses?

a. *F*
b. *t*
c. R square
d. Adjusted R square

60

## Assumptions for Linear Regression

- The mean of the Ys is accurately modeled by a linear function of the Xs.
- The random error term, ε, is assumed to have a normal distribution with a mean of zero.
- The random error term, ε, is assumed to have a constant variance, $\sigma^2$.
- The errors are independent.

62

Techniques to evaluate the validity of these assumptions are discussed in a later chapter.

## Multiple Linear Regression versus Simple Linear Regression

**Main Advantage**

Multiple linear regression enables you to investigate the relationship among Y and several independent variables simultaneously.

**Main Disadvantages**

Increased complexity makes it more difficult to do the following:

- ascertain which model is "best"
- interpret the models

63

The advantage of performing multiple linear regression over a series of simple linear regression models far outweighs the disadvantages. In practice, many responses depend on multiple factors that might interact in some way.

SAS tools help you decide upon a "best" model, a choice that might depend on the purposes of the analysis, as well as subject-matter expertise.

## Common Applications

Multiple linear regression is a powerful tool for the following tasks:

- Prediction – to develop a model to predict future values of a response variable (Y) based on its relationships with other predictor variables (Xs)
- Analytical or Explanatory Analysis – to develop an understanding of the relationships between the response variable and predictor variables

64

Even though multiple linear regression enables you to analyze many experimental designs, ranging from simple to complex, you focus on applications for analytical studies and predictive modeling. Other SAS procedures, such as GLM, are better suited for analyzing experimental data.

The distinction between using multiple regression for an analytic analysis and prediction modeling is somewhat artificial. A model developed for prediction is probably a good analytic model. Conversely, a model developed for an analytic study is probably a good prediction model.

Myers (1999) refers to four applications of regression:

- prediction
- variable screening
- model specifications
- parameter estimation

The term *analytical analysis* is similar to Myers' parameter estimation application and variable screening.

## Prediction

- The terms in the model, the values of their coefficients, and their statistical significance are of secondary importance.
- The focus is on producing a model that is the best at predicting future values of Y as a function of the Xs. The predicted value of Y is given by this formula:

$$\underline{\hat{Y}} = \hat{\beta}_0 + \hat{\beta}_1 X_1 + \ldots + \hat{\beta}_k X_k$$

65

Most investigators whose main goal is prediction do not ignore the terms in the model (the Xs), the values of their coefficients (the βs), or their statistical significance (the *p*-values). They use these statistics to help choose among models with different numbers of terms and predictive capabilities.

## Analytical or Explanatory Analysis

- The focus is on understanding the relationship between the dependent variable and the independent variables.
- Consequently, the statistical significance of the coefficients is important as well as the magnitudes and signs of the coefficients.

$$\hat{Y} = \underline{\hat{\beta}_0} + \underline{\hat{\beta}_1} X_1 + \ldots + \underline{\hat{\beta}_k} X_k$$

66

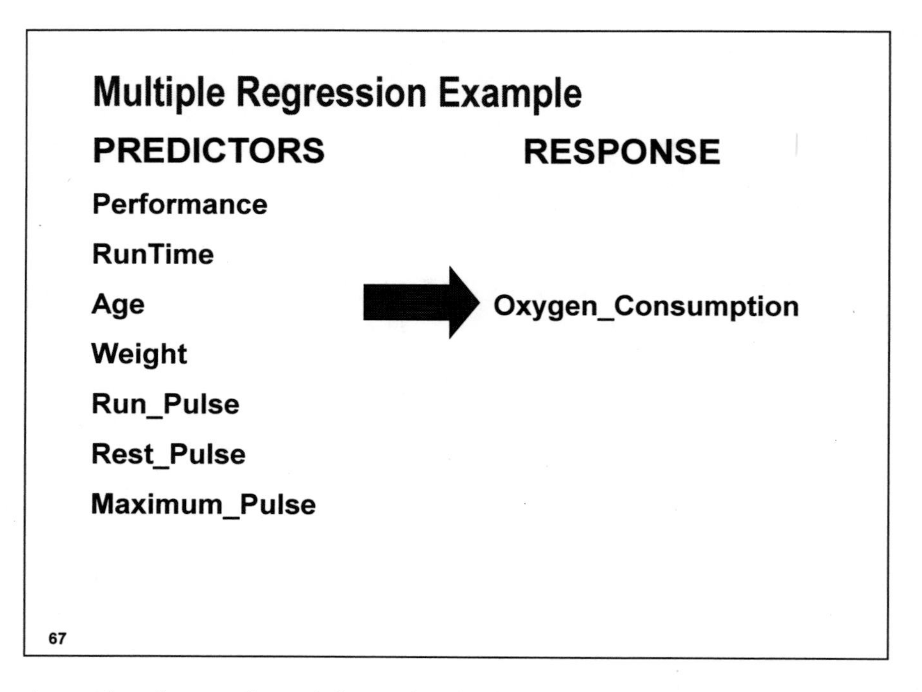


An analyst knows from doing a simple linear regression that the measure of performance is an important variable in explaining the oxygen consumption capability of a club member.

The analyst is interested in investigating other information to ascertain whether other variables are important in explaining the oxygen consumption capability.

Recall that you did a simple linear regression on **Oxygen_Consumption** with **RunTime** as the predictor variable.

The R square for this model was 0.7434, which suggests that 25.64% of the variation in **Oxygen_Consumption** is still unexplained.

Consequently, adding other variables to the model, such as **Performance** or **Age**, might provide a significantly better model.

## Adjusted R Square

$$R_{ADJ}^2 = 1 - \frac{(n-i)(1-R^2)}{n-p}$$

*i*=1 if there is an intercept and 0 otherwise

*n*=the number of observations used to fit the model

*p*=the number of parameters in the model

68

The R square always increases or stays the same as you include more terms in the model. Therefore, choosing the "best" model is not as simple as just making the R square as large as possible.

The adjusted R square is a measure similar to R square, but it takes into account the number of terms in the model. It can be thought of as a penalized version of R square with the penalty increasing with each parameter added to the model.

## Fitting a Multiple Linear Regression Model

Example: Invoke PROC REG and perform a multiple linear regression analysis of **Oxygen_Consumption** on **Performance** and **RunTime**. Interpret the output for the two-variable model.

```
/*st103d04.sas*/
ods graphics off;
proc reg data=sasuser.fitness;
   model Oxygen_Consumption=Performance RunTime;
   title 'Multiple Linear Regression for Fitness Data';
run;
quit;
ods graphics on;
```

The only required statement for PROC REG is the MODEL statement.

General form of the MODEL statement:

**MODEL** Y=X1 X2 … X*k*;

where

Y is the dependent variable.

X1 X2 … X*k*
is a list of the independent variables that are included in the model.

| | |
|---|---|
| **Number of Observations Read** | 31 |
| **Number of Observations Used** | 31 |

| Analysis of Variance | | | | | |
|---|---|---|---|---|---|
| **Source** | **DF** | **Sum of Squares** | **Mean Square** | **F Value** | **Pr > F** |
| **Model** | 2 | 646.33101 | 323.16550 | 44.09 | <.0001 |
| **Error** | 28 | 205.22355 | 7.32941 | | |
| **Corrected Total** | 30 | 851.55455 | | | |

PROC REG Output

| | |
|---|---|
| Model DF | is 2, the number of parameters minus 1. |
| Error DF | is 28, the total numbers of observations (31) minus the number of parameters in the model (3). |
| Corrected Total DF | is 30, the number of observations minus 1. |
| Model Sum of Squares | is the total variation in the Y explained by the model. |
| Error Sum of Squares | is the variation in the Y ***not*** explained by the model. |
| Corrected Total Sum of Squares | is the total variation in the Y. |
| Model Mean Square | is the Model Sum of Squares divided by the Model DF – also known as model variance. |
| Mean Square Error | is the Error Sum of Squares divided by the Error DF and is an estimate of $\sigma^2$, the variance of the random error term – also known as error variance. |
| F Value | is the (Mean Square Model)/(Mean Square Error). |

Pr>F is small. Therefore, you reject $H_0$: $\beta_1=\beta_2=0$ and conclude that at least one $\beta_i \neq 0$.

| | | | |
|---|---|---|---|
| **Root MSE** | 2.70729 | **R-Square** | 0.7590 |
| **Dependent Mean** | 47.37581 | **Adj R-Sq** | 0.7418 |
| **Coeff Var** | 5.71450 | | |

The R square for this model, 0.7590, is only slightly larger than the R square for the model in which **RunTime** is the only predictor variable, 0.7434.

The adjusted R square for this model is 0.7418, slightly higher than the adjusted R square of 0.7345 for the **RunTime** only model. This suggests, although mildly, that adding **Performance** does improve the model predicting **Oxygen_Consumption**.

| Parameter Estimates | | | | | |
|---|---|---|---|---|---|
| Variable | DF | Parameter Estimate | Standard Error | t Value | Pr > \|t\| |
| Intercept | 1 | 71.52626 | 8.93520 | 8.00 | <.0001 |
| Performance | 1 | 0.06360 | 0.04718 | 1.35 | 0.1885 |
| RunTime | 1 | -2.62163 | 0.62320 | -4.21 | 0.0002 |

Using the estimates for $\beta_0$, $\beta_1$, and $\beta_2$ above, this model can be written as the following:

**Oxygen_Consumption**=71.5626+0.06360***Performance**–2.62163***RunTime**

The *p*-value for **Performance** is large, which suggests that the slope is not significantly different from 0. The correlation that you saw between **Performance** and **Oxygen_Consumption** was large and statistically significant ($r$=.77890, $p$<.0001). The test for $\beta_i$=0 is conditioned on the other terms in the model. That is the reason that neither **Performance** nor **RunTime** have the same *p*-values (or parameter estimates) when used alone as when used in a model that includes both. The test for $\beta_1$=0 (for **Performance**) is conditional on (or adjusted for) $X_2$ (**RunTime**). Similarly, the test for $\beta_2$=0 is conditional on $X_1$ (**Performance**).

The significance level of the test does ***not*** depend on the order in which you list the independent variables in the MODEL statement, but it does depend on the variables included in the MODEL statement.

In a later section, you look at the difficulties involved with analyzing and selecting the best models due to the relationships among predictor variables.

# Exercises

3. **Performing Multiple Regression Using the REG Procedure**

   a. Using the **sasuser.BodyFat2** data set, run a regression of **PctBodyFat2** on the variables **Age**, **Weight**, **Height**, **Neck**, **Chest**, **Abdomen**, **Hip**, **Thigh**, **Knee**, **Ankle**, **Biceps**, **Forearm**, and **Wrist**.

      1) Compare the ANOVA table with that from the model with only **Weight** in the previous exercise. What is different?

      2) How do the R square and the adjusted R square compare with these statistics for the **Weight** regression demonstration?

      3) Did the estimate for the intercept change? Did the estimate for the coefficient of **Weight** change?

4. **Simplifying the Model**

   a. Rerun the model in **3a**, but eliminate the variable with the highest *p*-value. Compare the output with the Exercise **3a** model.

   b. Did the *p*-value for the model change notably?

   c. Did the R square and adjusted R square change notably?

   d. Did the parameter estimates and their *p*-values change notably?

5. **More Simplifying of the Model**

   a. Rerun the model in Exercise **4a**, but drop the variable with the highest *p*-value.

   b. How did the output change from the previous model?

   c. Did the number of parameters with a *p*-value less than 0.05 change?

## 3.05 Multiple Choice Poll

When **Oxygen_Consumption** is regressed on **RunTime**, **Age**, **Run_Pulse**, and **Maximum_Pulse**, the parameter estimate for **Age** is -2.78. What does this mean?

a. For each year older, the predicted value of oxygen consumption is 2.78 greater.
b. For each year older, the predicted value of oxygen consumption is 2.78 lower.
c. For every 2.78 years older, oxygen consumption doubles.
d. For every 2.78 years younger, oxygen consumption doubles.

* Assume that the values of all other predictors are held constant.

73

# 3.4 Model Building and Interpretation

## Objectives

- Explain the REG procedure options for model selection.
- Describe model selection options and interpret output to evaluate the fit of several models.

76

## Model Selection

Eliminating one variable at a time manually for small data sets is a reasonable approach.

However, eliminating one variable at a time manually for large data sets can take an extreme amount of time.

77

A process for selecting models might be to start with all the variables in the **sasuser.fitness** data set and eliminate the least significant terms, based on *p*-values.

For a small data set, a final model can be developed in a reasonable amount of time. If you start with a large model, however, eliminating one variable at a time can take an extreme amount of time. You would have to continue this process until only terms with *p*-values lower than some threshold value, such as 0.05 or 0.10, remain.

## Model Selection Options

The SELECTION= option in the MODEL statement of PROC REG supports these model selection techniques:

**Stepwise selection methods**

- STEPWISE, FORWARD, or BACKWARD

**All-possible regressions ranked using**

- RSQUARE, ADJRSQ, or CP

SELECTION=NONE is the default.

78

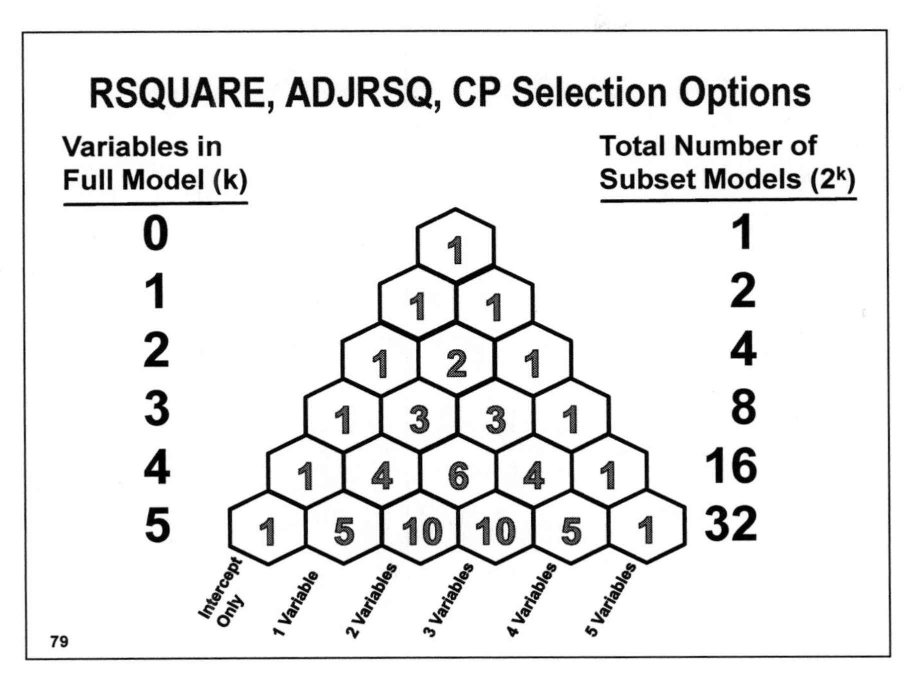


In the **sasuser.fitness** data set, there are seven possible independent variables. Therefore, there are $2^7$=128 possible regression models. There are seven possible one-variable models, 21 possible two-variable models, 35 possible three-variable models, and so on.

You can choose to only look at the best n (as measured by the model $R^2$ for $k$=1, 2, 3, ..., 7) by using the BEST= option on the model statement. The BEST= option only reduces the output. All regressions are still calculated.

If there were 20 possible independent variables, there would be more than 1,000,000 models. In a later demonstration, you see another technique that does not have to examine all the models to help you choose a set of candidate models.

## Mallows' $C_p$

- Mallows' $C_p$ is a simple indicator of effective variable selection within a model.
- Look for models with $C_p \leq p$, where $p$ equals the number of parameters in the model, including the intercept.

Mallows recommends choosing the first (fewest variables) model where $C_p$ approaches $p$.

80

Mallows' $C_p$ (1973) is estimated by $C_p = p + \frac{(MSE_p - MSE_{full})(n-p)}{MSE_{full}}$

where

| | |
|---|---|
| $MSE_p$ | is the mean squared error for the model with $p$ parameters. |
| $MSE_{full}$ | is the mean squared error for the full model used to estimate the true residual variance. |
| $n$ | is the number of observations. |
| $p$ | is the number of parameters, including an intercept parameter, if estimated. |

The choice of the best model based on $C_p$ is debatable, as will be shown in the slide about Hocking's criterion. Many choose the model with the smallest $C_p$ value. However, Mallows recommended that the best model will have a $C_p$ value approximating $p$. The most parsimonious model that fits that criterion is generally considered to be a good choice, although subject-matter knowledge should also be a guide in the selection from among competing models.

## Hocking's Criterion versus Mallows' $C_p$

Hocking (1976) suggests selecting a model based on the following:

- $C_p \leq p$ for prediction
- $C_p \leq 2p - p_{full} + 1$ for parameter estimation

81

Hocking suggested the use of the $C_p$ statistic, but with alternative criteria, depending on the purpose of the analysis. His suggestion of ($C_p \leq 2p - p_{full} + 1$) is included in the REG procedure's calculations of criteria reference plots for best models.

## Automated Model Selection

Example: Invoke PROC REG to produce a regression of **Oxygen_Consumption** on all the other variables in the **fitness** data set.

```
/*st103d05.sas*/  /*Part A*/
ods graphics / imagemap=on;
proc reg data=sasuser.fitness plots(only)=(rsquare adjrsq cp);
   ALL_REG: model oxygen_consumption=
                      Performance RunTime Age Weight
                      Run_Pulse Rest_Pulse Maximum_Pulse
            / selection=rsquare adjrsq cp;
   title 'Best Models Using All-Regression Option';
run;
quit;
```

Selected MODEL statement options:

SELECTION= enables you to choose the different selection methods – RSQUARE, ADJRSQ, and CP. The first listed method is the one that determines the sorting order in the output.

Selected SELECTION= option methods:

RSQUARE tells PROC REG to use the model R square to rank the model from best to worst for a given number of variables.

ADJRSQ prints the adjusted R square for each model.

CP prints Mallows' $C_p$ statistic for each model.

Partial HTML Output

| Number of Observations Read | 31 |
|---|---|
| Number of Observations Used | 31 |

| Model Index | Number in Model | R-Square | Adjusted R-Square | C(p) | Variables in Model |
|---|---|---|---|---|---|
| 1 | 1 | 0.7434 | 0.7345 | 11.9967 | RunTime |
| 2 | 1 | 0.6067 | 0.5931 | 32.7650 | Performance |
| 3 | 1 | 0.1595 | 0.1305 | 100.7200 | Rest_Pulse |
| 4 | 1 | 0.1585 | 0.1294 | 100.8736 | Run_Pulse |
| 5 | 1 | 0.0971 | 0.0660 | 110.1977 | Age |
| 6 | 1 | 0.0561 | 0.0235 | 116.4349 | Maximum_Pulse |
| 7 | 1 | 0.0265 | -0.0070 | 120.9214 | Weight |
| 8 | 2 | 0.7647 | 0.7479 | 10.7530 | RunTime Age |
| 9 | 2 | 0.7614 | 0.7444 | 11.2503 | RunTime Run_Pulse |
| 10 | 2 | 0.7590 | 0.7418 | 11.6205 | Performance RunTime |
| 11 | 2 | 0.7475 | 0.7295 | 13.3606 | Performance Run_Pulse |
| 12 | 2 | 0.7452 | 0.7270 | 13.7166 | RunTime Maximum_Pulse |
| 13 | 2 | 0.7449 | 0.7267 | 13.7588 | RunTime Weight |
| 14 | 2 | 0.7435 | 0.7252 | 13.9735 | RunTime Rest_Pulse |

There are many models to compare. It would be unwieldy to try to determine the best model by viewing the output tables. Therefore, it is advisable to look at the ODS plots.

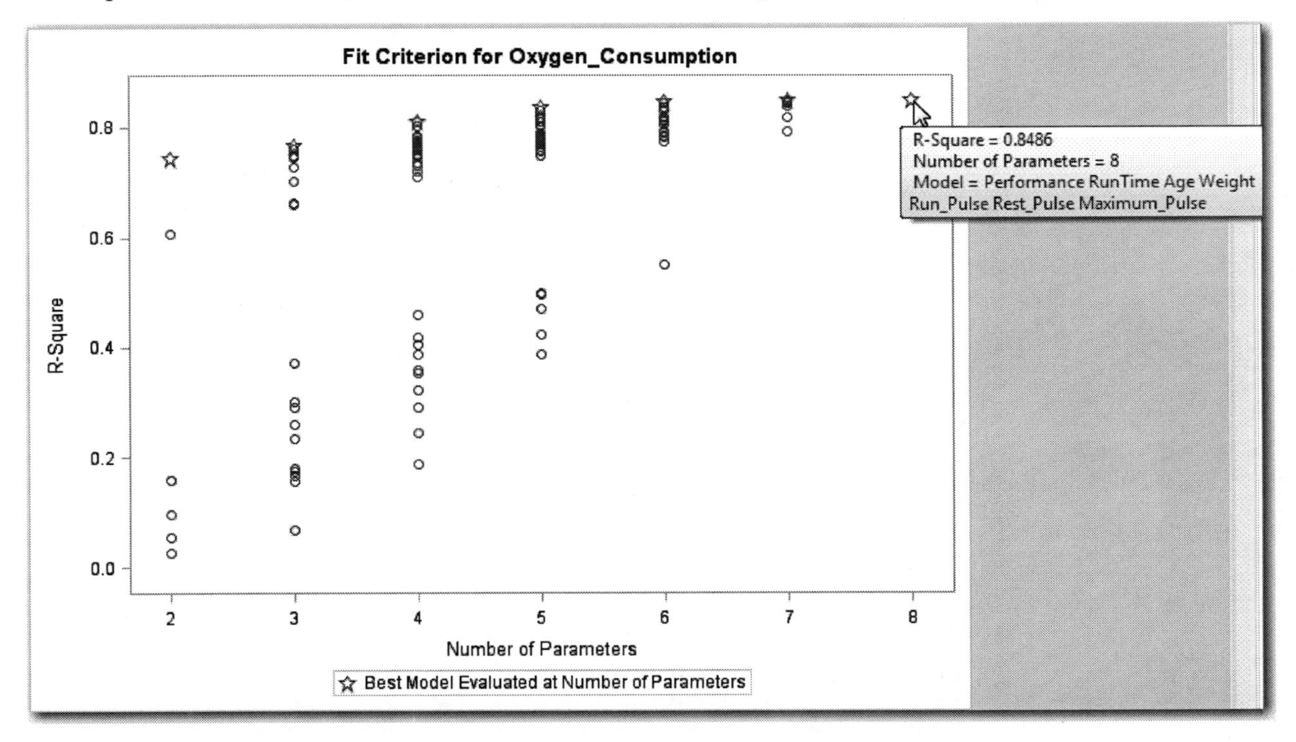


The R-square plot compares all models based on their R-square values. As noted earlier, adding variables to a model always increases R-square, and therefore the full model is always best. Therefore, you can only use the R-square value to compare models of equal numbers of parameters.

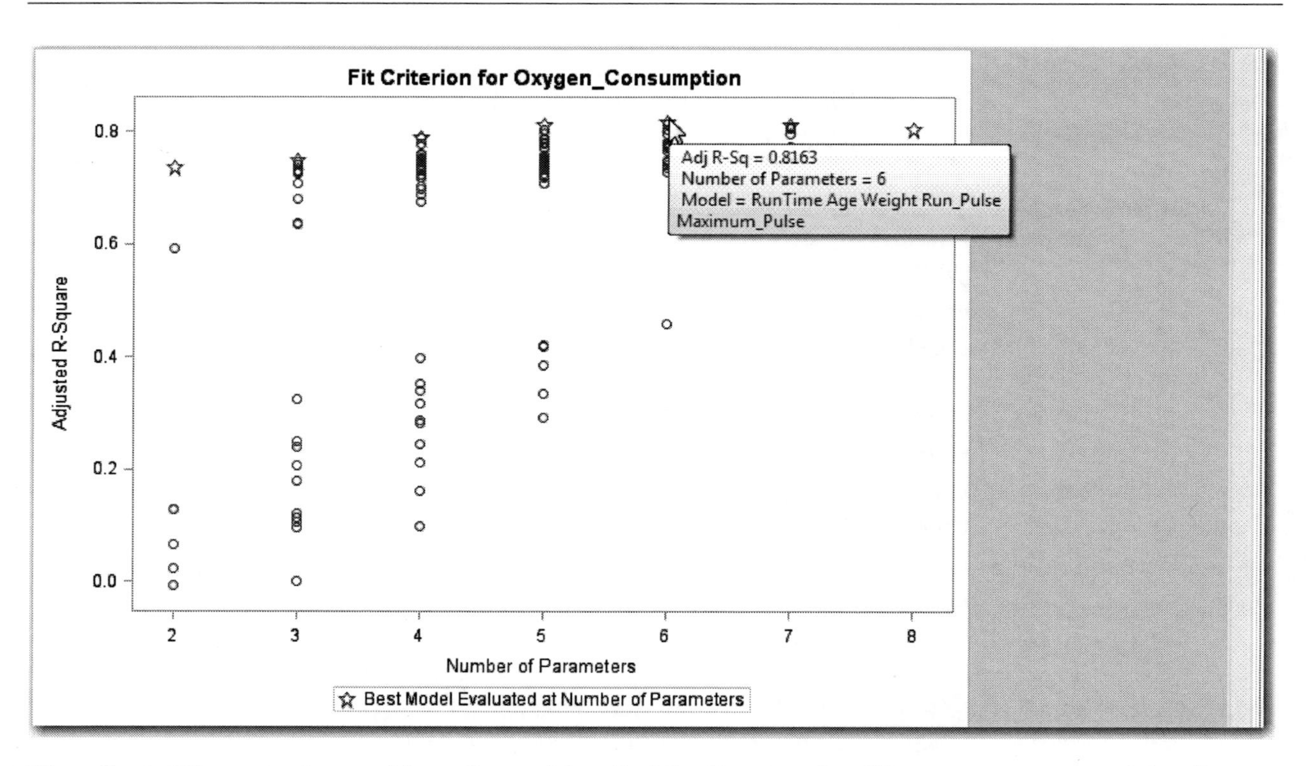


The adjusted R square does not have the problem that the R square has. You can compare models of different sizes. In this case, it is difficult to see which model has the higher adjusted R square, the starred model for six parameters or seven parameters.

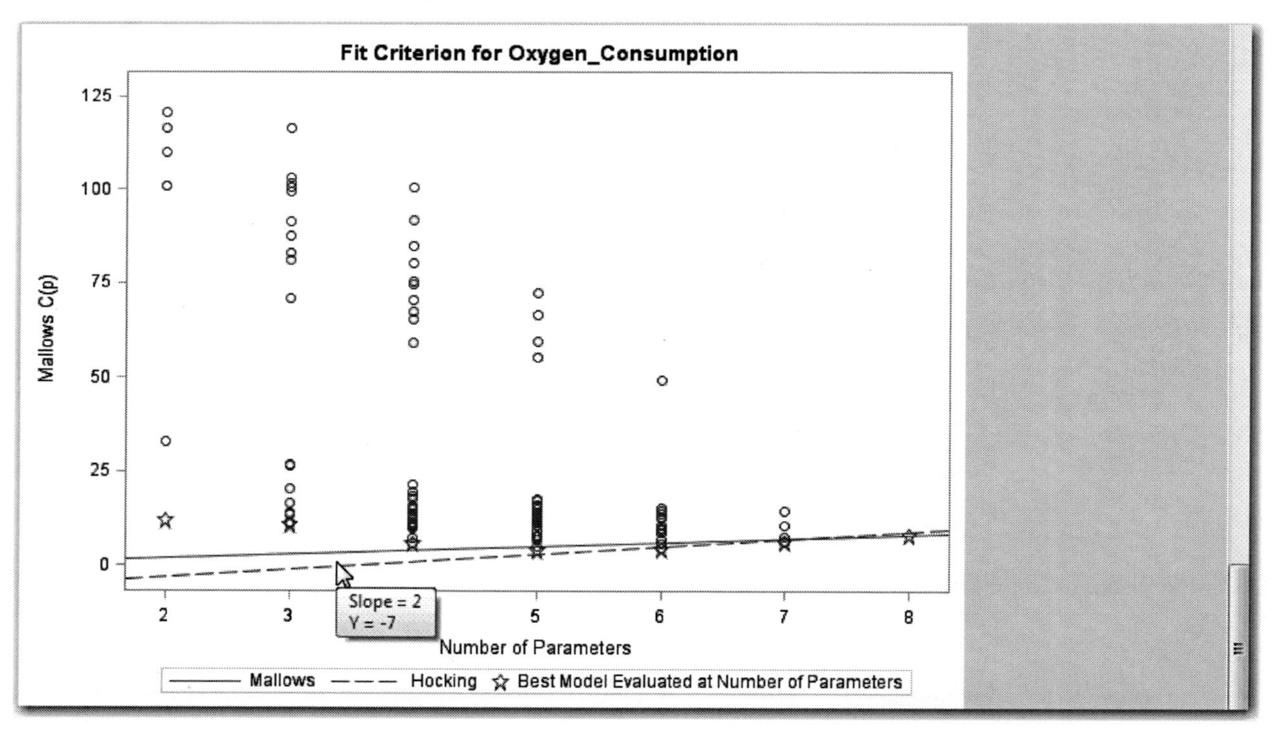

The line $C_p=p$ is plotted to help you identify models that satisfy the criterion $C_p \le p$ for prediction. The lower line is plotted to help identify which models satisfy Hocking's criterion $C_p \le 2p - p_{full} + 1$ for parameter estimation.

Use the graph and review the output to select a relatively short list of models that satisfy the criterion appropriate for your objective. The first model to fall below the line for Mallows' criterion has five parameters. The first model to fall below Hocking's criterion has six parameters.

It is often the case that the best model is difficult to see because of the range of $C_p$ values at the high end. These models are clearly not the best and therefore you can focus on the models near the bottom of the range of $C_p$.

```
/*st103d05.sas*/  /*Part B*/
ods graphics / imagemap=on;
proc reg data=sasuser.fitness plots(only)=(cp);
   ALL_REG: model oxygen_consumption=
                  Performance RunTime Age Weight
                  Run_Pulse Rest_Pulse Maximum_Pulse
         / selection=cp rsquare adjrsq best=20;
   title 'Best Models Using All-Regression Option';
run;
quit;
```

Selected SELECTION= option methods:

BEST=*n* limits the output to only the best *n* models.

| Model Index | Number in Model | C(p) | R-Square | Adjusted R-Square | Variables in Model |
|---|---|---|---|---|---|
| 1 | 4 | 4.0004 | 0.8355 | 0.8102 | RunTime Age Run_Pulse Maximum_Pulse |
| 2 | 5 | 4.2598 | 0.8469 | 0.8163 | RunTime Age Weight Run_Pulse Maximum_Pulse |
| 3 | 5 | 4.7158 | 0.8439 | 0.8127 | Performance RunTime Weight Run_Pulse Maximum_Pulse |
| 4 | 5 | 4.7168 | 0.8439 | 0.8127 | Performance RunTime Age Run_Pulse Maximum_Pulse |
| 5 | 4 | 4.9567 | 0.8292 | 0.8029 | Performance RunTime Run_Pulse Maximum_Pulse |
| 6 | 3 | 5.8570 | 0.8101 | 0.7890 | RunTime Run_Pulse Maximum_Pulse |
| 7 | 3 | 5.9367 | 0.8096 | 0.7884 | RunTime Age Run_Pulse |
| 8 | 5 | 5.9783 | 0.8356 | 0.8027 | RunTime Age Run_Pulse Rest_Pulse Maximum_Pulse |
| 9 | 5 | 5.9856 | 0.8356 | 0.8027 | Performance Age Weight Run_Pulse Maximum_Pulse |
| 10 | 6 | 6.0492 | 0.8483 | 0.8104 | Performance RunTime Age Weight Run_Pulse Maximum_Pulse |
| 11 | 6 | 6.1758 | 0.8475 | 0.8094 | RunTime Age Weight Run_Pulse Rest_Pulse Maximum_Pulse |
| 12 | 6 | 6.6171 | 0.8446 | 0.8057 | Performance RunTime Weight Run_Pulse Rest_Pulse Maximum_Pulse |
| 13 | 6 | 6.7111 | 0.8440 | 0.8049 | Performance RunTime Age Run_Pulse Rest_Pulse Maximum_Pulse |
| 14 | 4 | 6.8865 | 0.8165 | 0.7882 | Performance RunTime Age Run_Pulse |
| 15 | 5 | 6.9446 | 0.8293 | 0.7951 | Performance RunTime Run_Pulse Rest_Pulse Maximum_Pulse |
| 16 | 4 | 6.9623 | 0.8160 | 0.7877 | RunTime Weight Run_Pulse Maximum_Pulse |
| 17 | 4 | 7.0752 | 0.8152 | 0.7868 | RunTime Age Weight Run_Pulse |
| 18 | 3 | 7.1734 | 0.8014 | 0.7794 | Performance RunTime Run_Pulse |
| 19 | 6 | 7.7279 | 0.8373 | 0.7966 | Performance Age Weight Run_Pulse Rest_Pulse Maximum_Pulse |
| 20 | 4 | 7.7942 | 0.8105 | 0.7814 | RunTime Run_Pulse Rest_Pulse Maximum_Pulse |

Investigate the plot of Mallows' C(p).

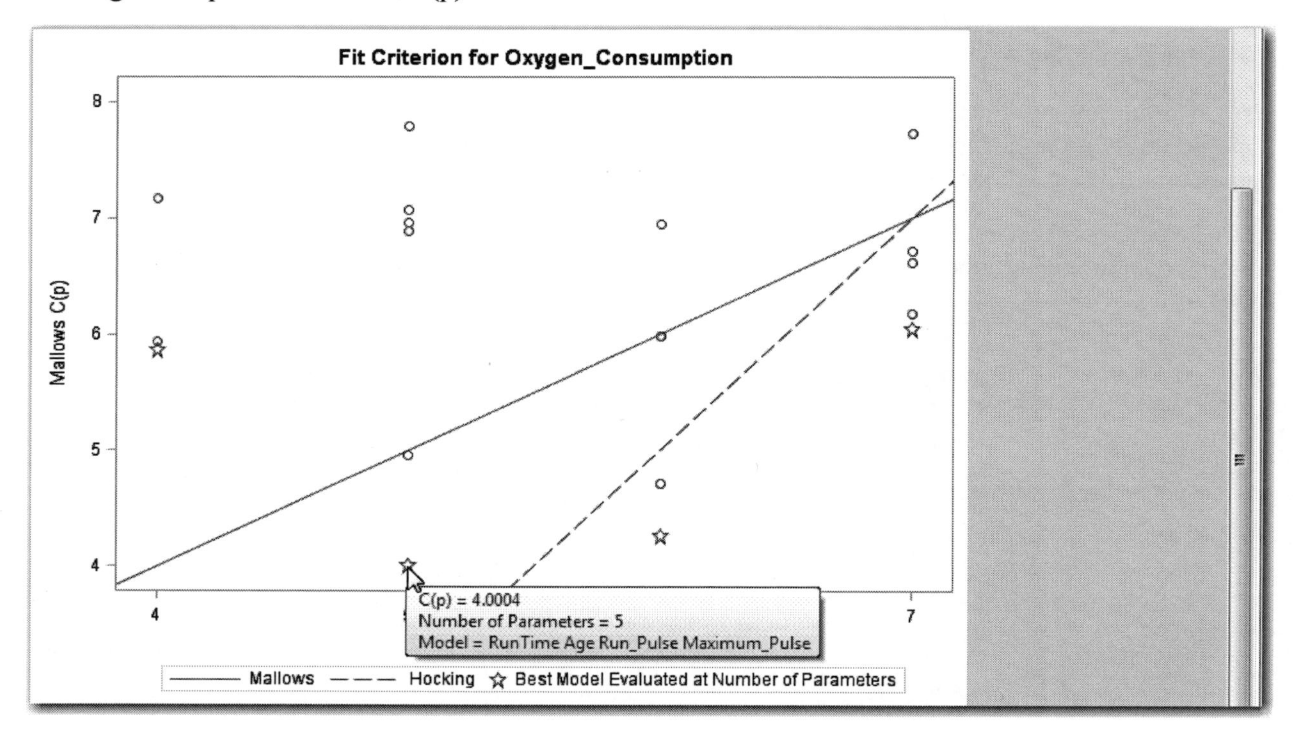


In this example the number of variables in the full model, $p_{full}$, equals 8 (seven variables plus the intercept).

The smallest model with an observation below the Mallows line has $p$=5 (which matches to Number in Model of 4 in the previous table). The model with the star at five parameters and the model above it are considered "best," based on Mallows' original criterion. The starred model has a $C_p$=4.004, satisfying Mallows' criterion (**Oxygen_Consumption=RunTime Age Run_Pulse Maximum_Pulse**) and the one above has a value of 4.9567 (**Oxygen_Consumption=Performance RunTime Run_Pulse Maximum_Pulse**). The only difference between the two models is that the first includes **Age** and the second includes **Performance**. By the strictest definition, the second model should be selected, because its $C_p$ value is closest to $p$.

The smallest model that falls under the Hocking line has $p$=6. The model with the smaller $C_p$ value will be considered the "best" explanatory model. The table shows that the first model with $p$=6 is **Oxygen_Consumption=RunTime Age Weight Run_Pulse Maximum_Pulse**, with a $C_p$ value of 4.2598. Two other models that are also below the Hocking line are **Oxygen_Consumption=Performance RunTime Weight Run_Pulse Maximum_Pulse** and **Oxygen_Consumption=Performance RunTime Age Run_Pulse Maximum_Pulse**. (They are nearly on top of one another in the plot.)

## "Best" Models – Prediction

The two best candidate models based on Mallows' original criterion includes these regressor variables:

| | | |
|---|---|---|
| *p*=5 | $C_p$=4.0004<br>$R^2$=0.8355<br>Adj. $R^2$=0.8102 | **RunTime, Age, Run_Pulse, Maximum_Pulse** |
| *p*=5 | $C_p$=4.9567<br>$R^2$=0.8292<br>Adj. $R^2$=0.8029 | **Performance, RunTime, Run_Pulse, Maximum_Pulse** |

83

Some models might be essentially equivalent based on their $C_p$, R square, or other measures. When, as in this case, there are several candidate "best" models, it is the responsibility of the investigator to determine which model makes the most sense based on theory and experience. The choice between these two models is essentially the choice between **Age** and **Performance**. Because age is much easier to measure than the subjective measure of performance, the first model is selected here.

A limitation of the evaluation that you did thus far is that you do not know the magnitude and signs of the coefficients of the candidate models or their statistical significance.

## "Best" Models – Parameter Estimation

The three best candidate models for analytic purposes, according to Hocking, include those listed below:

| | | |
|---|---|---|
| *p*=6 | $C_p$=4.2598<br>$R^2$=0.8469<br>Adj. $R^2$=0.8163 | **RunTime, Age, Weight, Run_Pulse, Maximum_Pulse** |
| *p*=6 | $C_p$=4.7158<br>$R^2$=0.8439<br>Adj. $R^2$=0.8127 | **Performance, RunTime, Weight, Run_Pulse, Maximum_Pulse** |
| *p*=6 | $C_p$=4.7168<br>$R^2$=0.8439<br>Adj. $R^2$=0.8127 | **Performance, RunTime, Age, Run_Pulse, Maximum_Pulse** |

84

The variables **RunTime**, **Run_Pulse**, and **Maximum_Pulse** once again appear in all candidate models. The choice of models depends on the selection of pairs from **Performance**, **Age**, and **Weight**. You again choose a model with objective measures, **Age** and **Weight**. That is the top model in the list. Your choice might differ.

# Estimating and Testing the Coefficients for the Selected Models

Example: Invoke PROC REG to compare the ANOVA tables and parameter estimates for the two-candidate models in the **fitness** data set.

```
/*st103d06.sas*/
ods graphics off;
proc reg data=sasuser.fitness;
   PREDICT: model Oxygen_Consumption=
                  RunTime Age Run_Pulse Maximum_Pulse;
   EXPLAIN: model Oxygen_Consumption=
                  RunTime Age Weight Run_Pulse Maximum_Pulse;
   title 'Check "Best" Two Candidate Models';
run;
quit;
ods graphics on;
```

PROC REG can have more than one MODEL statement. You can assign a label to each MODEL statement to identify the output generated for each model.

Output for the PREDICT Model

| | |
|---|---|
| **Number of Observations Read** | 31 |
| **Number of Observations Used** | 31 |

| Analysis of Variance | | | | | |
|---|---|---|---|---|---|
| **Source** | **DF** | **Sum of Squares** | **Mean Square** | **F Value** | **Pr > F** |
| **Model** | 4 | 711.45087 | 177.86272 | 33.01 | <.0001 |
| **Error** | 26 | 140.10368 | 5.38860 | | |
| **Corrected Total** | 30 | 851.55455 | | | |

| | | | |
|---|---|---|---|
| **Root MSE** | 2.32134 | **R-Square** | 0.8355 |
| **Dependent Mean** | 47.37581 | **Adj R-Sq** | 0.8102 |
| **Coeff Var** | 4.89984 | | |

| Parameter Estimates | | | | | |
|---|---|---|---|---|---|
| **Variable** | **DF** | **Parameter Estimate** | **Standard Error** | **t Value** | **Pr > \|t\|** |
| **Intercept** | 1 | 97.16952 | 11.65703 | 8.34 | <.0001 |
| **RunTime** | 1 | -2.77576 | 0.34159 | -8.13 | <.0001 |
| **Age** | 1 | -0.18903 | 0.09439 | -2.00 | 0.0557 |
| **Run_Pulse** | 1 | -0.34568 | 0.11820 | -2.92 | 0.0071 |
| **Maximum_Pulse** | 1 | 0.27188 | 0.13438 | 2.02 | 0.0534 |

The R square and adjusted R square are the same as calculated during the model selection program. If there are missing values in the data set, however, this might not be true.

The model *F* is large and highly significant. **Age** and **Maximum_Pulse** are not significant at the 0.05 level of significance. However, all terms are significant at alpha=0.10.

The adjusted R square is close to the R square, which suggests that there are not too many variables in the model.

Output for the EXPLAIN Model

| | |
|---|---|
| Number of Observations Read | 31 |
| Number of Observations Used | 31 |

| Analysis of Variance | | | | | |
|---|---|---|---|---|---|
| Source | DF | Sum of Squares | Mean Square | F Value | Pr > F |
| Model | 5 | 721.20532 | 144.24106 | 27.66 | <.0001 |
| Error | 25 | 130.34923 | 5.21397 | | |
| Corrected Total | 30 | 851.55455 | | | |

| | | | |
|---|---|---|---|
| Root MSE | 2.28341 | R-Square | 0.8469 |
| Dependent Mean | 47.37581 | Adj R-Sq | 0.8163 |
| Coeff Var | 4.81978 | | |

| Parameter Estimates | | | | | |
|---|---|---|---|---|---|
| Variable | DF | Parameter Estimate | Standard Error | t Value | Pr > \|t\| |
| Intercept | 1 | 101.33835 | 11.86474 | 8.54 | <.0001 |
| RunTime | 1 | -2.68846 | 0.34202 | -7.86 | <.0001 |
| Age | 1 | -0.21217 | 0.09437 | -2.25 | 0.0336 |
| Weight | 1 | -0.07332 | 0.05360 | -1.37 | 0.1836 |
| Run_Pulse | 1 | -0.37071 | 0.11770 | -3.15 | 0.0042 |
| Maximum_Pulse | 1 | 0.30603 | 0.13452 | 2.28 | 0.0317 |

The adjusted R square is slightly larger than in the PREDICT model and very close to the R square.

The model *F* is large, but smaller than in the PREDICT model. However, it is still highly significant. All terms included in the model are significant except **Weight**. The *p*-values for **Age, Run_Pulse**, and **Maximum_Pulse** are smaller in this model than they were in the PREDICT model.

Including the additional variable in the model changes the coefficients of the other terms and changes the *t* statistics for all.

## 3.06 Multiple Choice Poll

Which value tends to increase (can never decrease) as you add predictor variables to your regression model?

a. R square
b. Adjusted R square
c. Mallows' $C_p$
d. Both a and b
*e.* *F* statistic
f. All of the above

87

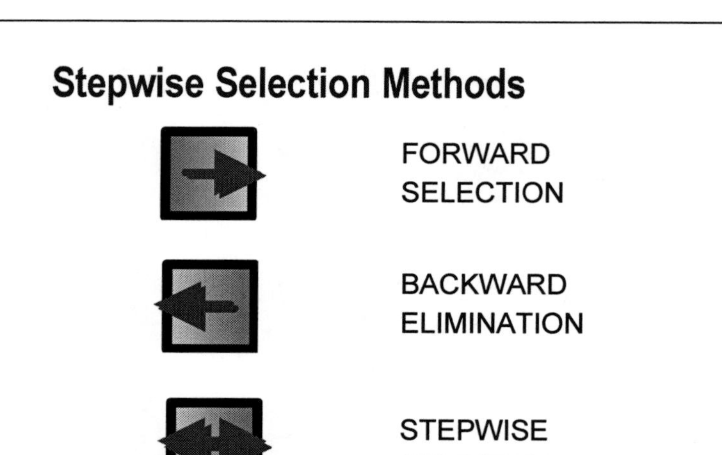


The all-possible regression technique that was discussed can be computer intensive, especially if there are a large number of potential independent variables.

PROC REG also offers the following stepwise SELECTION= options:

FORWARD first selects the best one-variable model. Then it selects the best two variables among those that contain the first selected variable. FORWARD continues this process, but stops when it reaches the point where no additional variables have *p*-value levels less than some stopping criterion (0.50, by default).

BACKWARD starts with the full model. Next, the variable that is least significant, given the other variables, is removed from the model. BACKWARD continues this process until all of the remaining variables have *p*-values less than a stopping criterion value (0.10, by default).

STEPWISE works like a combination of the FORWARD and BACKWARD method. The default entry *p*-value is 0.15 and the default stay *p*-value is also 0.15.

The SLENTRY= (for forward step stopping criteria) and SLSTAY= (for backward step stopping criteria) options can be used to change the default stopping values.

## Forward Selection

0
1
2
3
4
5
Stop

96

Forward selection starts with an empty model. The method computes an *F* statistic for each predictor variable not in the model and examines the largest of these statistics. If it is significant at a specified significance level (specified by the SLENTRY= option), the corresponding variable is added to the model. After a variable is entered in the model, it is never removed from the model. The process is repeated until none of the remaining variables meets the specified level for entry. By default, SLENTRY=0.50.

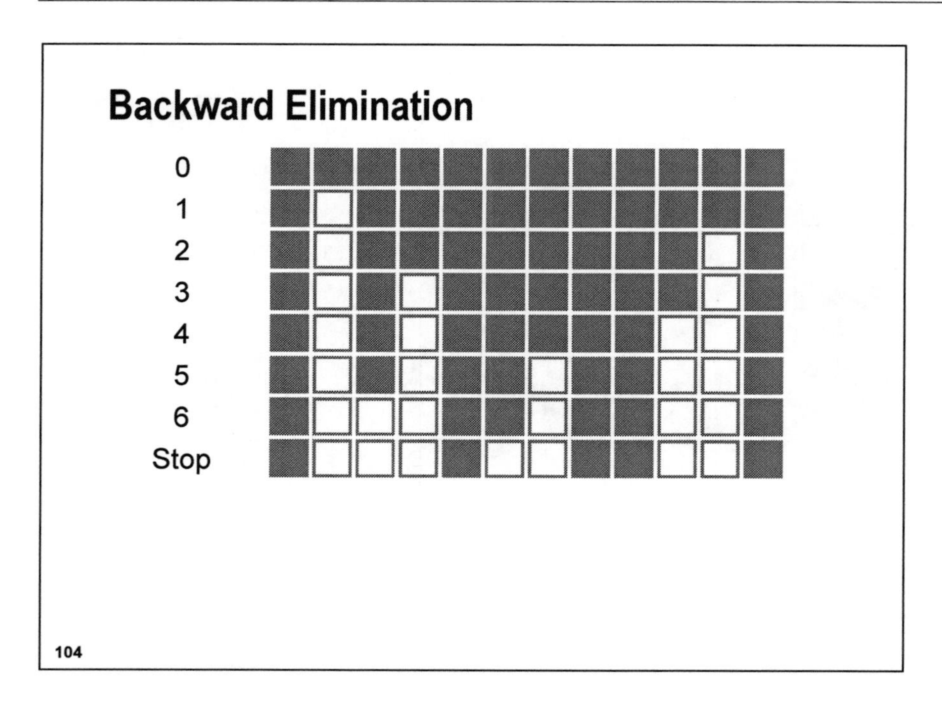


Backward elimination starts off with the full model. Results of the *F* test for individual parameter estimates are examined, and the least significant variable that falls above the specified significance level (specified by the SLSTAY= option) is removed. After a variable is removed from the model, it remains excluded. The process is repeated until no other variable in the model meets the specified significance level for removal. By default, SLSTAY=0.10.

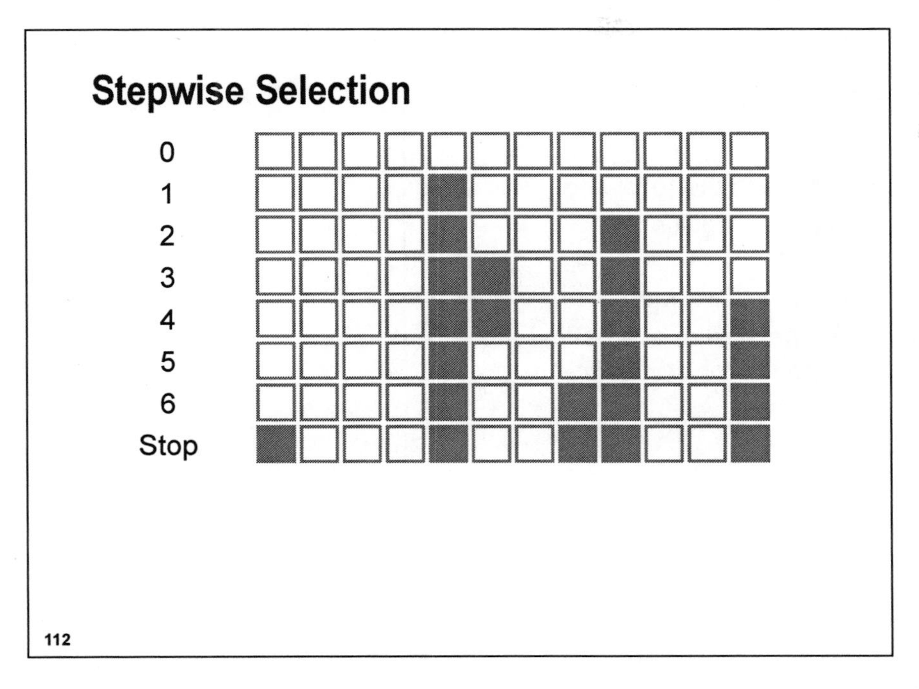


Stepwise selection is similar to forward selection in that it starts with an empty model and incrementally builds a model one variable at a time. However, the method differs from forward selection in that variables already in the model do not necessarily remain. The backward component of the method removes variables from the model that do not meet the significance criteria specified in the SLSTAY= option. The stepwise selection process terminates if no further variables can be added to the model or if the variable entered into the model is the only variable removed in the subsequent backward elimination. By default, SLENTRY=0.15 and SLSTAY=0.15.

Stepwise selection (Forward, Backward, and Stepwise) has some serious shortcomings. Simulation studies (Derksen and Keselman 1992) evaluating variable selection techniques found the following:

1. The degree of collinearity among the predictor variables affected the frequency with which authentic predictor variables found their way into the final model.

2. The number of candidate predictor variables affected the number of noise variables that gained entry to the model.

3. The size of the sample was of little practical importance in determining the number of authentic variables contained in the final model.

One recommendation is to use the variable selection methods to create several candidate models, and then use subject-matter knowledge to select the variables that result in the best model within the scientific or business context of the problem. Therefore, you are simply using these methods as a useful tool in the model-building process (Hosmer and Lemeshow 2000).

## Are *p*-values and Parameter Estimates Correct?

Automated model selection results in the following:

- biases in parameter estimates, predictions, and standard errors
- incorrect calculation of degrees of freedom
- *p*-values that tend to err on the side of overestimating significance (increasing Type I Error probability)

113

Statisticians give warnings and cautions about the appropriate interpretation of *p*-values from models chosen using any automated variable selection technique. Refitting many submodels in terms of an optimum fit to the data distorts the significance levels of conventional statistical tests. However, many researchers and users of statistical software neglect to report that the models that they ended up with were chosen using automated methods. They report statistical quantities such as standard errors, confidence limits, *p*-values, and R square as if the resulting model were entirely prespecified. These inferences are inaccurate, tending to err on the side of overstating the significance of predictors and making predictions with overly optimistic confidence. This problem is very evident when there are many iterative stages in model building. When there are many variables and you use stepwise selection to find a small subset of variables, inferences become less accurate (Chatfield 1995, Raftery 1994, Freedman 1983).

One solution to this problem is to split your data. One part can be used for finding the regression model and the other part can be used for inference. Another solution is to use bootstrapping methods to obtain the correct standard errors and *p*-values. *Bootstrapping* is a resampling method that tries to approximate the distribution of the parameter estimates to estimate the standard error.

## Stepwise Regression

Example: Select a model for predicting **Oxygen_Consumption** in the **fitness** data set by using the FORWARD, BACKWARD, and STEPWISE methods.

```
/*st103d07.sas*/
proc reg data=sasuser.fitness plots(only)=adjrsq;
   FORWARD:  model oxygen_consumption=
                      Performance RunTime Age Weight
                      Run_Pulse Rest_Pulse Maximum_Pulse
           / selection=forward;
   BACKWARD: model oxygen_consumption=
                      Performance RunTime Age Weight
                      Run_Pulse Rest_Pulse Maximum_Pulse
           / selection=backward;
   STEPWISE: model oxygen_consumption=
                      Performance RunTime Age Weight
                      Run_Pulse Rest_Pulse Maximum_Pulse
           / selection=stepwise;
   title 'Best Models Using Stepwise Selection';
run;
quit;
```

Partial PROC REG Output

| | |
|---|---|
| **Number of Observations Read** | 31 |
| **Number of Observations Used** | 31 |

**Forward Selection: Step 1**

**Variable RunTime Entered: R-Square = 0.7434 and C(p) = 11.9967**

| Analysis of Variance | | | | | |
|---|---|---|---|---|---|
| **Source** | **DF** | **Sum of Squares** | **Mean Square** | **F Value** | **Pr > F** |
| **Model** | 1 | 633.01458 | 633.01458 | 84.00 | <.0001 |
| **Error** | 29 | 218.53997 | 7.53586 | | |
| **Corrected Total** | 30 | 851.55455 | | | |

| Variable | Parameter Estimate | Standard Error | Type II SS | F Value | Pr > F |
|---|---|---|---|---|---|
| **Intercept** | 82.42494 | 3.85582 | 3443.63138 | 456.97 | <.0001 |
| **RunTime** | -3.31085 | 0.36124 | 633.01458 | 84.00 | <.0001 |

...

Partial PROC REG Output (Continued)

| Summary of Forward Selection | | | | | | | |
|---|---|---|---|---|---|---|---|
| Step | Variable Entered | Number Vars In | Partial R-Square | Model R-Square | C(p) | F Value | Pr > F |
| 1 | RunTime | 1 | 0.7434 | 0.7434 | 11.9967 | 84.00 | <.0001 |
| 2 | Age | 2 | 0.0213 | 0.7647 | 10.7530 | 2.54 | 0.1222 |
| 3 | Run_Pulse | 3 | 0.0449 | 0.8096 | 5.9367 | 6.36 | 0.0179 |
| 4 | Maximum_Pulse | 4 | 0.0259 | 0.8355 | 4.0004 | 4.09 | 0.0534 |
| 5 | Weight | 5 | 0.0115 | 0.8469 | 4.2598 | 1.87 | 0.1836 |

The model selected at each step is printed and a summary of the sequence of steps is given at the end of the output. In the summary, the variables are listed in the order in which they were selected. The partial R square shows the increase in the model R square as each term was added.

The model that FORWARD selected has the same variables as the model chosen using the all-regressions techniques with the Hocking criterion. This will not always be the case.

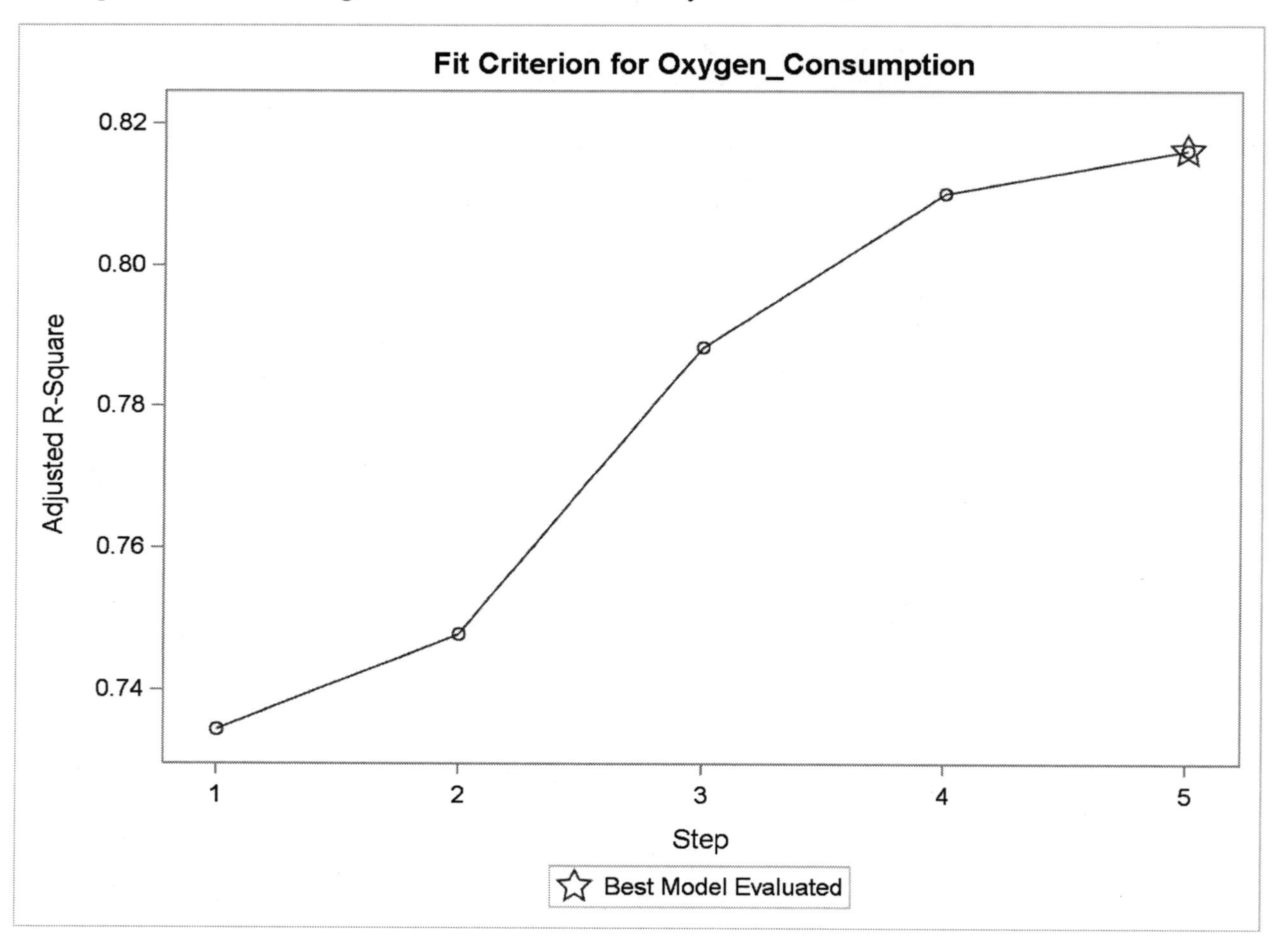


The Adjusted R-Square plot shows the progression of that statistic at each step. The star denotes the best model of the five that were tested. This is not necessarily the highest adjusted R-square value of all possible subsets, but is the best of the five tested in the Forward model.

Partial PROC REG Output (Continued)

**Backward Elimination: Step 0**

**All Variables Entered: R-Square = 0.8486 and C(p) = 8.0000**

| Analysis of Variance | | | | | |
|---|---|---|---|---|---|
| Source | DF | Sum of Squares | Mean Square | F Value | Pr > F |
| Model | 7 | 722.66124 | 103.23732 | 18.42 | <.0001 |
| Error | 23 | 128.89331 | 5.60406 | | |
| Corrected Total | 30 | 851.55455 | | | |

| Variable | Parameter Estimate | Standard Error | Type II SS | F Value | Pr > F |
|---|---|---|---|---|---|
| Intercept | 131.78249 | 72.20754 | 18.66607 | 3.33 | 0.0810 |
| Performance | -0.12619 | 0.30097 | 0.98519 | 0.18 | 0.6789 |
| RunTime | -3.86019 | 2.93659 | 9.68350 | 1.73 | 0.2016 |
| Age | -0.46082 | 0.58660 | 3.45842 | 0.62 | 0.4401 |
| Weight | -0.05812 | 0.06892 | 3.98514 | 0.71 | 0.4078 |
| Run_Pulse | -0.36207 | 0.12324 | 48.37354 | 8.63 | 0.0074 |
| Rest_Pulse | -0.01512 | 0.06817 | 0.27581 | 0.05 | 0.8264 |
| Maximum_Pulse | 0.30102 | 0.13981 | 25.97886 | 4.64 | 0.0420 |

**Bounds on condition number: 162.85, 2262.9**

**Backward Elimination: Step 1**

**Variable Rest_Pulse Removed: R-Square = 0.8483 and C(p) = 6.0492**

| Analysis of Variance | | | | | |
|---|---|---|---|---|---|
| Source | DF | Sum of Squares | Mean Square | F Value | Pr > F |
| Model | 6 | 722.38543 | 120.39757 | 22.37 | <.0001 |
| Error | 24 | 129.16912 | 5.38205 | | |
| Corrected Total | 30 | 851.55455 | | | |

| Variable | Parameter Estimate | Standard Error | Type II SS | F Value | Pr > F |
|---|---|---|---|---|---|
| Intercept | 133.73795 | 70.23358 | 19.51494 | 3.63 | 0.0689 |
| Performance | -0.13647 | 0.29144 | 1.18011 | 0.22 | 0.6438 |
| RunTime | -3.99624 | 2.81438 | 10.85139 | 2.02 | 0.1685 |
| Age | -0.47577 | 0.57106 | 3.73583 | 0.69 | 0.4130 |
| Weight | -0.05545 | 0.06650 | 3.74132 | 0.70 | 0.4126 |
| Run_Pulse | -0.36430 | 0.12037 | 49.29878 | 9.16 | 0.0058 |
| Maximum_Pulse | 0.30184 | 0.13696 | 26.13890 | 4.86 | 0.0374 |

...

Partial PROC REG Output (Continued)

| Summary of Backward Elimination | | | | | | | |
|---|---|---|---|---|---|---|---|
| Step | Variable Removed | Number Vars In | Partial R-Square | Model R-Square | C(p) | F Value | Pr > F |
| 1 | Rest_Pulse | 6 | 0.0003 | 0.8483 | 6.0492 | 0.05 | 0.8264 |
| 2 | Performance | 5 | 0.0014 | 0.8469 | 4.2598 | 0.22 | 0.6438 |
| 3 | Weight | 4 | 0.0115 | 0.8355 | 4.0004 | 1.87 | 0.1836 |

Using the BACKWARD elimination option and the default $p$-value, three independent variables were eliminated. By coincidence the final model is the same as the one considered best based on $C_p$, using the Mallows criterion.

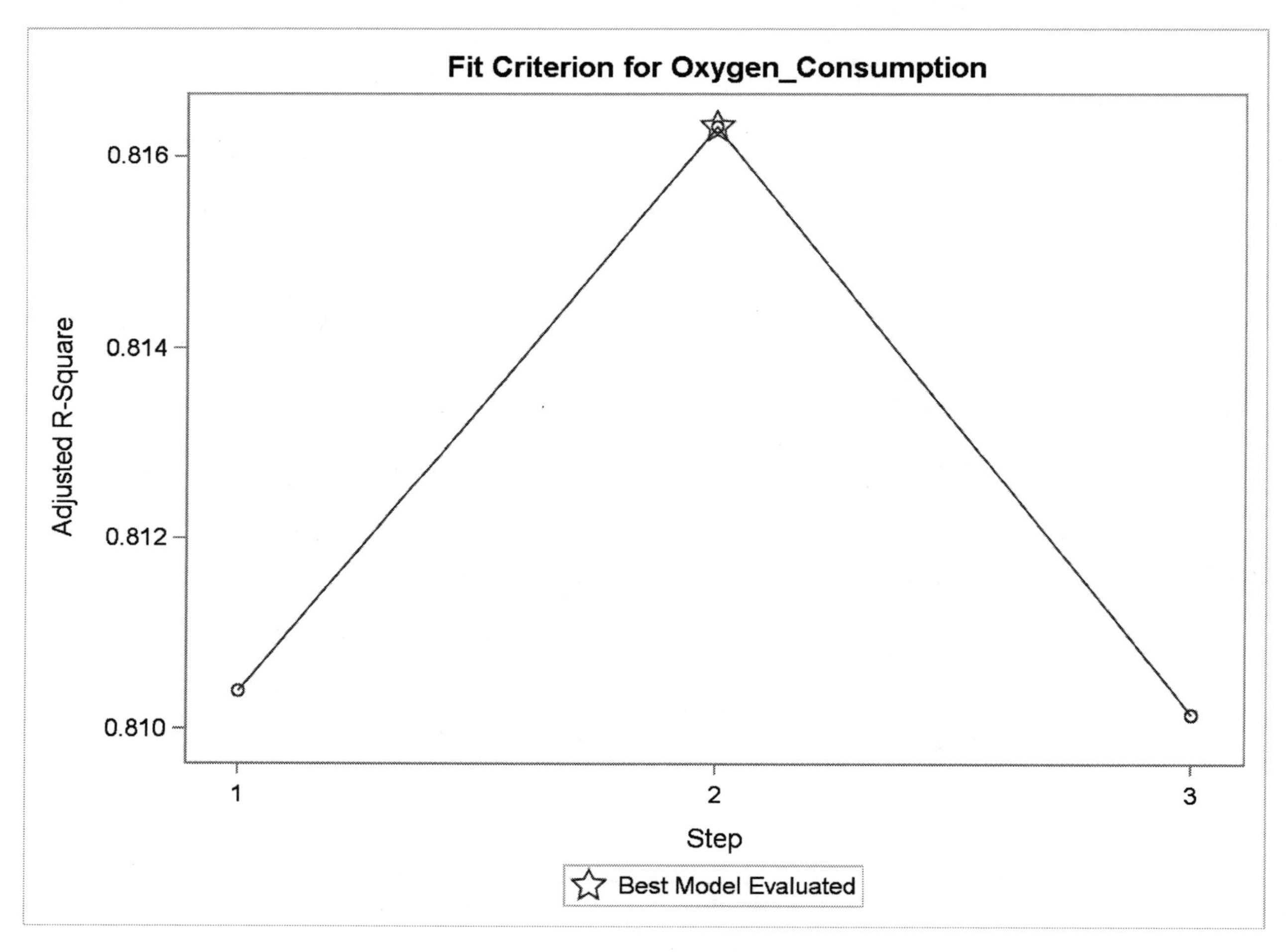


The adjusted R-square for the model at step 2 (before **Weight** was removed) was greatest of the three tested.

Partial PROC REG Output (Continued)

| Summary of Stepwise Selection | | | | | | | | |
|---|---|---|---|---|---|---|---|---|
| **Step** | **Variable Entered** | **Variable Removed** | **Number Vars In** | **Partial R-Square** | **Model R-Square** | **C(p)** | **F Value** | **Pr > F** |
| **1** | RunTime | | 1 | 0.7434 | 0.7434 | 11.9967 | 84.00 | <.0001 |
| **2** | Age | | 2 | 0.0213 | 0.7647 | 10.7530 | 2.54 | 0.1222 |
| **3** | Run_Pulse | | 3 | 0.0449 | 0.8096 | 5.9367 | 6.36 | 0.0179 |
| **4** | Maximum_Pulse | | 4 | 0.0259 | 0.8355 | 4.0004 | 4.09 | 0.0534 |

Using the STEPWISE option and the default variable entry and removal $p$-value criteria, the same subset resulted as that using the BACKWARD option.

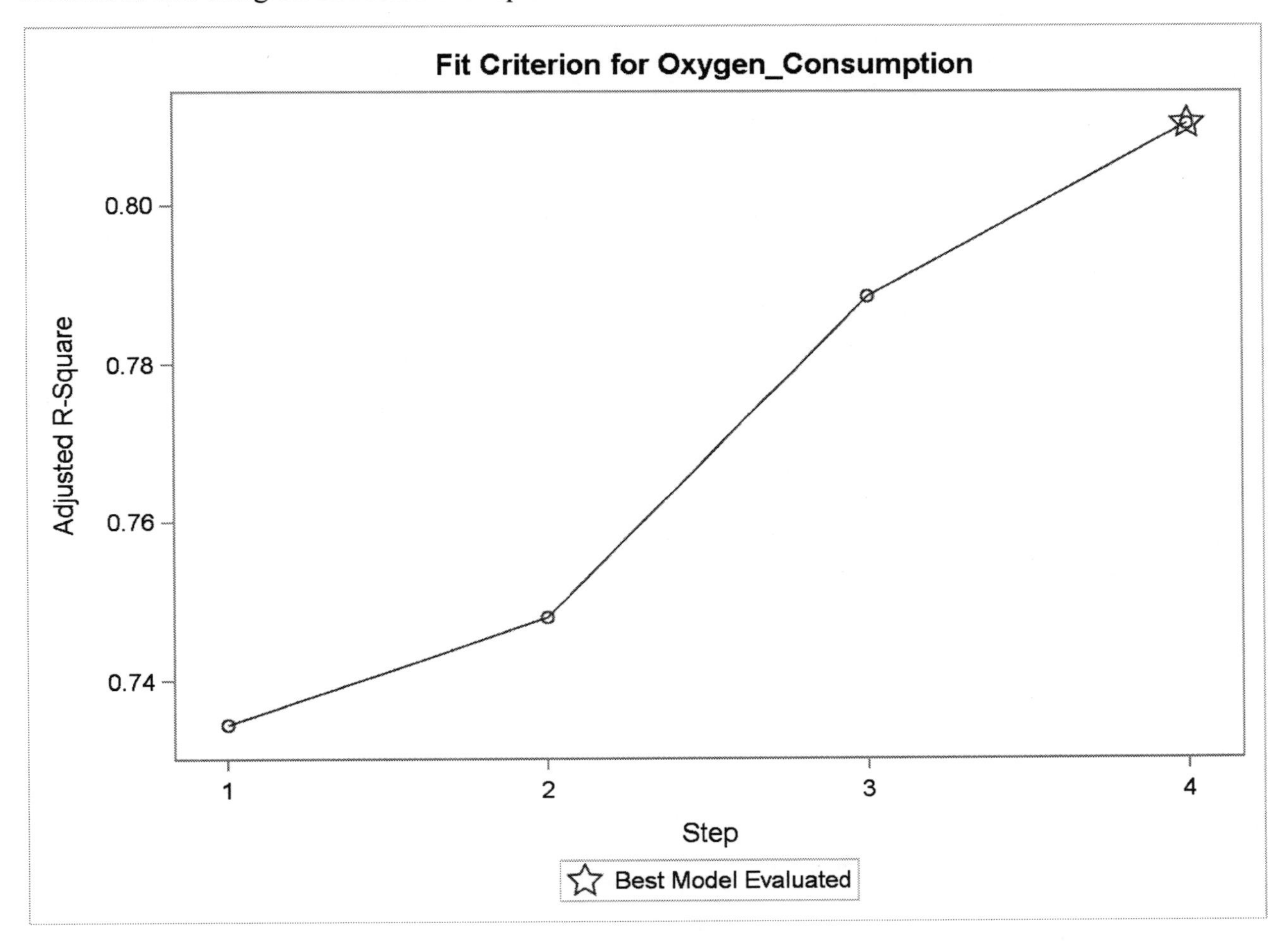


The SLENTRY= default criterion is $p<0.50$ for the FORWARD method and $p<.15$ for the STEPWISE method. After **RunTime** was entered into the model, **Age** was entered at step 2 with a $p$-value of 0.1222. If the SLENTRY= criterion were set to something less than 0.10, the final model would be quite different. It would include only one variable, **RunTime**. This underscores the precariousness of relying on one stepwise method for defining a "best" model.

The scale of the default Y axes in these plots might give misleading information about the effect of adding or removing variables. The same plots displayed side-by-side and using a common y-scale of 0 to 1 is shown below. The differences do not look nearly as great.

The “Bounds on the condition number” reported at each step of the output for the STEPWISE selection methods refer to a measurement of *collinearity* (correlation among predictor variables). (The concept of collinearity is discussed in a later chapter.)

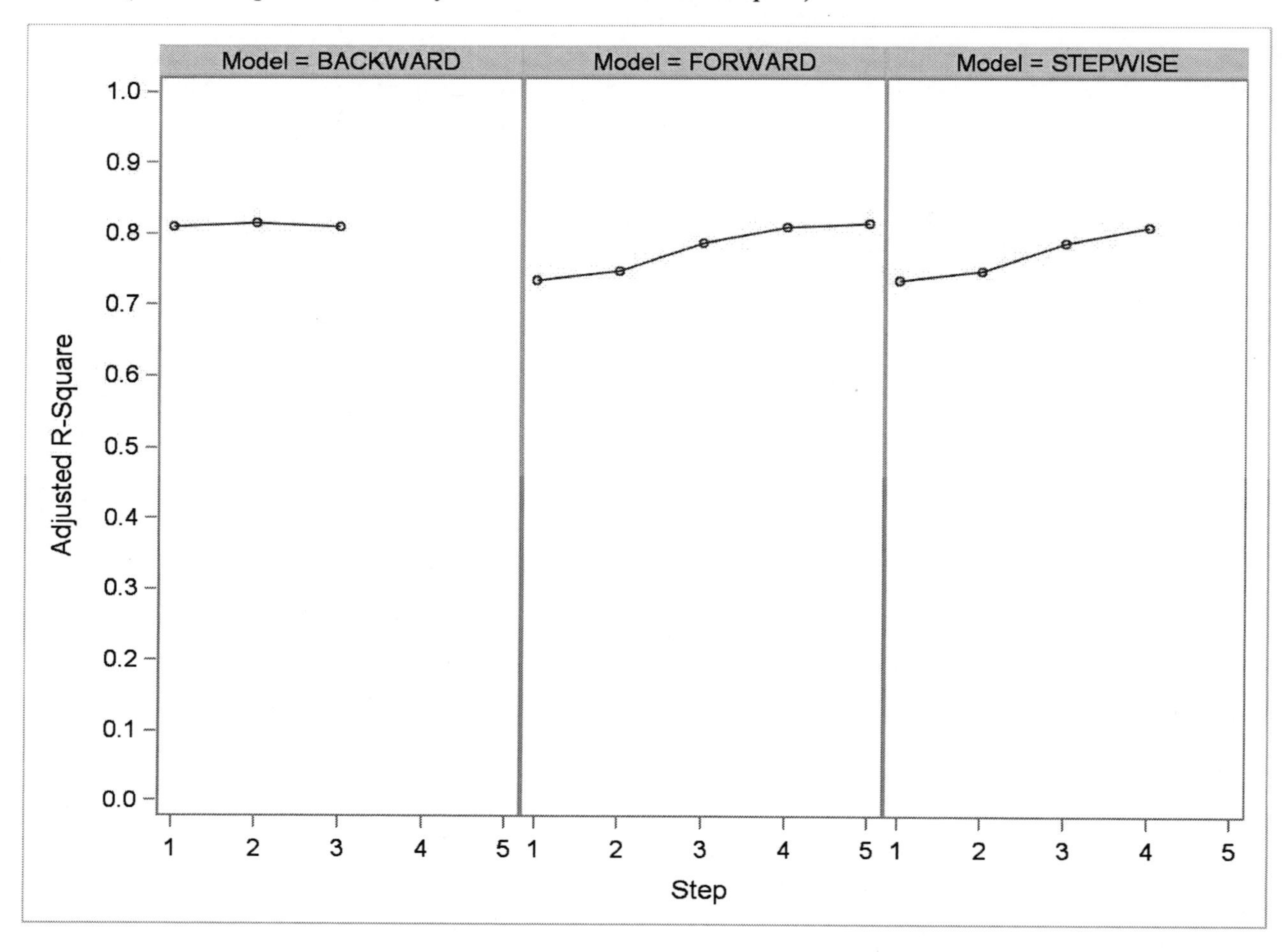

## Stepwise Regression Models*

| | |
|---|---|
| FORWARD | **RunTime**, **Age**, **Weight**, **Run_Pulse**, **Maximum_Pulse** |
| BACKWARD | **RunTime**, **Age**, **Run_Pulse**, **Maximum_Pulse** |
| STEPWISE | **RunTime**, **Age**, **Run_Pulse**, **Maximum_Pulse** |

*** Using default values of SLENTRY and SLSTAY**

115

The final models obtained using the default SLENTRY= and SLSTAY= criteria are displayed. It is important to note that the choice of criterion levels can greatly affect the final models that are selected using stepwise methods. Some analysts use the defaults to get models to a manageable size then do manual reduction instead of using low values for SLENTRY and SLSTAY.

## Stepwise Models, Alternative Criteria

| | |
|---|---|
| FORWARD (slentry=0.05) | **RunTime** |
| BACKWARD (slstay=0.05) | **RunTime**, **Run_Pulse**, **Maximum_Pulse** |
| STEPWISE (slentry=0.05, slstay=0.05) | **RunTime** |

116

The final models using 0.05 as the forward and backward step criteria resulted in very different models than those chosen using the default criteria.

## Comparison of Selection Methods

| | |
|---|---|
| **Stepwise regression** | uses fewer computer resources. |
| **All-possible regression** | generates more candidate models that might have nearly equal $R^2$ statistics and $C_p$ statistics. |

117

The stepwise regression methods have an advantage when there are a large number of independent variables.

With the all-possible regression techniques, you can compare essentially equivalent models and use your knowledge of the data set and subject area to select a model that is more easily interpreted.

## Exercises

**6. Using All-Regression Techniques**

Use the **sasuser.BodyFat2** data set to identify a set of "best" models.

**a.** With the SELECTION=CP option, use an all-possible regression technique to identify a set of candidate models that predict **PctBodyFat2** as a function of the variables **Age**, **Weight**, **Height**, **Neck**, **Chest**, **Abdomen**, **Hip**, **Thigh**, **Knee**, **Ankle**, **Biceps**, **Forearm**, and **Wrist**.

Hint: Select only the best 60 models based on $C_p$ to compare.

**b.** Use a stepwise regression method to select a candidate model. Try FORWARD, STEPWISE, and BACKWARD.

**c.** How many variables would result from a model using FORWARD selection and a significance level for entry criterion of 0.05, instead of the default SLENTRY of 0.50?

### 3.07 Poll

The STEPWISE, BACKWARD, and FORWARD strategies result in the same final model if the same significance levels are used in all three.

- ❍ True
- ❍ False

121

# 3.5 Solutions

## Solutions to Exercises

1. **Describing the Relationships between Continuous Variables**

   a. Generate scatter plots and correlations for the VAR variables **Age**, **Weight**, **Height**, and the circumference measures versus the WITH variable, **PctBodyFat2**.

Important! ODS Graphics in PROC CORR limits you to 10 VAR variables at a time, so for this exercise, look at the relationships with **Age**, **Weight**, and **Height** separately from the other variables.

Correlation tables can be created using more than 10 VAR variables at a time.

```
/*st103s01.sas*/  /*Part A*/
proc corr data=sasuser.BodyFat2 rank
          plots(only)=scatter(nvar=all ellipse=none);
   var Age Weight Height;
   with PctBodyFat2;
   title "Correlations and Scatter Plots with Body Fat %";
run;

proc corr data=sasuser.BodyFat2 rank
          plots(only)=scatter(nvar=all ellipse=none);
   var Neck Chest Abdomen Hip Thigh
       Knee Ankle Biceps Forearm Wrist;
   with PctBodyFat2;
   title "Correlations and Scatter Plots with Body Fat %";
run;
```

| 1 With Variables: | PctBodyFat2 | | |
|---|---|---|---|
| 3 Variables: | Age | Weight | Height |

| Simple Statistics | | | | | | |
|---|---|---|---|---|---|---|
| Variable | N | Mean | Std Dev | Sum | Minimum | Maximum |
| PctBodyFat2 | 252 | 19.15079 | 8.36874 | 4826 | 0 | 47.50000 |
| Age | 252 | 44.88492 | 12.60204 | 11311 | 22.00000 | 81.00000 |
| Weight | 252 | 178.92440 | 29.38916 | 45089 | 118.50000 | 363.15000 |
| Height | 252 | 70.30754 | 2.60958 | 17718 | 64.00000 | 77.75000 |

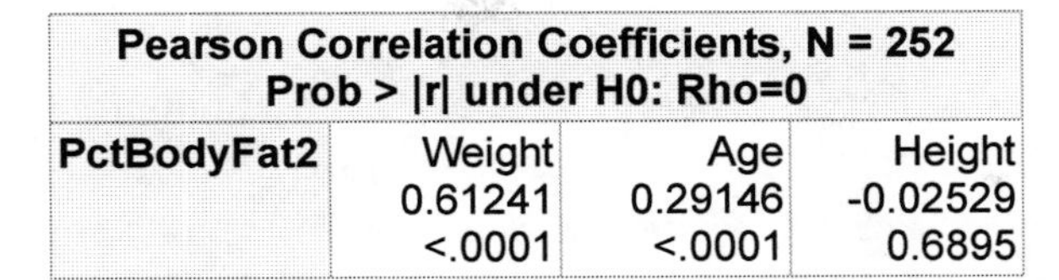

| Pearson Correlation Coefficients, N = 252<br>Prob > \|r\| under H0: Rho=0 | | | |
|---|---|---|---|
| PctBodyFat2 | Weight<br>0.61241<br><.0001 | Age<br>0.29146<br><.0001 | Height<br>-0.02529<br>0.6895 |

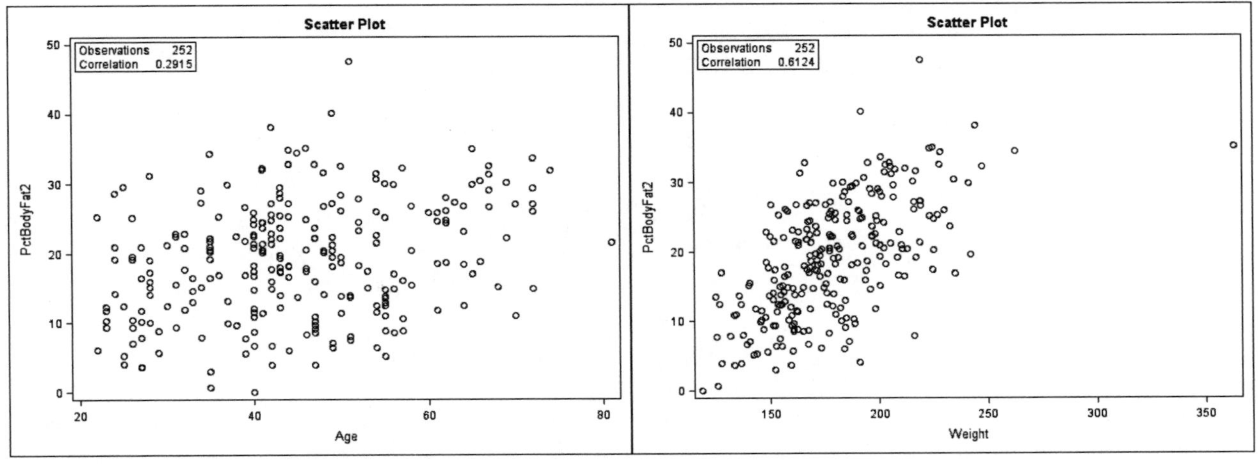


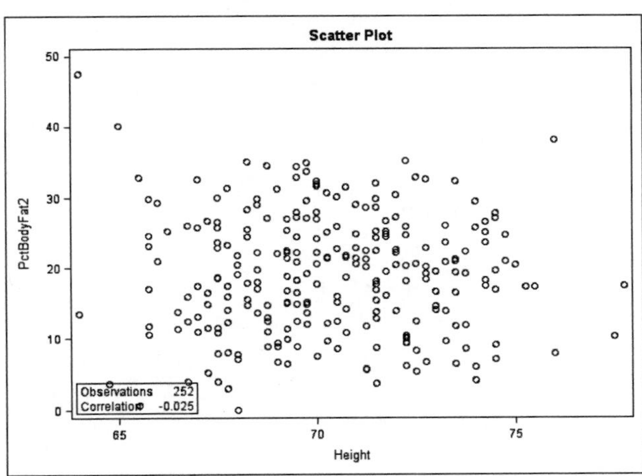


| 1 With Variables: | PctBodyFat2 | | | | | | | | | |
|---|---|---|---|---|---|---|---|---|---|---|
| 10 Variables: | Neck | Chest | Abdomen | Hip | Thigh | Knee | Ankle | Biceps | Forearm | Wrist |

| Simple Statistics | | | | | | |
|---|---|---|---|---|---|---|
| **Variable** | **N** | **Mean** | **Std Dev** | **Sum** | **Minimum** | **Maximum** |
| **PctBodyFat2** | 252 | 19.15079 | 8.36874 | 4826 | 0 | 47.50000 |
| **Neck** | 252 | 37.99206 | 2.43091 | 9574 | 31.10000 | 51.20000 |
| **Chest** | 252 | 100.82421 | 8.43048 | 25408 | 79.30000 | 136.20000 |
| **Abdomen** | 252 | 92.55595 | 10.78308 | 23324 | 69.40000 | 148.10000 |
| **Hip** | 252 | 99.90476 | 7.16406 | 25176 | 85.00000 | 147.70000 |
| **Thigh** | 252 | 59.40595 | 5.24995 | 14970 | 47.20000 | 87.30000 |
| **Knee** | 252 | 38.59048 | 2.41180 | 9725 | 33.00000 | 49.10000 |
| **Ankle** | 252 | 23.10238 | 1.69489 | 5822 | 19.10000 | 33.90000 |
| **Biceps** | 252 | 32.27341 | 3.02127 | 8133 | 24.80000 | 45.00000 |
| **Forearm** | 252 | 28.66389 | 2.02069 | 7223 | 21.00000 | 34.90000 |
| **Wrist** | 252 | 18.22976 | 0.93358 | 4594 | 15.80000 | 21.40000 |

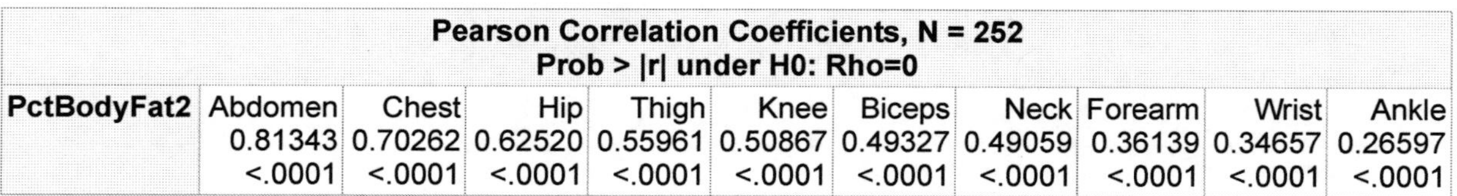

| Pearson Correlation Coefficients, N = 252<br>Prob > \|r\| under H0: Rho=0 | | | | | | | | | | |
|---|---|---|---|---|---|---|---|---|---|---|
| **PctBodyFat2** | Abdomen | Chest | Hip | Thigh | Knee | Biceps | Neck | Forearm | Wrist | Ankle |
| | 0.81343 | 0.70262 | 0.62520 | 0.55961 | 0.50867 | 0.49327 | 0.49059 | 0.36139 | 0.34657 | 0.26597 |
| | <.0001 | <.0001 | <.0001 | <.0001 | <.0001 | <.0001 | <.0001 | <.0001 | <.0001 | <.0001 |

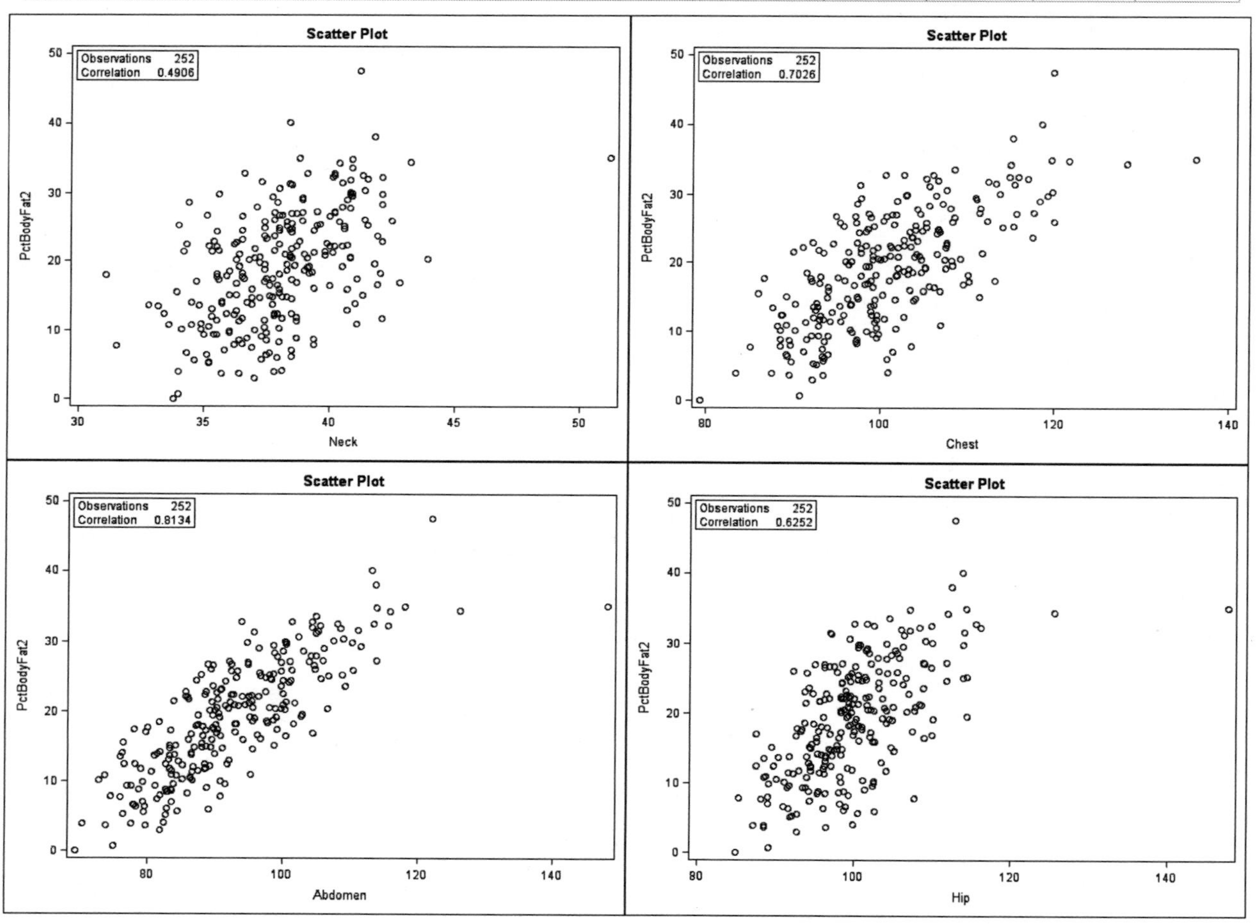

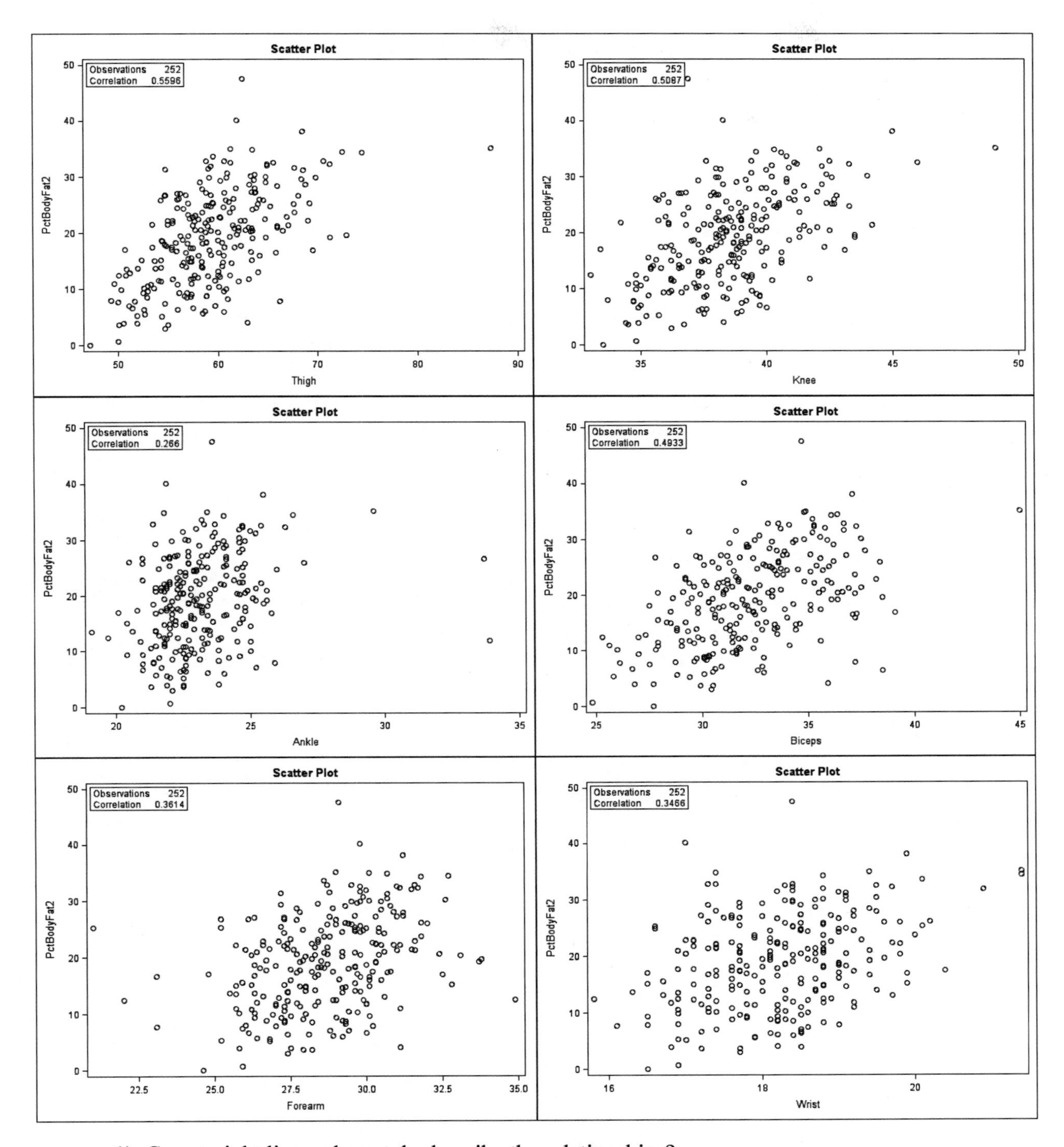


1) Can straight lines adequately describe the relationships?

   **Height seems to be the only variable that shows no real linear relationship. Age and Ankle show little linear trend.**

2) Are there any outliers that you should investigate?

   **The Weight outlier is present again, as well as Neck, Abdomen, Hip, Knee, and Biceps. There are two outliers for Ankle.**

3) What variable has the highest correlation with **PctBodyFat2**?

   **Abdomen**, with 0.81343, is the variable with the highest correlation with **PctBodyFat2**.

   a) What is the *p*-value for the coefficient?

      **<.0001**

   b) Is it statistically significant at the 0.05 level?

      **Yes**

**b.** Generate correlations among all of the VAR variables (**Age**, **Weight**, **Height**) among one another and among the circumference measures. Are there any notable relationships?

```
/*st103s01.sas*/  /*Part B*/
proc corr data=sasuser.BodyFat2 nosimple
          plots=matrix(nvar=all histogram);
   var Age Weight Height;
   title "Correlations and Scatter Plot Matrix of Basic Measures";
run;

proc corr data=sasuser.BodyFat2 nosimple
          plots=matrix(nvar=all histogram);
   var Neck Chest Abdomen Hip Thigh
       Knee Ankle Biceps Forearm Wrist;
   title "Correlations and Scatter Plot Matrix of Circumferences";
run;

proc corr data=sasuser.BodyFat2 nosimple
          plots=matrix(nvar=all histogram);
   var Neck Chest Abdomen Hip Thigh
       Knee Ankle Biceps Forearm Wrist;
   with Age Weight Height;
   title "Correlations and Scatter Plot Matrix of Circumferences";
run;
```

**Pearson Correlation Coefficients, N = 252**
**Prob > |r| under H0: Rho=0**

| | Age | Weight | Height |
|---|---|---|---|
| **Age** | 1.00000 | -0.01275<br>0.8404 | -0.24521<br><.0001 |
| **Weight** | -0.01275<br>0.8404 | 1.00000 | 0.48689<br><.0001 |
| **Height** | -0.24521<br><.0001 | 0.48689<br><.0001 | 1.00000 |

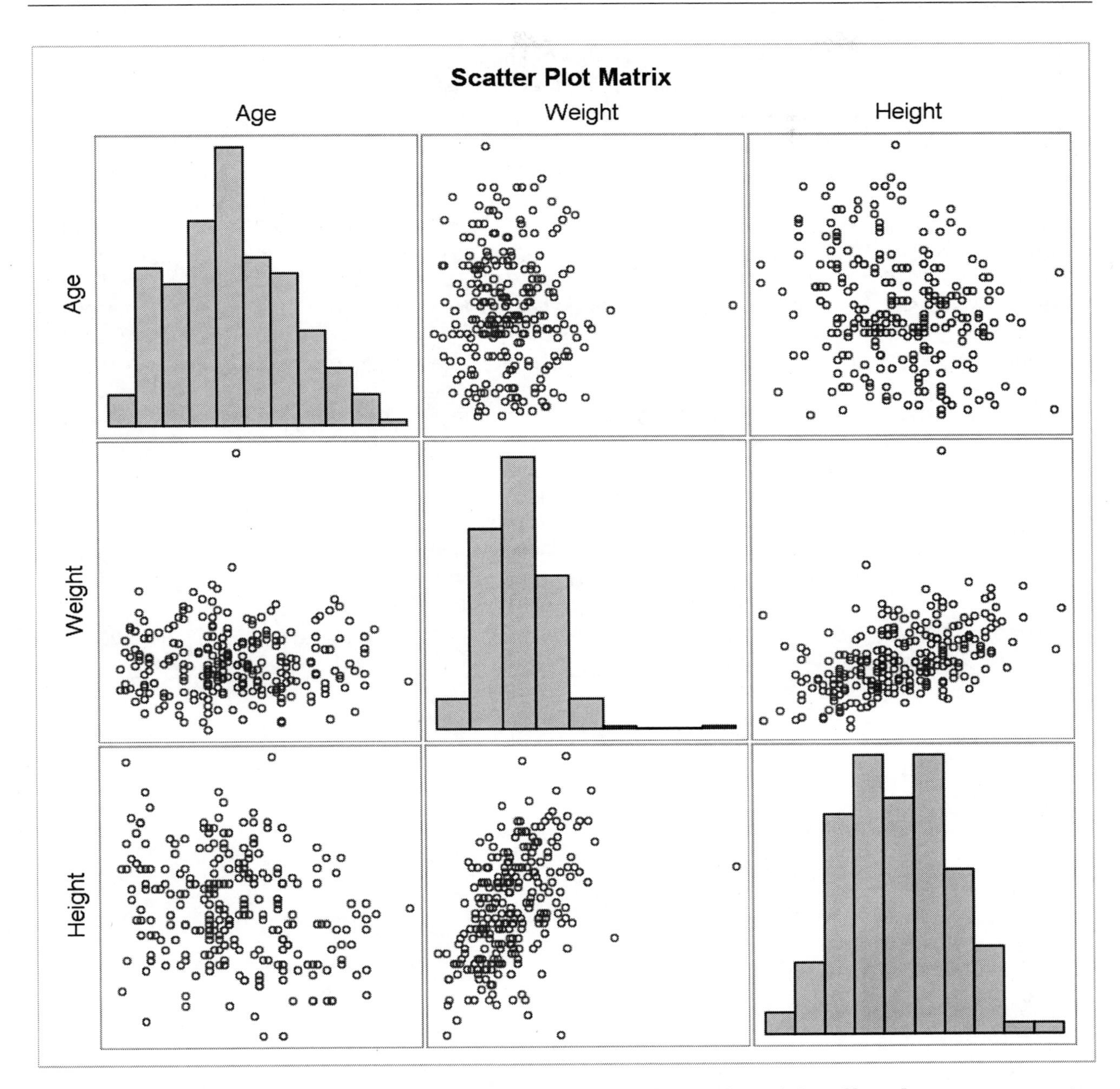


**Height and Weight seem to correlate relatively strongly. The outlier might affect the measurement of the relationship.**

| Pearson Correlation Coefficients, N = 252<br>Prob > \|r\| under H0: Rho=0 | | | | | | | | | | |
|---|---|---|---|---|---|---|---|---|---|---|
| | **Neck** | **Chest** | **Abdomen** | **Hip** | **Thigh** | **Knee** | **Ankle** | **Biceps** | **Forearm** | **Wrist** |
| **Neck** | 1.00000 | 0.78484<br><.0001 | 0.75408<br><.0001 | 0.73496<br><.0001 | 0.69570<br><.0001 | 0.67240<br><.0001 | 0.47789<br><.0001 | 0.73115<br><.0001 | 0.62366<br><.0001 | 0.74483<br><.0001 |
| **Chest** | 0.78484<br><.0001 | 1.00000 | 0.91583<br><.0001 | 0.82942<br><.0001 | 0.72986<br><.0001 | 0.71950<br><.0001 | 0.48299<br><.0001 | 0.72791<br><.0001 | 0.58017<br><.0001 | 0.66016<br><.0001 |
| **Abdomen** | 0.75408<br><.0001 | 0.91583<br><.0001 | 1.00000 | 0.87407<br><.0001 | 0.76662<br><.0001 | 0.73718<br><.0001 | 0.45322<br><.0001 | 0.68498<br><.0001 | 0.50332<br><.0001 | 0.61983<br><.0001 |
| **Hip** | 0.73496<br><.0001 | 0.82942<br><.0001 | 0.87407<br><.0001 | 1.00000 | 0.89641<br><.0001 | 0.82347<br><.0001 | 0.55839<br><.0001 | 0.73927<br><.0001 | 0.54501<br><.0001 | 0.63009<br><.0001 |
| **Thigh** | 0.69570<br><.0001 | 0.72986<br><.0001 | 0.76662<br><.0001 | 0.89641<br><.0001 | 1.00000 | 0.79917<br><.0001 | 0.53980<br><.0001 | 0.76148<br><.0001 | 0.56684<br><.0001 | 0.55868<br><.0001 |
| **Knee** | 0.67240<br><.0001 | 0.71950<br><.0001 | 0.73718<br><.0001 | 0.82347<br><.0001 | 0.79917<br><.0001 | 1.00000 | 0.61161<br><.0001 | 0.67871<br><.0001 | 0.55590<br><.0001 | 0.66451<br><.0001 |
| **Ankle** | 0.47789<br><.0001 | 0.48299<br><.0001 | 0.45322<br><.0001 | 0.55839<br><.0001 | 0.53980<br><.0001 | 0.61161<br><.0001 | 1.00000 | 0.48485<br><.0001 | 0.41905<br><.0001 | 0.56619<br><.0001 |
| **Biceps** | 0.73115<br><.0001 | 0.72791<br><.0001 | 0.68498<br><.0001 | 0.73927<br><.0001 | 0.76148<br><.0001 | 0.67871<br><.0001 | 0.48485<br><.0001 | 1.00000 | 0.67826<br><.0001 | 0.63213<br><.0001 |
| **Forearm** | 0.62366<br><.0001 | 0.58017<br><.0001 | 0.50332<br><.0001 | 0.54501<br><.0001 | 0.56684<br><.0001 | 0.55590<br><.0001 | 0.41905<br><.0001 | 0.67826<br><.0001 | 1.00000 | 0.58559<br><.0001 |
| **Wrist** | 0.74483<br><.0001 | 0.66016<br><.0001 | 0.61983<br><.0001 | 0.63009<br><.0001 | 0.55868<br><.0001 | 0.66451<br><.0001 | 0.56619<br><.0001 | 0.63213<br><.0001 | 0.58559<br><.0001 | 1.00000 |

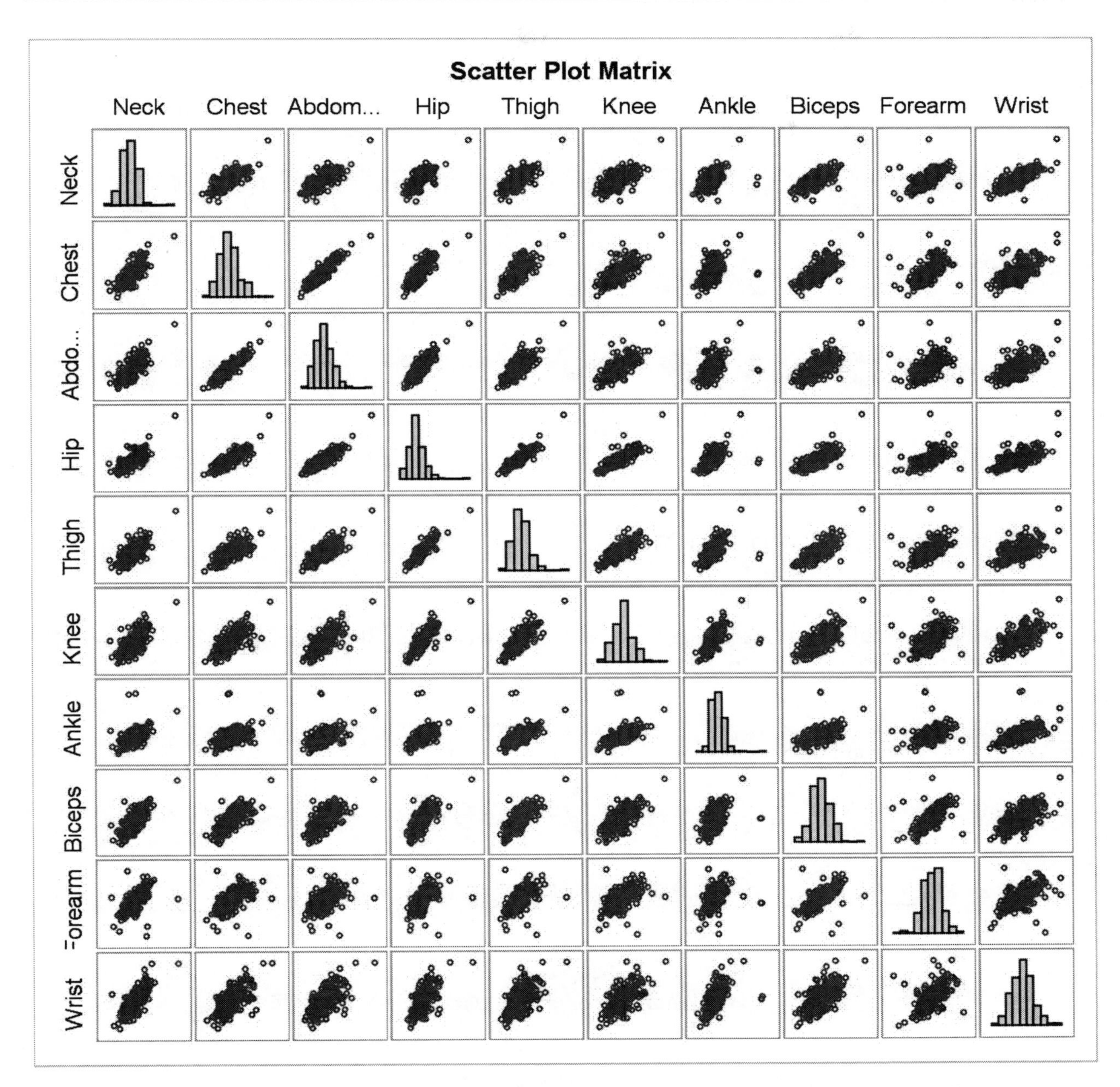


**There are several relationships that appear to have high correlations (such as those among Hip, Thigh, and Knee).**

| Pearson Correlation Coefficients, N = 252<br>Prob > \|r\| under H0: Rho=0 | | | | | | | | | | |
|---|---|---|---|---|---|---|---|---|---|---|
| | **Neck** | **Chest** | **Abdomen** | **Hip** | **Thigh** | **Knee** | **Ankle** | **Biceps** | **Forearm** | **Wrist** |
| **Age** | 0.11351<br>0.0721 | 0.17645<br>0.0050 | 0.23041<br>0.0002 | -0.05033<br>0.4263 | -0.20010<br>0.0014 | 0.01752<br>0.7820 | -0.10506<br>0.0961 | -0.04116<br>0.5154 | -0.08506<br>0.1783 | 0.21353<br>0.0006 |
| **Weight** | 0.83072<br><.0001 | 0.89419<br><.0001 | 0.88799<br><.0001 | 0.94088<br><.0001 | 0.86869<br><.0001 | 0.85317<br><.0001 | 0.61369<br><.0001 | 0.80042<br><.0001 | 0.63030<br><.0001 | 0.72977<br><.0001 |
| **Height** | 0.32114<br><.0001 | 0.22683<br>0.0003 | 0.18977<br>0.0025 | 0.37211<br><.0001 | 0.33856<br><.0001 | 0.50050<br><.0001 | 0.39313<br><.0001 | 0.31851<br><.0001 | 0.32203<br><.0001 | 0.39778<br><.0001 |

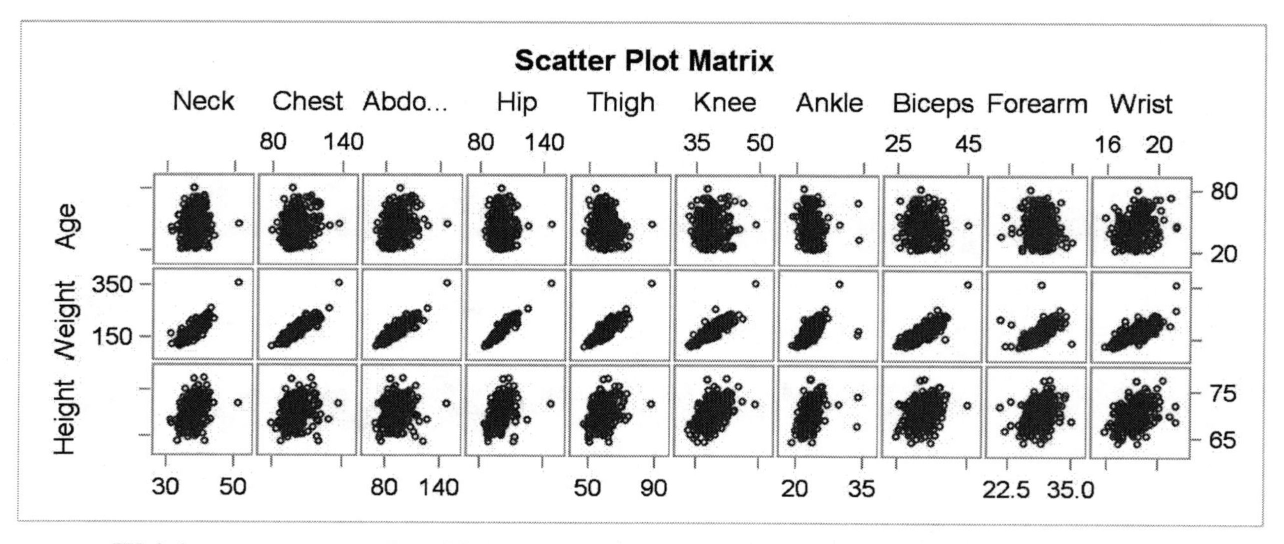


**Weight seems to correlate highly with all circumference variables.**

2. **Fitting a Simple Linear Regression Model**

   Use the **sasuser.BodyFat2** data set for this exercise.

   a. Perform a simple linear regression model with **PctBodyFat2** as the response variable and **Weight** as the predictor.

```
/*st103s02.sas*/  /*Part A*/
ods graphics off;
proc reg data=sasuser.BodyFat2;
   model PctBodyFat2=Weight;
   title "Regression of % Body Fat on Weight";
run;
quit;
ods graphics on;
```

| | |
|---|---|
| **Number of Observations Read** | 252 |
| **Number of Observations Used** | 252 |

| Analysis of Variance | | | | | |
|---|---|---|---|---|---|
| **Source** | **DF** | **Sum of Squares** | **Mean Square** | **F Value** | **Pr > F** |
| **Model** | 1 | 6593.01614 | 6593.01614 | 150.03 | <.0001 |
| **Error** | 250 | 10986 | 43.94389 | | |
| **Corrected Total** | 251 | 17579 | | | |

| | | | |
|---|---|---|---|
| **Root MSE** | 6.62902 | **R-Square** | 0.3751 |
| **Dependent Mean** | 19.15079 | **Adj R-Sq** | 0.3726 |
| **Coeff Var** | 34.61485 | | |

| Parameter Estimates | | | | | |
|---|---|---|---|---|---|
| Variable | DF | Parameter Estimate | Standard Error | t Value | Pr > \|t\| |
| Intercept | 1 | -12.05158 | 2.58139 | -4.67 | <.0001 |
| Weight | 1 | 0.17439 | 0.01424 | 12.25 | <.0001 |

1) What is the value of the *F* statistic and the associated *p*-value? How would you interpret this with regard to the null hypothesis?

   **The *F* value is 150.03 and the *p*-value is <.0001. You would reject the null hypothesis of no relationship.**

2) Write the predicted regression equation.

   **From the parameter estimates table, the predicted value equation is as follows: PctBodyFat2=-12.05158+0.17439*Weight.**

3) What is the value of the R-square statistic? How would you interpret this?

   **The R-square value of 0.3751 can be interpreted to mean that 37.51% of the variability in PctBodyFat2 can be explained by Weight.**

**b.** Produce predicted values for **PctBodyFat2** when **Weight** is 125, 150, 175, 200, and 225.

```
/*st103s02.sas*/  /*Part B*/
ods graphics off;
proc reg data=sasuser.BodyFat2 outest=Betas;
   PredBodyFat: model PctBodyFat2=Weight;
   title "Regression of % Body Fat on Weight";
run;
quit;
ods graphics on;

data ToScore;
   input Weight @@;
   datalines;
125 150 175 200 225
;
run;

proc score data=ToScore score=Betas
           out=Scored type=parms;
   var Weight;
run;

proc print data=Scored;
   title "Predicted % Body Fat from Weight 125 150 175 200 225";
run;
```

| Obs | Weight | PredBodyFat |
|---|---|---|
| 1 | 125 | 9.7470 |
| 2 | 150 | 14.1067 |
| 3 | 175 | 18.4664 |
| 4 | 200 | 22.8261 |
| 5 | 225 | 27.1859 |

What are the predicted values?

**The predicted values are as listed in the output above under PredBodyFat.**

3. **Performing Multiple Regression Using the REG Procedure**

   a. Using the **sasuser.BodyFat2** data set, run a regression of **PctBodyFat2** on the variables **Age**, **Weight**, **Height**, **Neck**, **Chest**, **Abdomen**, **Hip**, **Thigh**, **Knee**, **Ankle**, **Biceps**, **Forearm**, and **Wrist**.

      1) Compare the ANOVA table with that from the model with only **Weight** in the previous exercise. What is different?

```
/*st103s03.sas*/  /*Part A*/
proc reg data=sasuser.BodyFat2;
   model PctBodyFat2=Age Weight Height
         Neck Chest Abdomen Hip Thigh
         Knee Ankle Biceps Forearm Wrist;
   title 'Regression of PctBodyFat2 on All '
         'Predictors';
run;
quit;
```

PROC REG Output

| | |
|---|---|
| Number of Observations Read | 252 |
| Number of Observations Used | 252 |

| Analysis of Variance | | | | | |
|---|---|---|---|---|---|
| Source | DF | Sum of Squares | Mean Square | F Value | Pr > F |
| Model | 13 | 13159 | 1012.22506 | 54.50 | <.0001 |
| Error | 238 | 4420.06401 | 18.57170 | | |
| Corrected Total | 251 | 17579 | | | |

| | | | |
|---|---|---|---|
| Root MSE | 4.30949 | R-Square | 0.7486 |
| Dependent Mean | 19.15079 | Adj R-Sq | 0.7348 |
| Coeff Var | 22.50293 | | |

| Parameter Estimates | | | | | |
|---|---|---|---|---|---|
| Variable | DF | Parameter Estimate | Standard Error | t Value | Pr > \|t\| |
| Intercept | 1 | -21.35323 | 22.18616 | -0.96 | 0.3368 |
| Age | 1 | 0.06457 | 0.03219 | 2.01 | 0.0460 |
| Weight | 1 | -0.09638 | 0.06185 | -1.56 | 0.1205 |
| Height | 1 | -0.04394 | 0.17870 | -0.25 | 0.8060 |
| Neck | 1 | -0.47547 | 0.23557 | -2.02 | 0.0447 |
| Chest | 1 | -0.01718 | 0.10322 | -0.17 | 0.8679 |
| Abdomen | 1 | 0.95500 | 0.09016 | 10.59 | <.0001 |
| Hip | 1 | -0.18859 | 0.14479 | -1.30 | 0.1940 |
| Thigh | 1 | 0.24835 | 0.14617 | 1.70 | 0.0906 |
| Knee | 1 | 0.01395 | 0.24775 | 0.06 | 0.9552 |
| Ankle | 1 | 0.17788 | 0.22262 | 0.80 | 0.4251 |
| Biceps | 1 | 0.18230 | 0.17250 | 1.06 | 0.2917 |
| Forearm | 1 | 0.45574 | 0.19930 | 2.29 | 0.0231 |
| Wrist | 1 | -1.65450 | 0.53316 | -3.10 | 0.0021 |

**There are key differences between the ANOVA table for this model and the Simple Linear Regression model.**

- **The degrees of freedom for the model are much higher, 13 versus 1.**
- **The Mean Square model and the *F* ratio are much smaller.**

2) How do the R square and the adjusted R square compare with these statistics for the **Weight** regression demonstration?

**Both the R square and adjusted R square for the full models are larger than the simple linear regression. The multiple regression model explains almost 75% of the variation in the PctBodyFat2 variable versus only about 37.5% explained by the simple linear regression model.**

3) Did the estimate for the intercept change? Did the estimate for the coefficient of **Weight** change?

**Yes, including the other variables in the model changed the estimates both of the intercept and the slope for Weight. Also, the *p*-values for both changed dramatically. The slope of Weight is now not significantly different from zero.**

## 4. Simplifying the Model

**a.** Rerun the model in **3a.**, but eliminate the variable with the highest *p*-value. Compare the output with the Exercise **3a.** model.

This program reruns the regression with **Knee** removed because it has the largest *p*-value (0.9552).

```
/*st103s03.sas*/  /*Part B*/
proc reg data=sasuser.BodyFat2;
   model PctBodyFat2=Age Weight Height
         Neck Chest Abdomen Hip Thigh
         Ankle Biceps Forearm Wrist;
   title 'Remove Knee';
run;
quit;
```

PROC REG Output

| | |
|---|---|
| Number of Observations Read | 252 |
| Number of Observations Used | 252 |

| Analysis of Variance | | | | | |
|---|---|---|---|---|---|
| Source | DF | Sum of Squares | Mean Square | F Value | Pr > F |
| Model | 12 | 13159 | 1096.57225 | 59.29 | <.0001 |
| Error | 239 | 4420.12286 | 18.49424 | | |
| Corrected Total | 251 | 17579 | | | |

| | | | |
|---|---|---|---|
| Root MSE | 4.30049 | R-Square | 0.7486 |
| Dependent Mean | 19.15079 | Adj R-Sq | 0.7359 |
| Coeff Var | 22.45595 | | |

| Parameter Estimates | | | | | |
|---|---|---|---|---|---|
| Variable | DF | Parameter Estimate | Standard Error | t Value | Pr > \|t\| |
| Intercept | 1 | -21.30204 | 22.12123 | -0.96 | 0.3365 |
| Age | 1 | 0.06503 | 0.03108 | 2.09 | 0.0374 |
| Weight | 1 | -0.09602 | 0.06138 | -1.56 | 0.1191 |
| Height | 1 | -0.04166 | 0.17369 | -0.24 | 0.8107 |
| Neck | 1 | -0.47695 | 0.23361 | -2.04 | 0.0423 |
| Chest | 1 | -0.01732 | 0.10298 | -0.17 | 0.8666 |
| Abdomen | 1 | 0.95497 | 0.08998 | 10.61 | <.0001 |
| Hip | 1 | -0.18801 | 0.14413 | -1.30 | 0.1933 |
| Thigh | 1 | 0.25089 | 0.13876 | 1.81 | 0.0719 |
| Ankle | 1 | 0.18018 | 0.21841 | 0.82 | 0.4102 |
| Biceps | 1 | 0.18182 | 0.17193 | 1.06 | 0.2913 |
| Forearm | 1 | 0.45667 | 0.19820 | 2.30 | 0.0221 |
| Wrist | 1 | -1.65227 | 0.53057 | -3.11 | 0.0021 |

**b.** Did the $p$-value for the model change notably?

**The $p$-value for the model did not change out to four decimal places.**

**c.** Did the R square and adjusted R square change notably?

**The R square showed essentially no change. The adjusted R square increased from 0.7348 to 0.7359. When an adjusted R square increases by removing a variable from the model, it strongly implies that the removed variable was not necessary.**

**d.** Did the parameter estimates and their $p$-values change notably?

**Some of the parameter estimates and their $p$-values changed slightly, none to any large degree.**

## 5. More Simplifying of the Model

**a.** Rerun the model in Exercise **4a**, but drop the variable with the highest $p$-value.

This program reruns the regression with **Chest** removed, because it is the variable with the highest $p$-value in the previous model.

```
/*st103s03.sas*/  /*Part C*/
proc reg data=sasuser.BodyFat2;
   model PctBodyFat2=Age Weight Height
         Neck Abdomen Hip Thigh
         Ankle Biceps Forearm Wrist;
   title 'Remove Knee and Chest';
run;
quit;
```

PROC REG Output

| | |
|---|---|
| **Number of Observations Read** | 252 |
| **Number of Observations Used** | 252 |

**Analysis of Variance**

| Source | DF | Sum of Squares | Mean Square | F Value | Pr > F |
|---|---|---|---|---|---|
| **Model** | 11 | 13158 | 1196.21310 | 64.94 | <.0001 |
| **Error** | 240 | 4420.64572 | 18.41936 | | |
| **Corrected Total** | 251 | 17579 | | | |

| | | | |
|---|---|---|---|
| **Root MSE** | 4.29178 | **R-Square** | 0.7485 |
| **Dependent Mean** | 19.15079 | **Adj R-Sq** | 0.7370 |
| **Coeff Var** | 22.41044 | | |

| Parameter Estimates | | | | | |
|---|---|---|---|---|---|
| Variable | DF | Parameter Estimate | Standard Error | t Value | Pr > \|t\| |
| Intercept | 1 | -23.13736 | 19.20171 | -1.20 | 0.2294 |
| Age | 1 | 0.06488 | 0.03100 | 2.09 | 0.0374 |
| Weight | 1 | -0.10095 | 0.05380 | -1.88 | 0.0618 |
| Height | 1 | -0.03120 | 0.16185 | -0.19 | 0.8473 |
| Neck | 1 | -0.47631 | 0.23311 | -2.04 | 0.0421 |
| Abdomen | 1 | 0.94965 | 0.08406 | 11.30 | <.0001 |
| Hip | 1 | -0.18316 | 0.14092 | -1.30 | 0.1950 |
| Thigh | 1 | 0.25583 | 0.13534 | 1.89 | 0.0599 |
| Ankle | 1 | 0.18215 | 0.21765 | 0.84 | 0.4035 |
| Biceps | 1 | 0.18055 | 0.17141 | 1.05 | 0.2933 |
| Forearm | 1 | 0.45262 | 0.19634 | 2.31 | 0.0220 |
| Wrist | 1 | -1.64984 | 0.52930 | -3.12 | 0.0020 |

**b.** How did the output change from the previous model?

**The ANOVA table did not change greatly. The R square remained essentially unchanged. The adjusted R square increased again, which confirms that the variable Chest did not contribute to explaining the variation in PctBodyFat2 when the other variables are in the model.**

**c.** Did the number of parameters with *p*-values less than 0.05 change?

**The *p*-value for Weight changed more than any other and is now just above 0.05. The *p*-values and parameter estimates for other variables changed much less. There are no more variables in this model with *p*-values below 0.05, compared with the previous one.**

**6. Using All-Regression Techniques**

**a.** With the SELECTION=CP option, use an all-possible regression technique to identify a set of candidate models that predict **PctBodyFat2** as a function of the variables **Age**, **Weight**, **Height**, **Neck**, **Chest**, **Abdomen**, **Hip**, **Thigh**, **Knee**, **Ankle**, **Biceps**, **Forearm**, and **Wrist**.
Hint: Select only the best 60 models based on $C_p$ to compare.

```
/*st103s04.sas*/  /*Part A*/
ods graphics / imagemap=on;

proc reg data=sasuser.BodyFat2 plots(only)=(cp);
   model PctBodyFat2=Age Weight Height
         Neck Chest Abdomen Hip Thigh
         Knee Ankle Biceps Forearm Wrist
         / selection=cp best=60;
   title "Using Mallows Cp for Model Selection";
run;
quit;
```

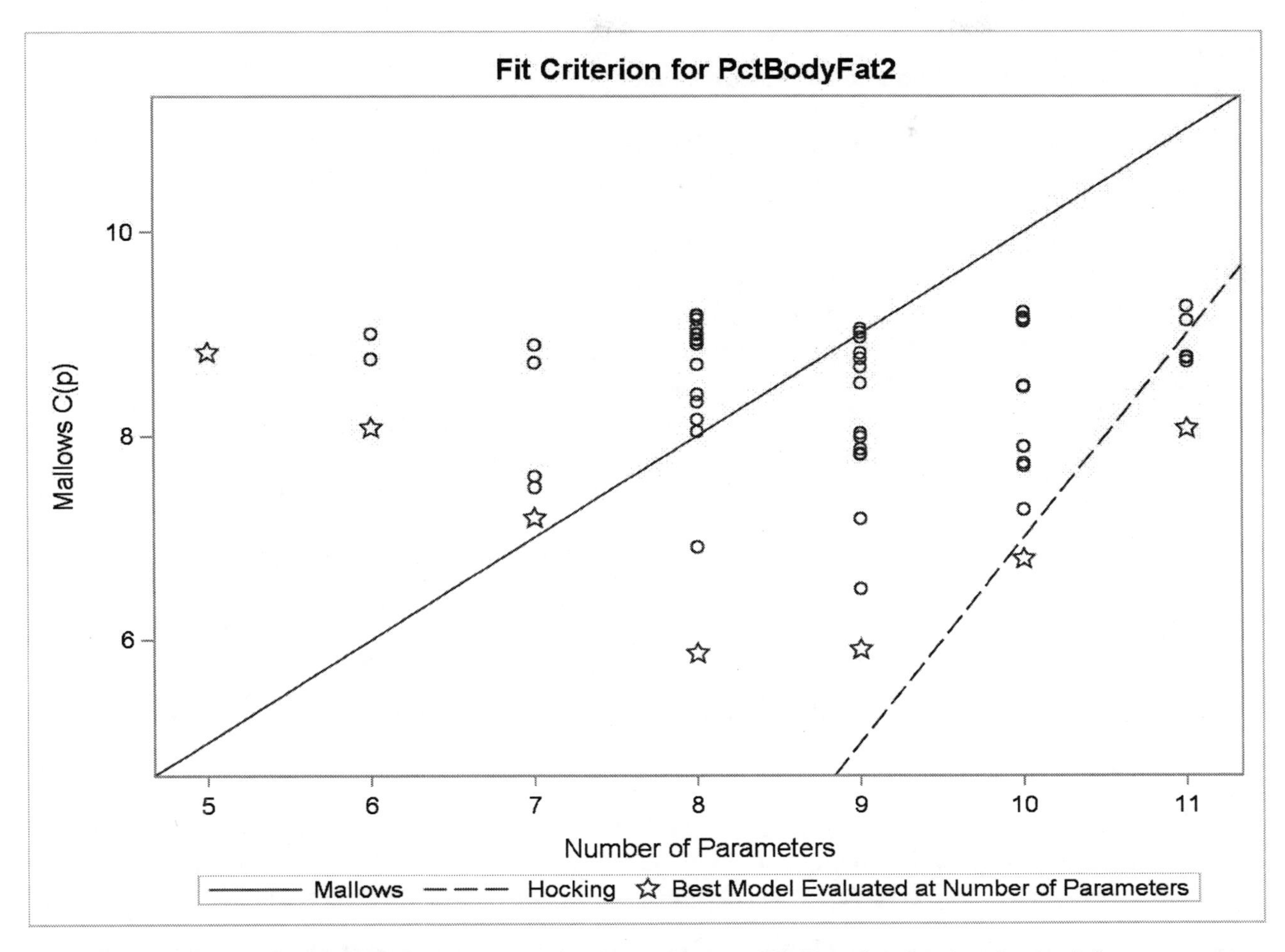


**The plot indicates that the best model according to Mallows' criterion is an eight-parameter (seven variables plus an intercept) model. The best model according to Hocking's criterion has 10 parameters (including the intercept).**

**A partial table of the 60 models, their C(p) values, and the numbers of variables in the models is displayed.**

| Model Index | Number in Model | C(p) | R-Square | Variables in Model |
|---|---|---|---|---|
| 1 | 7 | 5.8653 | 0.7445 | Age Weight Neck Abdomen Thigh Forearm Wrist |
| 2 | 8 | 5.8986 | 0.7466 | Age Weight Neck Abdomen Hip Thigh Forearm Wrist |
| 3 | 8 | 6.4929 | 0.7459 | Age Weight Neck Abdomen Thigh Biceps Forearm Wrist |
| 4 | 9 | 6.7834 | 0.7477 | Age Weight Neck Abdomen Hip Thigh Biceps Forearm Wrist |
| 5 | 7 | 6.9017 | 0.7434 | Age Weight Neck Abdomen Biceps Forearm Wrist |
| 6 | 8 | 7.1778 | 0.7452 | Age Weight Neck Abdomen Thigh Ankle Forearm Wrist |
| 7 | 6 | 7.1860 | 0.7410 | Age Weight Abdomen Thigh Forearm Wrist |
| 8 | 9 | 7.2729 | 0.7472 | Age Weight Neck Abdomen Hip Thigh Ankle Forearm Wrist |
| 9 | 6 | 7.4937 | 0.7406 | Age Weight Neck Abdomen Forearm Wrist |
| 10 | 6 | 7.6018 | 0.7405 | Weight Neck Abdomen Biceps Forearm Wrist |
| 11 | 9 | 7.7067 | 0.7468 | Age Weight Neck Abdomen Thigh Ankle Biceps Forearm Wrist |
| 12 | 9 | 7.7282 | 0.7467 | Age Weight Height Neck Abdomen Hip Thigh Forearm Wrist |
| 13 | 8 | 7.8146 | 0.7445 | Age Weight Height Neck Abdomen Thigh Forearm Wrist |
| 14 | 8 | 7.8246 | 0.7445 | Age Weight Neck Chest Abdomen Thigh Forearm Wrist |
| 15 | 8 | 7.8651 | 0.7445 | Age Weight Neck Abdomen Thigh Knee Forearm Wrist |
| 16 | 9 | 7.8966 | 0.7466 | Age Weight Neck Abdomen Hip Thigh Knee Forearm Wrist |
| 17 | 9 | 7.8986 | 0.7466 | Age Weight Neck Chest Abdomen Hip Thigh Forearm Wrist |
| 18 | 8 | 7.9907 | 0.7443 | Age Weight Neck Abdomen Ankle Biceps Forearm Wrist |

Number in Model does not include the intercept in this table.

**The best MALLOWS model is either the eight-parameter models, number 1 (includes the variables Age, Weight, Neck, Abdomen, Thigh, Forearm, and Wrist) or number 5 (includes the variables Age, Weight, Neck, Abdomen, Biceps, Forearm, and Wrist).**

**The best HOCKING model is number 4. It includes Hip, along with the variables in the best MALLOWS models listed above.**

**b.** Use a stepwise regression method to select a candidate model. Try FORWARD, STEPWISE, and BACKWARD.

```
/*st103s04.sas*/  /*Part B*/
proc reg data=sasuser.BodyFat2 plots(only)=adjrsq;
   FORWARD:  model PctBodyFat2=Age Weight Height
             Neck Chest Abdomen Hip Thigh
             Knee Ankle Biceps Forearm Wrist
             / selection=forward;
   BACKWARD: model PctBodyFat2=Age Weight Height
             Neck Chest Abdomen Hip Thigh
             Knee Ankle Biceps Forearm Wrist
             / selection=backward;
   STEPWISE: model PctBodyFat2=Age Weight Height
             Neck Chest Abdomen Hip Thigh
             Knee Ankle Biceps Forearm Wrist
             / selection=stepwise;
   title "Using Stepwise Methods for Model Selection";
run;
quit;
```

Partial Output

**Forward Selection: Step 10**

**Variable Ankle Entered: R-Square = 0.7485 and C(p) = 8.0682**

| Analysis of Variance | | | | | |
|---|---|---|---|---|---|
| Source | DF | Sum of Squares | Mean Square | F Value | Pr > F |
| Model | 10 | 13158 | 1315.76595 | 71.72 | <.0001 |
| Error | 241 | 4421.33035 | 18.34577 | | |
| Corrected Total | 251 | 17579 | | | |

| Variable | Parameter Estimate | Standard Error | Type II SS | F Value | Pr > F |
|---|---|---|---|---|---|
| Intercept | -25.99962 | 12.15316 | 83.96376 | 4.58 | 0.0334 |
| Age | 0.06509 | 0.03092 | 81.31425 | 4.43 | 0.0363 |
| Weight | -0.10740 | 0.04207 | 119.56769 | 6.52 | 0.0113 |
| Neck | -0.46749 | 0.22812 | 77.05006 | 4.20 | 0.0415 |
| Abdomen | 0.95772 | 0.07276 | 3178.52750 | 173.26 | <.0001 |
| Hip | -0.17912 | 0.13908 | 30.42960 | 1.66 | 0.1990 |
| Thigh | 0.25926 | 0.13389 | 68.78441 | 3.75 | 0.0540 |
| Ankle | 0.18453 | 0.21686 | 13.28232 | 0.72 | 0.3957 |
| Biceps | 0.18617 | 0.16858 | 22.37399 | 1.22 | 0.2705 |
| Forearm | 0.45303 | 0.19593 | 98.08072 | 5.35 | 0.0216 |
| Wrist | -1.65666 | 0.52706 | 181.25142 | 9.88 | 0.0019 |

**Bounds on condition number: 20.913, 668.17**

**No other variable met the 0.5000 significance level for entry into the model.**

| Summary of Forward Selection | | | | | | | |
|---|---|---|---|---|---|---|---|
| Step | Variable Entered | Number Vars In | Partial R-Square | Model R-Square | C(p) | F Value | Pr > F |
| 1 | Abdomen | 1 | 0.6617 | 0.6617 | 72.2434 | 488.93 | <.0001 |
| 2 | Weight | 2 | 0.0571 | 0.7188 | 20.1709 | 50.58 | <.0001 |
| 3 | Wrist | 3 | 0.0089 | 0.7277 | 13.7069 | 8.15 | 0.0047 |
| 4 | Forearm | 4 | 0.0073 | 0.7350 | 8.8244 | 6.78 | 0.0098 |
| 5 | Neck | 5 | 0.0029 | 0.7379 | 8.0748 | 2.73 | 0.1000 |
| 6 | Age | 6 | 0.0027 | 0.7406 | 7.4937 | 2.58 | 0.1098 |
| 7 | Thigh | 7 | 0.0038 | 0.7445 | 5.8653 | 3.66 | 0.0569 |
| 8 | Hip | 8 | 0.0021 | 0.7466 | 5.8986 | 1.99 | 0.1594 |
| 9 | Biceps | 9 | 0.0012 | 0.7477 | 6.7834 | 1.13 | 0.2888 |
| 10 | Ankle | 10 | 0.0008 | 0.7485 | 8.0682 | 0.72 | 0.3957 |

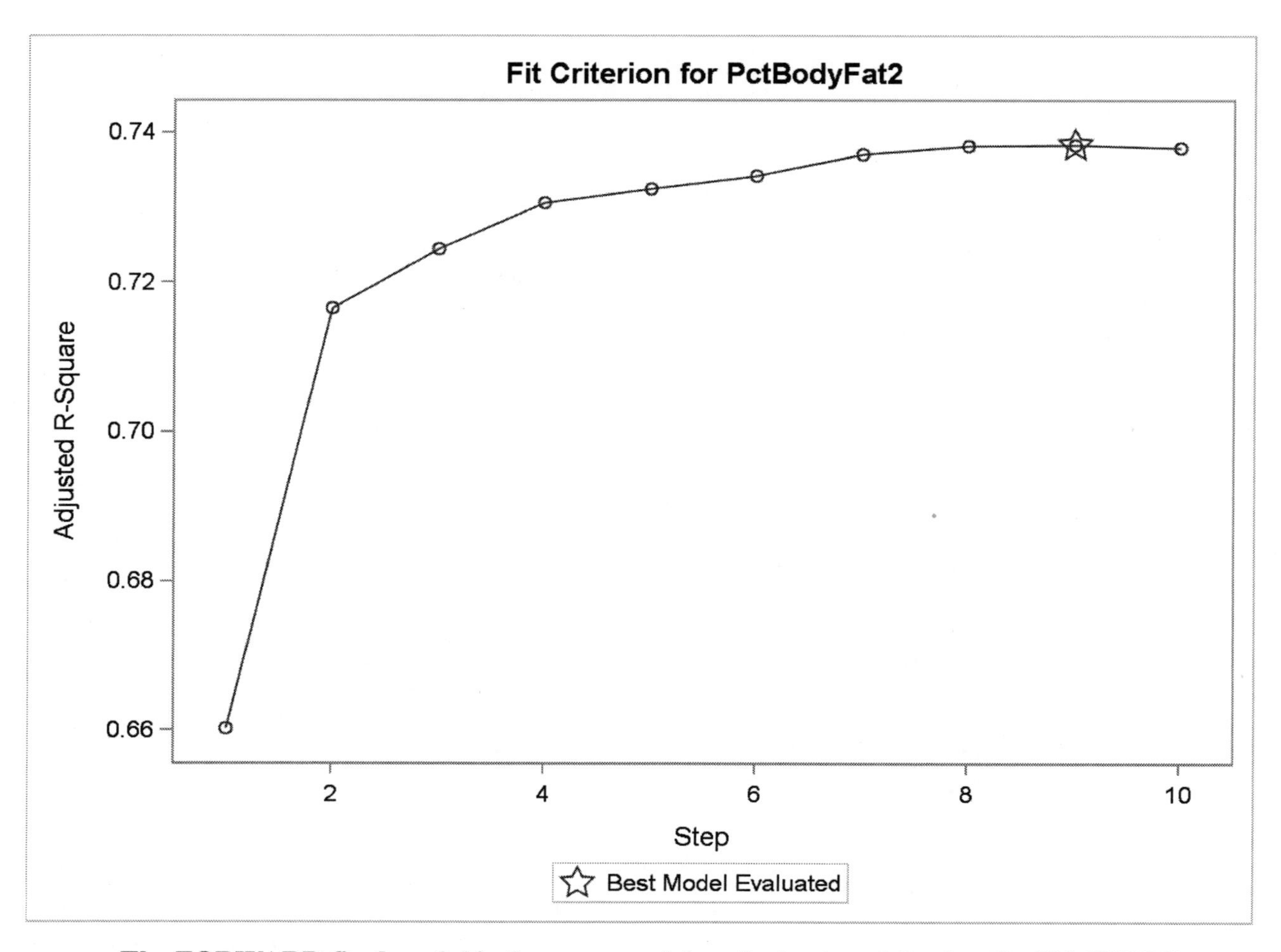


**The FORWARD final model is the same model as the best model using the HOCKING criterion plus Ankle (Abdomen, Weight, Wrist, Forearm, Neck, Age, Thigh, Hip, Biceps, and Ankle). The Criterion plot shows that the increase in adjusted R square is best for the model in Step 9. The increase is rather modest after about Step 4.**

**Backward Elimination: Step 6**

**Variable Hip Removed: R-Square = 0.7445 and C(p) = 5.8653**

| Analysis of Variance | | | | | |
|---|---|---|---|---|---|
| Source | DF | Sum of Squares | Mean Square | F Value | Pr > F |
| Model | 7 | 13087 | 1869.59160 | 101.56 | <.0001 |
| Error | 244 | 4491.84861 | 18.40922 | | |
| Corrected Total | 251 | 17579 | | | |

| Variable | Parameter Estimate | Standard Error | Type II SS | F Value | Pr > F |
|---|---|---|---|---|---|
| Intercept | -33.25799 | 9.00681 | 251.00658 | 13.63 | 0.0003 |
| Age | 0.06817 | 0.03079 | 90.22018 | 4.90 | 0.0278 |
| Weight | -0.11944 | 0.03403 | 226.84802 | 12.32 | 0.0005 |
| Neck | -0.40380 | 0.22062 | 61.67131 | 3.35 | 0.0684 |
| Abdomen | 0.91788 | 0.06950 | 3211.14250 | 174.43 | <.0001 |
| Thigh | 0.22196 | 0.11601 | 67.38659 | 3.66 | 0.0569 |
| Forearm | 0.55314 | 0.18479 | 164.95134 | 8.96 | 0.0030 |
| Wrist | -1.53240 | 0.51041 | 165.93323 | 9.01 | 0.0030 |

**Bounds on condition number: 13.634, 261.24**

**All variables left in the model are significant at the 0.1000 level.**

| Summary of Backward Elimination | | | | | | | |
|---|---|---|---|---|---|---|---|
| Step | Variable Removed | Number Vars In | Partial R-Square | Model R-Square | C(p) | F Value | Pr > F |
| 1 | Knee | 12 | 0.0000 | 0.7486 | 12.0032 | 0.00 | 0.9552 |
| 2 | Chest | 11 | 0.0000 | 0.7485 | 10.0313 | 0.03 | 0.8666 |
| 3 | Height | 10 | 0.0000 | 0.7485 | 8.0682 | 0.04 | 0.8473 |
| 4 | Ankle | 9 | 0.0008 | 0.7477 | 6.7834 | 0.72 | 0.3957 |
| 5 | Biceps | 8 | 0.0012 | 0.7466 | 5.8986 | 1.13 | 0.2888 |
| 6 | Hip | 7 | 0.0021 | 0.7445 | 5.8653 | 1.99 | 0.1594 |

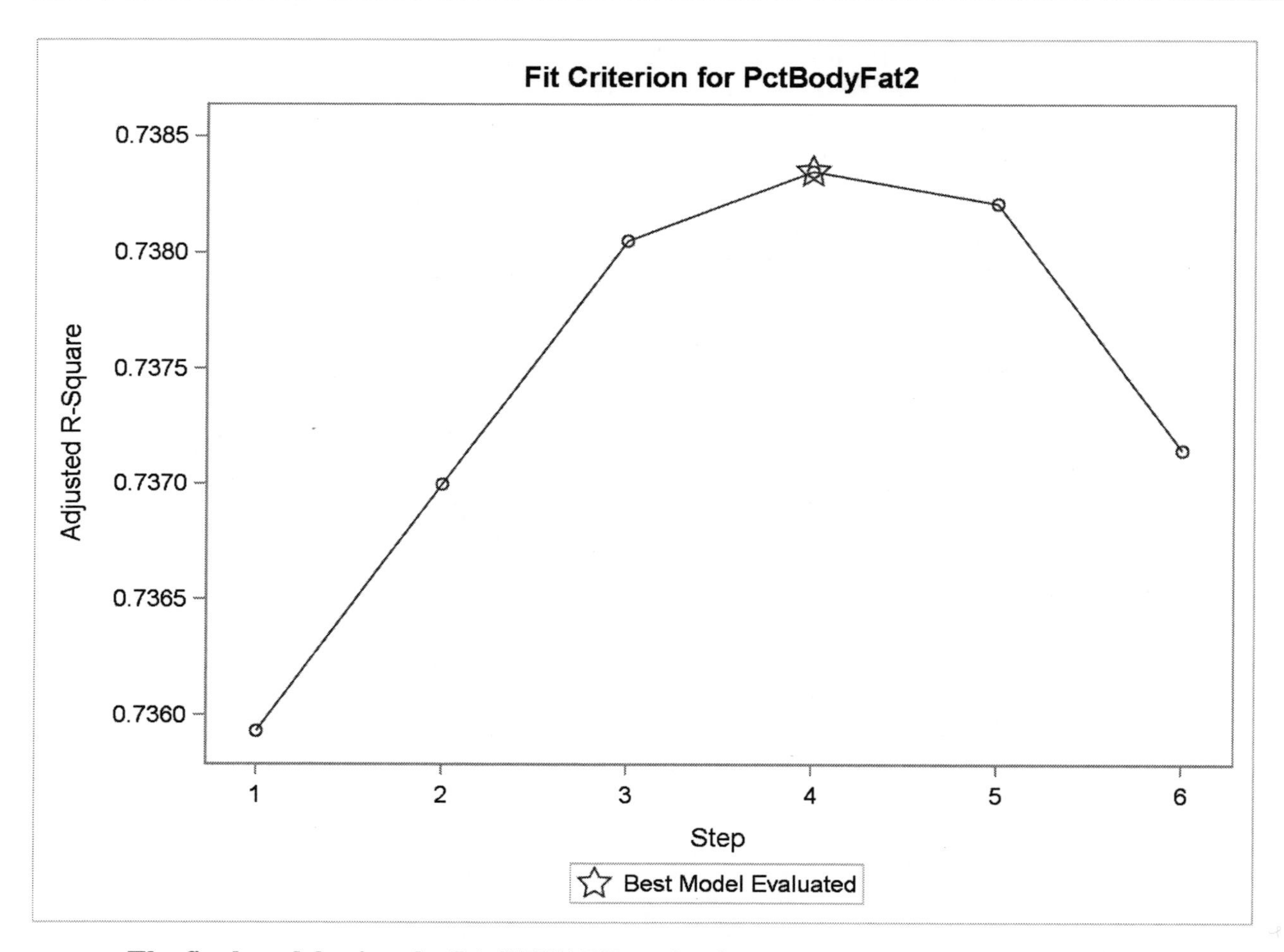


**The final model using the BACKWARD option is the same model as the one suggested by Mallows' criterion (Age, Weight, Neck, Abdomen, Thigh, Forearm, and Wrist).**

**The Criterion plot shows that the adjusted R square was best at Step 4. Be careful not to over-interpret this difference. The Y-axis only ranges from approximately 0.7360 to 0.7385. The differences are all minor.**

**Stepwise Selection: Step 7**

**Variable Thigh Entered: R-Square = 0.7445 and C(p) = 5.8653**

| Analysis of Variance | | | | | |
|---|---|---|---|---|---|
| Source | DF | Sum of Squares | Mean Square | F Value | Pr > F |
| Model | 7 | 13087 | 1869.59160 | 101.56 | <.0001 |
| Error | 244 | 4491.84861 | 18.40922 | | |
| Corrected Total | 251 | 17579 | | | |

| Variable | Parameter Estimate | Standard Error | Type II SS | F Value | Pr > F |
|---|---|---|---|---|---|
| Intercept | -33.25799 | 9.00681 | 251.00658 | 13.63 | 0.0003 |
| Age | 0.06817 | 0.03079 | 90.22018 | 4.90 | 0.0278 |
| Weight | -0.11944 | 0.03403 | 226.84802 | 12.32 | 0.0005 |
| Neck | -0.40380 | 0.22062 | 61.67131 | 3.35 | 0.0684 |
| Abdomen | 0.91788 | 0.06950 | 3211.14250 | 174.43 | <.0001 |
| Thigh | 0.22196 | 0.11601 | 67.38659 | 3.66 | 0.0569 |
| Forearm | 0.55314 | 0.18479 | 164.95134 | 8.96 | 0.0030 |
| Wrist | -1.53240 | 0.51041 | 165.93323 | 9.01 | 0.0030 |

**Bounds on condition number: 13.634, 261.24**

**All variables left in the model are significant at the 0.1500 level.**

**No other variable met the 0.1500 significance level for entry into the model.**

| Summary of Stepwise Selection | | | | | | | | |
|---|---|---|---|---|---|---|---|---|
| Step | Variable Entered | Variable Removed | Number Vars In | Partial R-Square | Model R-Square | C(p) | F Value | Pr > F |
| 1 | Abdomen | | 1 | 0.6617 | 0.6617 | 72.2434 | 488.93 | <.0001 |
| 2 | Weight | | 2 | 0.0571 | 0.7188 | 20.1709 | 50.58 | <.0001 |
| 3 | Wrist | | 3 | 0.0089 | 0.7277 | 13.7069 | 8.15 | 0.0047 |
| 4 | Forearm | | 4 | 0.0073 | 0.7350 | 8.8244 | 6.78 | 0.0098 |
| 5 | Neck | | 5 | 0.0029 | 0.7379 | 8.0748 | 2.73 | 0.1000 |
| 6 | Age | | 6 | 0.0027 | 0.7406 | 7.4937 | 2.58 | 0.1098 |
| 7 | Thigh | | 7 | 0.0038 | 0.7445 | 5.8653 | 3.66 | 0.0569 |

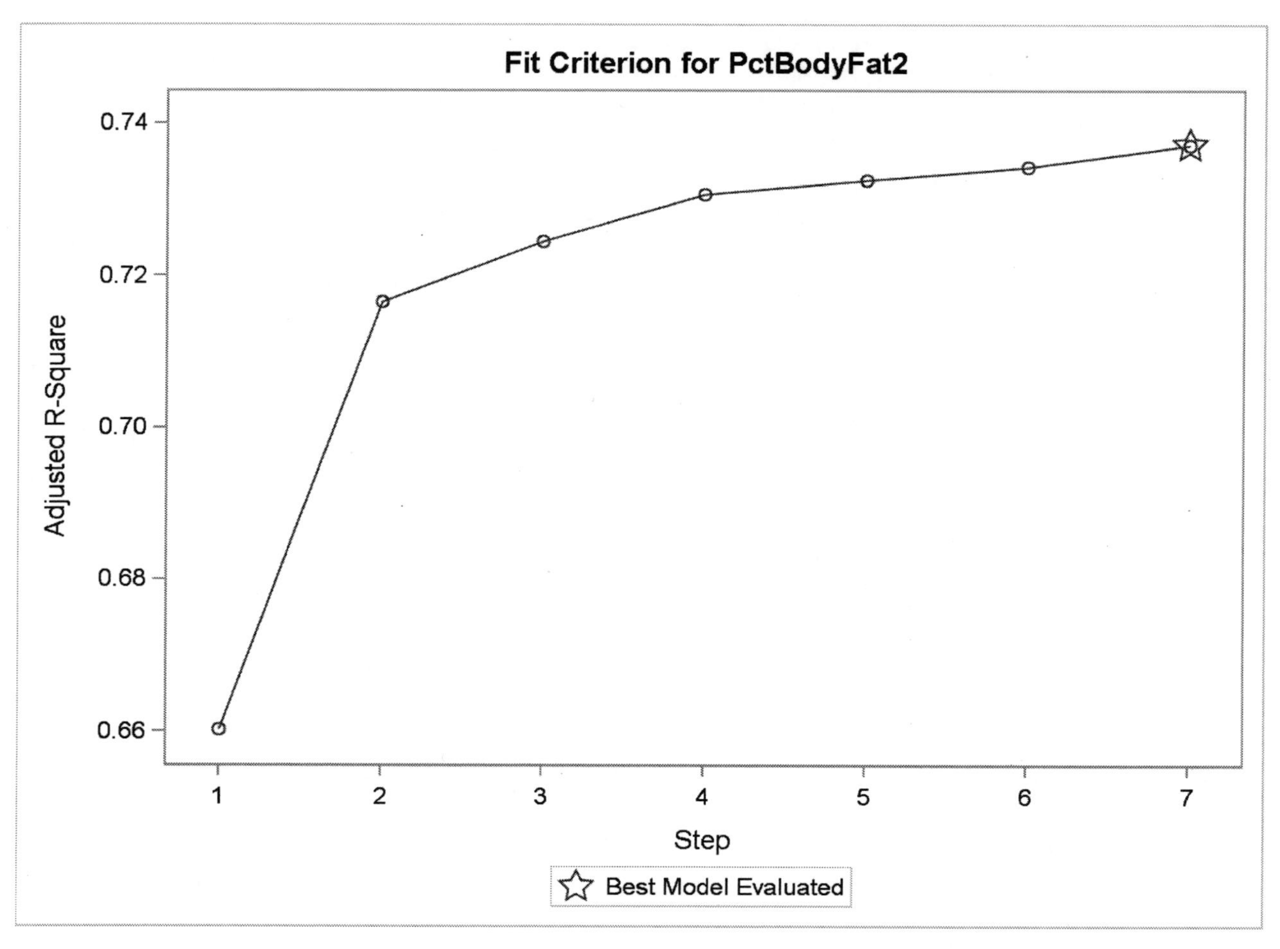


**The model using the STEPWISE option results in the same model as that using the BACKWARD option (Age, Weight, Neck, Abdomen, Thigh, Forearm, and Wrist).**

**c.** How many variables would result from a model using FORWARD selection and a significance level for entry criterion of 0.05, instead of the default SLENTRY of 0.50?

```
/*st103s04.sas*/  /*Part C*/
proc reg data=sasuser.BodyFat2 plots(only)=adjrsq;
   FORWARD05:model PctBodyFat2=Age Weight Height
              Neck Chest Abdomen Hip Thigh
              Knee Ankle Biceps Forearm Wrist
              / selection=forward slentry=0.05;
   title "Using Forward Stepwise with SLENTRY=0.05";
run;
quit;
```

Partial Output

**Forward Selection: Step 4**

**Variable Forearm Entered: R-Square = 0.7350 and C(p) = 8.8244**

| Analysis of Variance | | | | | |
|---|---|---|---|---|---|
| **Source** | **DF** | **Sum of Squares** | **Mean Square** | **F Value** | **Pr > F** |
| **Model** | 4 | 12921 | 3230.18852 | 171.28 | <.0001 |
| **Error** | 247 | 4658.23577 | 18.85925 | | |
| **Corrected Total** | 251 | 17579 | | | |

| Variable | Parameter Estimate | Standard Error | Type II SS | F Value | Pr > F |
|---|---|---|---|---|---|
| **Intercept** | -34.85407 | 7.24500 | 436.46987 | 23.14 | <.0001 |
| **Weight** | -0.13563 | 0.02475 | 566.43299 | 30.03 | <.0001 |
| **Abdomen** | 0.99575 | 0.05607 | 5948.85562 | 315.43 | <.0001 |
| **Forearm** | 0.47293 | 0.18166 | 127.81846 | 6.78 | 0.0098 |
| **Wrist** | -1.50556 | 0.44267 | 218.15750 | 11.57 | 0.0008 |

**Bounds on condition number: 7.0408, 63.886**

**No other variable met the 0.0500 significance level for entry into the model.**

| Summary of Forward Selection | | | | | | | |
|---|---|---|---|---|---|---|---|
| **Step** | **Variable Entered** | **Number Vars In** | **Partial R-Square** | **Model R-Square** | **C(p)** | **F Value** | **Pr > F** |
| 1 | Abdomen | 1 | 0.6617 | 0.6617 | 72.2434 | 488.93 | <.0001 |
| 2 | Weight | 2 | 0.0571 | 0.7188 | 20.1709 | 50.58 | <.0001 |
| 3 | Wrist | 3 | 0.0089 | 0.7277 | 13.7069 | 8.15 | 0.0047 |
| 4 | Forearm | 4 | 0.0073 | 0.7350 | 8.8244 | 6.78 | 0.0098 |

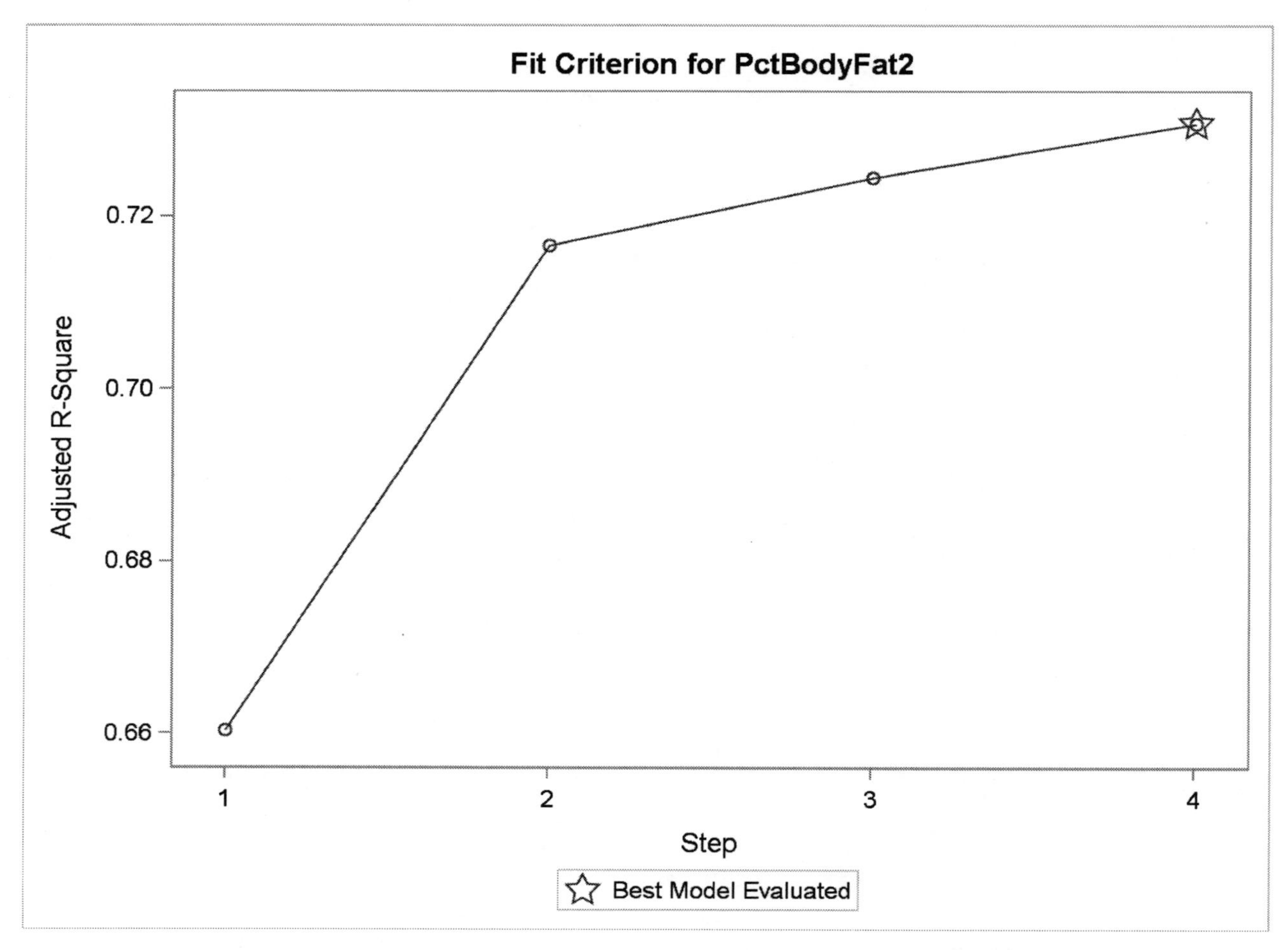


**The model using SLENTRY=0.05 has substantially fewer (4) variables than the default SELECTION=FORWARD final model (Weight, Abdomen, Forearm, and Wrist).**

**The Criterion plot, showing adjusted R square at each step, is also produced.**

## Solutions to Student Activities (Polls/Quizzes)

### 3.01 Multiple Choice Poll – Correct Answer

The correlation between tuition and rate of graduation at U.S. colleges is 0.55. What does this mean?

a. The way to increase graduation rates at your college is to raise tuition.

b. Increasing graduation rates is expensive, causing tuition to rise.

c. Students who are richer tend to graduate more often than poorer students.

(d.) None of the above.

26

### 3.02 Multiple Choice Poll – Correct Answer

Run PROC REG with this MODEL statement: `model y=x1;`. If the parameter estimate (slope) of x1 is 0, then the best guess (predicted value) of y when x1=13 is which of the following?

a. 13

(b.) the mean of y

c. a random number

d. the mean of x1

e. 0

42

## 3.03 Multiple Choice Poll – Correct Answer

What is the predicted value for **PctBodyFat2** when **Weight** is 150?

a. 0.17439
b. 150
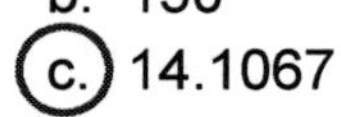
c. 14.1067

51

## 3.04 Multiple Choice Poll – Correct Answer

Which statistic in the ANOVA table is used to test the overall model hypotheses?

a. *F*
b. *t*
c. R square
d. Adjusted R square

61

## 3.05 Multiple Choice Poll – Correct Answer

When **Oxygen_Consumption** is regressed on **RunTime**, **Age**, **Run_Pulse**, and **Maximum_Pulse**, the parameter estimate for **Age** is -2.78. What does this mean?

a. For each year older, the predicted value of oxygen consumption is 2.78 greater.

(b.) For each year older, the predicted value of oxygen consumption is 2.78 lower.

c. For every 2.78 years older, oxygen consumption doubles.

d. For every 2.78 years younger, oxygen consumption doubles.

* Assume that the values of all other predictors are held constant.

74

## 3.06 Multiple Choice Poll – Correct Answer

Which value tends to increase (can never decrease) as you add predictor variables to your regression model?

(a.) R square

b. Adjusted R square

c. Mallows' $C_p$

d. Both a and b

*e.* *F* statistic

f. All of the above

88

## 3.07 Poll – Correct Answer

The STEPWISE, BACKWARD, and FORWARD strategies result in the same final model if the same significance levels are used in all three.

- ❍ True
- (❍) False (circled)

122

# Chapter 4 Regression Diagnostics

# 4.1 Examining Residuals

## Objectives

- Review the assumptions of linear regression.
- Examine the assumptions with scatter plots nd residual plots.

3

## Assumptions for Regression



4

Recall that the model for the linear regression has the form $Y = \beta_0 + \beta_1 X + \varepsilon$. When you perform a regression analysis, several assumptions about the error terms must be met to provide valid tests of hypothesis and confidence intervals. The assumptions are that the error terms

- have a mean of 0 at each value of the predictor variable
- are normally distributed at each value of the predictor variable
- have the same variance at each value of the predictor variable
- are independent.

## 4.01 Poll

Predictor variables are assumed to be normally distributed in linear regression models.

❍ True

❍ False

6

## Scatter Plot of Correct Model

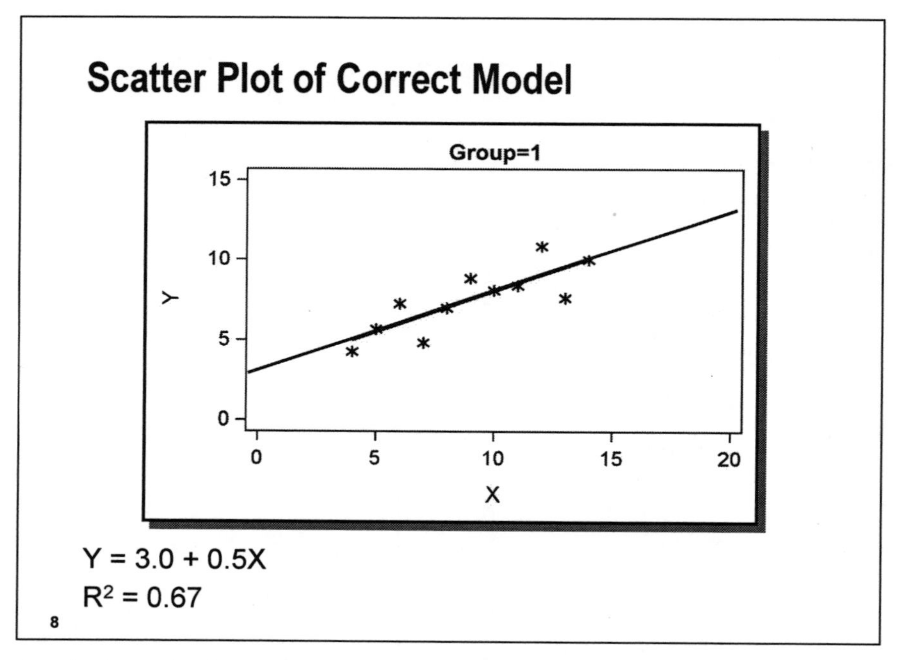


Y = 3.0 + 0.5X

$R^2$ = 0.67

8

To illustrate the importance of plotting data, four examples were developed by Anscombe (1973). In each example, the scatter plot of the data values is different. However, the regression equation and the R-square statistic are the same.

In the first plot, a regression line adequately describes the data.

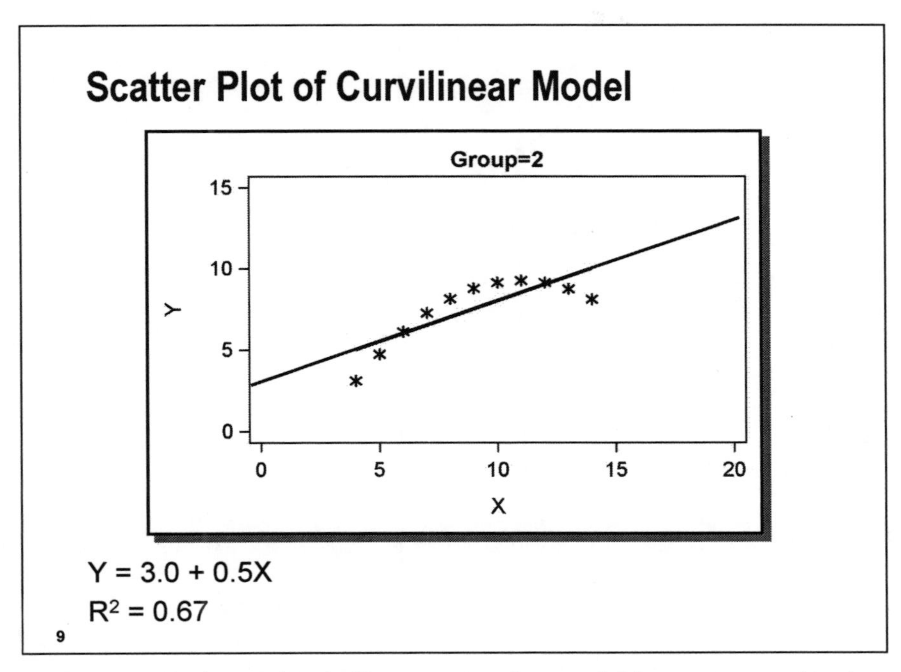


In the second plot, a simple linear regression model is not appropriate because you are fitting a straight line through a curvilinear relationship.

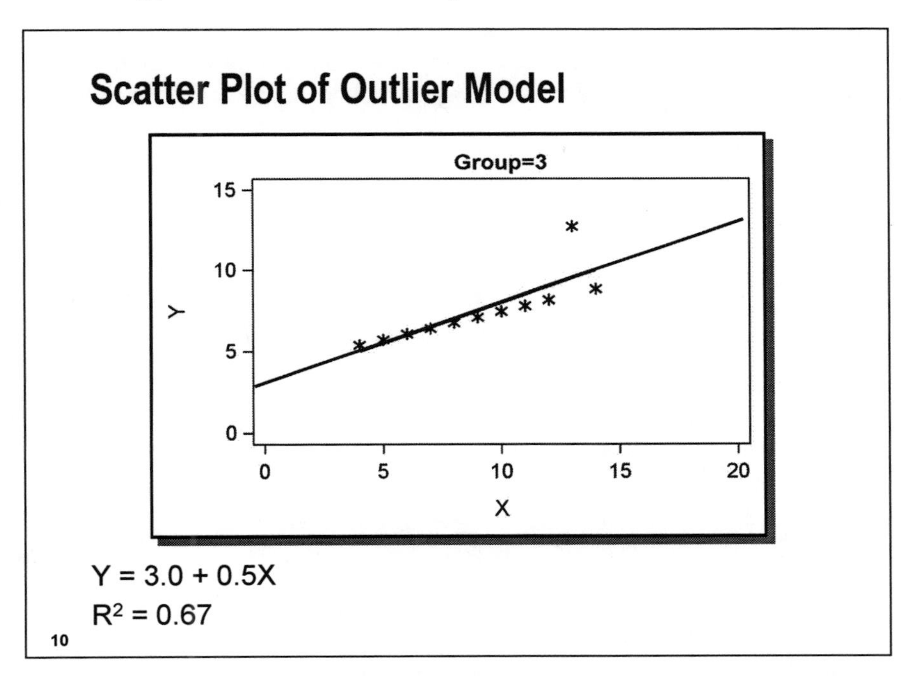


In the third plot, there seems to be an outlying data value that is affecting the regression line. This outlier is an influential data value in that it is substantially changing the fit of the regression line.

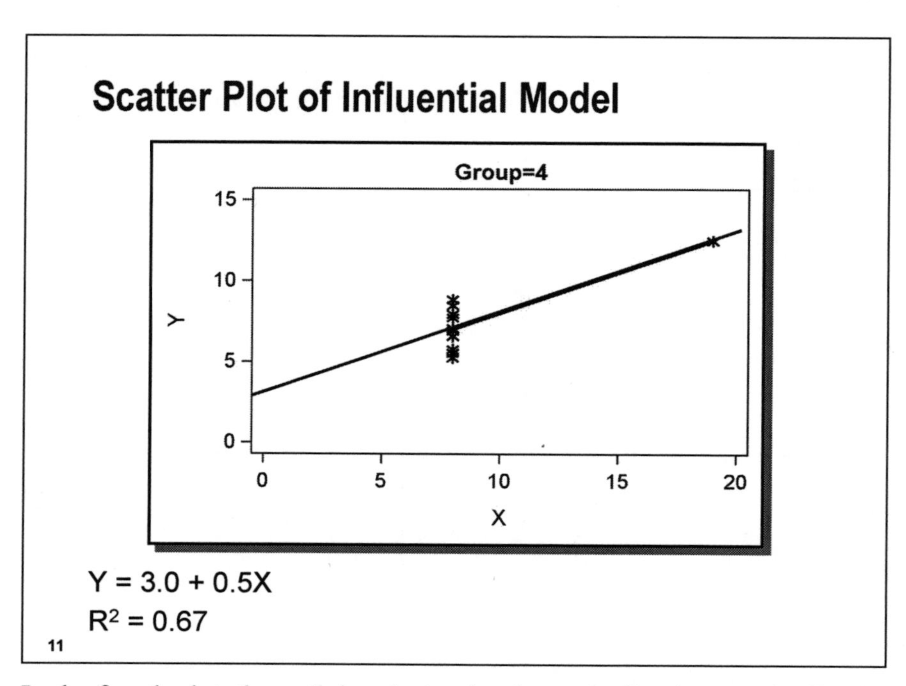


In the fourth plot, the outlying data point dramatically changes the fit of the regression line. In fact, the slope would be undefined without the outlier.

The four plots illustrate that relying on the regression output to describe the relationship between your variables can be misleading. The regression equations and the R-square statistics are the same even though the relationships between the two variables are different. Always produce a scatter plot before you conduct a regression analysis.

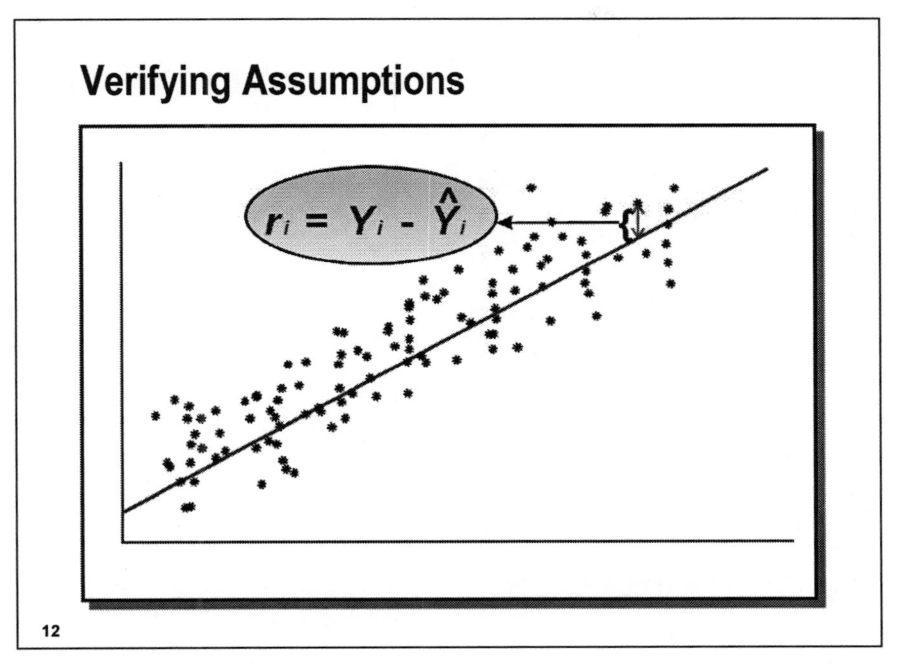


To verify the assumptions for regression, you can use the residual values from the regression analysis as your best estimates of the error terms. Residuals are defined as follows: $r_i = Y_i - \hat{Y}_i$

where $\hat{Y}_i$ is the predicted value for the $i^{th}$ value of the dependent variable.

You can examine two types of plots when verifying assumptions:

- the residuals versus the predicted values
- the residuals versus the values of the independent variables

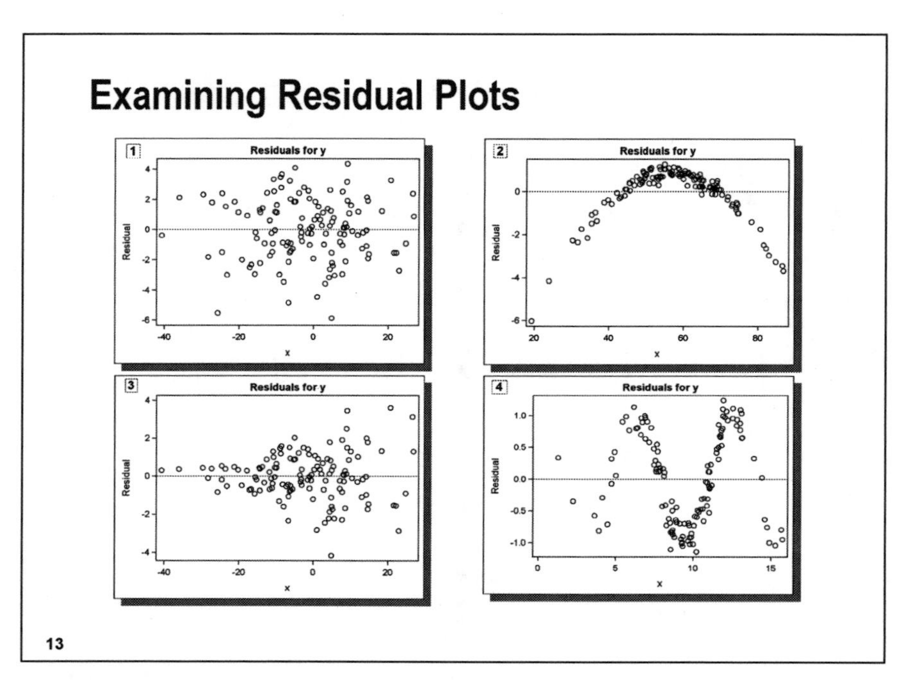


The graphs above are plots of residual values versus predicted values or predictor variable values for four models fit to different sets of data. If model assumptions are valid, then the residual values should be randomly scattered about a reference line at 0. Any patterns or trends in the residuals might indicate problems in the model.

1. The model form appears to be adequate because the residuals are randomly scattered about a reference line at 0 and no patterns appear in the residual values.

2. The model form is incorrect. The plot indicates that the model should take into account curvature in the data. One possible solution is to add a quadratic term as one of the predictor variables.

3. The variance is not constant. As you move from left to right, the variance increases. One possible solution is to transform your dependent variable. Another possible solution is to use either PROC GENMOD or PROC GLIMMIX, and choose a model that does not assume equal variances.

4. The observations are not independent. For this graph, the residuals tend to be followed by residuals with the same sign, which is called *autocorrelation*. This problem can occur when you have observations that were collected over time. A possible solution is to use the AUTOREG procedure in SAS/ETS software.

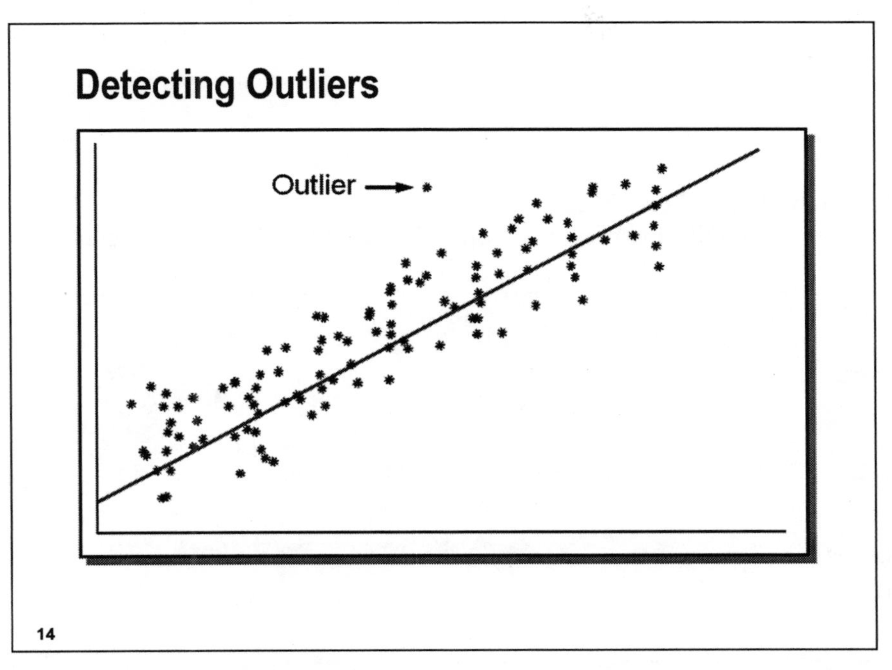


Besides verifying assumptions, it is also important to check for outliers. Observations that are far away from the bulk of your data are outliers. These observations are often data errors or reflect unusual circumstances. In either case, it is good statistical practice to detect these outliers and find out why they occurred.

# Residual Plots

Example: Invoke the REG procedure noticing the default graphics. Then use a PLOTS= option to produce full-sized ODS residual plots and diagnostic plots for the PREDICT model generated in the previous chapter.

```
/*st104d01.sas*/  /*Part A*/
proc reg data=sasuser.fitness;
   PREDICT: model Oxygen_Consumption=
                  RunTime Age Run_Pulse Maximum_pulse;
   id Name;
   title 'PREDICT Model - Plots of Diagnostic Statistics';
run;
quit;
```

The default graphs are shown below.

Partial Output

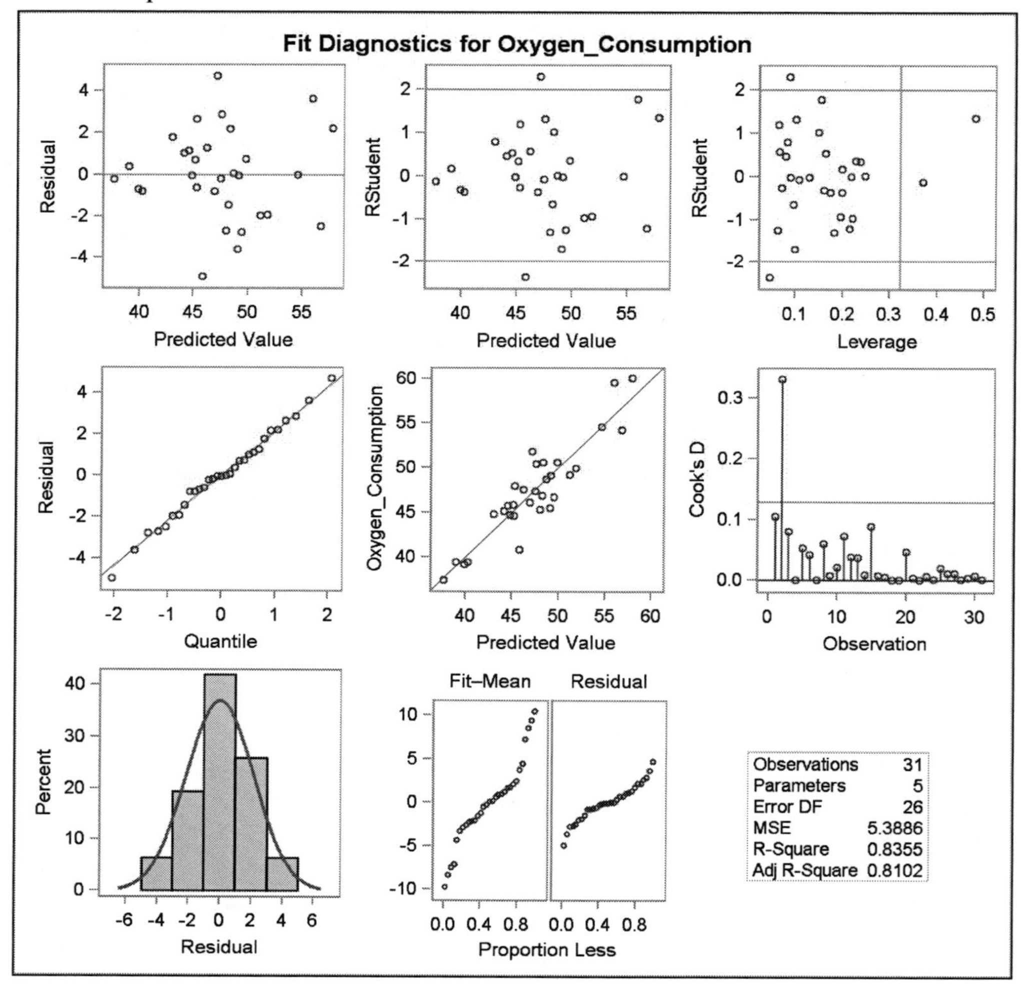

Residual and diagnostic plots are produced in the DIAGNOSTICS panel plot. (Several of these are discussed in more detail later in the chapter.)

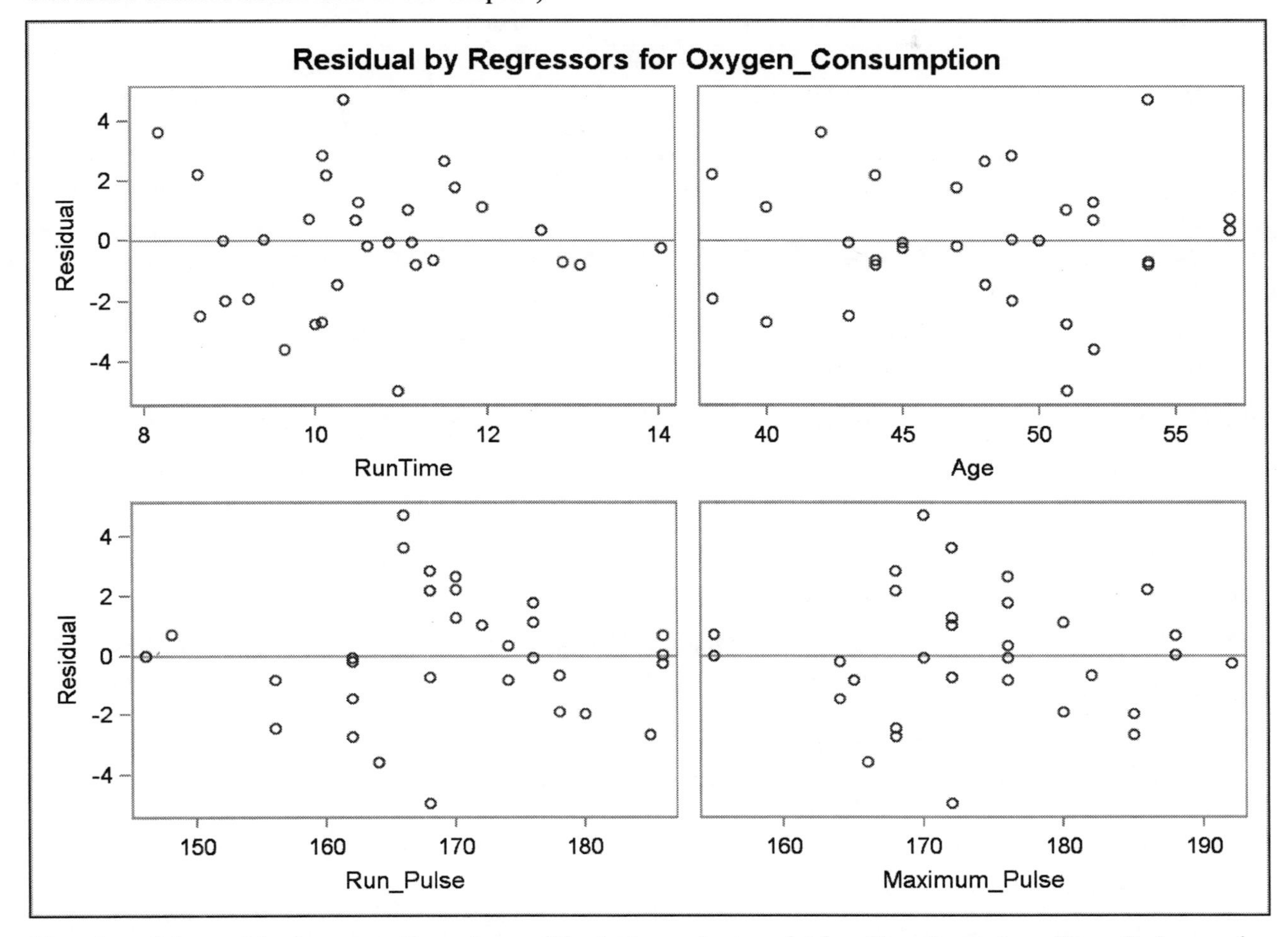


The plot of the residuals versus the values of the independent variables, **Runtime**, **Age**, **Run_Pulse**, and **Maximum_Pulse**, is shown above. They show no obvious trends or patterns in the residuals. Recall that independence of residual errors (no trends) is an assumption for linear regression, as is constant variance across all levels of all predictor variables (and across all levels of the predicted values, which is seen earlier).

When visually inspecting residual plots, the distinction of whether a pattern exists is to the discretion of the viewer. If there is any question to the presence of a pattern, a further investigation for possible causes of potential patterns should be performed.

Hint: If you want to view the DIAGNOSTICS panel plots separately, specify PLOTS=DIAGNOSTICS(UNPACK) in the PROC REG statement. You can also specify each plot individually by name. Individual plots are produced full sized.

```
/*st104d01.sas*/  /*Part B*/
proc reg data=sasuser.fitness
         plots(only)=(QQ RESIDUALBYPREDICTED RESIDUALS);
   PREDICT: model Oxygen_Consumption=
                  RunTime Age Run_Pulse Maximum_pulse;
   id Name;
   title 'PREDICT Model - Plots of Diagnostic Statistics';
run;
quit;
```

Selected REG statement PLOTS= options:

| | |
|---|---|
| PLOTS(ONLY)= | produces only the plots listed and suppresses printing of default plots. |
| QQ | produces residual Quantile-Quantile plot to assess the normality of the residual error. |
| RESIDUALBYPREDICTED | produces residuals by predicted values. |
| RESIDUALS | produces residuals by predictor variable values. |

You can also use the R option in the MODEL statement of PROC REG to obtain residual diagnostics. Output from the R option includes the values of the response variable, the predicted values of the response variable, the standard error of the predicted values, the residuals, the standard error of the residuals, the student residuals, and a summary of the student residuals in tabular rather than graphic form. The R option is used in the next section.

The plots of the residuals by predicted values of **Oxygen_Consumption** and by each of the predictor variables are shown below. The residual values appear to be randomly scattered about the reference line at 0. There are no apparent trends or patterns in the residuals.

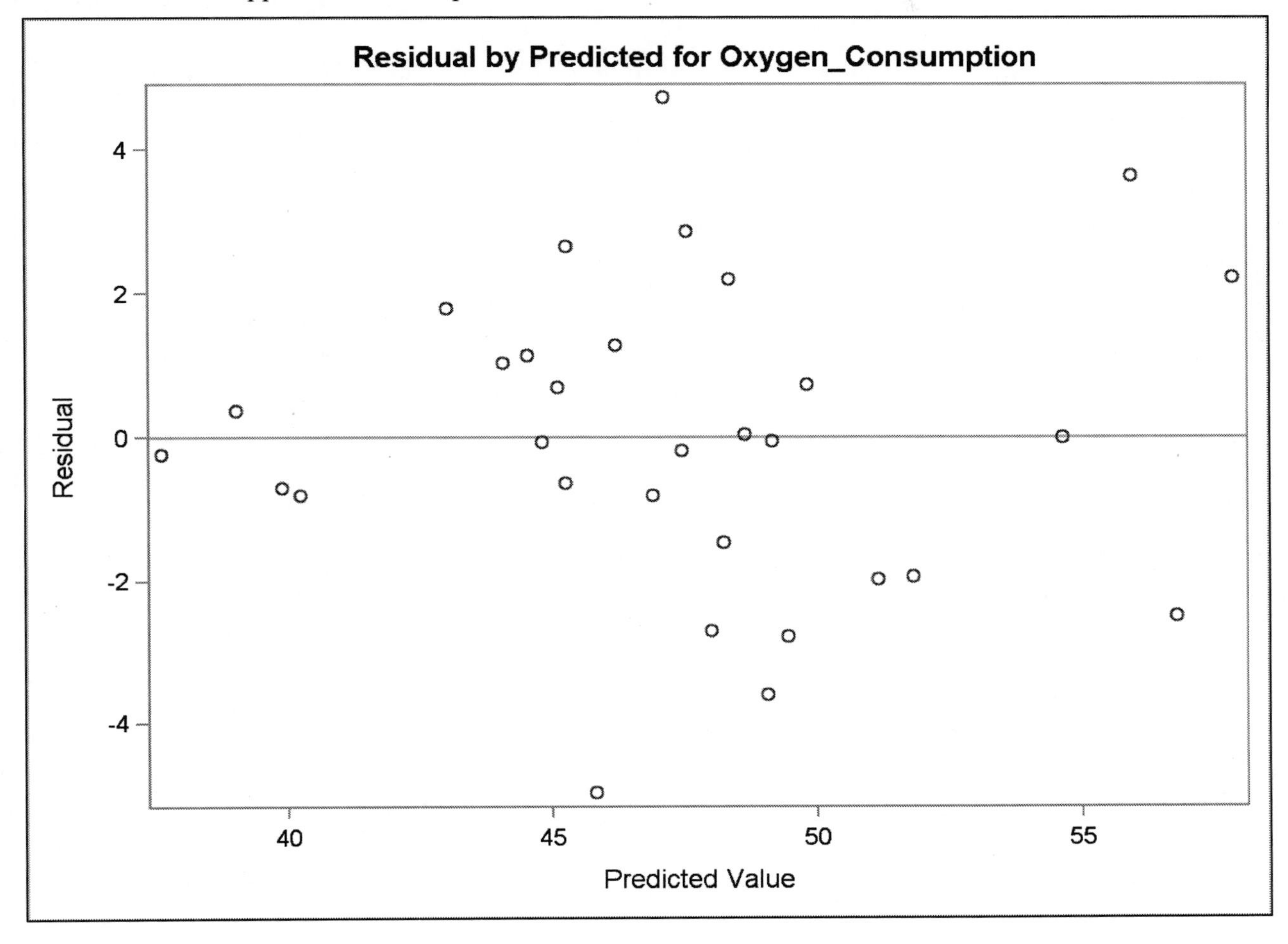

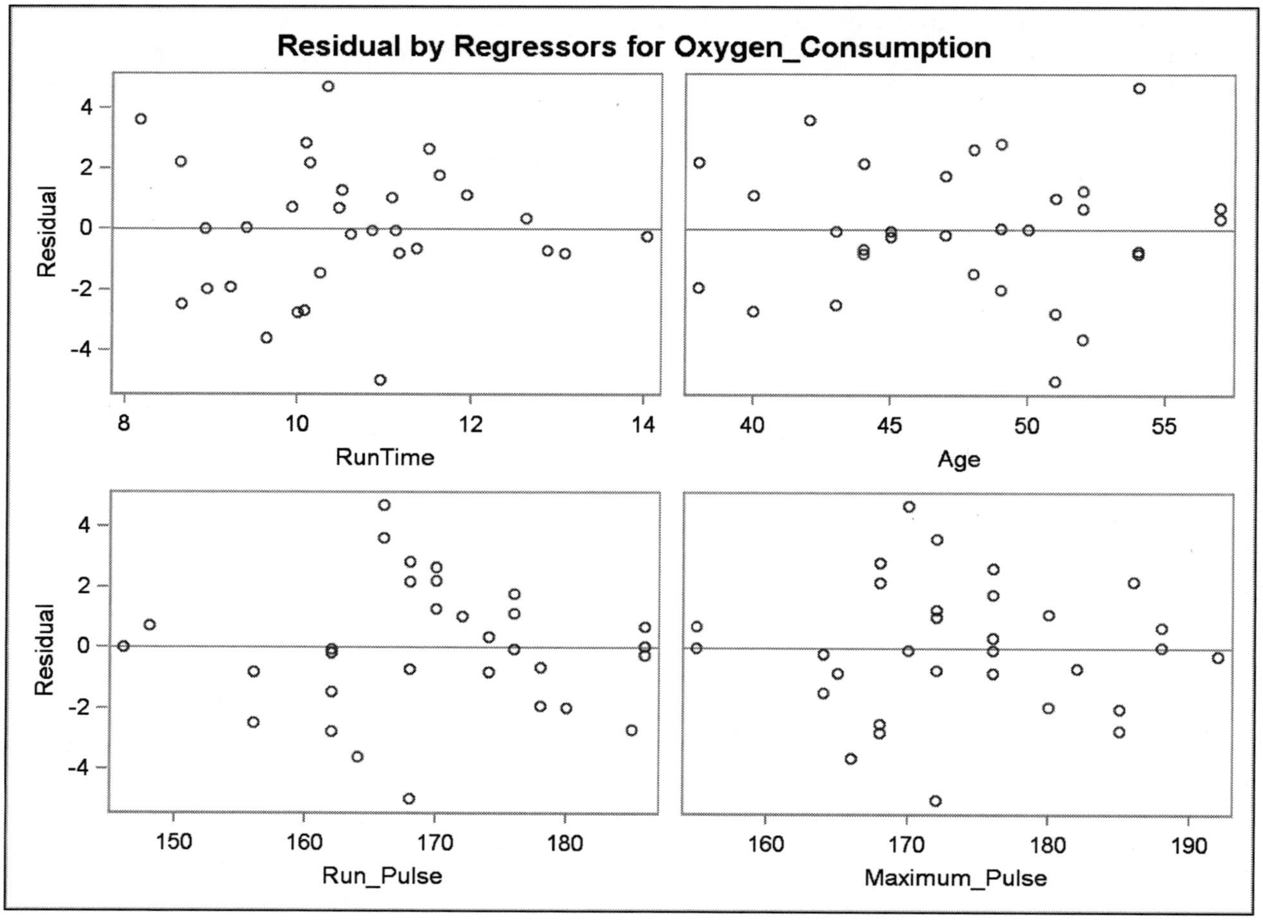
Residual by Regressors for Oxygen_Consumption
Residual
4
2
0
-2
-4
8
10
12
14
RunTime
40
45
50
55
Age
150
160
170
180
Run_Pulse
160
170
180
190
Maximum_Pulse

The plot of the residuals against the normal quantiles is shown below. If the residuals are normally distributed, the plot should appear to be a straight, diagonal line. If the plot deviates substantially from the reference line, then there is evidence against normality.

The plot below shows little deviation from the expected pattern. Thus, you can conclude that the residuals do not significantly violate the normality assumption. If the residuals did violate the normality assumption, then a transformation of the response variable or a different model might be warranted.

PROC REG Output (Continued)

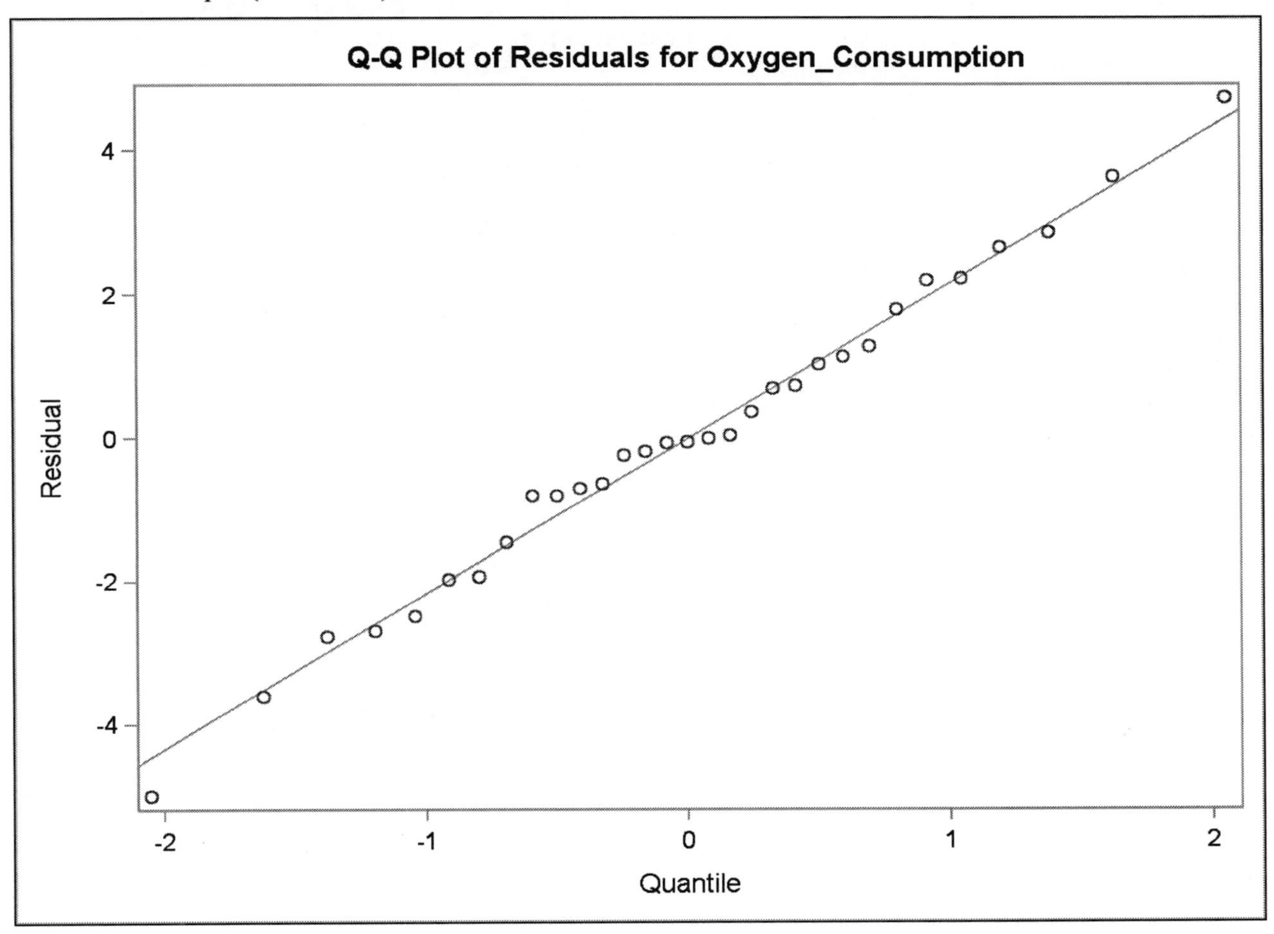


You can use the NORMAL option in the UNIVARIATE procedure to generate a hypothesis test on whether the residuals are normally distributed. This could be necessary if you feel that the plot above shows a violation of the normality assumption. First you must create an output data set with the residuals in PROC REG using an OUTPUT statement (as shown in Chapter 2 with an OUTPUT statement in the GLM procedure) or in the Output Delivery System. Then use that data set as the input data set in PROC UNIVARIATE. Recall that these tests of normality are extremely sensitive to sample sizes.

## Exercises

1. **Examining Residuals**

   Assess the model obtained from the final forward stepwise selection of predictors for the **sasuser.BodyFat2** data set. Run a regression of **PctBodyFat2** on **Abdomen**, **Weight**, **Wrist**, and **Forearm**. Create plots of the residuals by the four regressors and by the predicted values and a normal Quantile-Quantile plot.

   **a.** Do the residual plots indicate any problems with the constant variance assumption?

   **b.** Are there any outliers indicated by the evidence in any of the residual plots?

   **c.** Does the Quantile-Quantile plot indicate any problems with the normality assumption?

# 4.2 Influential Observations

## Objectives

- Use statistics to identify potentially influential observations.

19

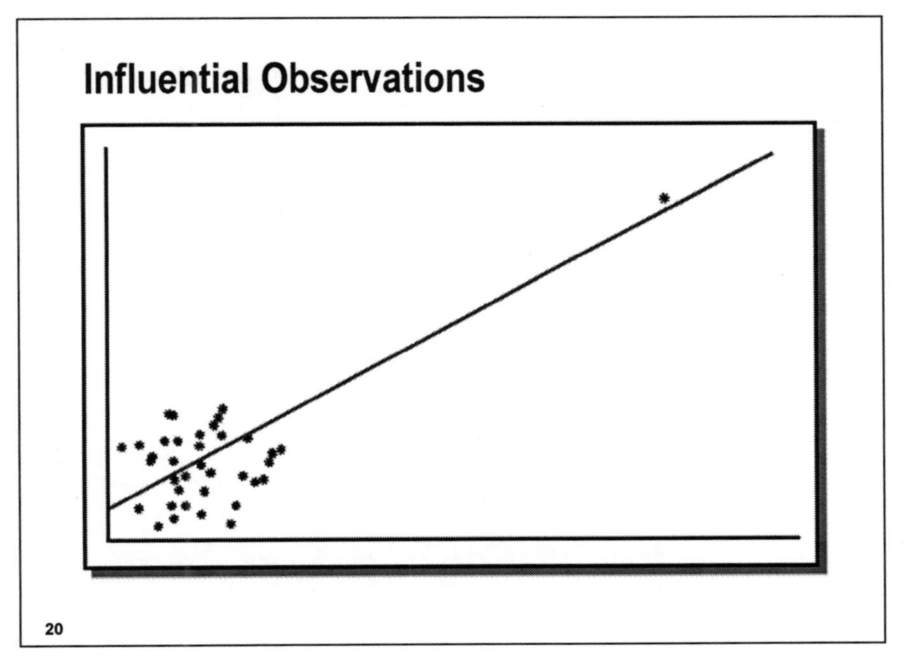


Recall in the previous section that you saw examples of data sets where the simple linear regression model fits were essentially the same. However, plotting the data revealed that the model fits were different.

One of the examples showed a highly influential observation similar to the example above.

Identifying influential observations in multiple linear regression is more complex because you have more predictors to consider.

The REG procedure has options to calculate statistics to identify influential observations.

## Diagnostic Statistics

Statistics that help identify influential observations are the following:

- Studentized residuals
- RSTUDENT residuals
- Cook's *D*
- DFFITS
- DFBETAS

21

The R option in the MODEL statement prints the studentized residuals and the Cook's D, as well as others discussed previously. The INFLUENCE option in the MODEL statement prints the RSTUDENT, DFFITS, and DFBETAS, as well as several others.

## Studentized (Standardized) Residuals

Studentized residuals (SR) are obtained by dividing the residuals by their standard errors.

Suggested cutoffs are as follows:

- |SR| > 2 for data sets with a relatively small number of observations
- |SR| > 3 for data sets with a relatively large number of observations

22

One way to check for outliers is to use the studentized residuals. These are calculated by dividing the residual values by their standard errors. For a model that fits the data well and has no outliers, most of the studentized residuals should be close to 0. In general, studentized residuals that have an absolute value less than 2.0 could easily occur by chance. Studentized residuals that are between an absolute value of 2.0 to 3.0 occur infrequently and could be outliers. Studentized residuals that are larger than an absolute value of 3.0 occur rarely by chance alone and should be investigated.

Studentized residuals are often referred to as "standardized residuals." The cutoff values are chosen based on the tail probabilities from the normal probability distribution that you learned about in Chapter 1.

## 4.02 Multiple Choice Poll

Given the properties of the standard normal distribution, you would expect about 95% of the studentized residuals to be between which two values?

a. -3 and 3
b. -2 and 2
c. -1 and 1
d. 0 and 1
e. 0 and 2
f. 0 and 3

24

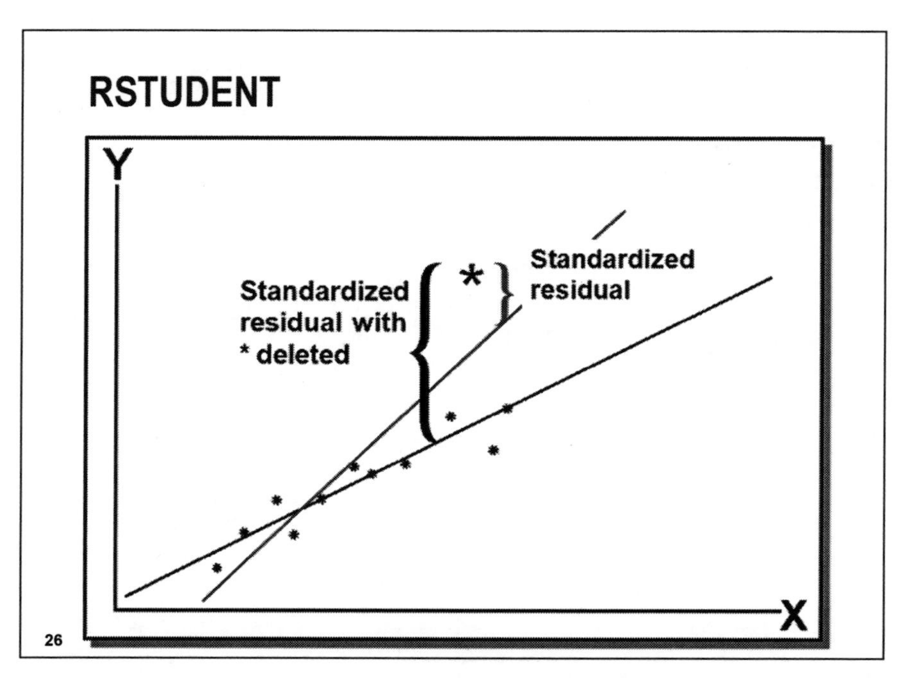


Studentized residuals are the ordinary residuals divided by their standard errors. The RSTUDENT residuals are similar to the studentized residuals except that they are calculated after deleting the $i^{th}$ observation. In other words, the RSTUDENT residual is the difference between the observed Y and the predicted value of Y excluding this observation from the regression.

There is a difference between the labels used in SAS and in SAS Enterprise Guide.

| SAS | | SAS Enterprise Guide |
|---|---|---|
| Studentized residuals | ⇨ | Standardized residuals |
| RSTUDENT residuals (studentized residual with the $i^{th}$ observation removed) | ⇨ | Studentized residuals |

## Cook's D Statistic

Cook's D statistic is a measure of the simultaneous change in the parameter estimates when the $i^{th}$ observation is deleted from the analysis.

A suggested cutpoint for influence is shown below:

$$\text{Cook's } D_i > \frac{4}{n}$$

27

To detect influential observations, you can use Cook's *D* statistic. This statistic measures the change in the parameter estimates that results from deleting each observation.

$$\text{Cook's } D_i = \left(\frac{1}{ps^2}\right)\left(\mathbf{b} - \mathbf{b}_{(i)}\right)' \left(\mathbf{X'X}\right)\left(\mathbf{b} - \mathbf{b}_{(i)}\right)$$

| | |
|---|---|
| $p$ | the number of regression parameters |
| $s^2$ | mean squared error of the regression model |
| **b** | the vector of parameter estimates |
| $\mathbf{b}_{(i)}$ | the vector of parameter estimates obtained after deleting the $i^{th}$ observation |
| **X'X** | corrected sum of squares and cross-products matrix |

Identify observations above the cutoff and investigate the reasons that they occurred.

## DFFITS

$DFFITS_i$ measures the impact that the $i^{th}$ observation has on the predicted value.

A suggested cutoff for influence is shown below:

$$|\,\mathbf{DFFITS_i}\,| > 2\sqrt{\frac{p}{n}}$$

28

$$\text{DFFITS}_i = \frac{\hat{Y}_i - \hat{Y}_{(i)}}{s(\hat{Y}_i)}$$

$\hat{Y}_i$ the $i^{th}$ predicted value

$\hat{Y}_{(i)}$ the $i^{th}$ predicted value when the $i^{th}$ observation is deleted

$s(\hat{Y}_i)$ the standard error of the $i^{th}$ predicted value

Belsey, Kuh, and Welsch (1980) provide this suggested cutoff: $|\text{DFFITS}_i| > 2\sqrt{\frac{p}{n}}$, where $p$ is the number of terms in the current model, including the intercept, and $n$ is the sample size.

## DFBETAS

- Measure of change in the $j^{th}$ parameter estimate with deletion of the $i^{th}$ observation
- One DFBETA per parameter per observation
- Helpful in explaining on which parameter coefficient the influence most lies

A suggested cutoff for influence is shown below:

$$|\mathbf{DFBETA}_{ij}| > 2\sqrt{\frac{1}{n}}$$

29

DFBETAS is abbreviated from Difference in Betas. They contain the standardized difference for each individual coefficient estimate resulting from the omission of the $i^{th}$ observation. They are identified by column headings with the name of the corresponding predictor in the Output window and also by plots, if requested in the PROC REG statement. Because there are many DFBETAS, it might be useful to examine only those corresponding to a large Cook's *D*. Large DFBETAS indicate which predictor(s) might be the cause of the influence.

$$\text{DFBETA}_{ij} = \frac{b_j - b_{(i)j}}{s(b_j)}$$

$b_j$ $j^{th}$ regression parameter estimate

$b_{(i)j}$ $j^{th}$ regression parameter estimate with observation i deleted

$s_{(bj)}$ standard error of $b_j$

Belsley, Kuh, and Welsch (1980) recommend 2 as a general cutoff value to indicate influential observations and $2\sqrt{\frac{1}{n}}$ as a size-adjusted cutoff.

## Looking for Influential Observations

Example: Generate the RStudent, DFFITS, DFBETAS, and Cook's D influence statistics and plots for the PREDICT model. Save the statistics to an output data set and create a data set with only observations that exceed the suggested cutoffs of the influence statistics.

```
/*st104d02.sas*/  /*Part A*/
ods output RSTUDENTBYPREDICTED=Rstud
           COOKSDPLOT=Cook
           DFFITSPLOT=Dffits
           DFBETASPANEL=Dfbs;

proc reg data=sasuser.fitness
         plots(only label)=
              (RSTUDENTBYPREDICTED
               COOKSD
               DFFITS
               DFBETAS);
   PREDICT: model Oxygen_Consumption=
                  RunTime Age Run_Pulse Maximum_Pulse;
   id Name;
   title 'PREDICT Model - Plots of Diagnostic Statistics';
run;

quit;
```

The ID statement makes the **Name** variable available for labeling of observations in plots.

Selected REG procedure PLOTS= options:

| | |
|---|---|
| PLOTS(LABEL)= | labels extreme observations in the plot with either the observation number or the value of an ID variable, if there is an ID statement. |
| RSTUDENTBYPREDICTED | RStudent by predicted values. |
| COOKSD | Cook's *D* plot. |
| DFFITS | DFFITS plot. |
| DFBETAS | DFBETAS plots. |

The ODS OUTPUT statement along with the PLOTS= option outputs the data from the influence plots into separate data sets.

PROC REG Output

| | |
|---|---|
| Number of Observations Read | 31 |
| Number of Observations Used | 31 |

| Analysis of Variance | | | | | |
|---|---|---|---|---|---|
| Source | DF | Sum of Squares | Mean Square | F Value | Pr > F |
| Model | 4 | 711.45087 | 177.86272 | 33.01 | <.0001 |
| Error | 26 | 140.10368 | 5.38860 | | |
| Corrected Total | 30 | 851.55455 | | | |

| | | | |
|---|---|---|---|
| Root MSE | 2.32134 | R-Square | 0.8355 |
| Dependent Mean | 47.37581 | Adj R-Sq | 0.8102 |
| Coeff Var | 4.89984 | | |

| Parameter Estimates | | | | | |
|---|---|---|---|---|---|
| Variable | DF | Parameter Estimate | Standard Error | t Value | Pr > \|t\| |
| Intercept | 1 | 97.16952 | 11.65703 | 8.34 | <.0001 |
| RunTime | 1 | -2.77576 | 0.34159 | -8.13 | <.0001 |
| Age | 1 | -0.18903 | 0.09439 | -2.00 | 0.0557 |
| Run_Pulse | 1 | -0.34568 | 0.11820 | -2.92 | 0.0071 |
| Maximum_Pulse | 1 | 0.27188 | 0.13438 | 2.02 | 0.0534 |

Partial PROC REG Output (Continued)

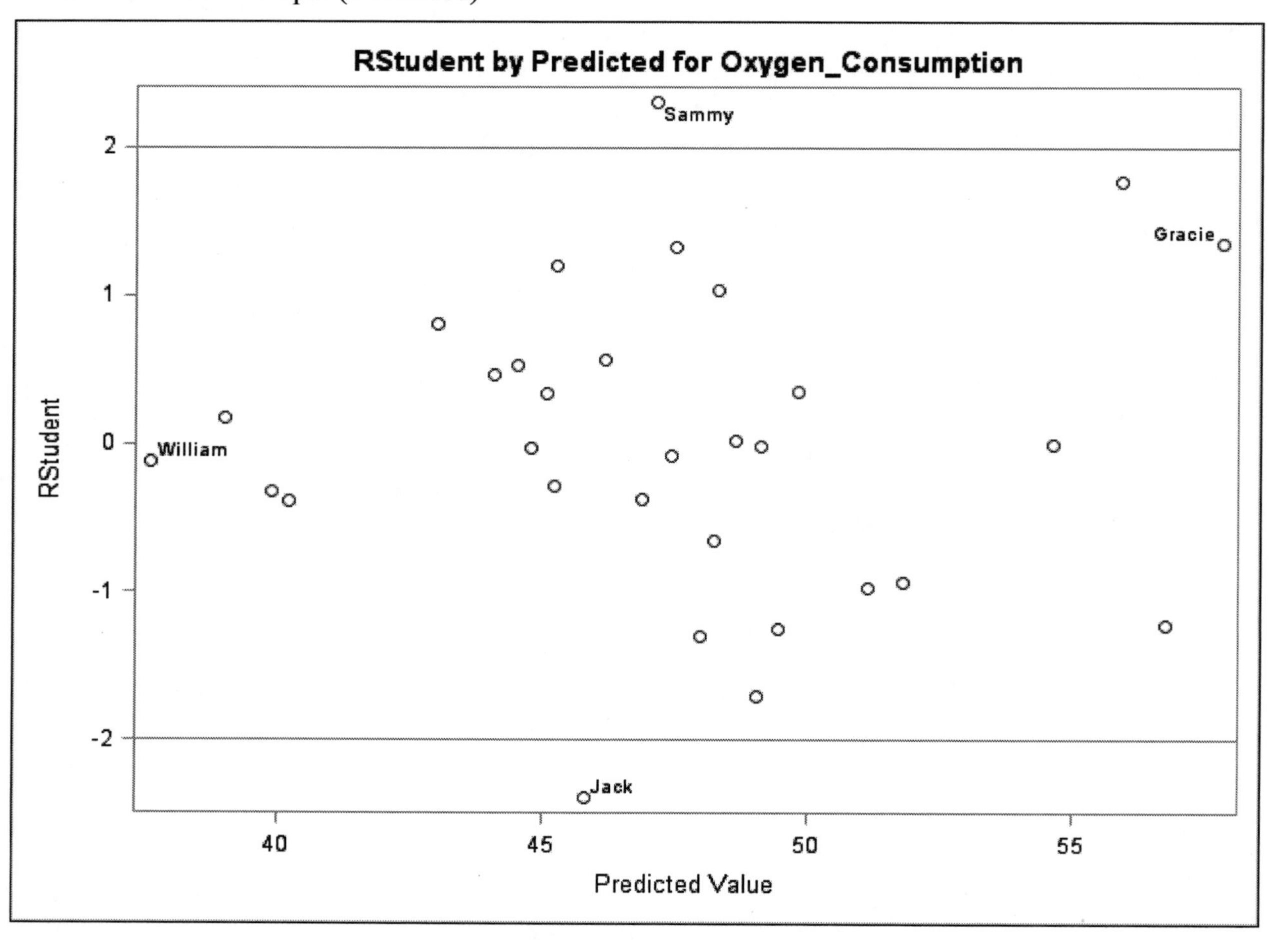


The RStudent plot shows two observations beyond two standard errors from the mean of 0. Those are identified as Sammy and Jack. Because you expect 5% of values to be beyond two standard errors from the mean (remember that RStudent residuals are assumed to be normally distributed), the fact that you have two that far outside the primary cluster gives no cause for concern. (Five percent of 31 is 1.55 expected observations.)

William and Gracie are also labeled in this plot because they have the most extreme predicted values. (Their leverage values are extreme.)

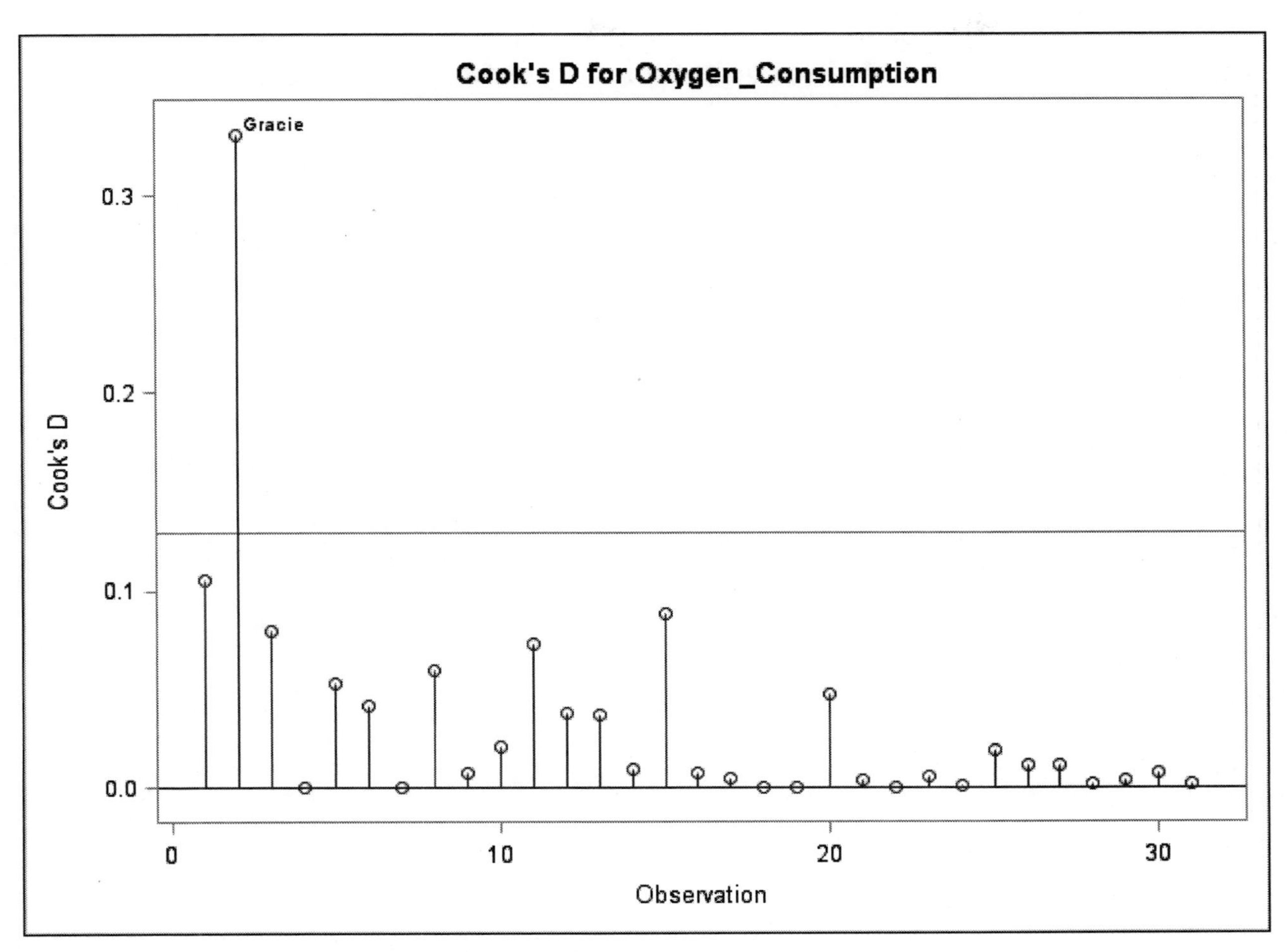


The Cook's *D* plot shows Gracie to be an influential point.

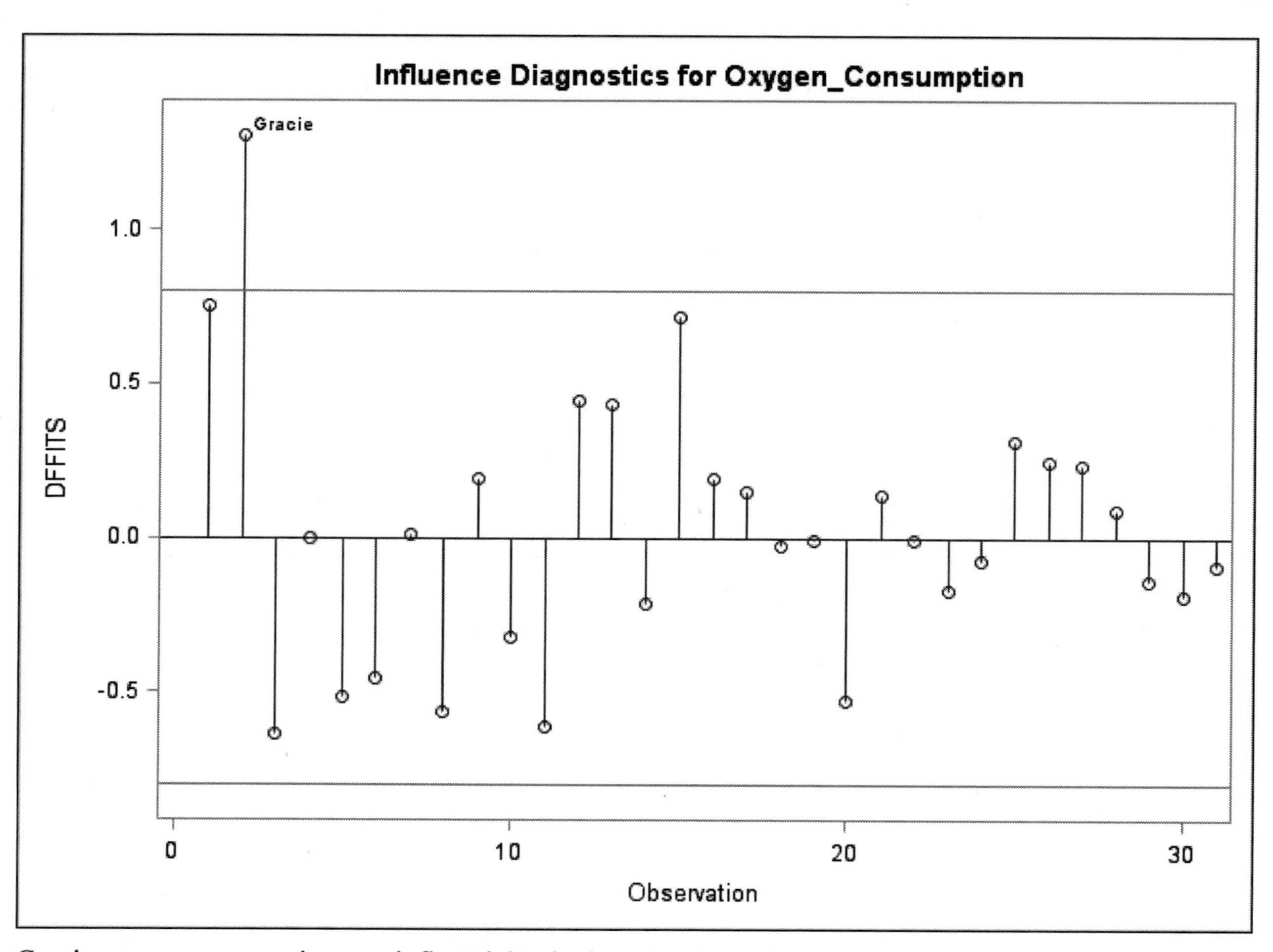


Gracie appears once again as an influential point based on her value on DFFITS.

At this point, it might be helpful to see which parameters Gracie might influence most. DFBETAS provides that information.

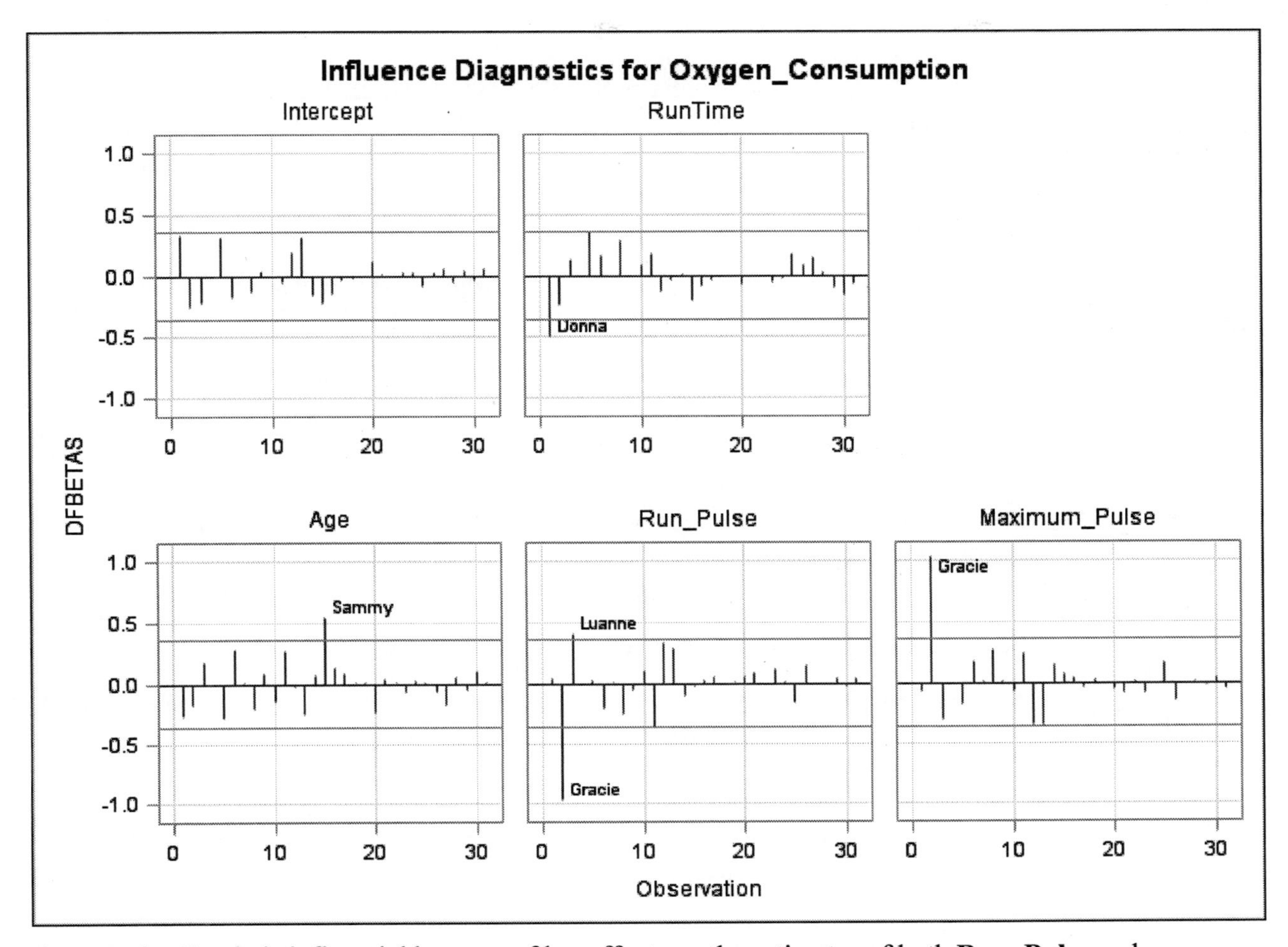


Apparently, Gracie is influential because of her effects on the estimates of both **Run_Pulse** and **Maximum_Pulse**.

Detection of outliers with plots is convenient for relatively small data sets, but for large data sets it can be very difficult to discern one observation from another. One method for extracting only the influential observations from a data set is to output the ODS plots data into data sets and then subset the influential observations.

The next part of the program prints the influential observations in the influence diagnostic data sets that were produced using ODS OUTPUT.

```
/*st104d02.sas*/  /*Part B*/
proc print data=Rstud;
run;
```

Partial Output

| Obs | Model | Dependent | RStudent | PredictedValue | outLevLabel | Observation | id1 |
|---|---|---|---|---|---|---|---|
| 1 | PREDICT | Oxygen_Consumption | 1.77178 | 55.9333 | | 1 | Donna |
| 2 | PREDICT | Oxygen_Consumption | 1.35265 | 57.8362 | Gracie | 2 | Gracie |
| 3 | PREDICT | Oxygen_Consumption | -1.21790 | 56.7812 | | 3 | Luanne |
| 4 | PREDICT | Oxygen_Consumption | -0.00041 | 54.6309 | | 4 | Mimi |

The variable **outLevLabel** is nonmissing only for an observation whose leverage was deemed high.

```
proc print data=Cook;
run;
```

Partial Output

| Obs | Model | Dependent | CooksD | Observation | CooksDLabel | id1 |
|---|---|---|---|---|---|---|
| 1 | PREDICT | Oxygen_Consumption | 0.10546 | 1 | | Donna |
| 2 | PREDICT | Oxygen_Consumption | 0.33051 | 2 | Gracie | Gracie |
| 3 | PREDICT | Oxygen_Consumption | 0.07999 | 3 | | Luanne |
| 4 | PREDICT | Oxygen_Consumption | 0.00000 | 4 | | Mimi |

The variable **CooksDLabel** identifies observations that are deemed influential due to high Cook's *D* values.

```
proc print data=Dffits;
run;
```

Partial Output

| Obs | Model | Dependent | Observation | DFFITS | id1 | DFFITSOUT |
|---|---|---|---|---|---|---|
| 1 | PREDICT | Oxygen_Consumption | 1 | 0.75543 | Donna | . |
| 2 | PREDICT | Oxygen_Consumption | 2 | . | Gracie | 1.30587 |
| 3 | PREDICT | Oxygen_Consumption | 3 | -0.63826 | Luanne | . |
| 4 | PREDICT | Oxygen_Consumption | 4 | -0.00022 | Mimi | . |

The variable **DFFITSOUT** identifies observations that are deemed influential due to high DFFITS values.

```
proc print data=Dfbs;
run;
```

Partial Output

| Obs | Model | Dependent | Observation | _DFBETAS1 | id1 | _DFBETASOUT1 | _DFBETAS2 |
|---|---|---|---|---|---|---|---|
| 1 | PREDICT | Oxygen_Consumption | 1 | 0.32241 | Donna | . | . |
| 2 | PREDICT | Oxygen_Consumption | 2 | -0.25010 | Gracie | . | -0.22777 |
| 3 | PREDICT | Oxygen_Consumption | 3 | -0.21273 | Luanne | . | 0.12802 |
| 4 | PREDICT | Oxygen_Consumption | 4 | -0.00012 | Mimi | . | 0.00004 |

The variables **_DFBETASOUT1** through **_DFBETASOUT5** identify the observations whose DFBETA values exceed the threshold for influence. **_DFBETASOUT1** represents the value for the intercept. The other four variables show influential outliers on each of the predictor variables in the MODEL statement in PROC REG.

✎ Use the optional DATA step to merge the results of the previous four data sets.

The next DATA step merges the four data sets containing the influence data and outputs only the observations that exceeded the respective influence cutoff levels.

The results are then displayed.

```
data influential;
/* Merge data sets from above. */
   merge Rstud
         Cook
         Dffits
         Dfbs;
   by observation;

/* Flag observations that have exceeded at least one cutpoint; */
   if (RStudent>3) or (Cooksdlabel ne ' ') or Dffitsout then flag=1;
   array dfbetas{*} _dfbetasout: ;
   do i=2 to dim(dfbetas);
      if dfbetas{i} then flag=1;
   end;

/* Set to missing values of influence statistics for those */
/* who have not exceeded cutpoints; */
   if RStudent<=3 then RStudent=.;
   if Cooksdlabel eq ' ' then CooksD=.;

/* Subset only observations that have been flagged. */
   if flag=1;
   drop i flag;
run;

proc print data=influential;
   id observation ID1;
   var RStudent CooksD Dffitsout _dfbetasout:;
run;
```

PROC PRINT Output

| Observation | id1 | RStudent | CooksD | DFFITSOUT | _DFBETASOUT1 | _DFBETASOUT2 |
|---|---|---|---|---|---|---|
| 1 | Donna | . | . | . | . | -0.48974 |
| 2 | Gracie | . | 0.33051 | 1.30587 | . | . |
| 3 | Luanne | . | . | . | . | . |
| 15 | Sammy | . | . | . | . | . |

| Observation | id1 | _DFBETASOUT3 | _DFBETASOUT4 | _DFBETASOUT5 |
|---|---|---|---|---|
| 1 | Donna | . | . | . |
| 2 | Gracie | . | -0.96166 | 1.02693 |
| 3 | Luanne | . | 0.40836 | . |
| 15 | Sammy | 0.54012 | . | . |

This table is a summary of the plots displayed previously. Gracie appears again as the sole influential outlier based on Cook's *D* and DFFITS. No observation had an RStudent value greater than 3. Donna, Luanne, and Sammy have some influence on one parameter value each.

## How to Handle Influential Observations

1. Recheck the data to ensure that no transcription or data entry errors occurred.
2. If the data is valid, one possible explanation is that the model is not adequate.

A model with higher-order terms, such as polynomials and interactions between the variables, might be necessary to fit the data well.

31

If the unusual data are erroneous, correct the errors and reanalyze the data.

(In this course, time does not permit discussion of higher order models in any depth. This discussion is in Statistics 2: ANOVA and Regression.)

Another possibility is that the observation, although valid, could be unusual. If you had a larger sample size, there might be more observations similar to the unusual ones.

You might have to collect more data to confirm the relationship suggested by the influential observation.

In general, do not exclude data. In many circumstances, some of the unusual observations contain important information.

If you do choose to exclude some observations, include a description of the types of observations that you exclude and provide an explanation. Also discuss the limitation of your conclusions, given the exclusions, as part of your report or presentation.

## Exercises

2. **Generating Potential Outliers**

   Using the **sasuser.BodyFat2** data set, run a regression model of **PctBodyFat2** on **Abdomen**, **Weight**, **Wrist**, and **Forearm**.

   **a.** Use plots to identify potential influential observations based on the suggested cutoff values.

   **b.** Output residuals to a data set, subset the data set by only those who are potentially influential outliers, and print the results.

### 4.03 Multiple Choice Poll

How many observations did you find that might substantially influence parameter estimates?

a. 0
b. 1
c. 4
d. 5
e. 7
f. 10

35

# 4.3 Collinearity

## Objectives

- Determine whether collinearity exists in a model.
- Generate output to evaluate the strength of the collinearity and what variables are involved in the collinearity.
- Determine methods that can minimize collinearity in a model.

38

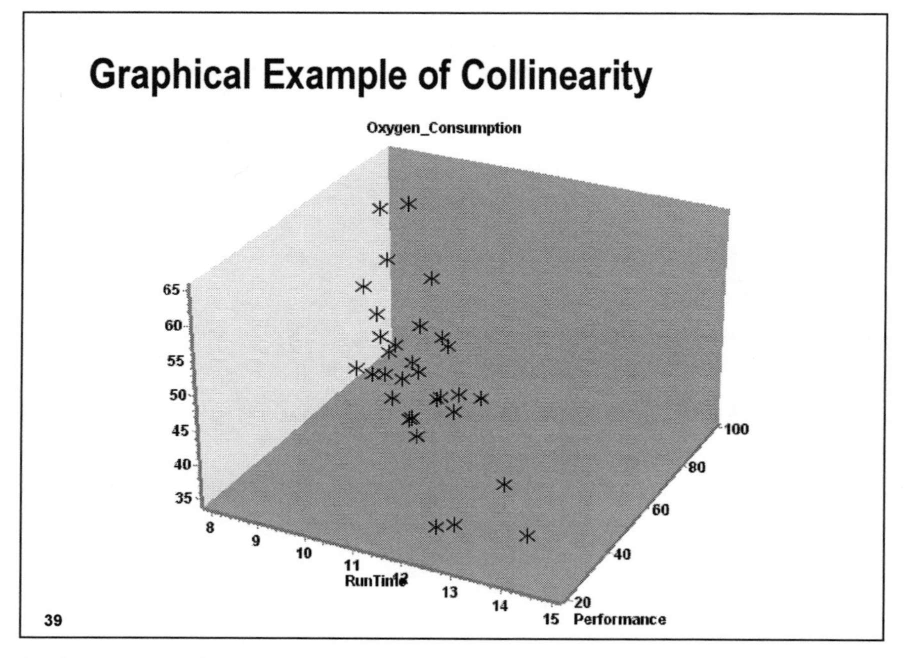


In the **Fitness** data set example, **RunTime** and **Oxygen_Consumption** have a strong linear relationship. Similarly, **Performance** has a strong relationship with **Oxygen_Consumption**.

The goal of multiple linear regression is to find a best fit plane through the data to predict **Oxygen_Consumption**. This perspective shows a very strong relationship between the predictor variables **RunTime** and **Performance**. You can picture that the prediction plane that you are trying to build is similar to a tabletop, where the observations guide the angle of the tabletop, relative to the floor, in the same way as the legs for the table. If the legs line up with one another, then the plane built on top of it tends to be unstable.

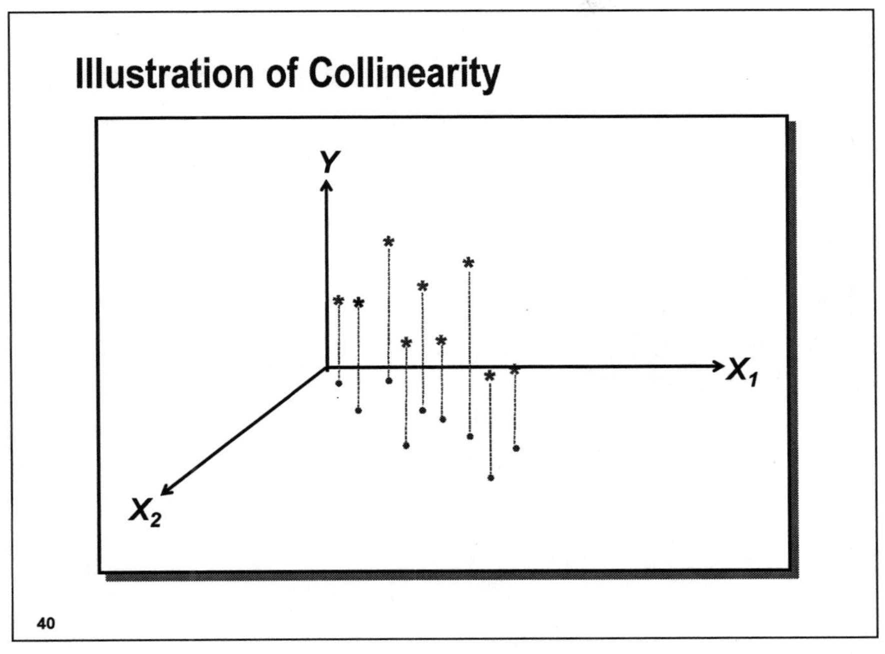


Here is another way of looking at the three dimensions of two predictor variables and a response variable. Where should the prediction plane be placed? The slopes of the prediction plane relative to each X and the Y are the parameter coefficient estimates.

$X_1$ and $X_2$ almost follow a straight line, that is, $X_1=X_2$ in the $(X_1, X_2)$ plane.

Why is this a problem? Two reasons exist.

1. Neither might appear to be significant when both are in the model. However, either might be significant when only one is in the model. Thus, collinearity can hide significant effects. (The reverse can be true as well. Collinearity can increase the apparent statistical significance of effects.)
2. Collinearity tends to increase the variance of parameter estimates and consequently increase prediction error.

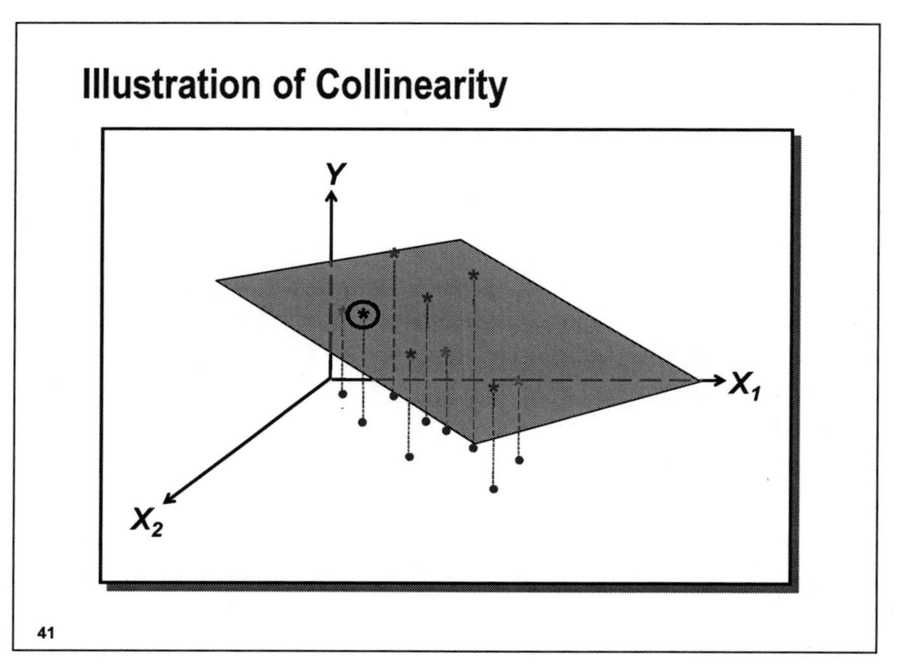


This is a representation of a best-fit plane through the data.

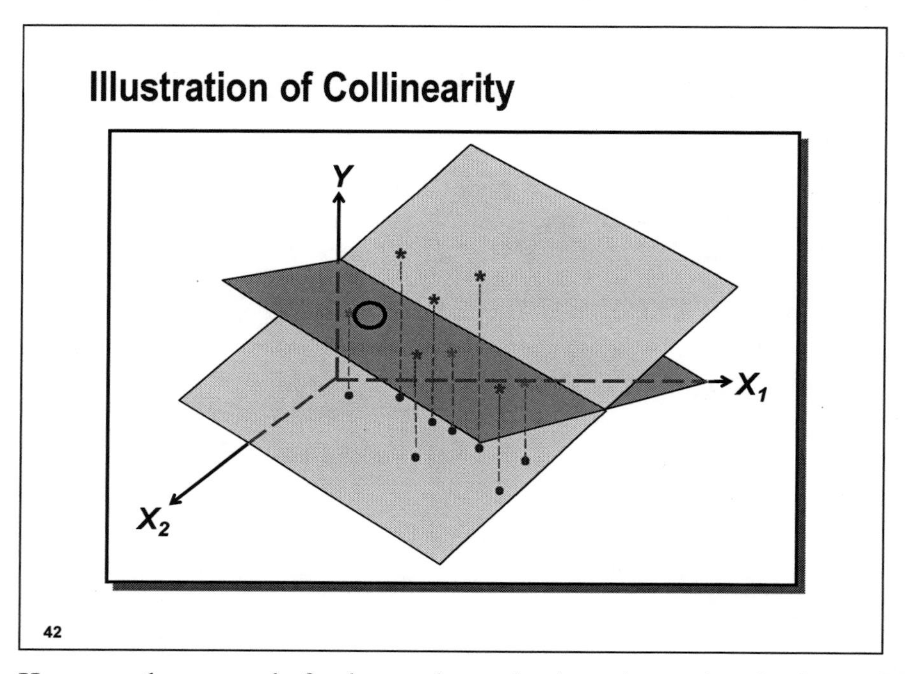


However, the removal of only one data point (or only moving the data point) results in a very different prediction plane (as represented by the lighter plane). This illustrates the variability of the parameter estimates when there is extreme collinearity.

When collinearity is a problem, the estimates of the coefficients are unstable. This means that they have a large variance. Consequently, the true relationship between Y and the Xs might be quite different from that suggested by the magnitude and sign of the coefficients.

Collinearity is ***not*** a violation of the assumptions of linear regression.

## Example of Collinearity

Example: Generate a regression model with **Oxygen_Consumption** as the dependent variable and **Performance**, **RunTime**, **Age**, **Weight**, **Run_Pulse**, **Rest_Pulse**, and **Maximum_Pulse** as the independent variables. Compare this model with the PREDICT model from the previous section.

```
/*st104d03.sas*/
ods graphics off;
proc reg data=sasuser.fitness;
   PREDICT: model Oxygen_Consumption=
                  RunTime Age Run_Pulse Maximum_pulse;
   FULLMODL: model Oxygen_Consumption=
                  Performance Runtime Age Weight
                  Run_Pulse Rest_Pulse Maximum_Pulse;
run;
quit;
ods graphics on;
```

PROC REG Output

**Model: PREDICT**
**Dependent Variable: Oxygen_Consumption**

| | |
|---|---|
| Number of Observations Read | 31 |
| Number of Observations Used | 31 |

| Analysis of Variance | | | | | |
|---|---|---|---|---|---|
| Source | DF | Sum of Squares | Mean Square | F Value | Pr > F |
| Model | 4 | 711.45087 | 177.86272 | 33.01 | <.0001 |
| Error | 26 | 140.10368 | 5.38860 | | |
| Corrected Total | 30 | 851.55455 | | | |

| | | | |
|---|---|---|---|
| Root MSE | 2.32134 | R-Square | 0.8355 |
| Dependent Mean | 47.37581 | Adj R-Sq | 0.8102 |
| Coeff Var | 4.89984 | | |

| Parameter Estimates | | | | | |
|---|---|---|---|---|---|
| Variable | DF | Parameter Estimate | Standard Error | t Value | Pr > \|t\| |
| Intercept | 1 | 97.16952 | 11.65703 | 8.34 | <.0001 |
| RunTime | 1 | -2.77576 | 0.34159 | -8.13 | <.0001 |
| Age | 1 | -0.18903 | 0.09439 | -2.00 | 0.0557 |
| Run_Pulse | 1 | -0.34568 | 0.11820 | -2.92 | 0.0071 |
| Maximum_Pulse | 1 | 0.27188 | 0.13438 | 2.02 | 0.0534 |

For the PREDICT model, the model R square is large, the *p*-value for the overall test of the model is small, and none of the *p*-values is greater than 0.0557.

**Model: FULLMODL**
**Dependent Variable: Oxygen_Consumption**

| Number of Observations Read | 31 |
|---|---|
| Number of Observations Used | 31 |

| Analysis of Variance | | | | | |
|---|---|---|---|---|---|
| Source | DF | Sum of Squares | Mean Square | F Value | Pr > F |
| Model | 7 | 722.66124 | 103.23732 | 18.42 | <.0001 |
| Error | 23 | 128.89331 | 5.60406 | | |
| Corrected Total | 30 | 851.55455 | | | |

| Root MSE | 2.36729 | R-Square | 0.8486 |
|---|---|---|---|
| Dependent Mean | 47.37581 | Adj R-Sq | 0.8026 |
| Coeff Var | 4.99683 | | |

| Parameter Estimates | | | | | |
|---|---|---|---|---|---|
| Variable | DF | Parameter Estimate | Standard Error | t Value | Pr > \|t\| |
| Intercept | 1 | 131.78249 | 72.20754 | 1.83 | 0.0810 |
| Performance | 1 | -0.12619 | 0.30097 | -0.42 | 0.6789 |
| RunTime | 1 | -3.86019 | 2.93659 | -1.31 | 0.2016 |
| Age | 1 | -0.46082 | 0.58660 | -0.79 | 0.4401 |
| Weight | 1 | -0.05812 | 0.06892 | -0.84 | 0.4078 |
| Run_Pulse | 1 | -0.36207 | 0.12324 | -2.94 | 0.0074 |
| Rest_Pulse | 1 | -0.01512 | 0.06817 | -0.22 | 0.8264 |
| Maximum_Pulse | 1 | 0.30102 | 0.13981 | 2.15 | 0.0420 |

For the full model, Model *F* is highly significant and the R square is large. These statistics suggest that the model fits the data well.

However, when you examine the *p*-values of the parameters, only **Run_Pulse** and **Maximum_Pulse** are statistically significant.

When you produced the correlation information between your predictors and the response, **Runtime** was ranked first with the strongest correlation to **Oxygen_Consumption**. You also saw that in a simple linear regression containing only **Runtime**, it was classified a significant predictor variable. This significance continued in the PREDICT model that included **Runtime**. However, in the full model, this same variable is not statistically significant (*p*-value=0.2016). The *p*-value for **Age** changed from 0.0557 to 0.4401 between the PREDICT model and the FULL model.

When you have a highly significant Model *F* but no (or few) highly significant terms, collinearity is a potential cause.

## 4.04 Multiple Choice Poll

Which of the following assumptions does collinearity violate?

a. Independent errors
b. Constant variance
c. Normally distributed errors
d. None of the above

45

## Collinearity Diagnostics

PROC REG offers these tools that help quantify the magnitude of the collinearity problems and identify the subset of Xs that is collinear:

- VIF
- COLLIN
- COLLINOINT

This course focuses on VIF.

47

Selected MODEL statement options:

| | |
|---|---|
| VIF | provides a measure of the magnitude of the collinearity (Variance Inflation Factor). |
| COLLIN | includes the intercept vector when analyzing the X′X matrix for collinearity. |
| COLLINOINT | excludes the intercept vector when analyzing the X′X matrix for collinearity. |

Two options, COLLIN and COLLINOINT, also provide a measure of the magnitude of the problem as well as give information that can be used to identify the sets of Xs that are the source of the problem.

(COLLIN and COLLINOINT diagnostics are described in Statistics 2: ANOVA and Regression.)

## Variance Inflation Factor (VIF)

The *VIF* is a relative measure of the increase in the variance because of collinearity. It can be thought of as this ratio:

$$VIF_i = \frac{1}{1 - R_i^2}$$

A $VIF_i > 10$ indicates that collinearity is a problem.

48

You can calculate a VIF for each term in the model.

Marquardt (1990) suggests that a VIF > 10 indicates the presence of strong collinearity in the model.

$VIF_i=1/(1-R_i^2)$, where $R_i^2$ is the R square of $X_i$, regressed on all the other Xs in the model.

For example, consider the model Y=X1 X2 X3 X4, *i*=1 to 4.

To calculate the R square for X3, fit the model X3=X1 X2 X4. Take the R square from the model with X3 as the dependent variable and replace it in the formula: $VIF_3=1/(1-R_3^2)$. If $VIF_3$ is greater than 10, X3 is possibly involved in collinearity.

## Collinearity Diagnostics

Example: Invoke PROC REG and use the VIF option to assess the magnitude of the collinearity problem and identify the terms involved in the problem.

```
/*st104d04.sas*/  /*Part A*/
ods graphics off;
proc reg data=sasuser.fitness;
   FULLMODL: model Oxygen_Consumption=
                   Performance RunTime Age Weight
                   Run_Pulse Rest_Pulse Maximum_Pulse
                   / vif;
   title 'Collinearity -- Full Model';
run;
quit;
ods graphics on;
```

Partial PROC REG Output

| | |
|---|---|
| **Number of Observations Read** | 31 |
| **Number of Observations Used** | 31 |

| Analysis of Variance | | | | | |
|---|---|---|---|---|---|
| **Source** | **DF** | **Sum of Squares** | **Mean Square** | **F Value** | **Pr > F** |
| **Model** | 7 | 722.66124 | 103.23732 | 18.42 | <.0001 |
| **Error** | 23 | 128.89331 | 5.60406 | | |
| **Corrected Total** | 30 | 851.55455 | | | |

| | | | |
|---|---|---|---|
| **Root MSE** | 2.36729 | **R-Square** | 0.8486 |
| **Dependent Mean** | 47.37581 | **Adj R-Sq** | 0.8026 |
| **Coeff Var** | 4.99683 | | |

| Parameter Estimates | | | | | | |
|---|---|---|---|---|---|---|
| **Variable** | **DF** | **Parameter Estimate** | **Standard Error** | **t Value** | **Pr > \|t\|** | **Variance Inflation** |
| **Intercept** | 1 | 131.78249 | 72.20754 | 1.83 | 0.0810 | 0 |
| **Performance** | 1 | -0.12619 | 0.30097 | -0.42 | 0.6789 | 162.85399 |
| **RunTime** | 1 | -3.86019 | 2.93659 | -1.31 | 0.2016 | 88.86251 |
| **Age** | 1 | -0.46082 | 0.58660 | -0.79 | 0.4401 | 51.01176 |
| **Weight** | 1 | -0.05812 | 0.06892 | -0.84 | 0.4078 | 1.76383 |
| **Run_Pulse** | 1 | -0.36207 | 0.12324 | -2.94 | 0.0074 | 8.54498 |
| **Rest_Pulse** | 1 | -0.01512 | 0.06817 | -0.22 | 0.8264 | 1.44425 |
| **Maximum_Pulse** | 1 | 0.30102 | 0.13981 | 2.15 | 0.0420 | 8.78755 |

Some of the VIFs are much larger than 10. A severe collinearity problem is present. At this point there are many ways to proceed. However, it is always a good idea to use some subject-matter expertise. For example, a quick conversation with the analyst and a view of the data-coding scheme revealed this bit of information.

Partial Code

```
data sasuser.fitness;
   input @1 Name $8. @10 Gender $1. @12 RunTime 5.2 @18 Age 2. @21
         Weight 5.2
         @27 Oxygen_Consumption 5.2 @33 Run_Pulse 3.
         @37 Rest_Pulse 2. @40 Maximum_Pulse 3.;
   Performance=260-round(10*runtime + 2*Age + 4*(Gender='F'));
   datalines;
...
run;
```

The variable **Performance** was not a measured variable. The researchers, on the basis of prior literature, created a summary variable, which is a weighted function of the three variables, **RunTime**, **Age**, and **Gender**. This is not at all an uncommon occurrence and illustrates an important point. If a summary variable is included in a model along with some or all of its composite measures, there is bound to be collinearity. In fact, this can be the source of great problems.

If the composite variable has meaning, it can be used as a stand-in measure for all three composite scores and you can remove the variables **RunTime** and **Age** from the analysis.

Summary measures have the disadvantage of losing some information about the individual variables. If this is of concern, then remove **Performance** from the analysis.

A decision was made to remove **Performance** from the analysis. Another check of collinearity is warranted.

```
/*st104d04.sas*/  /*Part B*/
ods graphics off;
proc reg data=sasuser.fitness;
   NOPERF: model Oxygen_Consumption=
                 RunTime Age Weight
                 Run_Pulse Rest_Pulse Maximum_Pulse
                 / vif;
   title 'Dealing with Collinearity';
run;
quit;
ods graphics on;
```

PROC REG Output

| Number of Observations Read | 31 |
|---|---|
| Number of Observations Used | 31 |

| Analysis of Variance | | | | | |
|---|---|---|---|---|---|
| Source | DF | Sum of Squares | Mean Square | F Value | Pr > F |
| Model | 6 | 721.67605 | 120.27934 | 22.23 | <.0001 |
| Error | 24 | 129.87851 | 5.41160 | | |
| Corrected Total | 30 | 851.55455 | | | |

| Root MSE | 2.32629 | R-Square | 0.8475 |
|---|---|---|---|
| Dependent Mean | 47.37581 | Adj R-Sq | 0.8094 |
| Coeff Var | 4.91028 | | |

| Parameter Estimates | | | | | | |
|---|---|---|---|---|---|---|
| Variable | DF | Parameter Estimate | Standard Error | t Value | Pr > \|t\| | Variance Inflation |
| Intercept | 1 | 101.96313 | 12.27174 | 8.31 | <.0001 | 0 |
| RunTime | 1 | -2.63994 | 0.38532 | -6.85 | <.0001 | 1.58432 |
| Age | 1 | -0.21848 | 0.09850 | -2.22 | 0.0363 | 1.48953 |
| Weight | 1 | -0.07503 | 0.05492 | -1.37 | 0.1845 | 1.15973 |
| Run_Pulse | 1 | -0.36721 | 0.12050 | -3.05 | 0.0055 | 8.46034 |
| Rest_Pulse | 1 | -0.01952 | 0.06619 | -0.29 | 0.7706 | 1.41004 |
| Maximum_Pulse | 1 | 0.30457 | 0.13714 | 2.22 | 0.0360 | 8.75535 |

The greatest VIF values are much smaller now. The variables **Maximum_Pulse** and **Run_Pulse** are also collinear, but for a natural reason. The pulse at the end of a run is highly likely to correlate with the maximum pulse during the run. You might be tempted to remove one variable from the model, but the small *p*-values for each indicate that this would adversely affect the model.

```
/*st104d04.sas*/  /*Part C*/
ods graphics off;
proc reg data=sasuser.fitness;
   NOPRFMAX: model Oxygen_Consumption=
                   RunTime Age Weight
                   Run_Pulse Rest_Pulse
                   / vif;
   title 'Dealing with Collinearity';
run;
quit;
ods graphics on;
```

PROC REG Output

| Number of Observations Read | 31 |
|---|---|
| Number of Observations Used | 31 |

| Analysis of Variance | | | | | |
|---|---|---|---|---|---|
| Source | DF | Sum of Squares | Mean Square | F Value | Pr > F |
| Model | 5 | 694.98323 | 138.99665 | 22.19 | <.0001 |
| Error | 25 | 156.57132 | 6.26285 | | |
| Corrected Total | 30 | 851.55455 | | | |

| Root MSE | 2.50257 | R-Square | 0.8161 |
|---|---|---|---|
| Dependent Mean | 47.37581 | Adj R-Sq | 0.7794 |
| Coeff Var | 5.28238 | | |

| Parameter Estimates | | | | | | |
|---|---|---|---|---|---|---|
| Variable | DF | Parameter Estimate | Standard Error | t Value | Pr > \|t\| | Variance Inflation |
| Intercept | 1 | 115.46115 | 11.46893 | 10.07 | <.0001 | 0 |
| RunTime | 1 | -2.71594 | 0.41288 | -6.58 | <.0001 | 1.57183 |
| Age | 1 | -0.27650 | 0.10217 | -2.71 | 0.0121 | 1.38477 |
| Weight | 1 | -0.05300 | 0.05811 | -0.91 | 0.3704 | 1.12190 |
| Run_Pulse | 1 | -0.12213 | 0.05207 | -2.35 | 0.0272 | 1.36493 |
| Rest_Pulse | 1 | -0.02485 | 0.07116 | -0.35 | 0.7298 | 1.40819 |

With **Maximum_Pulse** removed, all of the VIF values are low, but the R square and Adjusted R square values were reduced and the *p*-value for **Run_Pulse** actually increased!

Even with collinearity still present in the model, it might be advisable to keep the previous model including **Maximum_Pulse**.

Collinearity can have a substantial effect on the outcome of a stepwise procedure for model selection. Because the significance of important variables can be masked by collinearity, the final model might not include very important variables. This is why it is advisable to deal with collinearity before using any automated model selection tool.

There are other approaches to dealing with collinearity. Two techniques are *ridge regression* and *principal components regression*. In addition, *recentering* the predictor variables can sometimes eliminate collinearity problems, especially in a polynomial regression and in ANCOVA models.

## 4.05 Poll

If there is no correlation among the predictor variables, can there still be collinearity in the model?

- ❍ Yes
- ❍ No

51

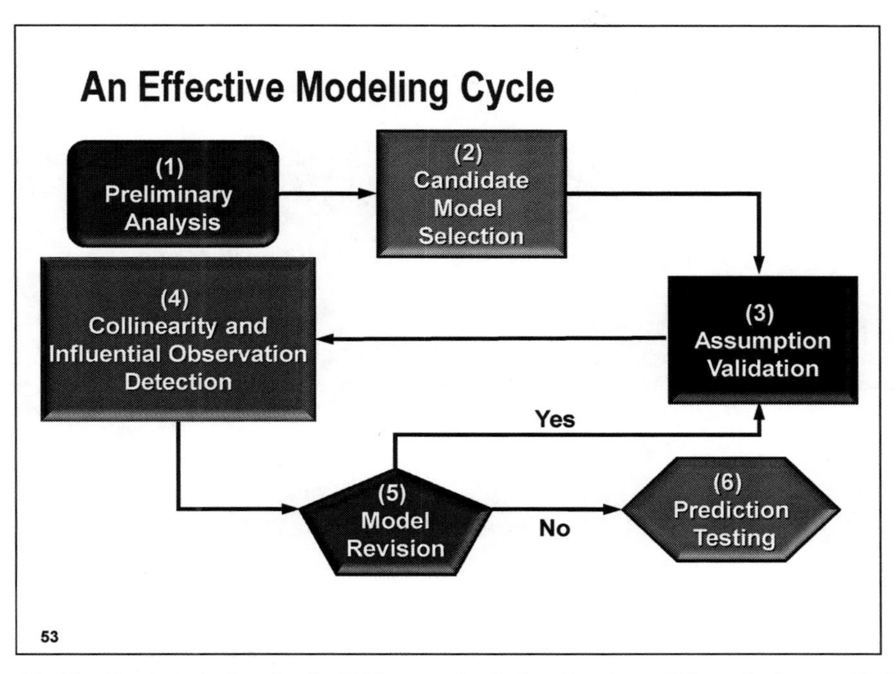


(1) **Preliminary Analysis**: This step includes the use of descriptive statistics, graphs, and correlation analysis.

(2) **Candidate Model Selection**: This step uses the numerous selection options in PROC REG to identify one or more candidate models.

(3) **Assumption Validation**: This step includes the plots of residuals and graphs of the residuals versus the predicted values. It also includes a test for equal variances.

(4) **Collinearity and Influential Observation Detection**: The former includes the use of the VIF statistic, condition indices, and variation proportions; the latter includes the examination of R-Student residuals, Cook's D statistic, and DFFITS statistics.

(5) **Model Revision**: If steps (3) and (4) indicate the need for model revision, generate a new model by returning to these two steps.

(6) **Prediction Testing**: If possible, validate the model with data not used to build the model.

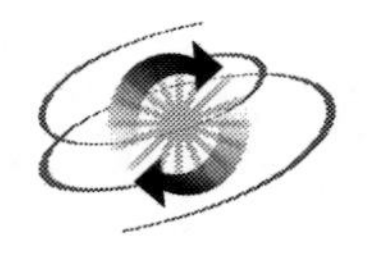

# Exercises

**3. Assessing Collinearity**

Using the **sasuser.BodyFat2** data set, run a regression of **PctBodyFat2** on all the other numeric variables in the file.

**a.** Determine whether there is a collinearity problem.

**b.** If so, decide what you would like to do about that. Will you remove any variables? Why or why not?

# 4.4 Solutions

## Solutions to Exercises

1. **Examining Residuals**

   Assess the model obtained from the final forward stepwise selection of predictors for the **sasuser.BodyFat2** data set. Run a regression of **PctBodyFat2** on **Abdomen**, **Weight**, **Wrist**, and **Forearm**. Create plots of the residuals by the four regressors and by the predicted values and a normal Quantile-Quantile plot.

```
/*st104s01.sas*/
ods graphics / imagemap=on;
proc reg data=sasuser.BodyFat2
         plots(only)=(QQ RESIDUALBYPREDICTED RESIDUALS);
   FORWARD: model PctBodyFat2=
                  Abdomen Weight Wrist Forearm;
   id Case;
   title 'FORWARD Model - Plots of Diagnostic Statistics';
run;
quit;
```

   **a.** Do the residual plots indicate any problems with the constant variance assumption?

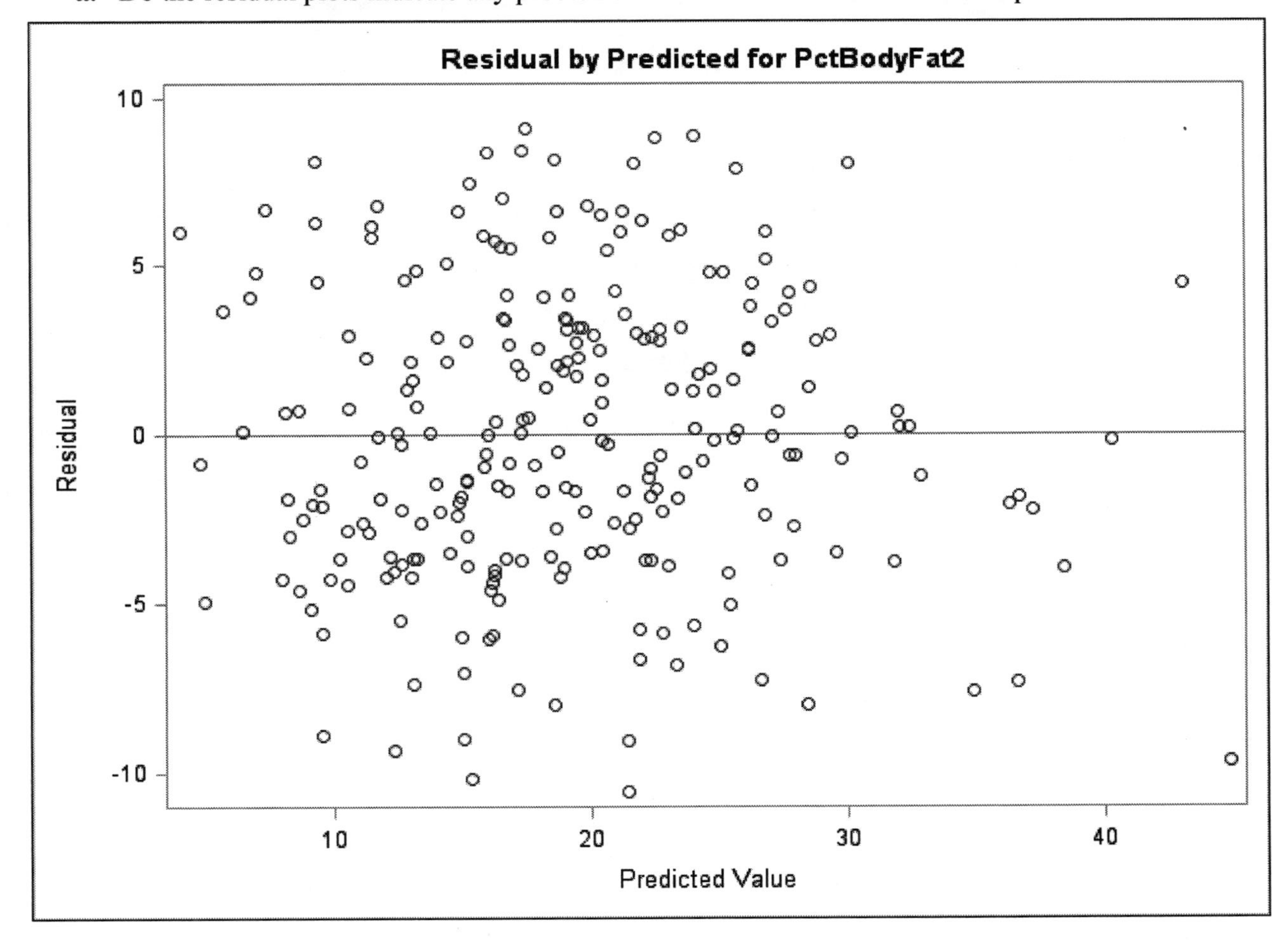

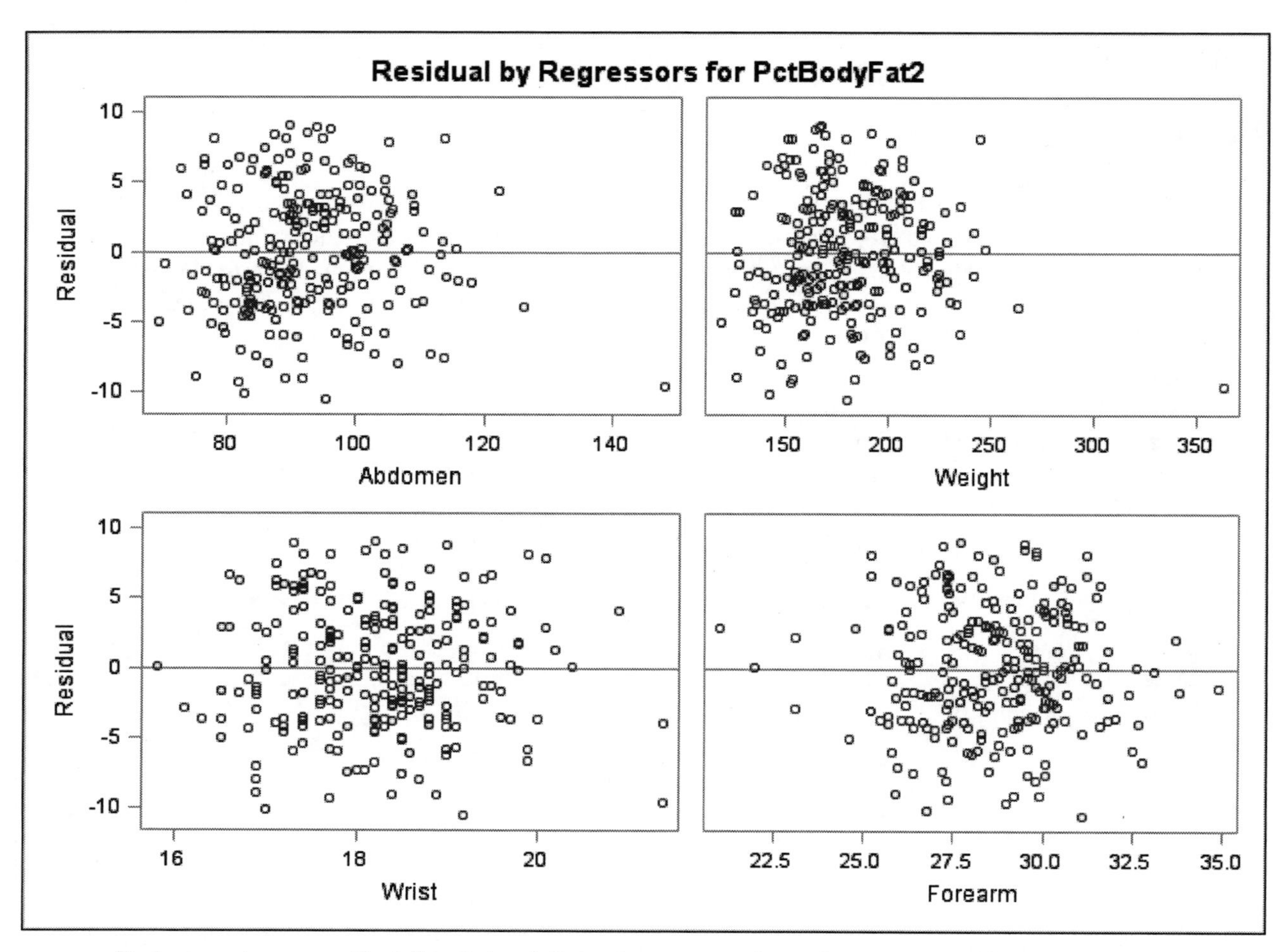


**It does not appear that the data violate the assumption of constant variance. Also, the residuals show nice random scatter and indicate no problem with model specification.**

**b.** Are there any outliers indicated by the evidence in any of the residual plots?

**There are a few outliers for Wrist and Forearm and one clear outlier in each of Abdomen and Weight values.**

**c.** Does the Quantile-Quantile plot indicate any problems with the normality assumption?

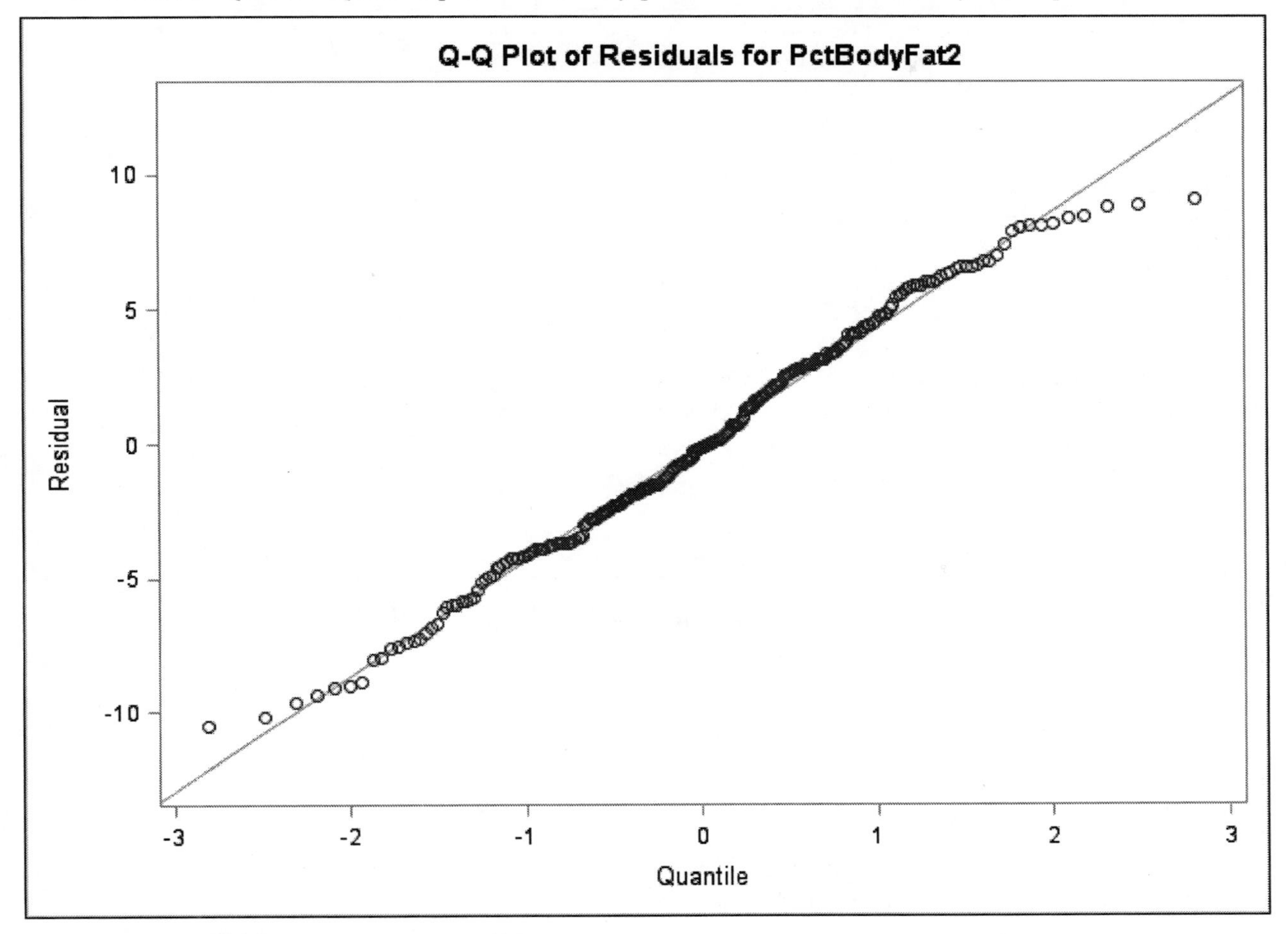


**The normality assumption seems to be met.**

2. **Generating Potential Outliers**

   Using the **sasuser.BodyFat2** data set, run a regression model of **PctBodyFat2** on **Abdomen, Weight, Wrist**, and **Forearm**..

**a.** Use plots to identify potential influential observations based on the suggested cutoff values.

```
/*st104s02.sas*/  /*Part A*/
ods output RSTUDENTBYPREDICTED=Rstud
           COOKSDPLOT=Cook
           DFFITSPLOT=Dffits
           DFBETASPANEL=Dfbs;
proc reg data=sasuser.BodyFat2
         plots(only label)=
              (RSTUDENTBYPREDICTED
               COOKSD
               DFFITS
               DFBETAS);
   FORWARD: model PctBodyFat2=
                  Abdomen Weight Wrist Forearm;
   id Case;
   title 'FORWARD Model - Plots of Diagnostic Statistics';
run;
quit;
```

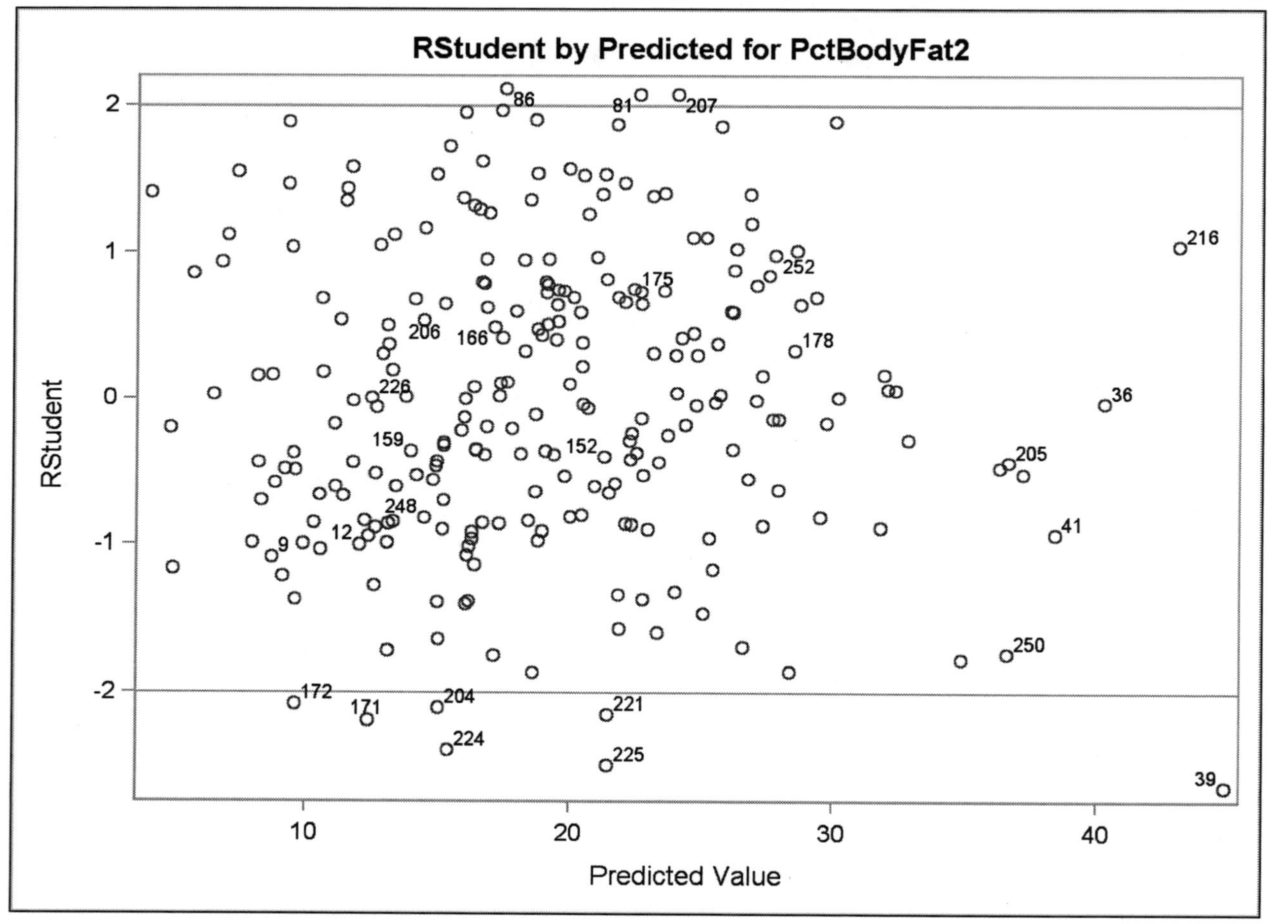


**There are only a modest number of observations farther than two standard error units from the mean of 0.**

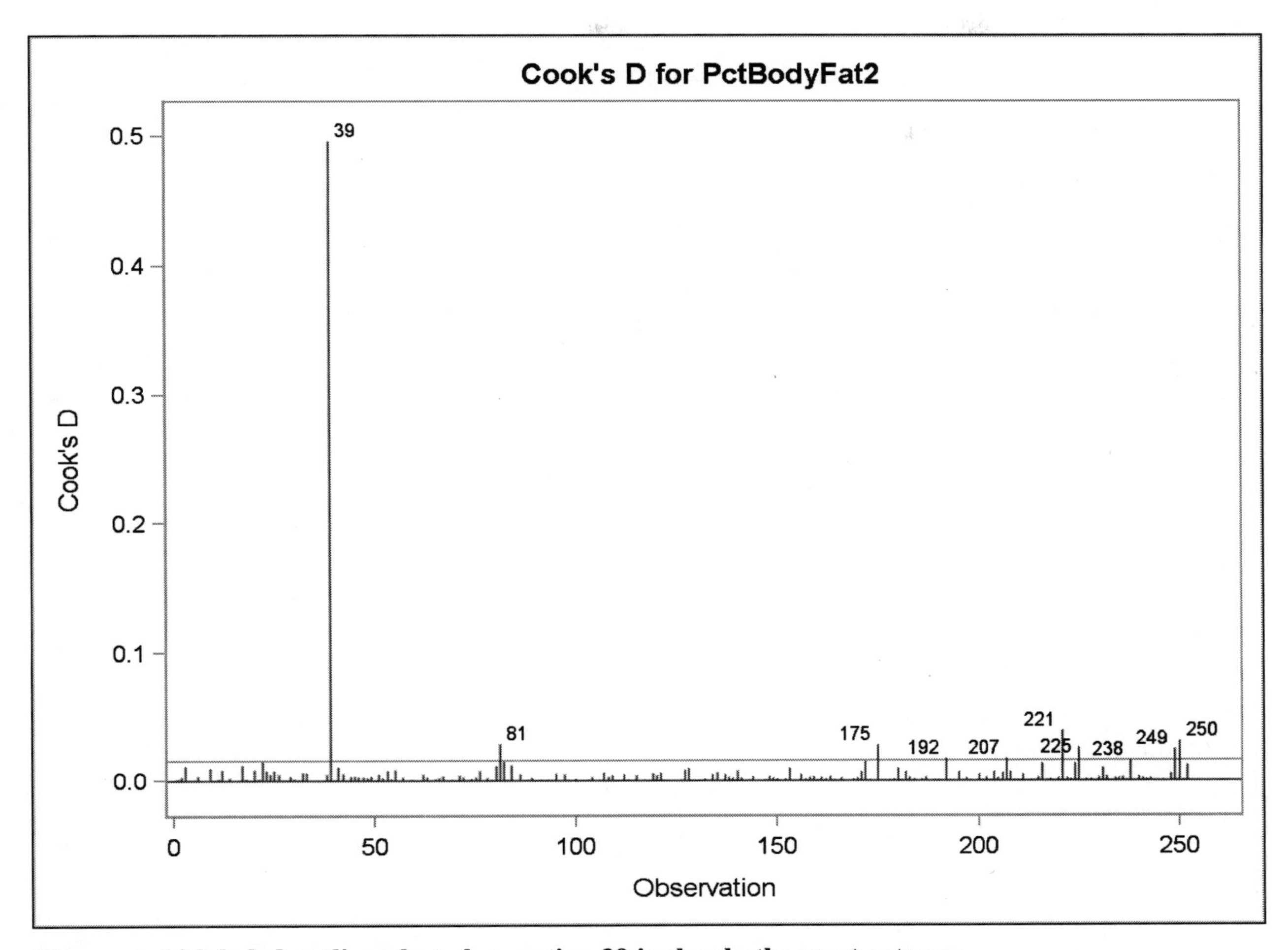


**There are 10 labeled outliers, but observation 39 is clearly the most extreme.**

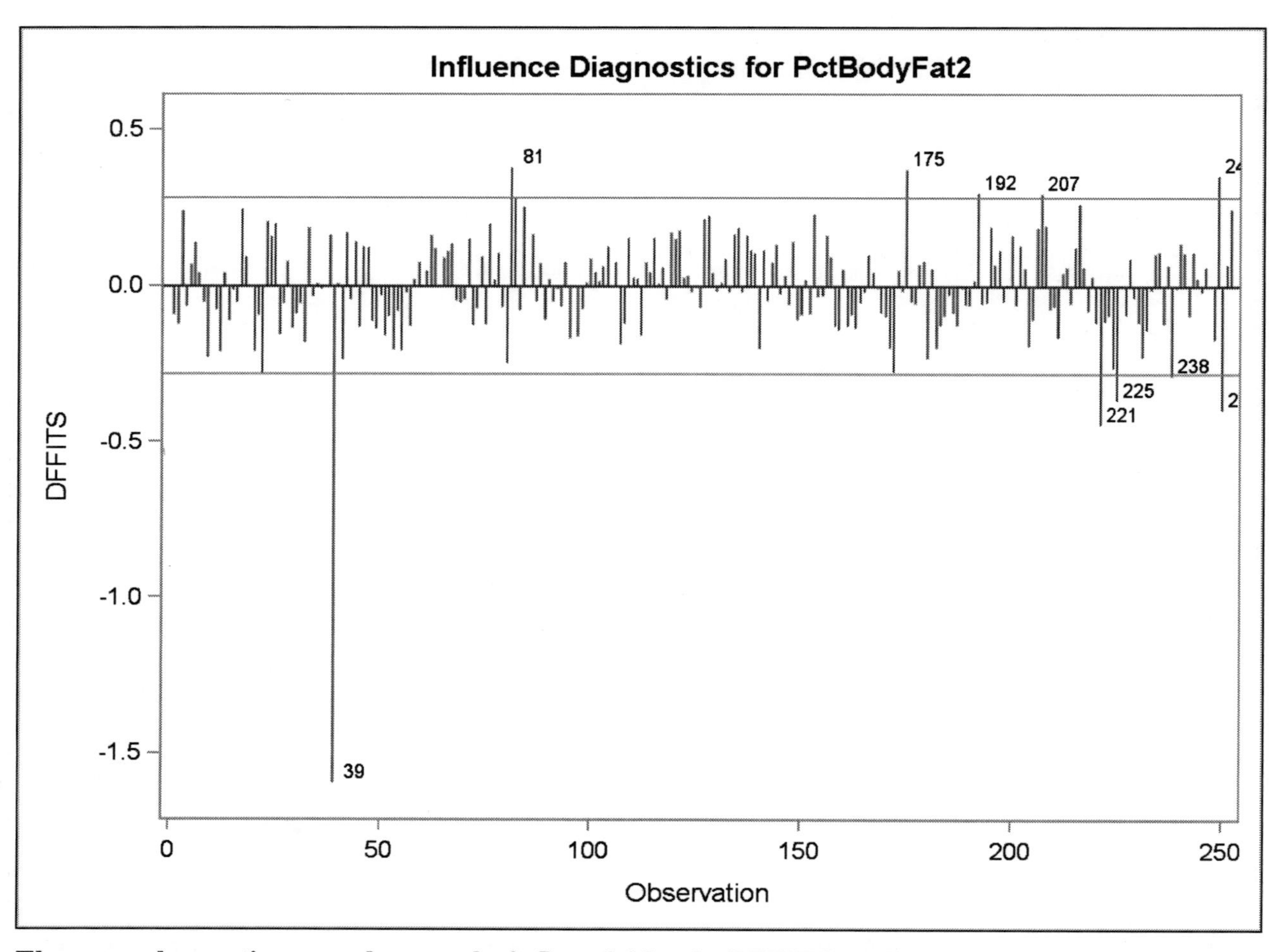


**The same observations are shown to be influential by the DFFITS statistic.**

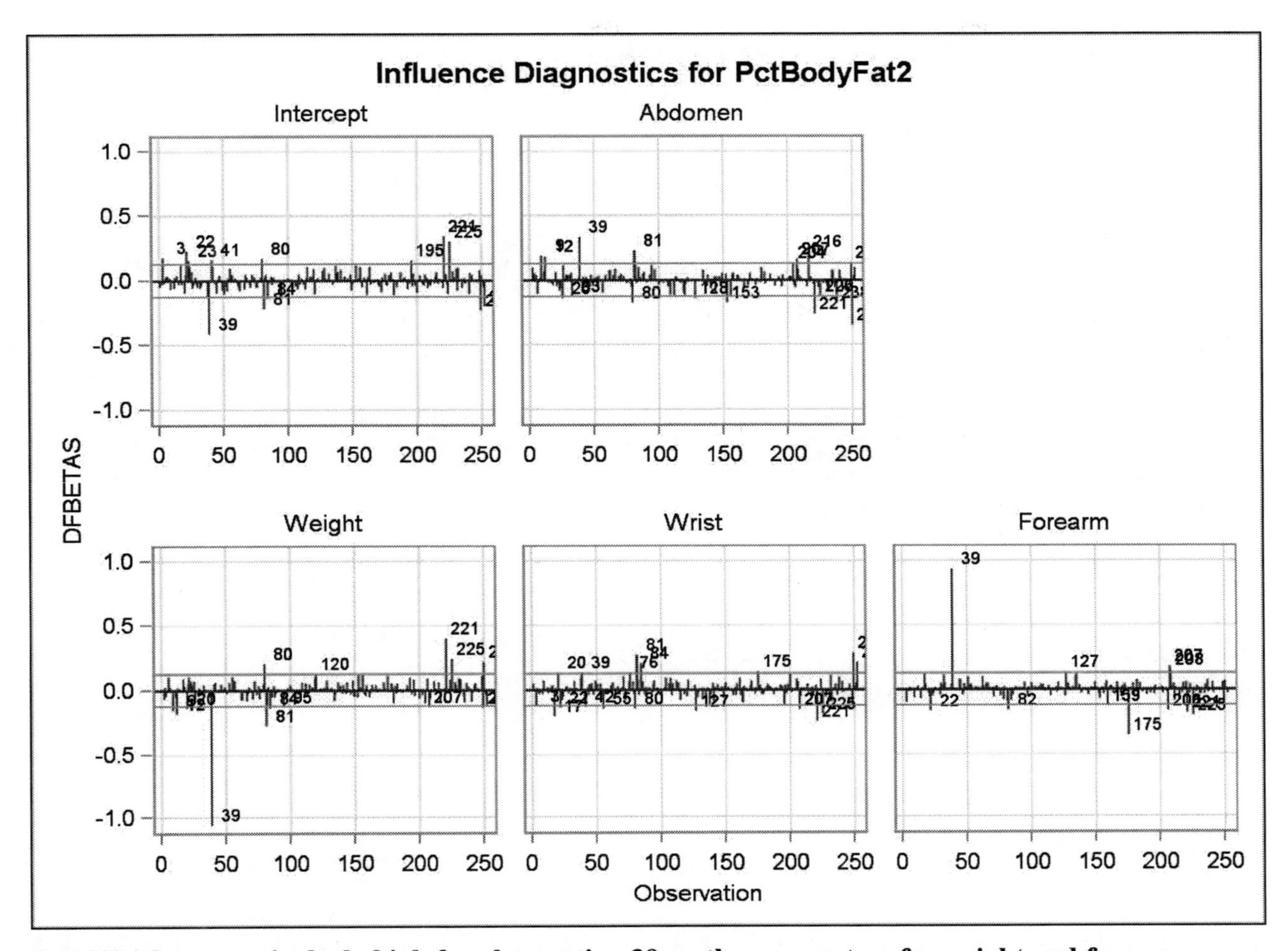


**DFBETAS are particularly high for observation 39 on the parameters for weight and forearm circumference.**

**b.** Output residuals to a data set, subset the data set by only those who are potentially influential outliers, and print the results.

```
/* st104s02.sas */  /* Part B */
data influential;
/* Merge data sets from above. */
   merge Rstud
         Cook
         Dffits
         Dfbs;
   by observation;

/* Flag observations that have exceeded at least one cutpoint; */
   if (Rstudent>3) or (Cooksdlabel ne ' ') or Dffitsout then flag=1;
   array dfbetas{*} _dfbetasout: ;
   do i=2 to dim(dfbetas);
      if dfbetas{i} then flag=1;
   end;

/* Set to missing values of influence statistics for those */
/* who have not exceeded cutpoints; */
   if Rstudent<=3 then RStudent=.;
   if Cooksdlabel eq ' ' then CooksD=.;

/* Subset only observations that have been flagged. */
   if flag=1;
   drop i flag;
run;

proc print data=influential;
   id observation ID1;
   var Rstudent CooksD Dffitsout _dfbetasout:;
run;
```

| Observation | id1 | RStudent | CooksD | DFFITSOUT | _DFBETAS OUT1 | _DFBETAS OUT2 | _DFBETAS OUT3 | _DFBETAS OUT4 | _DFBETAS OUT5 |
|---|---|---|---|---|---|---|---|---|---|
| **3** | **3** | . | . | . | 0.17943 | . | . | -0.12815 | . |
| **9** | **9** | . | . | . | . | 0.18911 | -0.15600 | . | . |
| **12** | **12** | . | . | . | . | 0.18169 | -0.18076 | . | . |
| **17** | **17** | . | . | . | . | . | . | -0.20902 | . |
| **20** | **20** | . | . | . | . | . | -0.13786 | 0.13273 | . |
| **22** | **22** | . | . | . | 0.22887 | . | . | -0.14080 | -0.16797 |
| **25** | **25** | . | . | . | . | -0.14080 | . | . | . |
| **33** | **33** | . | . | . | . | -0.12765 | . | . | . |
| **39** | **39** | . | 0.49632 | -1.59408 | -0.41792 | 0.33576 | -1.05761 | 0.13217 | 0.93125 |
| **42** | **42** | . | . | . | . | . | . | -0.13688 | . |
| **55** | **55** | . | . | . | . | . | . | -0.14907 | . |
| **76** | **76** | . | . | . | . | . | . | 0.13108 | . |
| **80** | **80** | . | . | . | 0.17122 | -0.17507 | 0.20391 | -0.14744 | . |
| **81** | **81** | . | 0.02858 | 0.38053 | -0.22179 | 0.22631 | -0.27484 | 0.26977 | . |
| **82** | **82** | . | . | . | . | . | . | . | -0.16453 |
| **84** | **84** | . | . | . | -0.14277 | . | -0.13915 | 0.20279 | . |
| **95** | **95** | . | . | . | . | . | -0.13519 | . | . |
| **120** | **120** | . | . | . | . | . | 0.12609 | . | . |
| **127** | **127** | . | . | . | . | . | . | -0.16625 | 0.13285 |
| **128** | **128** | . | . | . | . | -0.13838 | . | . | . |
| **153** | **153** | . | . | . | . | -0.17467 | . | . | . |
| **159** | **159** | . | . | . | . | . | . | . | -0.13278 |
| **175** | **175** | . | 0.02787 | 0.37296 | . | . | . | 0.14200 | -0.35339 |
| **192** | **192** | . | 0.01752 | 0.29750 | . | . | . | . | . |
| **204** | **204** | . | . | . | . | 0.13453 | . | . | . |
| **206** | **206** | . | . | . | . | . | . | . | -0.17242 |
| **207** | **207** | . | 0.01716 | 0.29490 | . | 0.16026 | -0.13169 | -0.15412 | 0.17410 |
| **208** | **208** | . | . | . | . | . | . | . | 0.14747 |
| **216** | **216** | . | . | . | . | 0.21712 | . | . | . |
| **221** | **221** | . | 0.03911 | -0.44540 | 0.34282 | -0.26106 | 0.39789 | -0.24565 | -0.18174 |
| **225** | **225** | . | 0.02633 | -0.36660 | 0.30270 | -0.12914 | 0.23904 | -0.19078 | -0.20840 |
| **238** | **238** | . | 0.01629 | -0.28661 | . | -0.17388 | . | . | . |
| **249** | **249** | . | 0.02463 | 0.35266 | -0.23435 | 0.13125 | -0.14344 | 0.28748 | . |
| **250** | **250** | . | 0.03108 | -0.39579 | . | -0.35320 | 0.21925 | . | . |
| **252** | **252** | . | . | . | -0.20349 | . | -0.12708 | 0.21088 | . |

**The same observations appear on this listing as in the plots.**

Examine the values of observation 39 to see what is causing problems. You might find it interesting.

**3. Assessing Collinearity**

Using the **sasuser.BodyFat2** data set, run a regression of **PctBodyFat2** on all the other numeric variables in the file.

**a.** Determine whether there is a collinearity problem.

```
/*st104s03.sas*/  /*Part A*/
ods graphics off;
proc reg data=sasuser.BodyFat;
   FULLMODL: model PctBodyFat2=
                  Age Weight Height
                  Neck Chest Abdomen Hip Thigh
                  Knee Ankle Biceps Forearm Wrist
                / vif;
   title 'Collinearity -- Full Model';
run;
quit;
ods graphics on;
```

| | |
|---|---|
| **Number of Observations Read** | 252 |
| **Number of Observations Used** | 252 |

| **Analysis of Variance** | | | | | |
|---|---|---|---|---|---|
| **Source** | **DF** | **Sum of Squares** | **Mean Square** | **F Value** | **Pr > F** |
| **Model** | 13 | 13168 | 1012.88783 | 54.65 | <.0001 |
| **Error** | 238 | 4411.44804 | 18.53550 | | |
| **Corrected Total** | 251 | 17579 | | | |

| | | | |
|---|---|---|---|
| **Root MSE** | 4.30529 | **R-Square** | 0.7490 |
| **Dependent Mean** | 19.15079 | **Adj R-Sq** | 0.7353 |
| **Coeff Var** | 22.48098 | | |

| Parameter Estimates | | | | | | |
|---|---|---|---|---|---|---|
| Variable | DF | Parameter Estimate | Standard Error | t Value | Pr > \|t\| | Variance Inflation |
| Intercept | 1 | -18.18849 | 17.34857 | -1.05 | 0.2955 | 0 |
| Age | 1 | 0.06208 | 0.03235 | 1.92 | 0.0562 | 2.25045 |
| Weight | 1 | -0.08844 | 0.05353 | -1.65 | 0.0998 | 33.50932 |
| Height | 1 | -0.06959 | 0.09601 | -0.72 | 0.4693 | 1.67459 |
| Neck | 1 | -0.47060 | 0.23247 | -2.02 | 0.0440 | 4.32446 |
| Chest | 1 | -0.02386 | 0.09915 | -0.24 | 0.8100 | 9.46088 |
| Abdomen | 1 | 0.95477 | 0.08645 | 11.04 | <.0001 | 11.76707 |
| Hip | 1 | -0.20754 | 0.14591 | -1.42 | 0.1562 | 14.79652 |
| Thigh | 1 | 0.23610 | 0.14436 | 1.64 | 0.1033 | 7.77786 |
| Knee | 1 | 0.01528 | 0.24198 | 0.06 | 0.9497 | 4.61215 |
| Ankle | 1 | 0.17400 | 0.22147 | 0.79 | 0.4329 | 1.90796 |
| Biceps | 1 | 0.18160 | 0.17113 | 1.06 | 0.2897 | 3.61974 |
| Forearm | 1 | 0.45202 | 0.19913 | 2.27 | 0.0241 | 2.19249 |
| Wrist | 1 | -1.62064 | 0.53495 | -3.03 | 0.0027 | 3.37751 |

**There seems to be high collinearity associated with Weight and less so with Hip, Abdomen, Chest, and Thigh.**

**b.** If so, decide what you would like to do about that. Will you remove any variables? Why or why not?

**The answer is not so easy. True, Weight is collinear with some set of the other variables, but as you saw before in your model-building process, Weight actually is a relatively significant predictor in the "best" models. The answer is for a subject-matter expert to determine.**

**If you want to remove Weight, simply run the model again without that variable.**

```
/*st104s03.sas*/  /*Part B*/
ods graphics off;
proc reg data=sasuser.BodyFat;
   NOWT: model PctBodyFat2=
               Age Height
               Neck Chest Abdomen Hip Thigh
               Knee Ankle Biceps Forearm Wrist
             / vif;
   title 'Collinearity -- No Weight';
run;
quit;
ods graphics on;
```

| Number of Observations Read | 252 |
|---|---|
| Number of Observations Used | 252 |

| Analysis of Variance | | | | | |
|---|---|---|---|---|---|
| Source | DF | Sum of Squares | Mean Square | F Value | Pr > F |
| Model | 12 | 13117 | 1093.07775 | 58.55 | <.0001 |
| Error | 239 | 4462.05682 | 18.66969 | | |
| Corrected Total | 251 | 17579 | | | |

| Root MSE | 4.32084 | R-Square | 0.7462 |
|---|---|---|---|
| Dependent Mean | 19.15079 | Adj R-Sq | 0.7334 |
| Coeff Var | 22.56222 | | |

| Parameter Estimates | | | | | | |
|---|---|---|---|---|---|---|
| Variable | DF | Parameter Estimate | Standard Error | t Value | Pr > \|t\| | Variance Inflation |
| Intercept | 1 | 7.54528 | 7.67169 | 0.98 | 0.3263 | 0 |
| Age | 1 | 0.07316 | 0.03176 | 2.30 | 0.0221 | 2.15369 |
| Height | 1 | -0.14157 | 0.08586 | -1.65 | 0.1005 | 1.32980 |
| Neck | 1 | -0.58279 | 0.22314 | -2.61 | 0.0096 | 3.95560 |
| Chest | 1 | -0.09077 | 0.09083 | -1.00 | 0.3187 | 7.88319 |
| Abdomen | 1 | 0.92587 | 0.08497 | 10.90 | <.0001 | 11.28546 |
| Hip | 1 | -0.33792 | 0.12318 | -2.74 | 0.0065 | 10.46928 |
| Thigh | 1 | 0.22264 | 0.14465 | 1.54 | 0.1251 | 7.75310 |
| Knee | 1 | -0.08666 | 0.23483 | -0.37 | 0.7124 | 4.31235 |
| Ankle | 1 | 0.10688 | 0.21850 | 0.49 | 0.6252 | 1.84379 |
| Biceps | 1 | 0.13168 | 0.16905 | 0.78 | 0.4368 | 3.50690 |
| Forearm | 1 | 0.44842 | 0.19984 | 2.24 | 0.0258 | 2.19223 |
| Wrist | 1 | -1.74681 | 0.53138 | -3.29 | 0.0012 | 3.30871 |

**Some collinearity still exists in the model. If Abdomen, the remaining variable with the highest VIF, is removed then the R square (and adjusted R square) value is reduced by approximately 0.13.**

## Solutions to Student Activities (Polls/Quizzes)

### 4.01 Poll – Correct Answer

Predictor variables are assumed to be normally distributed in linear regression models.

❍ True

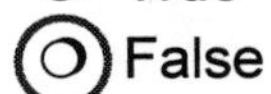 False

7

### 4.02 Multiple Choice Poll – Correct Answer

Given the properties of the standard normal distribution, you would expect about 95% of the studentized residuals to be between which two values?

a. -3 and 3
(b.) -2 and 2
c. -1 and 1
d. 0 and 1
e. 0 and 2
f. 0 and 3

25

## 4.03 Multiple Choice Poll – Correct Answer

How many observations did you find that might substantially influence parameter estimates?

a. 0
b. 1
c. 4
d. 5
e. 7
f. 10 (circled)

36

## 4.04 Multiple Choice Poll – Correct Answer

Which of the following assumptions does collinearity violate?

a. Independent errors
b. Constant variance
c. Normally distributed errors
d. None of the above (circled)

46

## 4.05 Poll – Correct Answer

If there is no correlation among the predictor variables, can there still be collinearity in the model?

❍ Yes

No

52

# Chapter 5 Categorical Data Analysis

# 5.1 Describing Categorical Data

## Objectives

- Examine the distribution of categorical variables.
- Do preliminary examinations of associations between variables.

3

## Examining Categorical Variables

By examining the distributions of categorical variables, you can do the following:

- determine the frequencies of data values.
- recognize possible associations among variables

4

## Categorical Variables Association

- An association exists between two categorical variables if the distribution of one variable changes when the level (or value) of the other variable changes.
- If there is no association, the distribution of the first variable is the same regardless of the level of the other variable.

5

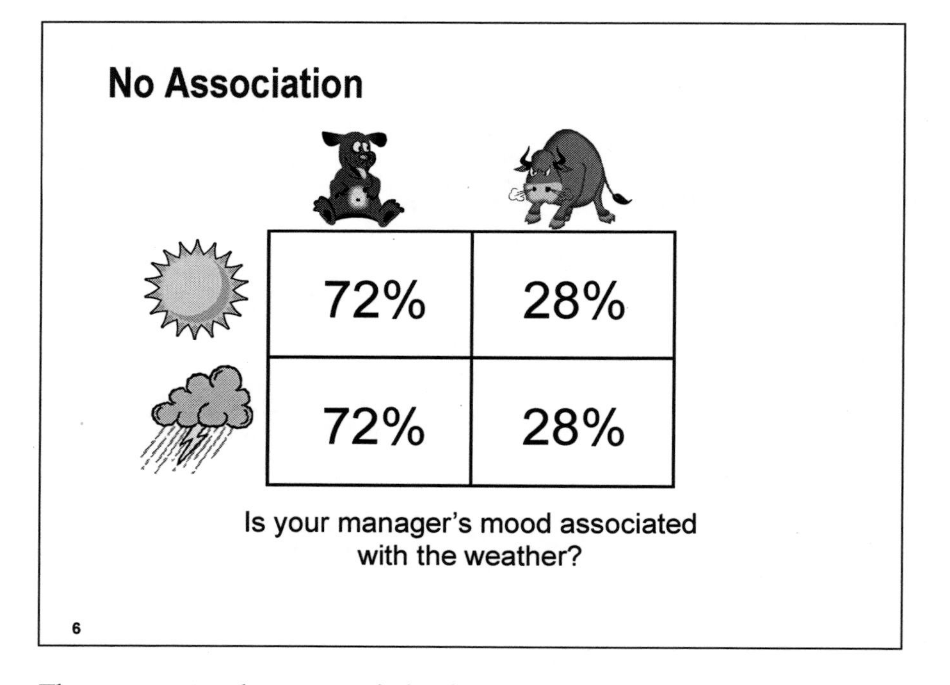


There appears to be no association between your manager's mood and the weather here because the row percentages are the ***same*** in each column.

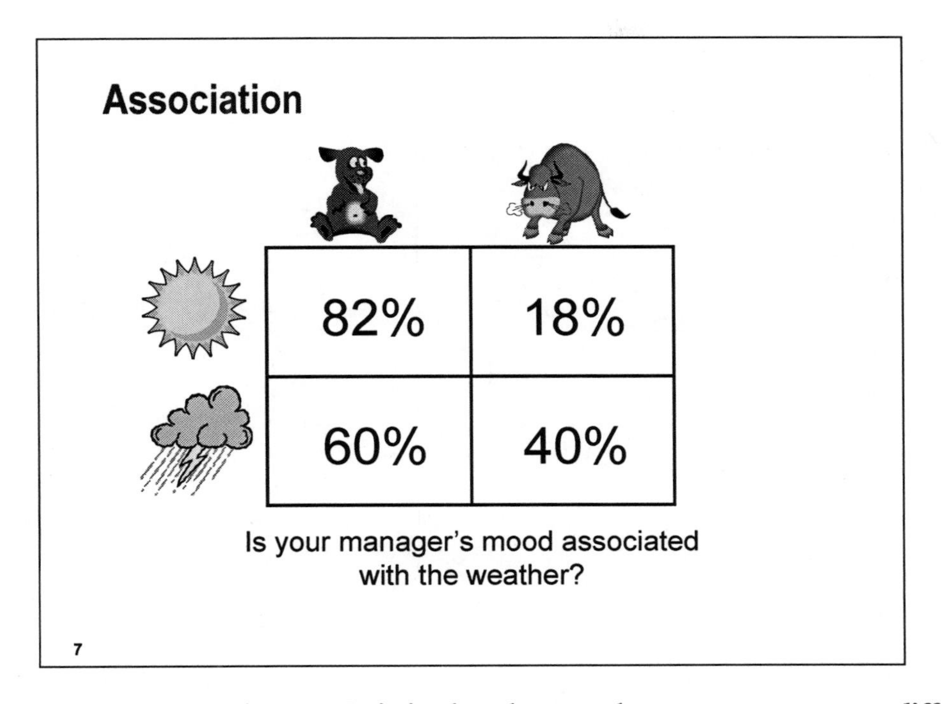


There appears to be an association here because the row percentages are ***different*** in each column.

## Frequency Tables

A frequency table shows the number of observations that occur in certain categories or intervals. A one-way frequency table examines one variable.

| Income | Frequency | Percent | Cumulative Frequency | Cumulative Percent |
|---|---|---|---|---|
| High | 155 | 36 | 155 | 36 |
| Low | 132 | 31 | 287 | 67 |
| Medium | 144 | 33 | 431 | 100 |

8

Typically, there are four types of frequency measures included in a frequency table:

| | |
|---|---|
| Frequency | is the number of times the value appears in the data set. |
| Percent | represents the percentage of the data that has this value. |
| Cumulative Frequency | accumulates the frequency of each of the values by adding the second frequency to the first, and so on. |
| Cumulative Percent | accumulates the percentage by adding the second percentage to the first, and so on. |

## Crosstabulation Tables

A *crosstabulation* table shows the number of observations for each combination of the row and column variables.

| | column 1 | column 2 | ... | column c |
|---|---|---|---|---|
| row 1 | $cell_{11}$ | $cell_{12}$ | ... | $cell_{1c}$ |
| row 2 | $cell_{21}$ | $cell_{22}$ | ... | $cell_{2c}$ |
| ... | ... | ... | ... | ... |
| row r | $cell_{r1}$ | $cell_{r2}$ | ... | $cell_{rc}$ |

9

By default, a crosstabulation table has four measures in each cell:

Frequency — Number of observations falling into a category formed by the row variable value and the column variable value

Percent — Number of observations in each cell as a percentage of the total number of observations

Row Pct — Number of observations in each cell as a percentage of the total number of observations in that row

Col Pct — Number of observations in each cell as a percentage of the total number of observations in that column

## The FREQ Procedure

General form of the FREQ procedure:

```
PROC FREQ DATA=SAS-data-set;
     TABLES table-requests </ options>;
RUN;
```

10

Selected FREQ procedure statement:

TABLES requests tables and specifies options for producing tests. The general form of a table request is *variable1*variable2*...*, where any number of these requests can be made in a single TABLES statement. For two-way crosstabulation tables, the first variable represents the rows and the second variable represents the columns.

PROC FREQ can generate large volumes of output as the number of variables or the number of variable levels (or both) increases.

## Titanic Example

On the 10th of April, 1912, the RMS Titanic set out on its maiden voyage across the Atlantic Ocean carrying 2,223 passengers. On the 14th of April, it hit an iceberg and sank. There were 1,517 fatalities. Identifying information was not available for all passengers.

11

Example: The data are stored in the **sasuser.Titanic** data set.

These are the variables in the data set:

**Survival** survival status (1=`Survived`, 0=`Died`)

**Age** age of passenger in years

**Gender** gender of passenger (`male`, `female`)

**Class** ticket class (`1`, `2`, `3`)

**Fare** ticket fare (This variable is misleading because it is shown as the cumulative total for a purchase for each person in a party.)

This is a publically available data set.

## 5.01 Multiple Answer Poll

Which of the following would likely not be considered categorical in the data?

a. **Gender**
b. **Fare**
c. **Survival**
d. **Age**
e. **Class**

13

## Examining Distributions

Example: Invoke PROC FREQ and create one-way frequency tables for the variables **Gender**, **Class**, and **Survival** and create two-way frequency tables for the variables **Survival** by **Gender**, and **Survival** by **Class**. For the continuous variable, **Age**, create histograms for each level of **Survival**. Use a CLASS statement in PROC UNIVARIATE.

Use the FORMAT procedure to format the values of **Survival**.

```
/*st105d01.sas*/
title;
proc format;
   value survfmt 1="Survived"
                 0="Died"
                 ;
run;

proc freq data=sasuser.Titanic;
   tables Survived Gender Class
          Gender*Survived Class*Survived /
          plots(only)=freqplot(scale=percent);
   format Survived survfmt.;
run;

proc univariate data=sasuser.Titanic noprint;
   class Survived;
   var Age;
   histogram Age;
   inset mean std median min max / format=5.2 position=ne;
   format Survived survfmt.;
run;
```

Selected TABLES statement PLOTS option and suboptions:

FREQPLOT(<*suboptions*>) requests a frequency plot. Frequency plots are available for frequency and crosstabulation tables. For multiway tables, PROC FREQ provides a two-way frequency plot for each stratum.

(SCALE=) specifies the scale of the frequencies to display. The default is SCALE=FREQ, which displays unscaled frequencies. SCALE=PERCENT displays percentages (relative frequencies).

PROC FREQ Output

| Survived | Frequency | Percent | Cumulative Frequency | Cumulative Percent |
|---|---|---|---|---|
| Died | 809 | 61.80 | 809 | 61.80 |
| Survived | 500 | 38.20 | 1309 | 100.00 |

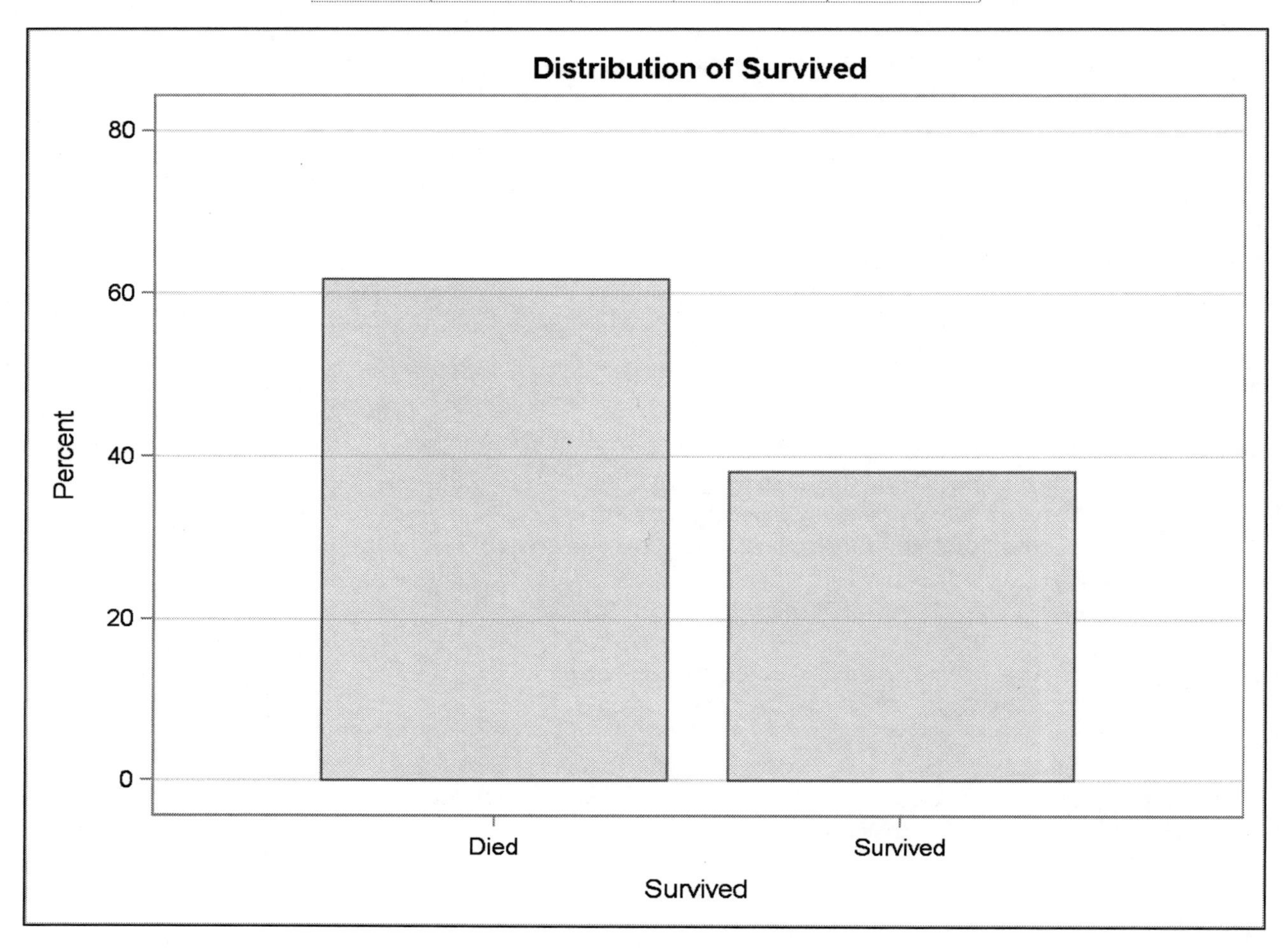

| Gender | Frequency | Percent | Cumulative Frequency | Cumulative Percent |
|---|---|---|---|---|
| female | 466 | 35.60 | 466 | 35.60 |
| male | 843 | 64.40 | 1309 | 100.00 |

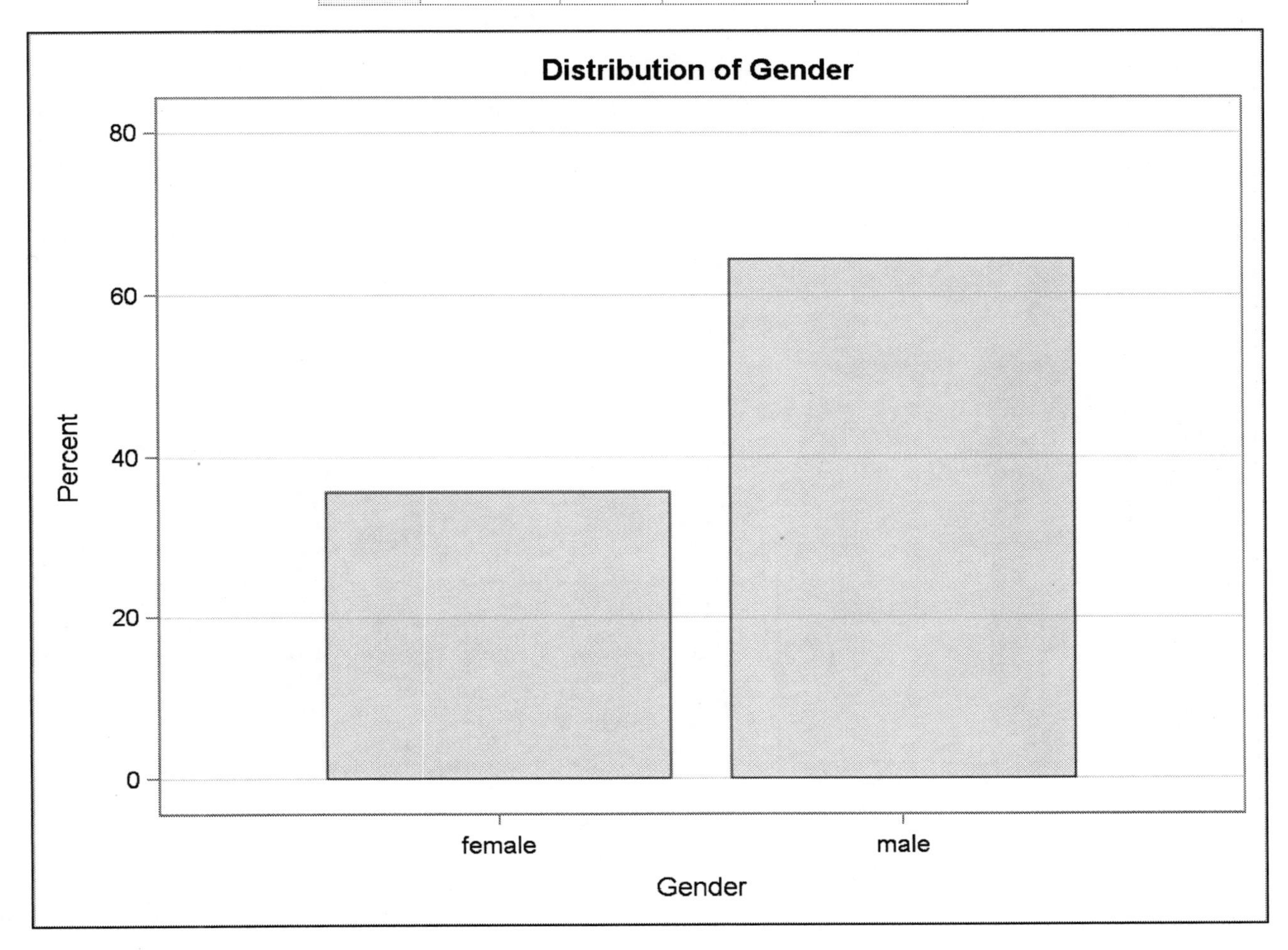

| Class | Frequency | Percent | Cumulative Frequency | Cumulative Percent |
|---|---|---|---|---|
| 1 | 323 | 24.68 | 323 | 24.68 |
| 2 | 277 | 21.16 | 600 | 45.84 |
| 3 | 709 | 54.16 | 1309 | 100.00 |

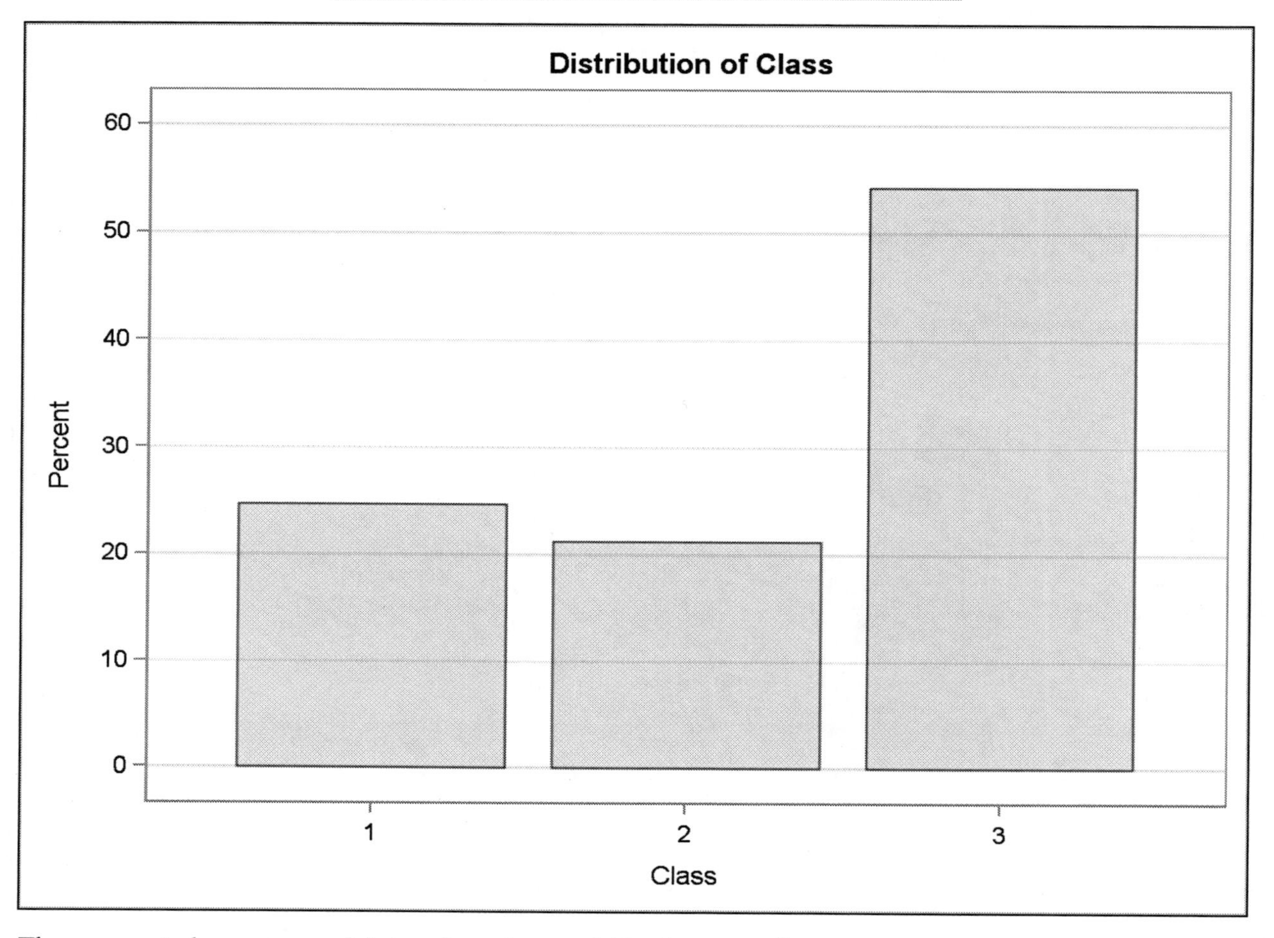


There seem to be no unusual data values that could be due to coding errors for any of the categorical variables.

The requested two-way frequency tables follow. You can get a preliminary idea whether there are associations between the outcome variable, **Survival,** and the predictor variables, **Gender** and **Class,** by examining the distribution of **Survival** at each value of the predictors.

| Table of Gender by Survived | | | |
|---|---|---|---|
| **Gender** | **Survived** | | |
| **Frequency**<br>**Percent**<br>**Row Pct**<br>**Col Pct** | **Died** | **Survived** | **Total** |
| **female** | 127<br>9.70<br>27.25<br>15.70 | 339<br>25.90<br>72.75<br>67.80 | 466<br>35.60 |
| **male** | 682<br>52.10<br>80.90<br>84.30 | 161<br>12.30<br>19.10<br>32.20 | 843<br>64.40 |
| **Total** | 809<br>61.80 | 500<br>38.20 | 1309<br>100.00 |

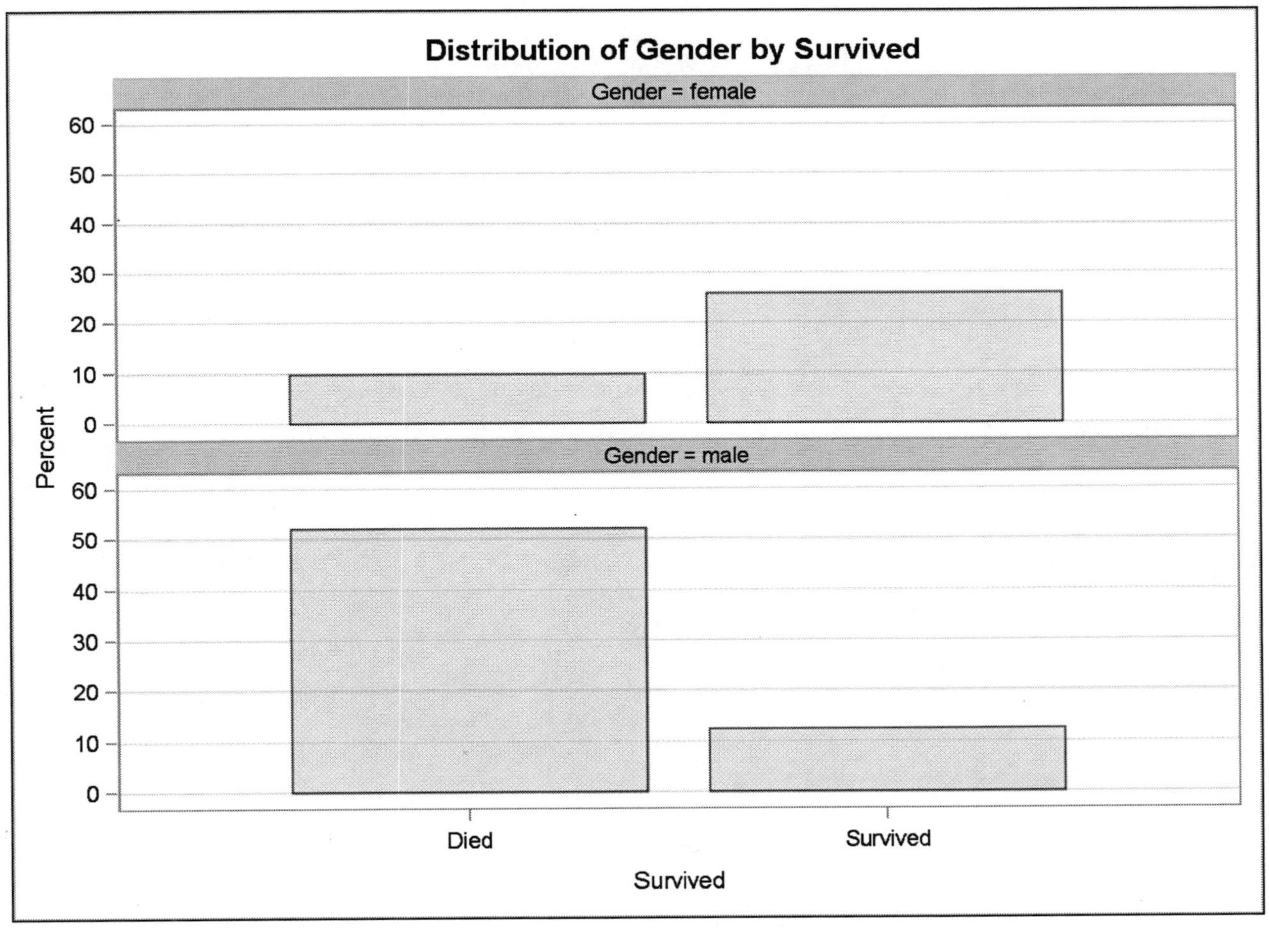


By examining the row percentages, you see that **Survival** is associated with **Gender**.

| Table of Class by Survived | | | |
|---|---|---|---|
| Class | Survived | | |
| Frequency<br>Percent<br>Row Pct<br>Col Pct | Died | Survived | Total |
| 1 | 123<br>9.40<br>38.08<br>15.20 | 200<br>15.28<br>61.92<br>40.00 | 323<br>24.68 |
| 2 | 158<br>12.07<br>57.04<br>19.53 | 119<br>9.09<br>42.96<br>23.80 | 277<br>21.16 |
| 3 | 528<br>40.34<br>74.47<br>65.27 | 181<br>13.83<br>25.53<br>36.20 | 709<br>54.16 |
| Total | 809<br>61.80 | 500<br>38.20 | 1309<br>100.00 |

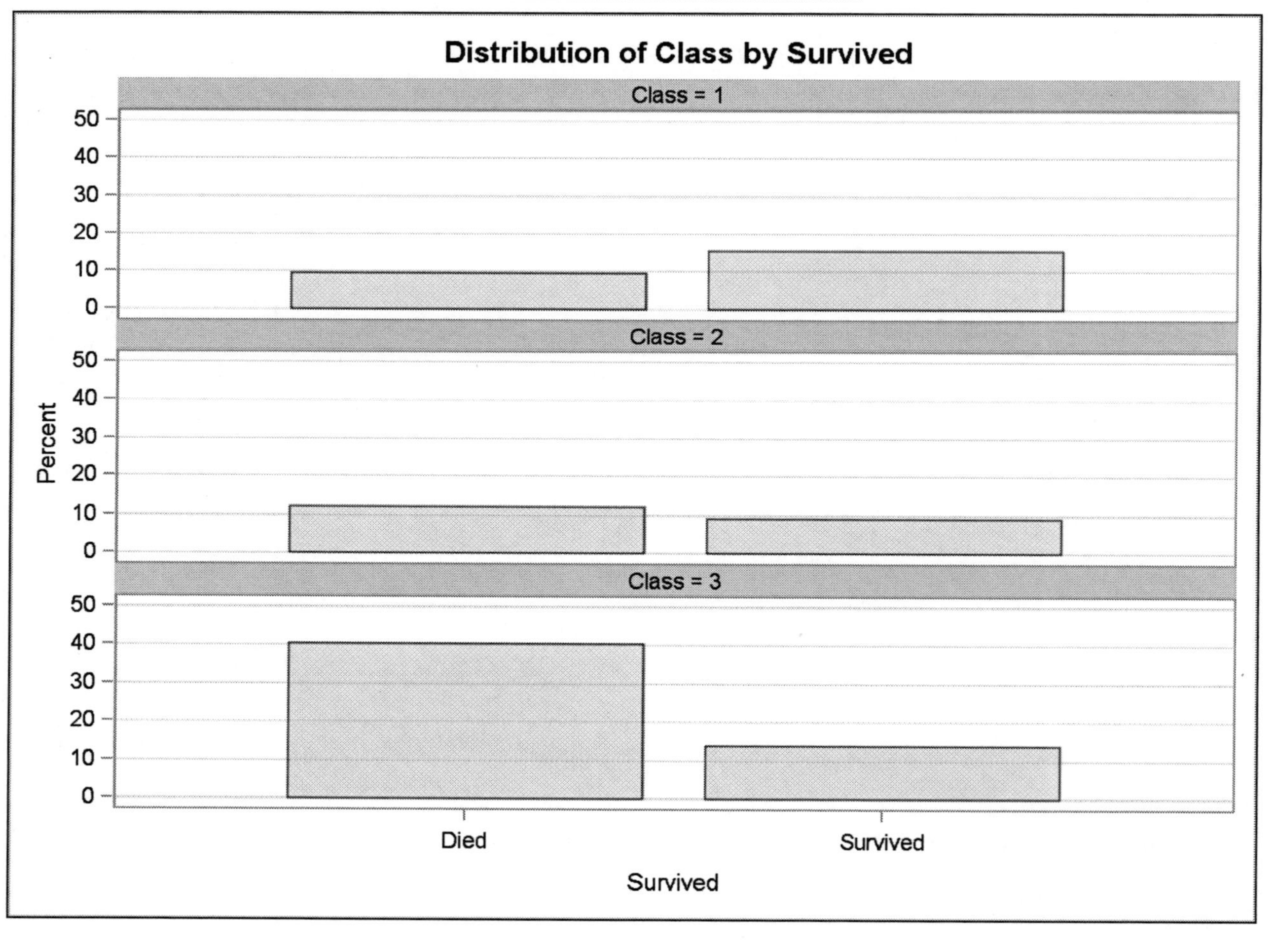


There also seems to be an association between **Survival** and **Class**, with a far greater chance of surviving in higher classes.

The plot below shows the distribution of the continuous variable, **Age**, by survival status.

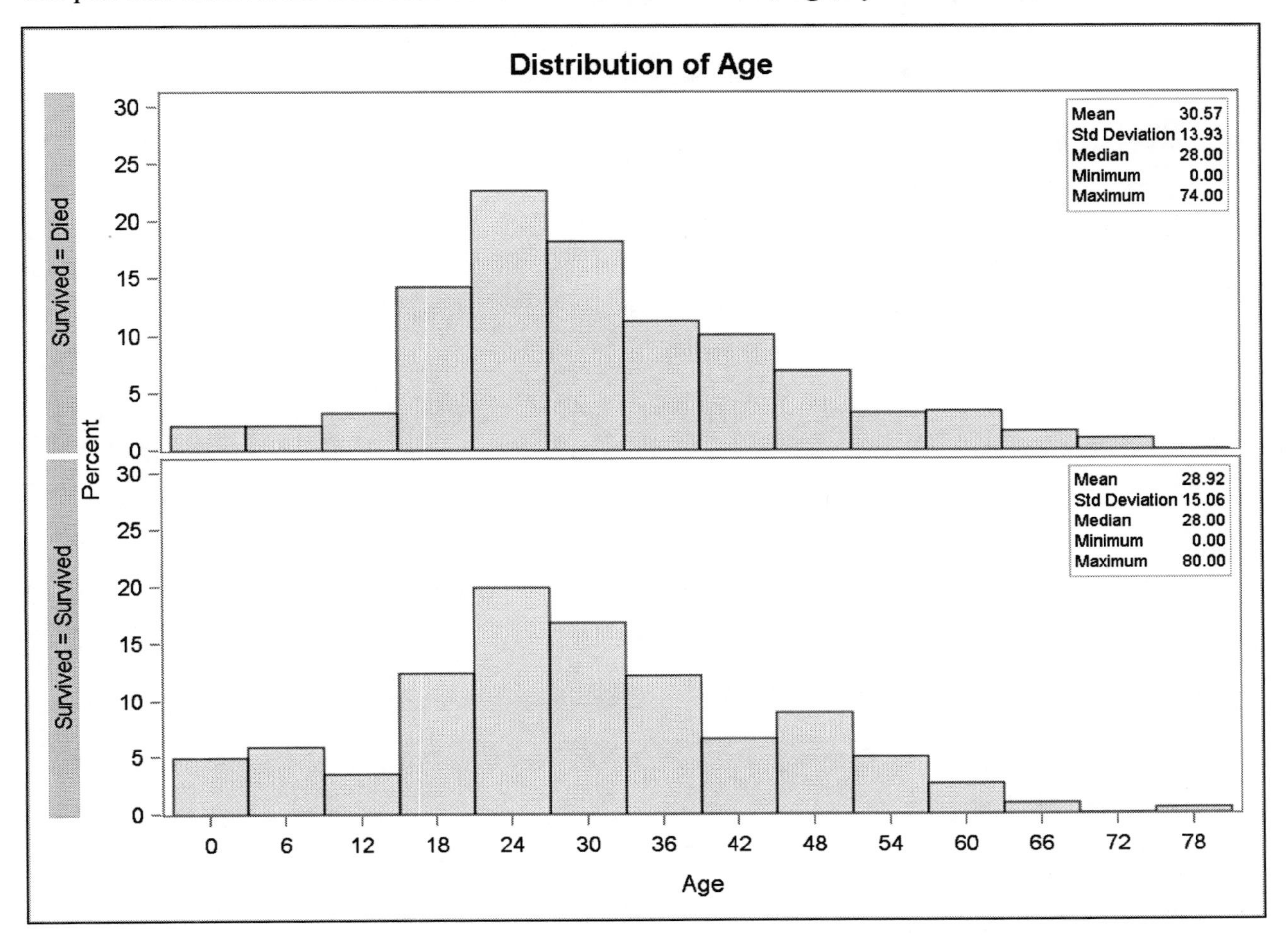


The distribution of **Age** appears to have no obvious outliers or strange shape for either group.

# 5.2 Tests of Association

## Objectives

- Perform a chi-square test for association.
- Examine the strength of the association.
- Calculate exact *p*-values.
- Perform a Mantel-Haenszel chi-square test.

18

## Overview

| Type of Predictors / Type of Response | **Categorical** | **Continuous** | **Continuous and Categorical** |
|---|---|---|---|
| Continuous | Analysis of Variance (ANOVA) | Ordinary Least Squares (OLS) Regression | Analysis of Covariance (ANCOVA) |
| **Categorical** | **Contingency Table Analysis** or Logistic Regression | Logistic Regression | Logistic Regression |

19

## Introduction

| Table of Gender by Survival | | | |
|---|---|---|---|
| **Gender** | **Purchase** | | |
| **Row Pct** | **Died** | **Survived** | **Total** |
| **female** | 27.75% | 72.25% | N=466 |
| **male** | 80.90% | 19.10% | N=843 |
| **Total** | N=809 | N=500 | N=1309 |

20

There appears to be an association between **Gender** and **Survival** because the row probabilities are different in each column. To test for this association, you assess whether the difference between the probabilities of females surviving (72.25%) and males surviving (19.10%) is greater than would be expected by chance.

## Null Hypothesis

- There is no association between **Gender** and **Survival**.
- The probability of surviving the Titanic crash was the same whether you were male or female.

### Alternative Hypothesis

- There ***is*** an association between **Gender** and **Survival**.
- The probability of surviving the Titanic crash was not the same for males and females.

21

## Chi-Square Test

***NO ASSOCIATION***

observed frequencies=expected frequencies

***ASSOCIATION***

observed frequencies≠expected frequencies

The expected frequencies are calculated by the formula: (row total*column total) / sample size.

22

A commonly used test that examines whether there is an association between two categorical variables is the Pearson chi-square test. The chi-square test measures the difference between the observed cell frequencies and the cell frequencies that are expected if there is no association between the variables. If you have a significant chi-square statistic, there is strong evidence that an association exists between your variables.

Under the null hypothesis of no association between Row and Column variable, the “expected” percentage in any R*C cell will be equal to the percent in that cell’s row (R / T) times the percent in the cell’s column (C / T). The expected count is then only that expected percentage times the total sample size. The expected count=(R/T)*(C/T)*T=(R*C)/T.

## Chi-Square Tests

Chi-square tests and the corresponding *p*-values

- determine whether an association exists
- do not measure the strength of an association
- depend on and reflect the sample size.

$$\chi^2 = \sum_{i=1}^{R}\sum_{j=1}^{C}\frac{(Obs_{ij} - Exp_{ij})^2}{Exp_{ij}}$$

23

The *p*-value for the chi-square test only indicates how confident you can be that the null hypothesis of no association is false. It does not tell you the magnitude of an association. The value of the chi-square statistic also does not tell you the magnitude of the association. If you double the size of your sample by duplicating each observation, you double the value of the chi-square statistic, even though the strength of the association does not change.

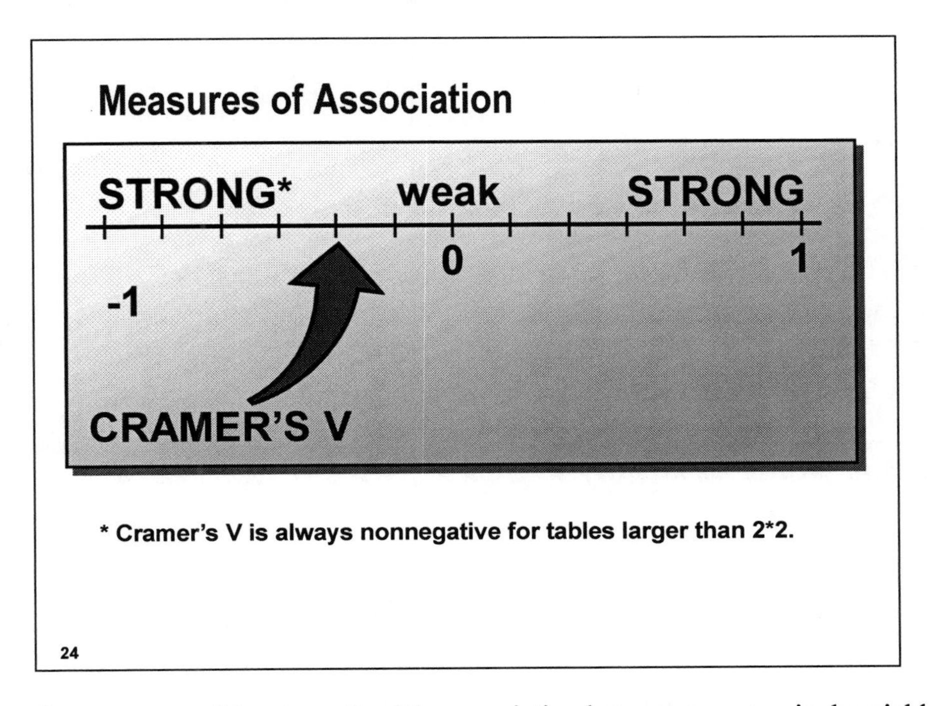


One measure of the strength of the association between two nominal variables is Cramer's V statistic. It has a range of –1 to 1 for 2-by-2 tables and 0 to 1 for larger tables. Values farther from 0 indicate stronger association. Cramer's V statistic is derived from the Pearson chi-square statistic.

## Odds Ratios

An *odds ratio* indicates how much more likely, with respect to odds, a certain event occurs in one group relative to its occurrence in another group.

Example: How do the odds of males surviving compare to those of females?

$$\text{Odds} = \frac{p_{event}}{1 - p_{event}}$$

25

The odds ratio can be used as a measure of the strength of association for 2 * 2 tables. Do not mistake odds for probability. Odds are calculated from probabilities as shown in the next slides.

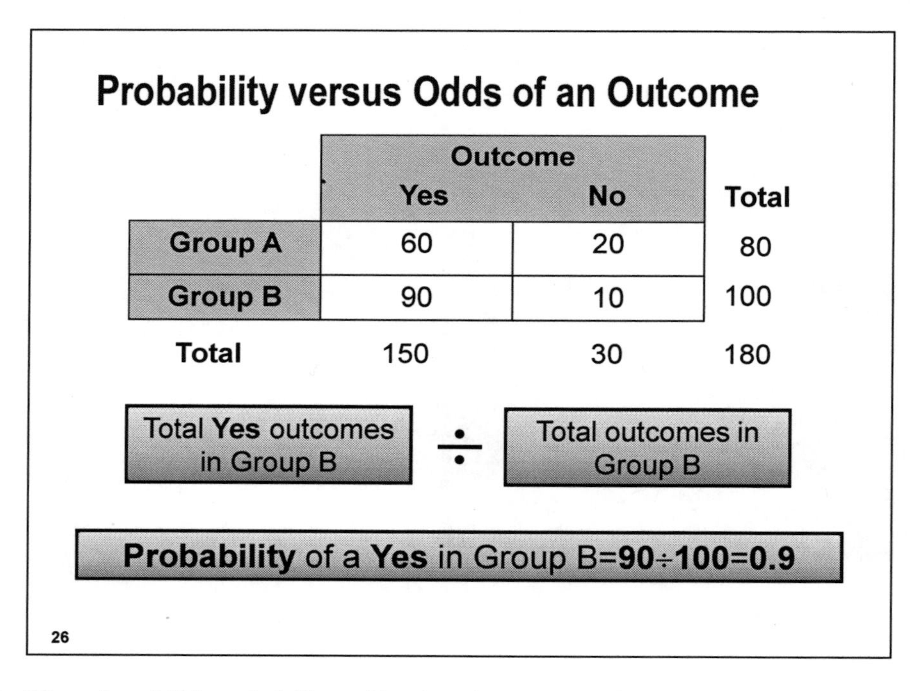


| | Outcome | | |
|---|---|---|---|
| | Yes | No | Total |
| Group A | 60 | 20 | 80 |
| Group B | 90 | 10 | 100 |
| Total | 150 | 30 | 180 |



There is a 90% probability of having the outcome in group B. What is the probability of having the outcome in group A?

## Probability versus Odds of an Outcome

| | Outcome: Yes | Outcome: No | Total |
|---|---|---|---|
| **Group A** | 60 | 20 | 80 |
| **Group B** | 90 | 10 | 100 |
| **Total** | 150 | 30 | 180 |

Probability of **Yes** in Group B=0.90 ÷ Probability of **No** in Group B=0.10

Odds of **Yes** in Group B=**0.90÷0.10=9**

27

The odds of an outcome are the ratio of the expected probability that the outcome will occur to the expected probability that the outcome will ***not*** occur. The odds for group B are 9, which indicate that you expect nine times as many occurrences as non-occurrences in group B.

What are the odds of having the outcome in group A?

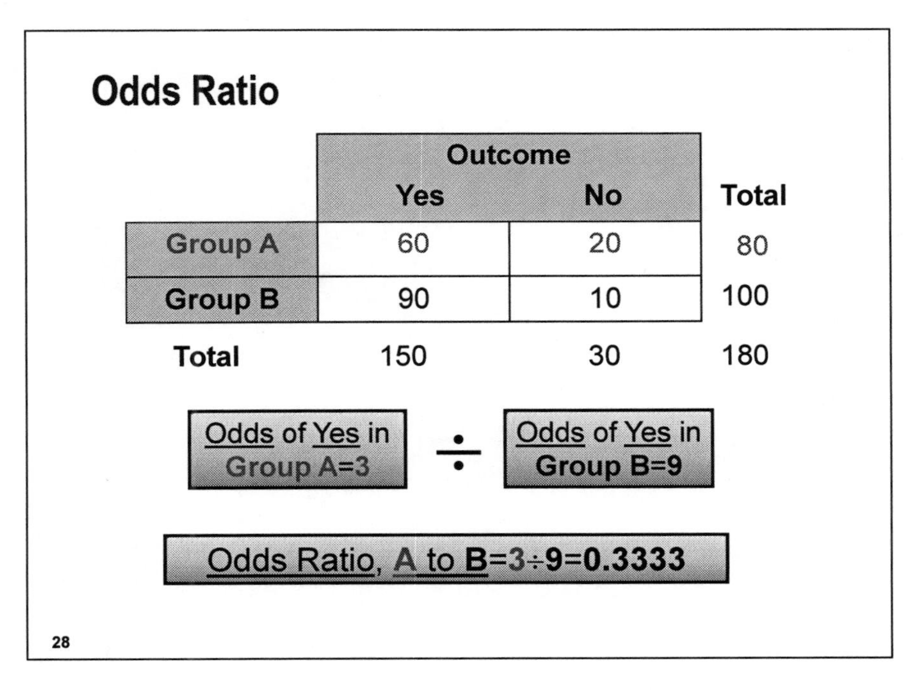


The odds ratio of group A to group B equals 1/3, or 0.3333, which indicates that the odds of getting the outcome in group A are one third those in group B. If you were interested in the odds ratio of group B to group A, you would simply take the inverse of 1/3 to arrive at 3.

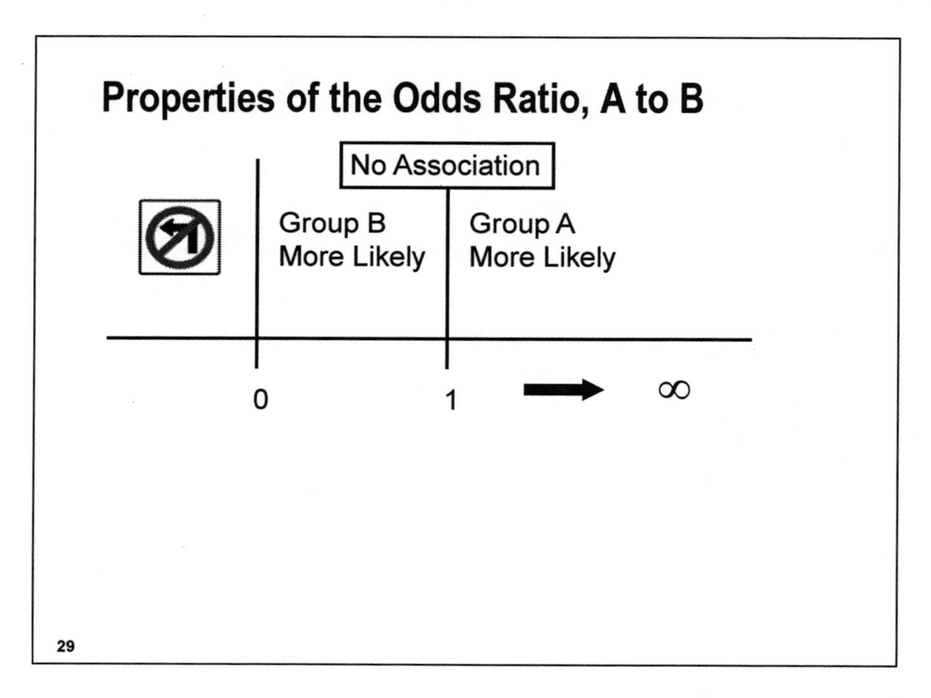


The odds ratio shows the strength of the association between the predictor variable and the outcome variable. If the odds ratio is 1, then there is no association between the predictor variable and the outcome. If the odds ratio is greater than 1, then group A, the numerator group, is more likely to have the outcome. If the odds ratio is less than 1, then group B, the denominator group, is more likely to have the outcome.

## Chi-Square Test

Example: Use the FREQ procedure to test for an association between the variables **Gender** and **Survived**. Also generate the expected cell frequencies and the cell's contribution to the total chi-square statistic.

```
/*st105d02.sas*/
ods graphics off;
proc freq data=sasuser.Titanic;
   tables (Gender Class)*Survived
         / chisq expected cellchi2 nocol nopercent
           relrisk;
   format Survived survfmt.;
   title1 'Associations with Survival';
run;
ods graphics on;
```

Selected TABLES statement options:

| | |
|---|---|
| CHISQ | produces the chi-square test of association and the measures of association based on the chi-square statistic. |
| EXPECTED | prints the expected cell frequencies under the hypothesis of no association. |
| CELLCHI2 | prints each cell's contribution to the total chi-square statistic. |
| NOCOL | suppresses printing the column percentages. |
| NOPERCENT | suppresses printing the cell percentages. |
| RELRISK | prints a table with risk ratios (probability ratios) and odds ratios. |

The frequency table is shown below.

| Table of Gender by Survived | | | |
|---|---|---|---|
| **Gender** | **Survived** | | |
| **Frequency**<br>**Expected**<br>**Cell Chi-Square**<br>**Row Pct** | **Died** | **Survived** | **Total** |
| **female** | 127<br>288<br>90.005<br>27.25 | 339<br>178<br>145.63<br>72.75 | 466 |
| **male** | 682<br>521<br>49.753<br>80.90 | 161<br>322<br>80.501<br>19.10 | 843 |
| **Total** | 809 | 500 | 1309 |

It appears that the cell for **Survived=`1`** (**`Survived`**) and **Gender=`female`** contributes the most to the chi-square statistic. The Cell Chi-Square value is 145.63.

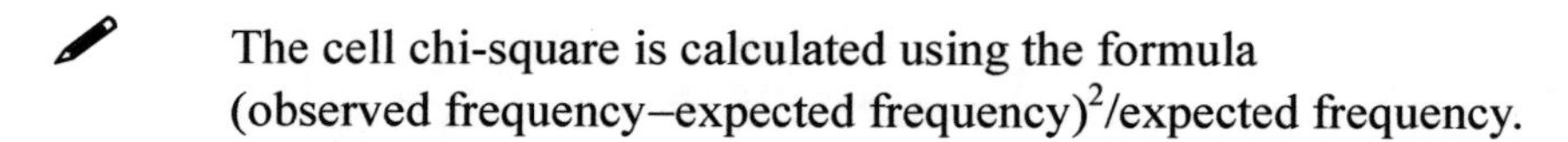

The cell chi-square is calculated using the formula (observed frequency–expected frequency)$^2$/expected frequency.

The overall chi-square statistic is calculated by adding the cell chi-square values over all rows and columns: $\Sigma\Sigma((\text{observed}_{rc}-\text{expected}_{rc})^2/\text{expected}_{rc})$.

Below is the table that shows the chi-square test and Cramer's V.

| Statistic | DF | Value | Prob |
|---|---|---|---|
| Chi-Square | 1 | 365.8869 | <.0001 |
| Likelihood Ratio Chi-Square | 1 | 372.9213 | <.0001 |
| Continuity Adj. Chi-Square | 1 | 363.6179 | <.0001 |
| Mantel-Haenszel Chi-Square | 1 | 365.6074 | <.0001 |
| Phi Coefficient | | -0.5287 | |
| Contingency Coefficient | | 0.4674 | |
| Cramer's V | | -0.5287 | |

Because the *p*-value for the chi-square statistic is <.0001, which is below .05, you reject the null hypothesis at the 0.05 level and conclude that there is evidence of an association between **Gender** and **Survived**. Cramer's V of -0.5287 indicates that the association detected with the chi-square test is relatively strong.

| Fisher's Exact Test | |
|---|---|
| Cell (1,1) Frequency (F) | 127 |
| Left-sided Pr <= F | 7.351E-83 |
| Right-sided Pr >= F | 1.0000 |
| | |
| Table Probability (P) | 6.705E-83 |
| Two-sided Pr <= P | 7.918E-83 |

Exact tests are often useful where asymptotic distributional assumptions are not met. The usual guidelines for the asymptotic chi-square test are generally 20-25 total observations for a $2 \times 2$ table, with 80% of the table cells having counts greater than 5. Fisher's Exact Test is provided by PROC FREQ when tests of association are requested for 2*2 tables. Otherwise, the exact test must be requested using an EXACT statement. The two-sided *p*-value of $7.918 * 10^{-83}$ is exceedingly small and statistically significant.

| Estimates of the Relative Risk (Row1/Row2) | | | |
|---|---|---|---|
| Type of Study | Value | 95% Confidence Limits | |
| Case-Control (Odds Ratio) | 0.0884 | 0.0677 | 0.1155 |
| Cohort (Col1 Risk) | 0.3369 | 0.2894 | 0.3921 |
| Cohort (Col2 Risk) | 3.8090 | 3.2797 | 4.4239 |

The Relative Risk table shows another measure of strength of association.

The odds ratio is shown in the first row of the table, along with the 95% confidence limits. The odds ratio can be interpreted as the odds of a top row (`female`, in this case) value to be in the left column (`Died`), compared with the same odds in the bottom row (`male`). The value of 0.0884 says that a female has about 9% of the odds of dying, compared with a male. This is equivalent to saying that a male has about 9% of the odds of surviving, compared with a female.

Cohort estimates for each column are interpreted as probability ratios, rather than odds ratios. You get a choice of assessing probabilities of the left column (Col1) or the right column (Col2). For example, the Col1 risk shows the ratio of the probabilities of females to males being in the left column (27.25/80.90=0.3369).

If is often easier to report odds ratios by first transforming the decimal value to a percent difference value. The formula for doing that is (OR-1) * 100. In the example, you have (0.0884-1)*100=-91.16%. In other words, males have 91.16 percent lower odds of surviving compared with females.

The 95% odds ratio confidence interval goes from 0.0677 to 0.1155. That interval does not include 1. This confirms the statistically significant (at alpha=0.05) result of the Pearson chi-square test of association. A confidence interval that included the value 1 (equality of odds) would be a non-significant result.

**Table of Class by Survived**

| Class | Survived | | |
|---|---|---|---|
| Frequency<br>Expected<br>Cell Chi-Square<br>Row Pct | Died | Survived | Total |
| 1 | 123<br>199.62<br>29.411<br>38.08 | 200<br>123.38<br>47.587<br>61.92 | 323 |
| 2 | 158<br>171.19<br>1.0169<br>57.04 | 119<br>105.81<br>1.6453<br>42.96 | 277 |
| 3 | 528<br>438.18<br>18.411<br>74.47 | 181<br>270.82<br>29.788<br>25.53 | 709 |
| Total | 809 | 500 | 1309 |

**Statistics for Table of Class by Survived**

| Statistic | DF | Value | Prob |
|---|---|---|---|
| Chi-Square | 2 | 127.8592 | <.0001 |
| Likelihood Ratio Chi-Square | 2 | 127.7655 | <.0001 |
| Mantel-Haenszel Chi-Square | 1 | 127.7093 | <.0001 |
| Phi Coefficient | | 0.3125 | |
| Contingency Coefficient | | 0.2983 | |
| Cramer's V | | 0.3125 | |

**Sample Size=1309**

There also seems to be an association between **Class** and **Survival** (Chi-Square(2 df)=127.8592, p<.0001). Cramer's V for that association is 0.3125.

Mantel-Haenszel chi-square is a test of an ordinal association between **Class** and **Survival.**

## 5.02 Multiple Answer Poll

What tends to happen when sample size decreases?

a. The chi-square value increases.
b. The *p*-value increases.
c. Cramer's V increases.
d. The Odds Ratio increases.
e. The width of the CI for the Odds Ratio increases.

32

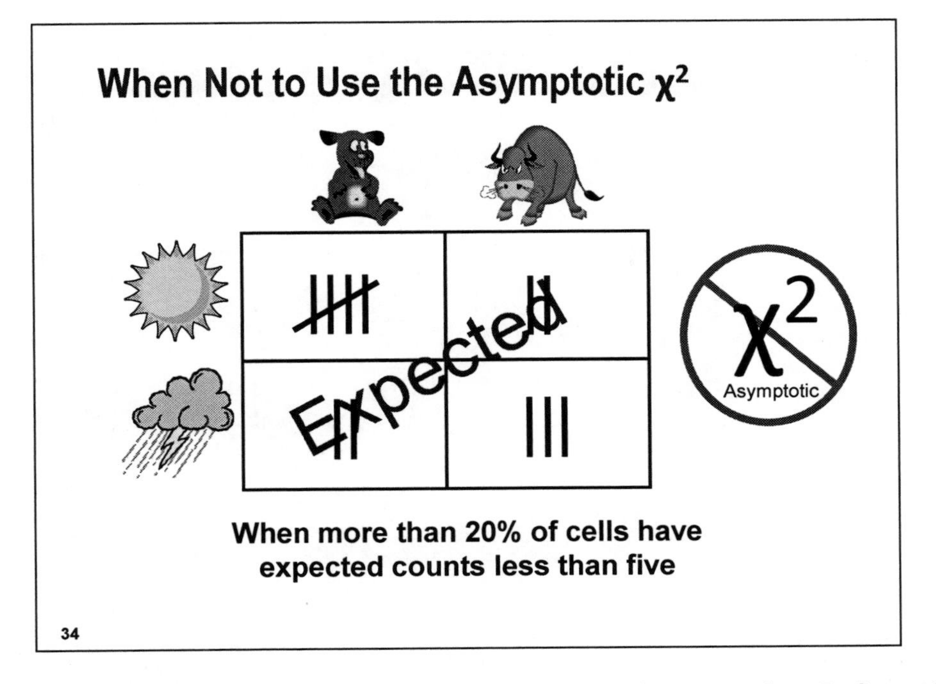


There are times when the chi-square test might not be appropriate. In fact, when more than 20% of the cells have expected cell frequencies of less than 5, the chi-square test might not be valid. This is because the *p*-values are based on the assumption that the test statistic follows a particular distribution when the sample size is sufficiently large. Therefore, when the sample sizes are small, the asymptotic (large sample) *p*-values might not be valid.

## Observed versus Expected Values

| Table of Row by Column | | | | |
|---|---|---|---|---|
| Row | Column | | | |
| Frequency<br>Expected | 1 | 2 | 3 | Total |
| 1 | 1<br>**3.4286** | 5<br>**4.5714** | 8<br>6 | 14 |
| 2 | 5<br>**4.4082** | 6<br>5.8776 | 7<br>7.7143 | 18 |
| 3 | 6<br>**4.1633** | 5<br>5.551 | 6<br>7.2857 | 17 |
| Total | 12 | 16 | 21 | 49 |

35

The criterion for the chi-square test is based on the expected values, not the observed values. In the slide above, 1 out of 9, or 11% of the cells, has an ***observed*** count less than 5. However, 4 out of 9, or 44%, of the cells have ***expected*** counts less than 5. Therefore, the chi-square test might not be valid.

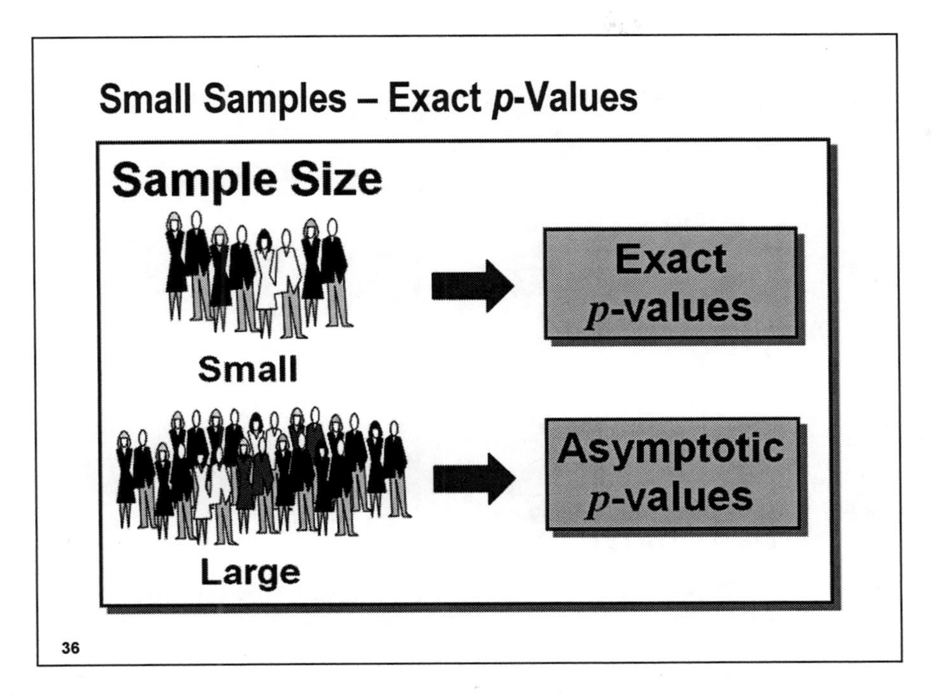


The EXACT statement provides exact *p*-values for many tests in the FREQ procedure. Exact *p*-values are useful when the sample size is small. In this case, the asymptotic *p*-values might not be useful.

However, large data sets (in terms of sample size, number of rows, and number of columns) can require a prohibitive amount of time and memory for computing exact *p*-values. For large data sets, consider whether exact *p*-values are needed or whether asymptotic *p*-values might be quite close to the exact *p*-values.

## Exact *p*-Values for Pearson Chi-Square

Observed Table

| | | |
|---|---|---|
| 0 | 3 | 3 |
| 2 | 2 | 4 |
| 2 | 5 | 7 |

Expected Table

| | | |
|---|---|---|
| .86 | 2.14 | 3 |
| 1.14 | 2.86 | 4 |
| 2 | 5 | 7 |

A *p*-value gives the probability of the value of the $\chi^2$ value being as extreme or more extreme than the one observed, just by chance.

Could the underlined sample values occur just by chance?

37

Consider the table at left above. With such a small sample size, the asymptotic *p*-values would not be valid, because the accuracy of those *p*-values depends on large enough expected values in all cells.

Exact *p*-values reflect the probability of observing a table with at least as much evidence of an association as the one actually observed, given there is no association between the variables.

Recall that expected count within each cell is calculated by expected count=(R*C)/T.

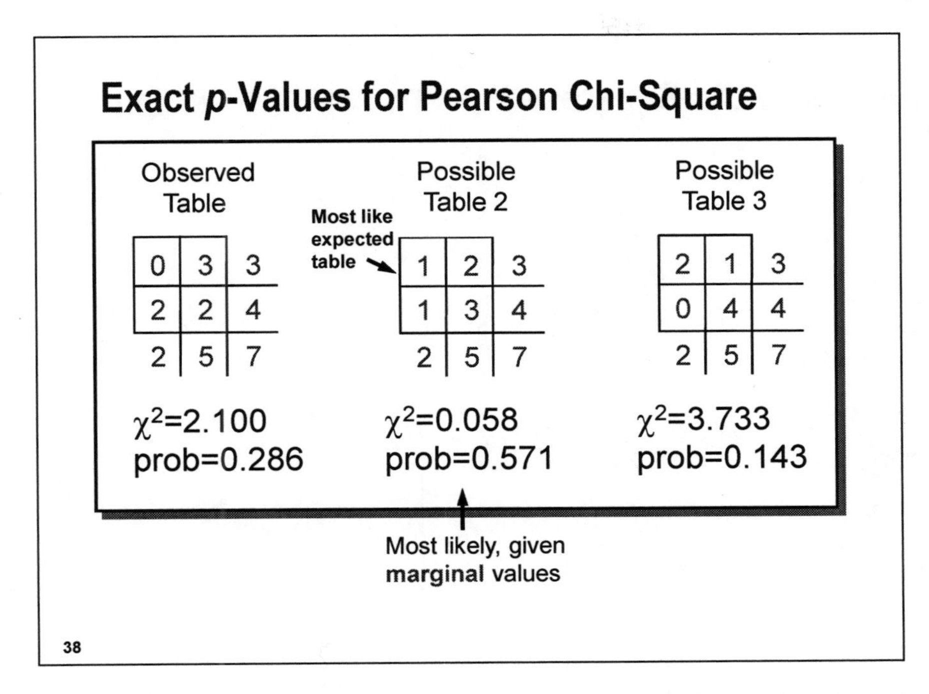


A key assumption behind the computation of exact *p*-values is that the column totals and row totals are fixed. There are only three possible tables, including the observed table, given the fixed marginal totals.

Possible Table 2 is most like the Expected Table of the previous slide. So, the probability (0.571) that its cell values would occur in a table, given these row and column total values, is greatest of any possible table that could occur by chance.

## Exact *p*-Values for Pearson Chi-Square

Observed Table

| 0 | 3 | 3 |
|---|---|---|
| 2 | 2 | 4 |
| 2 | 5 | 7 |

$\chi^2$=2.100
prob=0.286

Possible Table 2

| 1 | 2 | 3 |
|---|---|---|
| 1 | 3 | 4 |
| 2 | 5 | 7 |

$\chi^2$=0.058
prob=0.571

Possible Table 3

| 2 | 1 | 3 |
|---|---|---|
| 0 | 4 | 4 |
| 2 | 5 | 7 |

$\chi^2$=3.733
prob=0.143

The exact *p*-value is the sum of probabilities of all tables with $\chi^2$ values as great or greater than that of the Observed Table:

*p*-value=0.286+0.143=0.429

39

To compute an exact *p*-value for this example, examine the chi-square value for each table and the probability that the table should occur by chance if the null hypothesis of no association were true. (The probabilities add up to 1.)

Remember the definition of a *p*-value. It is the probability, if the null hypothesis is true, that you would obtain a sample statistic **as great as or greater than** the one you observed just by chance.

In this example, this means the probability of obtaining a table with a $\chi^2$ value as great as or greater than the 2.100 for the Observed Table. The probability associated with every table with a $\chi^2$ value of 2.100 or higher would be summed to compute the two-sided exact *p*-value.

The exact *p*-value would be 0.286 (Observed Table)+0.143 (Possible Table 3)=0.429. This means you have a 42.9% chance of obtaining a table with at least as much of an association as the observed table simply by random chance.

# Fisher's Exact *p*-Values for the Pearson Chi-Square Test

Example: Invoke PROC FREQ and produce exact *p*-values for the Pearson chi-square test. Use the **sasuser.exact** data set, which has the data from the previous example.

```
/*st105d03.sas*/
ods graphics off;
proc freq data=sasuser.exact;
   tables A*B / chisq expected cellchi2 nocol nopercent;
   title "Exact P-Values";
run;
ods graphics on;
```

The frequency table is shown below.

| Table of A by B | | | |
|---|---|---|---|
| A | B | | |
| Frequency<br>Expected<br>Cell Chi-Square<br>Row Pct | 1 | 2 | Total |
| 1 | 0<br>0.8571<br>0.8571<br>0.00 | 3<br>2.1429<br>0.3429<br>100.00 | 3 |
| 2 | 2<br>1.1429<br>0.6429<br>50.00 | 2<br>2.8571<br>0.2571<br>50.00 | 4 |
| Total | 2 | 5 | 7 |

| Statistic | DF | Value | Prob |
|---|---|---|---|
| Chi-Square | 1 | 2.1000 | 0.1473 |
| Likelihood Ratio Chi-Square | 1 | 2.8306 | 0.0925 |
| Continuity Adj. Chi-Square | 1 | 0.3646 | 0.5460 |
| Mantel-Haenszel Chi-Square | 1 | 1.8000 | 0.1797 |
| Phi Coefficient | | -0.5477 | |
| Contingency Coefficient | | 0.4804 | |
| Cramer's V | | -0.5477 | |
| **WARNING: 100% of the cells have expected counts less than 5. Chi-Square may not be a valid test.** | | | |

The warning tells you that you should not trust the reported *p*-value in this table.

| Fisher's Exact Test | |
|---|---|
| Cell (1,1) Frequency (F) | 0 |
| Left-sided Pr <= F | 0.2857 |
| Right-sided Pr >= F | 1.0000 |
| | |
| Table Probability (P) | 0.2857 |
| Two-sided Pr <= P | 0.4286 |

The Two-sided Pr <= P value is the one you will report. Notice the difference between the exact *p*-value (0.4286) and the asymptotic *p*-value (0.1473) in the Pearson chi-square test table. The exact *p*-values are larger. Exact tests tend to be more conservative than asymptotic tests.

For tables larger than 2*2, an EXACT statement must be submitted to obtain exact *p*-values. For large tables, this can take a long time and use a great deal of computational resources.

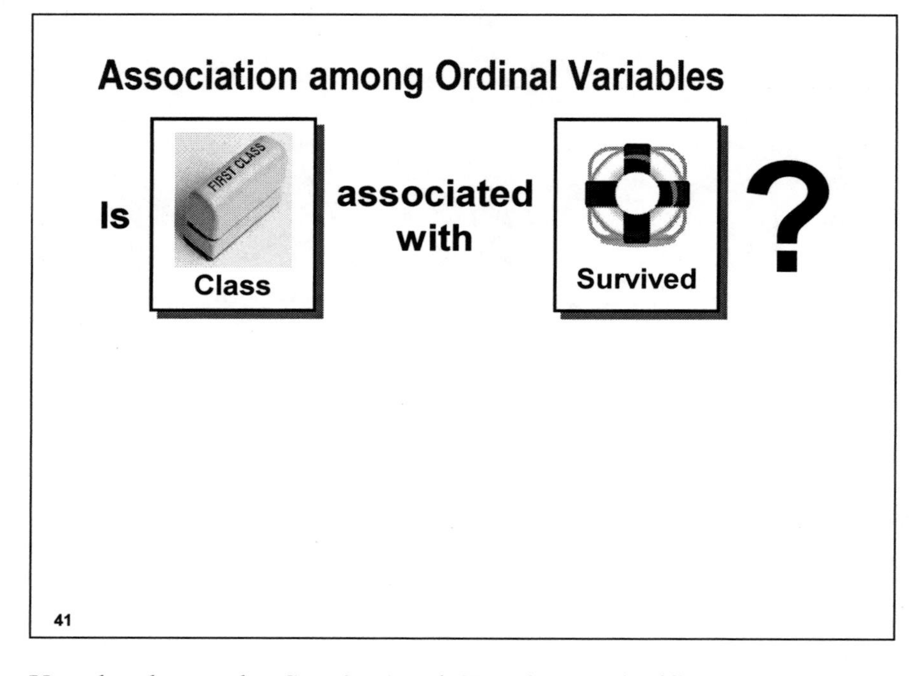


You already saw that **Survived** and **Class** have a significant general association. Another question that you can ask is whether **Survived** and **Class** have a significant ordinal association. The appropriate test for ordinal associations is the Mantel-Haenszel chi-square test.

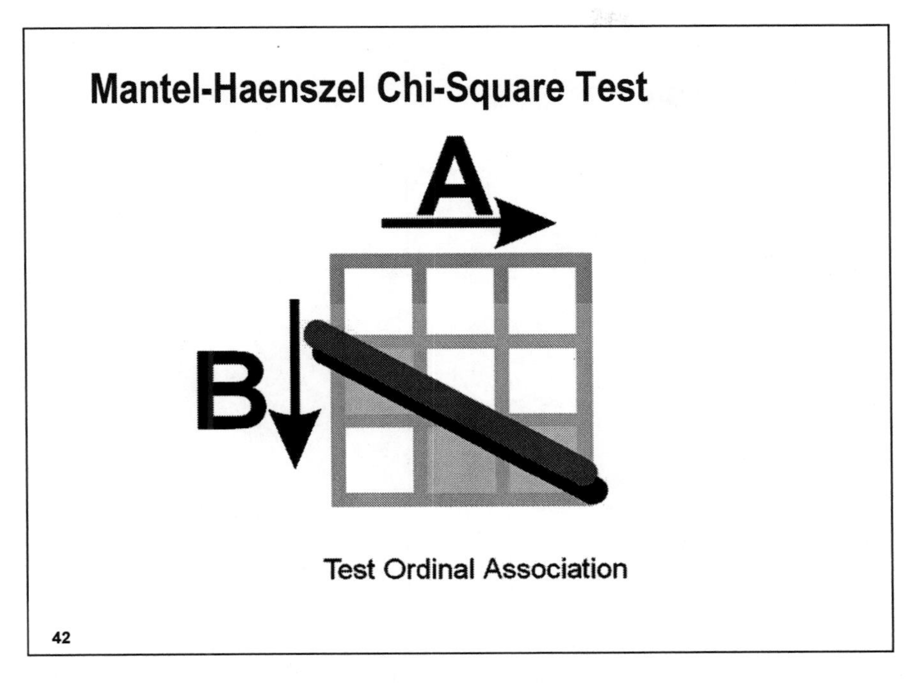


The Mantel-Haenszel chi-square test is particularly sensitive to ordinal associations. An *ordinal association* implies that as one variable increases, the other variable tends to increase, or decrease. For the test results to be meaningful when there are variables with more than two levels, the levels must be in a logical order.

| | |
|---|---|
| Null hypothesis: | There is no ordinal association between the row and column variables. |
| Alternative hypothesis: | There is an ordinal association between the row and column variables. |

## Mantel-Haenszel Chi-Square Test

- Determines whether an ordinal association exists
- Does not measure the strength of the ordinal association
- Depends on and reflects the sample size

43

The Mantel-Haenszel chi-square statistic is more powerful than the general association chi-square statistic for detecting an ordinal association. The reasons are that

- all of the Mantel-Haenszel statistic's power is concentrated toward that objective
- the power of the general association statistic is dispersed over a greater number of alternatives.

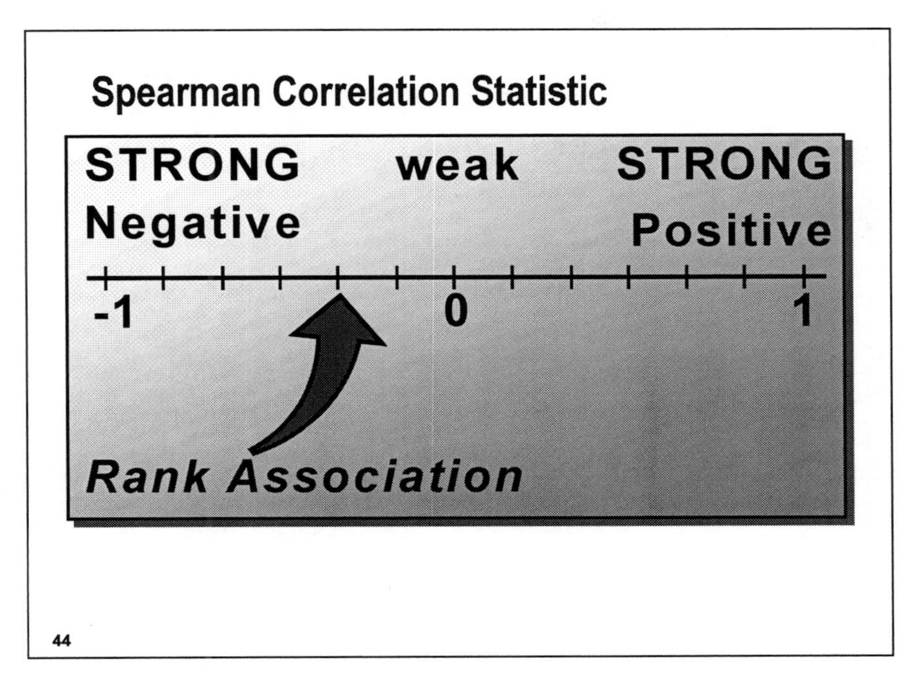


To measure the strength of the ordinal association, you can use the Spearman correlation statistic. This statistic

- has a range between –1 and 1
- has values close to 1 if there is a relatively high degree of positive correlation
- has values close to –1 if there is a relatively high degree of negative correlation
- is appropriate only if both variables are ordinal scaled and the values are in a logical order.

## Spearman versus Pearson

- The Spearman correlation uses ranks of the data.
- The Pearson correlation uses the observed values when the variable is numeric.

45

The Spearman statistic can be interpreted as the Pearson correlation between the ranks on variable X and the ranks on variable Y.

For character values, SAS assigns, by default, a 1 to column 1, a 2 to column 2, and so on. You can change the default with the SCORES= option in the TABLES statement.

# Detecting Ordinal Associations

Example: Use PROC FREQ to test whether an ordinal association exists between **Survived** and **Class**.

```
/*st105d04.sas*/
ods graphics off;
proc freq data=sasuser.Titanic;
   tables Class*Survived / chisq measures cl;
   format Survived survfmt.;
   title1 'Ordinal Association between CLASS and SURVIVAL?';
run;
ods graphics on;
```

Selected TABLES statement options:

CHISQ produces the Pearson chi-square, the likelihood-ratio chi-square, and the Mantel-Haenszel chi-square. It also produces measures of association based on chi-square such as the phi coefficient, the contingency coefficient, and Cramer's V.

MEASURES produces the Spearman correlation statistic along with other measures of association.

CL produces confidence bounds for the MEASURES statistics.

The crosstabulation is shown below.

| Table of Class by Survived | | | |
|---|---|---|---|
| **Class** | **Survived** | | |
| **Frequency<br>Percent<br>Row Pct<br>Col Pct** | **Died** | **Survived** | **Total** |
| **1** | 123<br>9.40<br>38.08<br>15.20 | 200<br>15.28<br>61.92<br>40.00 | 323<br>24.68 |
| **2** | 158<br>12.07<br>57.04<br>19.53 | 119<br>9.09<br>42.96<br>23.80 | 277<br>21.16 |
| **3** | 528<br>40.34<br>74.47<br>65.27 | 181<br>13.83<br>25.53<br>36.20 | 709<br>54.16 |
| **Total** | 809<br>61.80 | 500<br>38.20 | 1309<br>100.00 |

The results of the Mantel-Haenszel chi-square test are shown below.

| Statistic | DF | Value | Prob |
|---|---|---|---|
| Chi-Square | 2 | 127.8592 | <.0001 |
| Likelihood Ratio Chi-Square | 2 | 127.7655 | <.0001 |
| Mantel-Haenszel Chi-Square | 1 | 127.7093 | <.0001 |
| Phi Coefficient | | 0.3125 | |
| Contingency Coefficient | | 0.2983 | |
| Cramer's V | | 0.3125 | |

Because the *p*-value of the Mantel-Haenszel chi-square is <.0001, you can conclude at the 0.05 significance level that there is evidence of an ordinal association between **Survived** and **Class**.

The Spearman correlation statistic and the 95% confidence bounds are shown below.

| Statistic | Value | ASE | 95% Confidence Limits | |
|---|---|---|---|---|
| Gamma | -0.5067 | 0.0375 | -0.5801 | -0.4332 |
| Kendall's Tau-b | -0.2948 | 0.0253 | -0.3444 | -0.2451 |
| Stuart's Tau-c | -0.3141 | 0.0274 | -0.3677 | -0.2604 |
| Somers' D C\|R | -0.2613 | 0.0226 | -0.3056 | -0.2170 |
| Somers' D R\|C | -0.3326 | 0.0286 | -0.3887 | -0.2765 |
| Pearson Correlation | -0.3125 | 0.0267 | -0.3647 | -0.2602 |
| Spearman Correlation | -0.3097 | 0.0266 | -0.3619 | -0.2576 |
| Lambda Asymmetric C\|R | 0.1540 | 0.0331 | 0.0892 | 0.2188 |
| Lambda Asymmetric R\|C | 0.0317 | 0.0320 | 0.0000 | 0.0944 |
| Lambda Symmetric | 0.0873 | 0.0292 | 0.0301 | 0.1445 |
| Uncertainty Coefficient C\|R | 0.0734 | 0.0127 | 0.0485 | 0.0983 |
| Uncertainty Coefficient R\|C | 0.0485 | 0.0084 | 0.0320 | 0.0650 |
| Uncertainty Coefficient Symmetric | 0.0584 | 0.0101 | 0.0386 | 0.0782 |

The Spearman Correlation (-0.3097) indicates that there is a moderate, negative ordinal relationship between **Class** and **Survived** (that is, as **Class** levels increase, **Survived** tends to decrease).

The ASE is the asymptotic standard error (0.0266), which is an appropriate measure of the standard error for larger samples.

Because the 95% confidence interval (-0.3619, -0.2576) for the Spearman correlation statistic does not contain 0, the relationship is significant at the 0.05 significance level.

The confidence bounds are valid only if your sample size is large. A general guideline is to have a sample size of at least 25 for each degree of freedom in the Pearson chi-square statistic.

## Exercises

### 1. Performing Tests and Measures of Association

An insurance company wants to relate the safety of vehicles to several other variables. A score is given to each vehicle model, using the frequency of insurance claims as a basis. The data are in the **sasuser.safety** data set.

The variables in the data set are as follows:

| | |
|---|---|
| **Unsafe** | dichotomized safety score (`1=Below Average`, `0=Average or Above`) |
| **Type** | type of car (`Large`, `Medium`, `Small`, `Sport/Utility`, `Sports`) |
| **Region** | manufacturing region (`Asia`, `N America`) |
| **Weight** | weight in 1000s of pounds |
| **Size** | trichotomized version of **Type** (`1=Small or Sports`, `2=Medium`, `3=Large or Sport/Utility`). |

**a.** Invoke the FREQ procedure and create one-way frequency tables for the categorical variables.

1) What is the measurement scale of each variable?

| Variable | Measurement Scale |
|---|---|
| **Unsafe** | ______________ |
| **Type** | ______________ |
| **Region** | ______________ |
| **Weight** | ______________ |
| **Size** | ______________ |

2) What is the proportion of cars made in North America?

3) For the variables **Unsafe**, **Size**, **Region**, and **Type**, are there any unusual data values that warrant further investigation?

**b.** Use PROC FREQ to examine the crosstabulation of the variables **Region** by **Unsafe**. Generate a temporary format to clearly identify the values of **Unsafe**. Along with the default output, generate the expected frequencies, the chi-square test of association, and the odds ratio.

Use the following code for the format:

```
proc format;
   value safefmt 0='Average or Above'
                 1='Below Average';
run;
```

1) For the cars made in Asia, what percentage had a below-average safety score?

2) For the cars with an average or above safety score, what percentage was made in North America?

3) Do you see a statistically significant (at the 0.05 level) association between **Region** and **Unsafe**?

4) What does the odds ratio compare and what does this one say about the difference in odds between Asian and North American cars?

**c.** Use the variable named **Size**. Examine the ordinal association between **Size** and **Unsafe**. Use PROC FREQ.

1) What statistic should you use to detect an ordinal association between **Size** and **Unsafe**?

2) Do you reject or fail to reject the null hypothesis at the 0.05 level?

3) What is the strength of the ordinal association between **Size** and **Unsafe**?

4) What is the 95% confidence interval around that statistic?

## 5.03 Multiple Answer Poll

A researcher wants to measure the strength of an association between two binary variables. Which statistic(s) can he use?

a. Hansel and Gretel Correlation
b. Mantel-Haenszel Chi-Square
c. Pearson Chi-Square
d. Odds Ratio
e. Spearman Correlation

50

# 5.3 Introduction to Logistic Regression

## Objectives

- Define the concepts of logistic regression.
- Fit a binary logistic regression model using the LOGISTIC procedure.
- Describe the standard output from the LOGISTIC procedure with one continuous predictor variable.
- Read and interpret odds ratio tables and plots.

54

## Overview

| Type of Predictors / Type of Response | Categorical | Continuous | Continuous and Categorical |
|---|---|---|---|
| Continuous | Analysis of Variance (ANOVA) | Ordinary Least Squares (OLS) Regression | Analysis of Covariance (ANCOVA) |
| **Categorical** | Contingency Table Analysis or Logistic Regression | **Logistic Regression** | Logistic Regression |

55

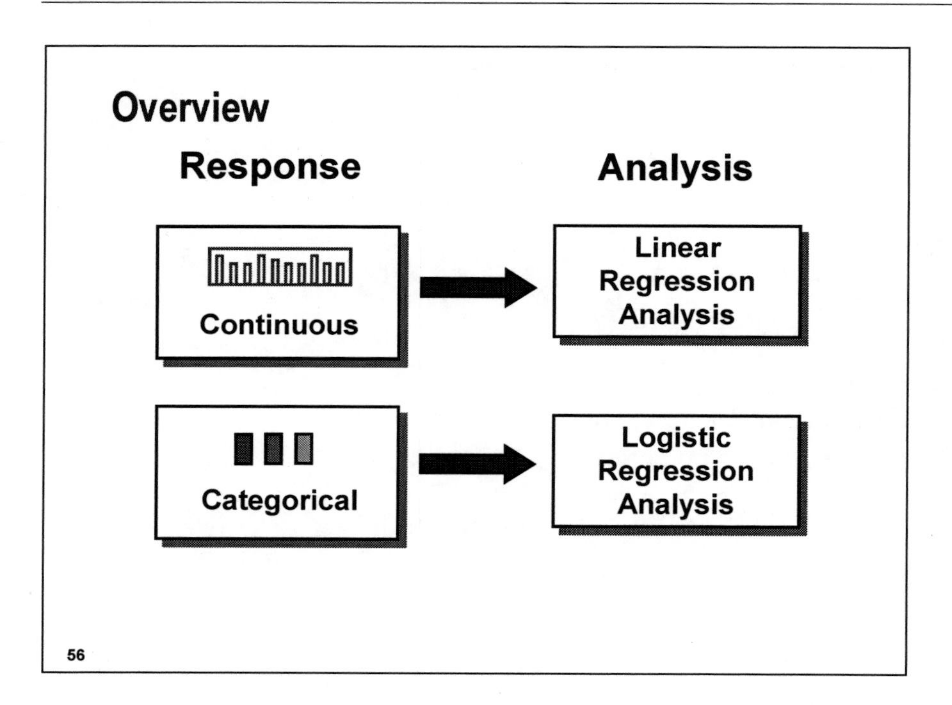


*Regression analysis* enables you to characterize the relationship between a response variable and one or more predictor variables. In linear regression, the response variable is continuous. In *logistic regression*, the response variable is categorical.

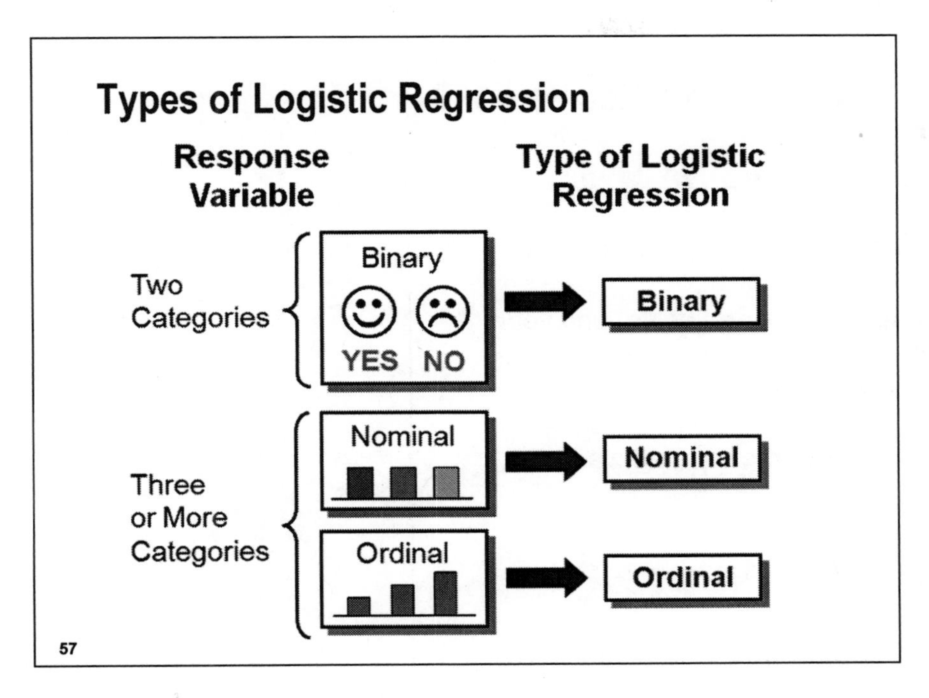


If the response variable is dichotomous (two categories), the appropriate logistic regression model is binary logistic regression.

If you have more than two categories (levels) within the response variable, then there are two possible logistic regression models:

1. If the response variable is nominal, you fit a nominal logistic regression model.
2. If the response variable is ordinal, you fit an ordinal logistic regression model.

## Why Not Ordinary Least Squares Regression?

*OLS Regression:* $Y_i = \beta_0 + \beta_1 X_{1i} + \varepsilon_i$

- If the response variable is categorical, then how do you code the response numerically?
- If the response is coded (1=Yes and 0=No) and your regression equation predicts 0.5 or 1.1 or -0.4, what does that mean practically?
- If there are only two (or a few) possible response levels, is it reasonable to assume constant variance and normality?

58

You might be tempted to analyze a regression model with a binary response variable using PROC REG. However, there are problems with that. Besides the arbitrary nature of the coding, there is the problem that the predicted values will take on values that have no intrinsic meaning, with regard to your response variable. There is also the mathematical inconvenience of not being able to assume normality and constant variance when the response variable has only two values.

## What about a Linear Probability Model?

*Linear Probability Model:* $p_i=\beta_0+\beta_1 X_{1i}$

- Probabilities are bounded, but linear functions can take on any value. (Once again, how do you interpret a predicted value of -0.4 or 1.1?)
- Given the bounded nature of probabilities, can you assume a linear relationship between X and *p* throughout the possible range of X?
- Can you assume a random error with constant variance?
- What is the observed probability for an observation?

59

Instead of modeling the zeros and ones directly, another way of thinking about modeling a binary variable is to model the probability of either the zero or the one. If you can model the probability of the one (called *p*), then you also modeled the probability of the zero, which would be $(1-p)$. Probabilities are truly continuous and so this line of thinking might sound compelling at first.

One problem is that the predicted values from a linear model can assume, theoretically, any value. However, probabilities are by definition bounded between 0 and 1.

Another problem is that the relationship between the probability of the outcome and a predictor variable is usually nonlinear rather than linear. In fact, the relationship often resembles an S-shaped curve (a "sigmoidal" relationship).

Probabilities do not have a random normal error associated with them, but rather a binomial error of $p*(1-p)$. That error is greatest at probabilities close to 0.5 and lowest near 0 and 1.

As mentioned above, probabilities have a binomial error of the form $p*(1-p)=(p-p^2)$. Taking the derivative of this expression with respect to *p* yields the expression $1-2*p$. Setting the derivative equal to zero and solving for *p* returns a value of 0.5. This binomial error equation is a downward facing parabola, which means that the greatest value is at 0.5 and lowest values are near 0 and 1.

Finally, there is no such thing as an "observed probability" and therefore least squares methods cannot be used. The response variable is always either 0 or 1 and therefore the probability of the event is either 0% or 100%. This is another reason why it is untenable to assume a normal distribution of error.

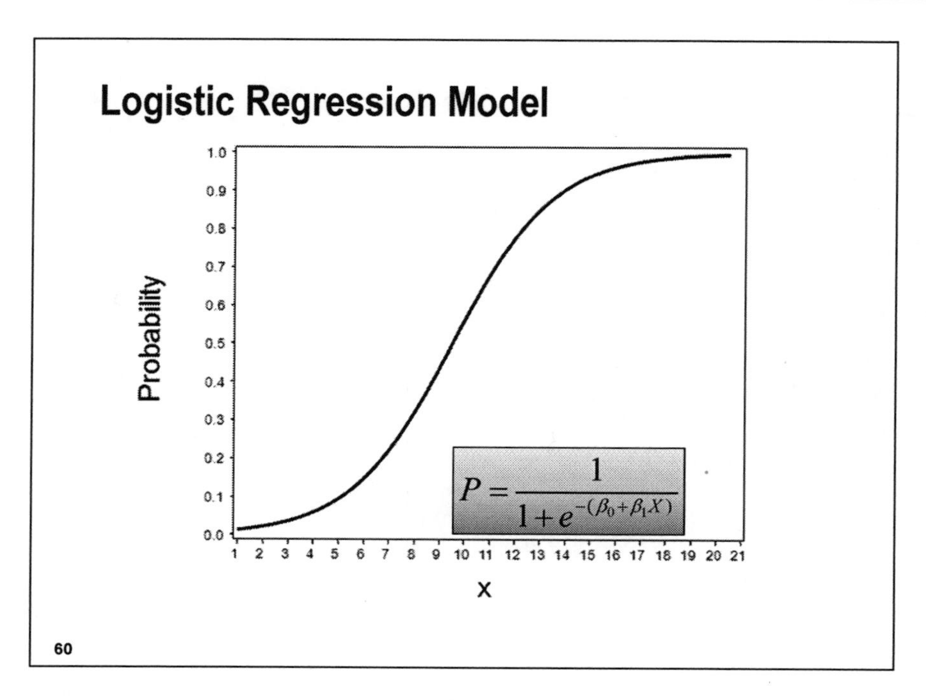


This plot shows a model of the relationship between a continuous predictor and the probability of an event or outcome. The linear model clearly does not fit if this is the true relationship between X and the probability. In order to model this relationship directly, you must use a nonlinear function. One such function is displayed. The S-shape of the function is known as a *sigmoid.*

The rate of change parameter of this function ($\beta_1$) determines the rate of increase or decrease of the curve. When the parameter value is greater than 0, the probability of the outcome increases as the predictor variable values increase. When the parameter is less than 0, the probability decreases as the predictor variable values increase. As the absolute value of the parameter increases, the curve has a steeper rate of change. When the parameter value is equal to 0, the curve can be represented by a straight, horizontal line that shows an equal probability of the event for everyone.

The $\beta$ values for this model cannot be computed in PROC REG because this is not a linear model.

## Logit Transformation

Logistic regression models transformed probabilities, called *logits**,

$$\text{logit}(p_i) = \ln\left(\frac{p_i}{(1-p_i)}\right)$$

where

| | |
|---|---|
| $i$ | indexes all cases (observations) |
| $p_i$ | is the probability that the event (for example, a sale) occurs in the $i^{th}$ case |
| ln | is the natural log (to the base e). |

* The logit is the natural log of the odds.

61

A logistic regression model applies a logit transformation to the probabilities. Two of the problems that you saw with modeling the probability directly were that probabilities were bounded between 0 and 1, and that there was not likely a straight line relationship between predictors and probabilities.

First, deal with the problem of restricted range of the probability. What about the range of a logit? As $p$ approaches its maximum value of 1, the value $\ln(p/(1-p))$ goes to infinity. As $p$ approaches its minimum value of 0, $p/(1-p)$ approaches 0. The natural log of something approaching 0 is something that goes to negative infinity. So, the logit has no upper or lower bounds.

If you can model the logit, then simple algebra enables you to model the odds or the probability. The logit transformation ensures that the model generates estimated probabilities between 0 and 1.

The logit is the natural log of the odds. The odds and odds ratios were discussed in a previous section. This relationship between the odds and the logit will become important later in this section.

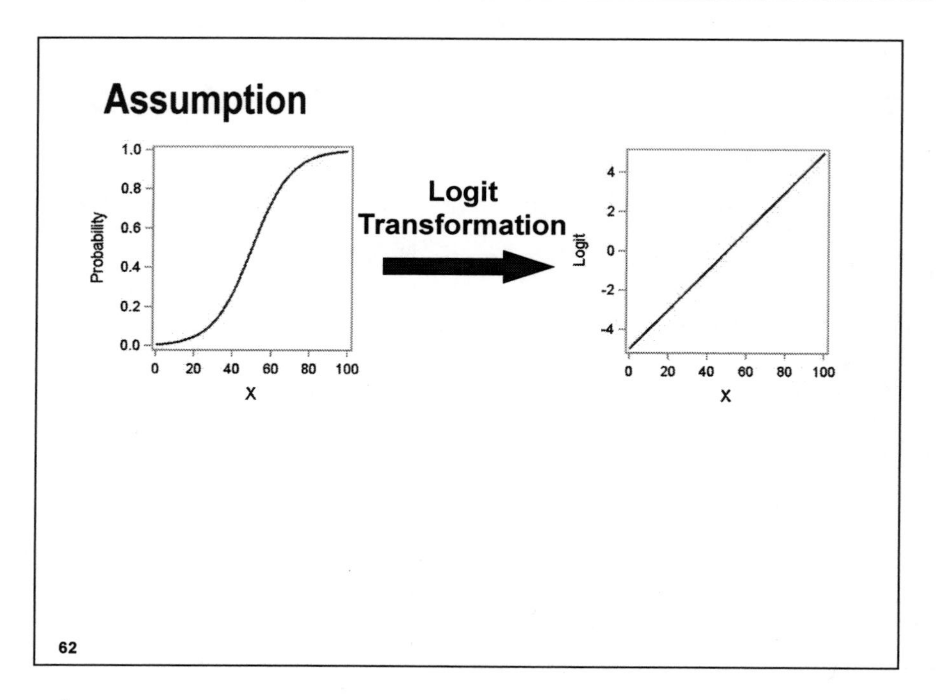


Assumption in logistic regression: The logit has a linear relationship with the predictor variables.

If the hypothesized nature of the direct relationship between X and $p$ are correct, then the logit has a linear relationship with X through the parameters. In other words, a linear function of X, additive in relation to the parameters, can be used to model the logit. In that way, you can indirectly model the probability.

To verify this assumption, it would be useful to plot the logits by the predictor variable. (Logit plots are illustrated in a later section.)

## Logistic Regression Model

$$\text{logit}(p_i)=\beta_0+\beta_1 X_{1i}+\ldots+\beta_k X_{ki}$$

where

**logit** $(p_i)$= logit of the probability of the event

$\beta_0$= intercept of the regression equation

$\beta_k$= parameter estimate of the $k^{th}$ predictor variable

63

For a binary response variable, the linear logistic model with one predictor variable has the form above.

Unlike linear regression, the logit is not normally distributed and the variance is not constant. Therefore, logistic regression requires a more computationally complex estimation method, named the *Method of Maximum Likelihood*, to estimate the parameters. This method finds the values of the parameters that make the observed data most likely. This is accomplished by maximizing the *likelihood function* that expresses the probability of the observed data as a function of the unknown parameters.

## 5.04 Multiple Choice Poll

What are the upper and lower bounds for a logit?

a. Lower=0, Upper=1
b. Lower=0, No upper bound
c. No lower bound, No upper bound
d. No lower bound, Upper=1

$$\text{logit}(p_i)=\ln\left(\frac{p_i}{(1-p_i)}\right)$$

65

## LOGISTIC Procedure

General form of the LOGISTIC procedure:

```
PROC LOGISTIC DATA=SAS-data-set <options>;
     CLASS variables </ options>;
     MODEL response=predictors </ options>;
     UNITS independent1=list ... </ options>;
     ODDSRATIO <'label'> variable </ options>;
     OUTPUT OUT=SAS-data-set keyword=name
                      </ options>;
RUN;
```

67

Selected LOGISTIC procedure statements:

CLASS names the classification variables to be used in the analysis. The CLASS statement must precede the MODEL statement. By default, these variables will be analyzed using effects coding parameterization. This can be changed with the PARAM= option.

MODEL specifies the response variable and the predictor variables.

OUTPUT creates an output data set containing all the variables from the input data set and any requested statistics.

UNITS enables you to obtain an odds ratio estimate for a specified change in a predictor variable. The unit of change can be a number, standard deviation (SD), or a number times the standard deviation (for example, 2*SD).

ODDSRATIO produces odds ratios for variables even when the variables are involved in interactions with other covariates, and for classification variables that use any parameterization. You can specify several ODDSRATIO statements.

## Simple Logistic Regression Model

Example: Fit a binary logistic regression model in PROC LOGISTIC. Select **Survived** as the outcome variable and **Age** as the predictor variable. Use the EVENT= option to model the probability of surviving and request profile likelihood confidence intervals around the estimated odds ratios.

```
/*st105d05.sas*/
proc logistic data=sasuser.Titanic alpha=.05
              plots(only)=(effect oddsratio);
   model Survived(event='1')=Age / clodds=pl;
   title1 'LOGISTIC MODEL (1):Survived=Age';
run;
```

Selected PLOTS options:

EFFECT requests a plot of the predicted probability on the Y axis by the predictor on the X axis. If there is more than one predictor variable in the model, the partial effect plot can be requested using the option (X=<*variable*>).

ODDSRATIO requests a plot of the odds ratios, along with its (1-ALPHA) confidence limits. The width of the confidence limits can be changed from the default of 95% using an ALPHA= option in the PROC LOGISTIC statement. The chosen alpha level applies to all confidence intervals produced in all tables and plots in that run of PROC LOGISTIC.

Selected MODEL statement options:

(EVENT=) specifies the event category for the binary response model. PROC LOGISTIC models the probability of the event category. You can specify the value (formatted if a format is applied) of the event category in quotation marks or you can specify one of the following keywords. The default is EVENT=FIRST.

| | |
|---|---|
| FIRST | designates the first ordered category as the event. |
| LAST | designates the last ordered category as the event. |

CLODDS=PL requests profile likelihood confidence intervals for the odds ratios of all predictor variables, which are desirable for small sample sizes. The CLODDS= option also enables production of the ODDSRATIO plot.

SAS Output

| Model Information | |
|---|---|
| **Data Set** | SASUSER.TITANIC |
| **Response Variable** | Survived |
| **Number of Response Levels** | 2 |
| **Model** | binary logit |
| **Optimization Technique** | Fisher's scoring |

The Model Information table describes the data set, the response variable, the number of response levels, the type of model, the algorithm used to obtain the parameter estimates, and the number of observations read and used.

The Optimization Technique is the iterative numerical technique that PROC LOGISTIC uses to estimate the model parameters.

The model is assumed to be "binary logit" when there are exactly two response levels.

| | |
|---|---|
| **Number of Observations Read** | 1309 |
| **Number of Observations Used** | 1046 |

The Number of Observations Used is the count of all observations that are nonmissing for all variables specified in the MODEL statement. The ages of 263 of these 1309 passengers cannot be determined and cannot be used to estimate the model.

| Response Profile | | |
|---|---|---|
| **Ordered Value** | **Survived** | **Total Frequency** |
| **1** | 0 | 619 |
| **2** | 1 | 427 |

The Response Profile table shows the response variable values listed according to their ordered values. By default, PROC LOGISTIC orders the response variable alphanumerically so that it bases the logistic regression model on the probability of the smallest value. Because you used the EVENT=option in this example, the model is based on the probability of surviving (**Survived**=1). The Response Profile table also shows frequencies of response values.

**Probability modeled is Survived=1.**

It is advisable to check that the modeled response level is the one that you intended.

**Note: 263 observations were deleted due to missing values for the response or explanatory variables.**

| Model Convergence Status |
|---|
| Convergence criterion (GCONV=1E-8) satisfied. |

The Model Convergence Status simply informs you that the convergence criterion was met. There are a number of options to control the convergence criterion.

The optimization technique does not always converge to a maximum likelihood solution. When this is the case, the output after this point cannot be trusted. Always check to see that the Convergence criterion is satisfied.

| Model Fit Statistics | | |
|---|---|---|
| **Criterion** | **Intercept Only** | **Intercept and Covariates** |
| **AIC** | 1416.620 | 1415.301 |
| **SC** | 1421.573 | 1425.207 |
| **-2 Log L** | 1414.620 | 1411.301 |

The Model Fit Statistics provides three tests:

- AIC is Akaike's 'A' information criterion.
- SC is the Schwarz criterion.
- –2 Log L is –2 times the natural log of the likelihood.

-2 Log L, AIC, and SC are goodness-of-fit measures that you can use to compare one model to another. ***These statistics measure relative fit among models, but they do not measure absolute fit of any single model.*** Smaller values for all of these measures indicate better fit. However, -2 Log L can be reduced by simply adding more regression parameters to the model. Therefore, it is not used to compare the fit of models that use different numbers of parameters. AIC adjusts for the number of predictor variables, and SCs adjust for the number of predictor variables and the number of observations. SC uses a bigger penalty for extra variables and therefore favors more parsimonious models.

| Testing Global Null Hypothesis: BETA=0 | | | |
|---|---|---|---|
| **Test** | **Chi-Square** | **DF** | **Pr > ChiSq** |
| **Likelihood Ratio** | 3.3191 | 1 | 0.0685 |
| **Score** | 3.3041 | 1 | 0.0691 |
| **Wald** | 3.2932 | 1 | 0.0696 |

The Testing Global Null Hypothesis: BETA=0 table provides three statistics to test the null hypothesis that all regression coefficients of the model are 0.

A significant *p*-value for these tests provides evidence that at least one of the regression coefficients for an explanatory variable is significantly different from 0. In this way, they are similar to the overall *F* test in linear regression. The Likelihood Ratio Chi-Square is calculated as the difference between the -2 Log L value of the baseline model (Intercept Only) and the -2 Log L value of the hypothesized model (Intercept and Covariates). The statistic is a distributed asymptotically chi-square with degrees of freedom equal to the difference in number of parameters between the hypothesized model and the baseline model. The Score and Wald tests are also used to test whether all the regression coefficients are 0. The likelihood ratio test is the most reliable, especially for small sample sizes (Agresti 1996). All three tests are asymptotically equivalent and often give very similar values.

Wald statistics (*p*-values and confidence limits) require fewer computations to perform and are therefore the default for most output in PROC LOGISTIC.

| Analysis of Maximum Likelihood Estimates | | | | | |
|---|---|---|---|---|---|
| Parameter | DF | Estimate | Standard Error | Wald Chi-Square | Pr > ChiSq |
| Intercept | 1 | -0.1335 | 0.1448 | 0.8501 | 0.3565 |
| Age | 1 | -0.00800 | 0.00441 | 3.2932 | 0.0696 |

The Analysis of Maximum Likelihood Estimates table lists the estimated model parameters, their standard errors, Wald Chi-Square values, and *p*-values.

The parameter estimates are the estimated coefficients of the fitted logistic regression model. The logistic regression equation is logit( $\hat{p}$ )=–0.1335+(-0.00800)***Age** for this example.

The Wald chi-square and its associated *p*-value tests whether the parameter estimate is significantly different from 0. For this example, the *p*-values for the variable **Age** is not significant at the 0.05 significance level (p=0.0696). It cannot be concluded that **Age** is not important in a multivariate model.

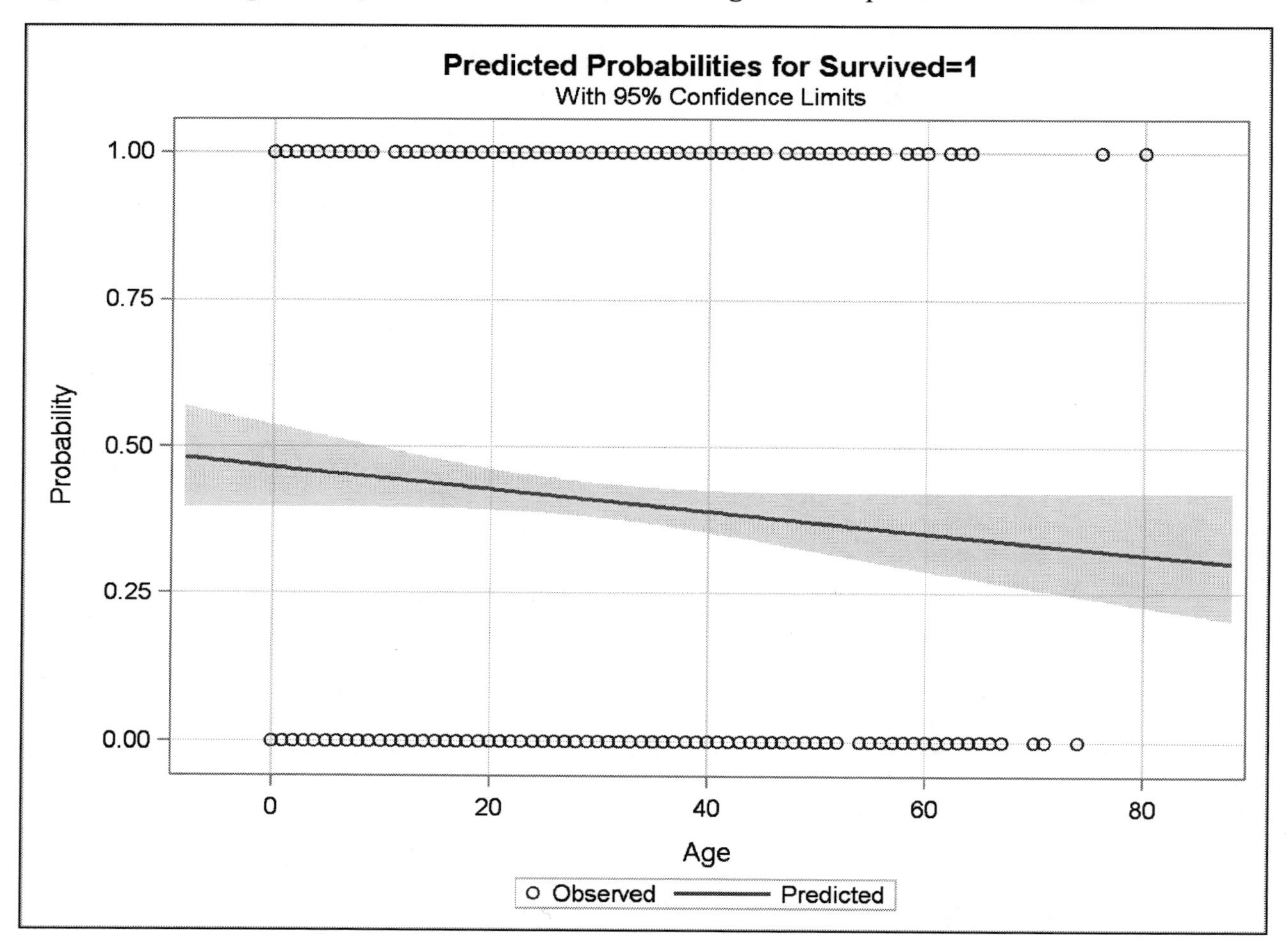


The estimated model is displayed on the probability scale in the Effect plot. The observed values are plotted at probabilities 1.00 and 0.00.

| Association of Predicted Probabilities and Observed Responses | | | |
|---|---|---|---|
| Percent Concordant | 51.3 | Somers' D | 0.050 |
| Percent Discordant | 46.4 | Gamma | 0.051 |
| Percent Tied | 2.3 | Tau-a | 0.024 |
| Pairs | 264313 | c | 0.525 |

| Profile Likelihood Confidence Interval for Odds Ratios | | | | |
|---|---|---|---|---|
| Effect | Unit | Estimate | 95% Confidence Limits | |
| Age | 1.0000 | 0.992 | 0.983 | 1.001 |

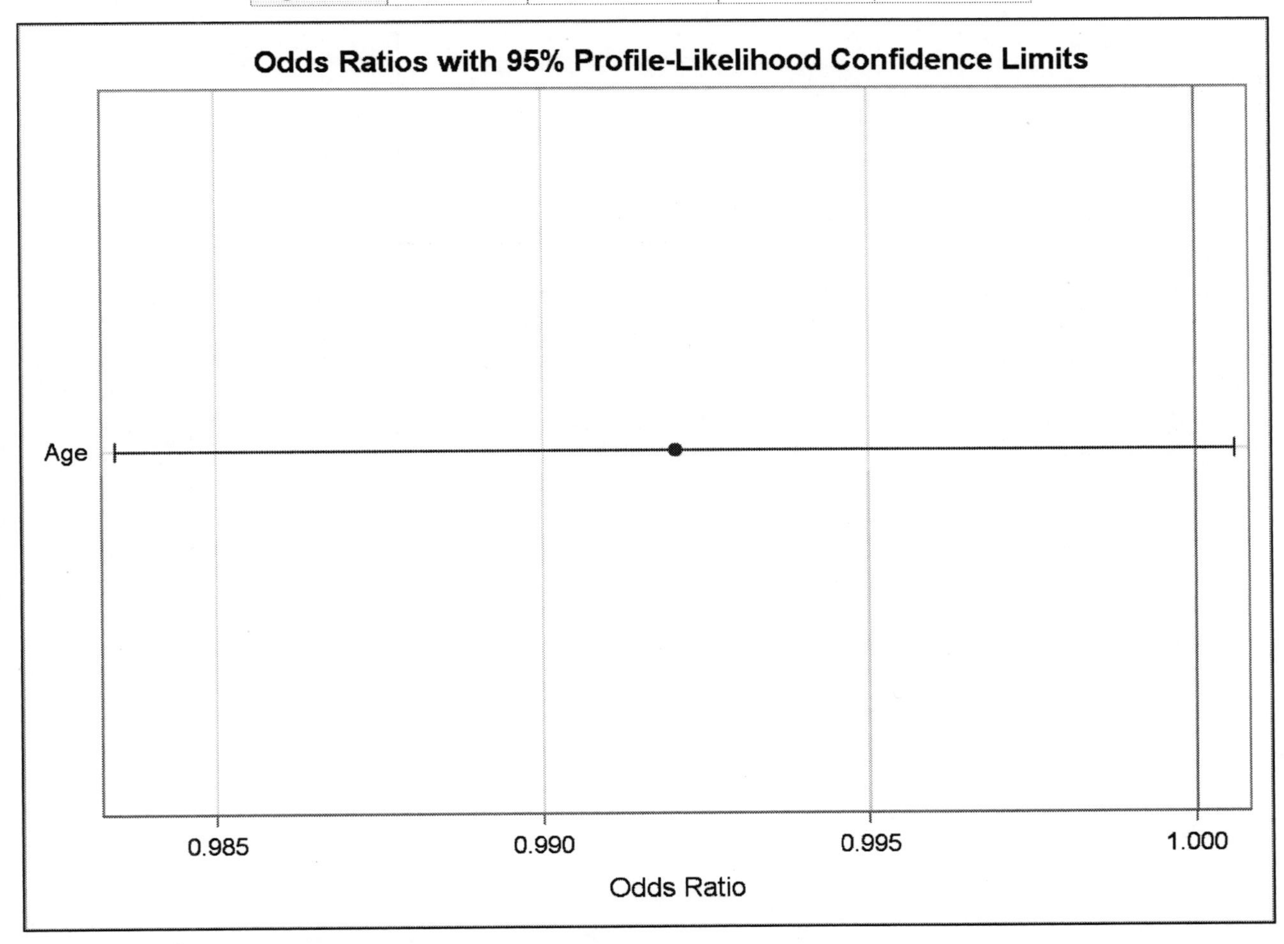


The above tables and plots are described in detail in the next slides.

## Odds Ratio Calculation from the Current Logistic Regression Model

Logistic regression model:

$$\text{logit}(\hat{p}) = \log(odds) = \beta_0 + \beta_1 * (\text{Age})$$

Odds ratio (1-year difference in Age):

$$\text{odds}_{\text{older}} = e^{\beta_0 + \beta_1 * (Age+1)}$$

$$\text{odds}_{\text{younger}} = e^{\beta_0 + \beta_1 * (Age)}$$

$$\text{Odds Ratio} = \frac{e^{\beta_0 + \beta_1 * (Age+1)}}{e^{\beta_0 + \beta_1 * (Age)}} = e^{\beta_1}$$

$$= e^{(-.008)} = 0.992$$

69

The odds ratio for a continuous predictor calculates the estimated relative odds for subjects that are one unit apart on the continuous measure. For example, in the Titanic example, **Age** is the continuous measure. If you remember, the logit is the natural log of the odds. Because you can calculate an estimated logit from the logistic model, the odds can be calculated by simply exponentiating that value. An odds ratio for a one-unit difference is then the ratio of the exponentiated predicted logits for two people who are one unit apart.

The odds ratio for age indicates that the odds of surviving decrease by 0.8% for each year older.

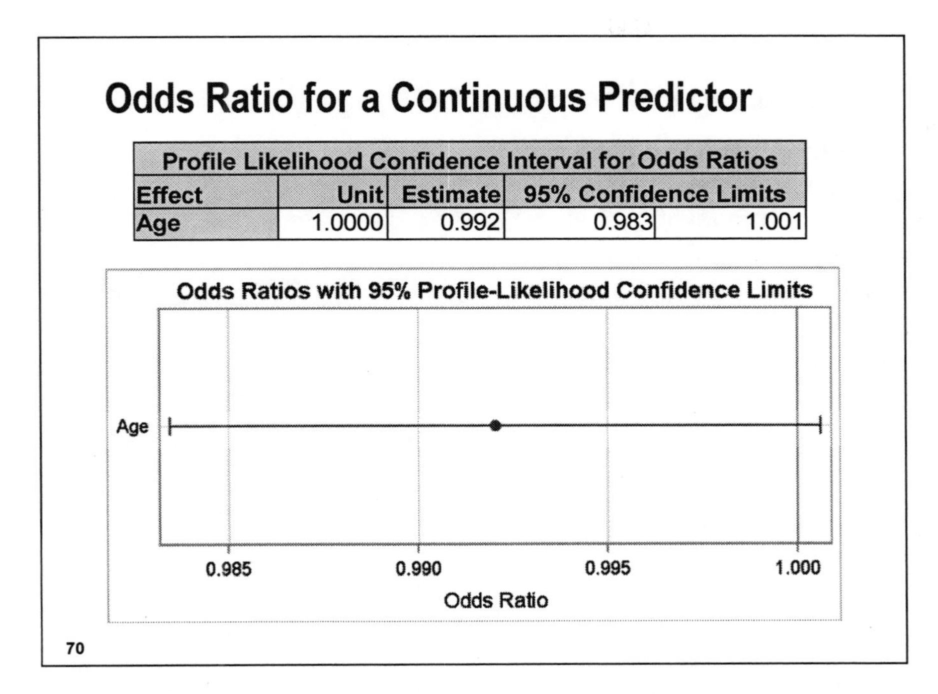


The 95% confidence limits indicate that you are 95% confident that the true odds ratio is between 0.983 and 1.001. Because the 95% confidence interval includes 1.000, the odds ratio is not significant at the .05 alpha level.

If you want a different significance level for the confidence intervals, you can use the ALPHA= option in the MODEL statement. The value must be between 0 and 1. The default value of .05 results in the calculation of a 95% confidence interval.

The profile likelihood confidence intervals are different from the Wald-based confidence intervals. This difference is because the Wald confidence intervals use a normal error approximation, whereas the profile likelihood confidence intervals are based on the value of the log-likelihood. These likelihood-ratio confidence intervals require a much greater number of computations, but are generally preferred to the Wald confidence intervals, especially for sample sizes less than 50 (Allison 1999).

The Odds Ratio plot displays the results of the Odds Ratio table graphically. A reference line shows the null hypothesis. When the confidence interval crosses the reference line, the effect of the variable is not significant.

## Model Assessment: Comparing Pairs

- Counting concordant, discordant, and tied pairs is a way to assess how well the model predicts its own data and therefore how well the model fits.
- In general, you want a high percentage of concordant pairs and low percentages of discordant and tied pairs.

71

## Comparing Pairs

To find concordant, discordant, and tied pairs, compare everyone who had the outcome of interest against everyone who did not.

Died

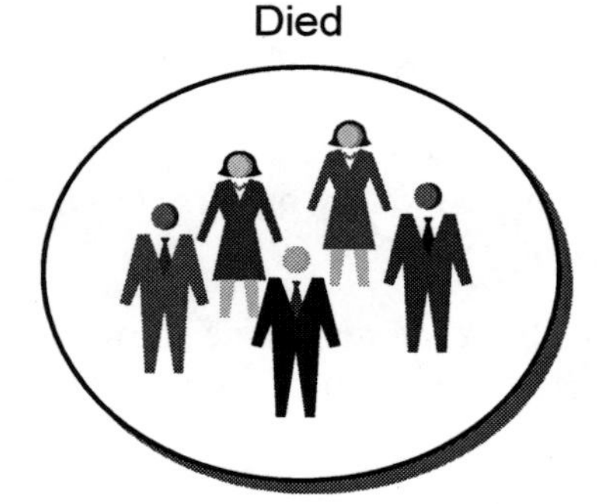

Survived

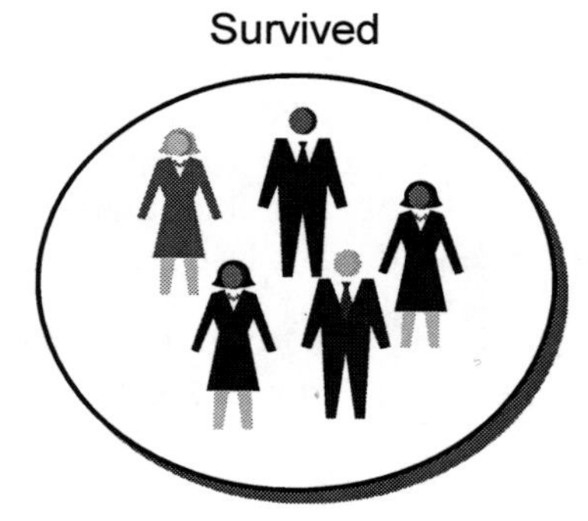

72

## Concordant Pair

Compare a 20-year-old who survived with a 30-year-old who did not.

| Died, Age 30 | Survived, Age 20 |
|---|---|
|  |  |
| P(Survived)=.4077 | P(Survived)=.4272 |

The actual sorting agrees with the model.
This is a **concordant** pair.

73

For all pairs of observations with different values of the response variable, a pair is *concordant* if the observation with the outcome has a ***higher*** predicted outcome probability (based on the model) than the observation without the outcome.

## Discordant Pair

Compare a 45-year-old who survived with a 35-year-old who did not.

| Died, Age 35 | Survived, Age 45 |
|---|---|
|  |  |
| P(Survived)=.3981 | P(Survived)=.3791 |

The actual sorting disagrees with the model.
This is a **discordant** pair.

74

A pair is *discordant* if the observation with the outcome has a ***lower*** predicted outcome probability than the observation without the outcome.

## Tied Pair

Compare two 50-year-olds. One survived and the other did not.

Died, Age 50

P(Survived)=.3697

Survived, Age 50

P(Survived)=.3697

The model cannot distinguish between the two. This is a **tied** pair.

75

A pair is *tied* if it is neither concordant nor discordant. (The probabilities are the same.)

## Model: Concordant, Discordant, and Tied Pairs

| Association of Predicted Probabilities and Observed Responses | | | |
|---|---|---|---|
| Percent Concordant | 51.3 | Somers' D | 0.050 |
| Percent Discordant | 46.4 | Gamma | 0.051 |
| Percent Tied | 2.3 | Tau-a | 0.024 |
| Pairs | 264313 | c | 0.525 |

76

The Association of Predicted Probabilities and Observed Responses table lists several measures of association to help you assess the predictive ability of the logistic model.

The number of pairs used to calculate the values of this table is equal to the product of the counts of observations with positive responses and negative responses. In this example, that value is 427*619=264,313.

You can use these percentages as goodness-of-fit measures to compare one model to another. In general, higher percentages of concordant pairs and lower percentages of discordant pairs indicate a more desirable model.

The four rank correlation indices (Somer's D, Gamma, Tau-a, and *c*) are computed from the numbers of concordant, discordant, and tied pairs of observations. In general, a model with higher values for these indices has better predictive ability than a model with lower values for these indices.

The *c* (concordance) statistic estimates the probability of an observation with the outcome having a higher predicted probability than an observation without the outcome. It is calculated as the percent concordant plus one half the percent tied. The range of possible values is 0.500 (no better predictive power than flipping a fair coin) to 1.000 (perfect prediction). The value of 0.525 shows a very weak ability of **Age** to discriminate between those who survived and those who did not.

## Exercises

2. **Performing a Logistic Regression Analysis**

   Fit a simple logistic regression model using **sasuser.safety** with **Unsafe** as the outcome variable and **Weight** as the predictor variable. Use the EVENT= option to model the probability of below-average safety scores. Request Profile Likelihood confidence limits and an odds ratio plot along with an effect plot.

   a. Do you reject or fail to reject the global null hypothesis that all regression coefficients of the model are 0?

   b. Write the logistic regression equation.

   c. Interpret the odds ratio for **Weight**.

# 5.4 Logistic Regression with Categorical Predictors

## Objectives

- State how a logistic model with categorical predictors does and does not differ from one with continuous predictors.
- Describe what a CLASS statement does.
- Define the standard output from the LOGISTIC procedure with categorical predictor variables.

80

## Overview

| Type of Response \ Type of Predictors | **Categorical** | **Continuous** | **Continuous and Categorical** |
|---|---|---|---|
| Continuous | Analysis of Variance (ANOVA) | Ordinary Least Squares (OLS) Regression | Analysis of Covariance (ANCOVA) |
| **Categorical** | Contingency Table Analysis or **Logistic Regression** | Logistic Regression | Logistic Regression |

81

## What Does a CLASS Statement Actually Do?

- The CLASS statement creates a set of "design variables" representing the information in the categorical variables.
  - Character variables cannot be used, as is, in a model.
  - The design variables are the ones actually used in model calculations.
  - There are several "parameterizations" available in PROC LOGISTIC.

82

The CLASS statement creates a set of "design variables" representing the information contained in any categorical variables. These design variables are incorporated into the model calculations rather than the original categorical variables. Character variables cannot be used, as is, in the model. SAS cannot use a variable with values such as 'yes' or 'no' adequately in the determination of a model.

Even if categorical variables are represented by numbers such as 1, 2, 3, the CLASS statement tells SAS to set up design variables to represent the categories. This is necessary because the numeric values that are assigned to the levels of the categorical variable are generally arbitrary and might not truly reflect distances between levels.

## Effect (Default) Coding: Three Levels

| CLASS | Value | Label | Design Variables 1 | Design Variables 2 |
|---|---|---|---|---|
| **IncLevel** | 1 | Low Income | 1 | 0 |
| | 2 | Medium Income | 0 | 1 |
| | 3 | High Income | -1 | -1 |

83

For *effect coding* (also called *deviation from the mean coding*), the number of design variables created is the number of levels of the CLASS variable minus 1. For example, because the variable **IncLevel** has three levels, two design variables were created. For the last level of the CLASS variable (**`High Income`**), all the design variables have a value of –1. Parameter estimates of the CLASS main effects using this coding scheme estimate the **difference** between the effect of each level and the average effect over all levels.

## Effect Coding: An Example

$$\text{logit}(p)=\beta_0+\beta_1{*}D_{\text{Low income}}+\beta_2{*}D_{\text{Medium income}}$$

$\beta_0$= the average value of the logit across all categories

$\beta_1$= the difference between the logit for Low income and the average logit

$\beta_2$= the difference between the logit for Medium income and the average logit

| Analysis of Maximum Likelihood Estimates | | | | | | |
|---|---|---|---|---|---|---|
| Parameter | | DF | Estimate | Standard Error | Wald Chi-Square | Pr > ChiSq |
| Intercept | | 1 | -0.5363 | 0.1015 | 27.9143 | <.0001 |
| IncLevel | 1 | 1 | -0.2259 | 0.1481 | 2.3247 | 0.1273 |
| IncLevel | 2 | 1 | -0.2200 | 0.1447 | 2.3111 | 0.1285 |

84

If you use Effect Coding for a CLASS variable, then the parameter estimates and *p*-values reflect differences from the mean logit value over all levels. So, for **IncLevel**, the Estimate shows the estimated difference in logit values between **IncLevel**=1 (Low Income) and the average logit across all income levels.

## Reference Cell Coding: Three Levels

| CLASS | Value | Label | Design Variables 1 | Design Variables 2 |
|---|---|---|---|---|
| **IncLevel** | 1 | Low Income | 1 | 0 |
| | 2 | Medium Income | 0 | 1 |
| | 3 | High Income | 0 | 0 |

85

For *reference cell coding*, parameter estimates of the CLASS main effects estimate the difference between the effect of each level and the last level, called the *reference level*. For example, the effect for the level **`Low`** estimates the logit difference between **`Low`** and **`High`**. You can choose the reference level in the CLASS statement.

## Reference Cell Coding: An Example

$$\text{logit}(p)=\beta_0+\beta_1{}^*D_{\text{Low income}}+\beta_2{}^*D_{\text{Medium income}}$$

$\beta_0$= the value of the logit when income is High

$\beta_1$= the difference between the logits for Low and High income

$\beta_2$= the difference between the logits for Medium and High income

| Analysis of Maximum Likelihood Estimates | | | | | | |
|---|---|---|---|---|---|---|
| Parameter | | DF | Estimate | Standard Error | Wald Chi-Square | Pr > ChiSq |
| Intercept | | 1 | -0.0904 | 0.1608 | 0.3159 | 0.5741 |
| IncLevel | 1 | 1 | -0.6717 | 0.2465 | 7.4242 | 0.0064 |
| IncLevel | 2 | 1 | -0.6659 | 0.2404 | 7.6722 | 0.0056 |

86

Notice the difference between this table and the previous parameter estimates table. Because you used Reference Cell Coding, instead of Effect Coding, the meanings of the parameter estimates and *p*-values are different. Now, the parameter estimate and *p*-value for **IncLevel**=1 reflect the difference between **IncLevel**=1 and **Inclevel**=3 (the reference level).

It is important to know what type of parameterization you are using in order to interpret and report the results of this table.

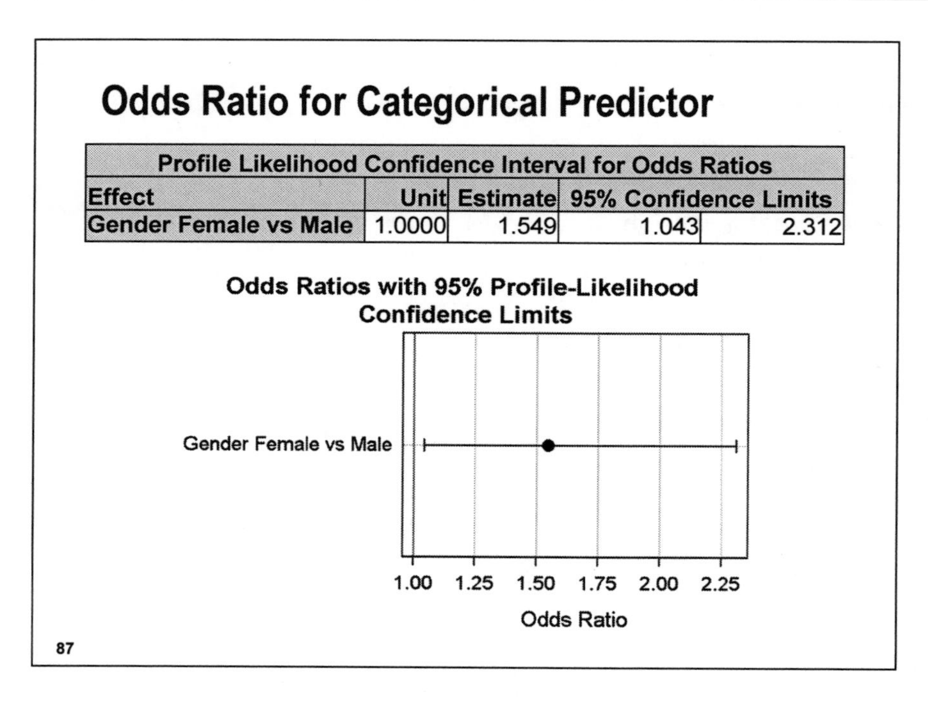


| Profile Likelihood Confidence Interval for Odds Ratios | | | | |
|---|---|---|---|---|
| Effect | Unit | Estimate | 95% Confidence Limits | |
| Gender Female vs Male | 1.0000 | 1.549 | 1.043 | 2.312 |

Odds ratios for categorical predictors are reported for bi-group comparisons in PROC LOGISTIC, no matter which parameterization is chosen. Thus, even if Effect Coding is selected for the **Gender** variable, the odds ratio tables display odds comparisons between females and males (and not females versus the average of both).

## 5.05 Multiple Choice Poll

In the Analysis of Maximum Likelihood table, using effect coding, what is the estimated logit for someone at **IncLevel**=2?

a. -.5363
b. -.6717
c. -.6659
d. -.7563
e. Cannot tell from the information provided

90

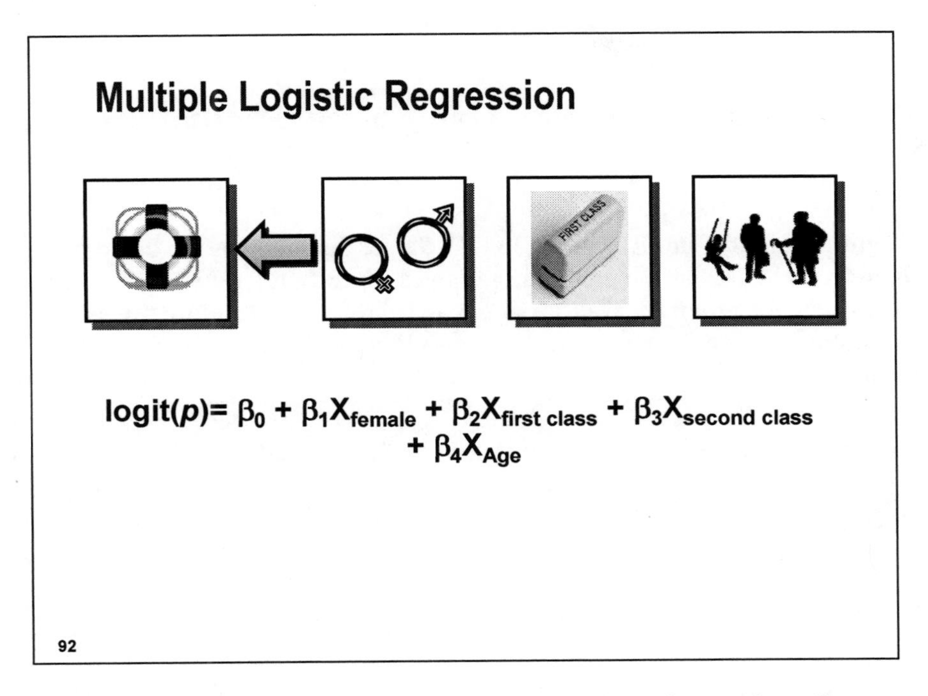


Each design variable is assigned its own beta value. The number of parameters in the logistic model take into account the intercept, the number of continuous predictors, and the number of design variables assigned to CLASS variables.

# Multiple Logistic Regression with Categorical Predictors

Example: Fit a binary logistic regression model in PROC LOGISTIC. Select **Survived** as the outcome variable and **Age**, **Gender**, and **Class** as the predictor variables. Specify reference cell coding and specify **male** as the reference group for **Gender** and **3** as the reference level for **Class**. Also use the EVENT= option to model the probability of surviving and request profile likelihood confidence intervals around the estimated odds ratios.

```
/*st105d06.sas*/
proc logistic data=sasuser.Titanic plots(only)=(effect oddsratio);
   class Gender(ref='male') Class(ref='3') / param=ref;
   model Survived(event='1')=Age Gender Class / clodds=pl;
   units age=10;
   title1 'LOGISTIC MODEL (2):Survived=Age Gender Class';
run;
```

Selected PROC LOGISTIC statement:

UNITS enables you to specify units of change for the continuous explanatory variables so that customized odds ratios can be estimated.

Selected CLASS statement options:

(REF='level') specifies the event category chosen as the reference level when using Reference or Effect parameterization. You can specify the value (formatted if a format is applied) of the reference category in quotation marks or you can specify one of the following keywords. The default is REF=LAST.

FIRST designates the first ordered category as the reference level.

LAST designates the last ordered category as the reference level.

PARAM= specifies the parameterization. This value can be specified for each CLASS variable by typing it within parentheses after the variable name, or for all CLASS variables, by typing it after the options slash (/) at the end of the list of CLASS variables.

If there are numerous levels in the CLASS variable, you might want to use subject-matter knowledge to reduce the number of levels. This is especially important when the levels have few or no observations.

| Model Information | |
|---|---|
| Data Set | SASUSER.TITANIC |
| Response Variable | Survived |
| Number of Response Levels | 2 |
| Model | binary logit |
| Optimization Technique | Fisher's scoring |

| | |
|---|---|
| Number of Observations Read | 1309 |
| Number of Observations Used | 1046 |

| Response Profile | | |
|---|---|---|
| Ordered Value | Survived | Total Frequency |
| 1 | 0 | 619 |
| 2 | 1 | 427 |

**Probability modeled is Survived=1.**

| Class Level Information | | | |
|---|---|---|---|
| Class | Value | Design Variables | |
| Gender | female | 1 | |
| | male | 0 | |
| Class | 1 | 1 | 0 |
| | 2 | 0 | 1 |
| | 3 | 0 | 0 |

The Class Level Information table includes the predictor variable in the CLASS statement. Because you used the PARAM=REF and REF='`male`' options, this table reflects your choice of **Gender**='`male`' as the reference level. The design variable is 1 when **Gender**='`female`' and 0 when **Gender**='`male`'. The reference level for **Class** is 3, so there or two design variables, each coded 0 for observations where **Class**=3.

| Model Convergence Status |
|---|
| Convergence criterion (GCONV=1E-8) satisfied. |

| Model Fit Statistics | | |
|---|---|---|
| **Criterion** | **Intercept Only** | **Intercept and Covariates** |
| **AIC** | 1416.620 | 992.315 |
| **SC** | 1421.573 | 1017.079 |
| **-2 Log L** | 1414.620 | 982.315 |

The SC value in the **Age** only model was 1425.207. Here it is 1017.079. Recalling that smaller values imply better fit, you can conclude that this model is better fitting.

| Testing Global Null Hypothesis: BETA=0 | | | |
|---|---|---|---|
| **Test** | **Chi-Square** | **DF** | **Pr > ChiSq** |
| **Likelihood Ratio** | 432.3052 | 4 | <.0001 |
| **Score** | 386.1522 | 4 | <.0001 |
| **Wald** | 277.3202 | 4 | <.0001 |

This model is statistically significant, indicating at least one of the predictors in the model is useful in predicting survival.

| Type 3 Analysis of Effects | | | |
|---|---|---|---|
| **Effect** | **DF** | **Wald Chi-Square** | **Pr > ChiSq** |
| **Age** | 1 | 29.6314 | <.0001 |
| **Gender** | 1 | 226.2235 | <.0001 |
| **Class** | 2 | 103.3575 | <.0001 |

The Type 3 Analysis of Effects table is generated when a predictor variable is used in the CLASS statement. This analysis is similar to the individual tests in the GLM procedure parameter estimates table. Just as in PROC GLM and PROC REG, these are adjusted effects.

All effects, including the **Age** effect, which was not statistically significant in the univariate model, are statistically significant.

| Analysis of Maximum Likelihood Estimates | | | | | | |
|---|---|---|---|---|---|---|
| **Parameter** | | **DF** | **Estimate** | **Standard Error** | **Wald Chi-Square** | **Pr > ChiSq** |
| **Intercept** | | 1 | -1.2628 | 0.2030 | 38.7108 | <.0001 |
| **Age** | | 1 | -0.0345 | 0.00633 | 29.6314 | <.0001 |
| **Gender** | **female** | 1 | 2.4976 | 0.1661 | 226.2235 | <.0001 |
| **Class** | **1** | 1 | 2.2907 | 0.2258 | 102.8824 | <.0001 |
| **Class** | **2** | 1 | 1.0093 | 0.1984 | 25.8849 | <.0001 |

For CLASS variables, effects are displayed for each of the design variables. Because reference cell coding was used, each effect is measured against the reference level. For example, the estimate for **Gender | female** shows the difference in logits between females and males. **Class | 1** shows the logit difference between first-class passengers and third-class passengers and **Class | 2** shows the difference in logits between second class and third class. All of these contrasts are statistically significant.

| Association of Predicted Probabilities and Observed Responses | | | |
|---|---|---|---|
| **Percent Concordant** | 83.8 | **Somers' D** | 0.680 |
| **Percent Discordant** | 15.8 | **Gamma** | 0.683 |
| **Percent Tied** | 0.4 | **Tau-a** | 0.329 |
| **Pairs** | 264313 | **c** | 0.840 |

The c (Concordance) statistic value is 0.840 for this model, indicating that 84% of the positive and negative response pairs are correctly sorted using **Age**, **Gender**, and **Class**.

| Profile Likelihood Confidence Interval for Odds Ratios | | | | |
|---|---|---|---|---|
| **Effect** | **Unit** | **Estimate** | **95% Confidence Limits** | |
| **Age** | 10.0000 | 0.708 | 0.625 | 0.801 |
| **Gender female vs male** | 1.0000 | 12.153 | 8.823 | 16.925 |
| **Class 1 vs 3** | 1.0000 | 9.882 | 6.395 | 15.513 |
| **Class 2 vs 3** | 1.0000 | 2.744 | 1.863 | 4.059 |

The odds ratios show that, adjusting for the other predictor variables, females had 12.153 times the male odds of surviving. First-class passengers had nearly 10 times the odds (9.882) of third-class passengers and second-class passengers had 174.4% greater odds than third-class passengers. The UNITS statement applies to the odds ratio table requested by the CLODDS=PL option. The table shows that a 10-year-older age is associated with a 29.2% decrease in survival odds. The ODDSRATIO plot displays these values graphically.

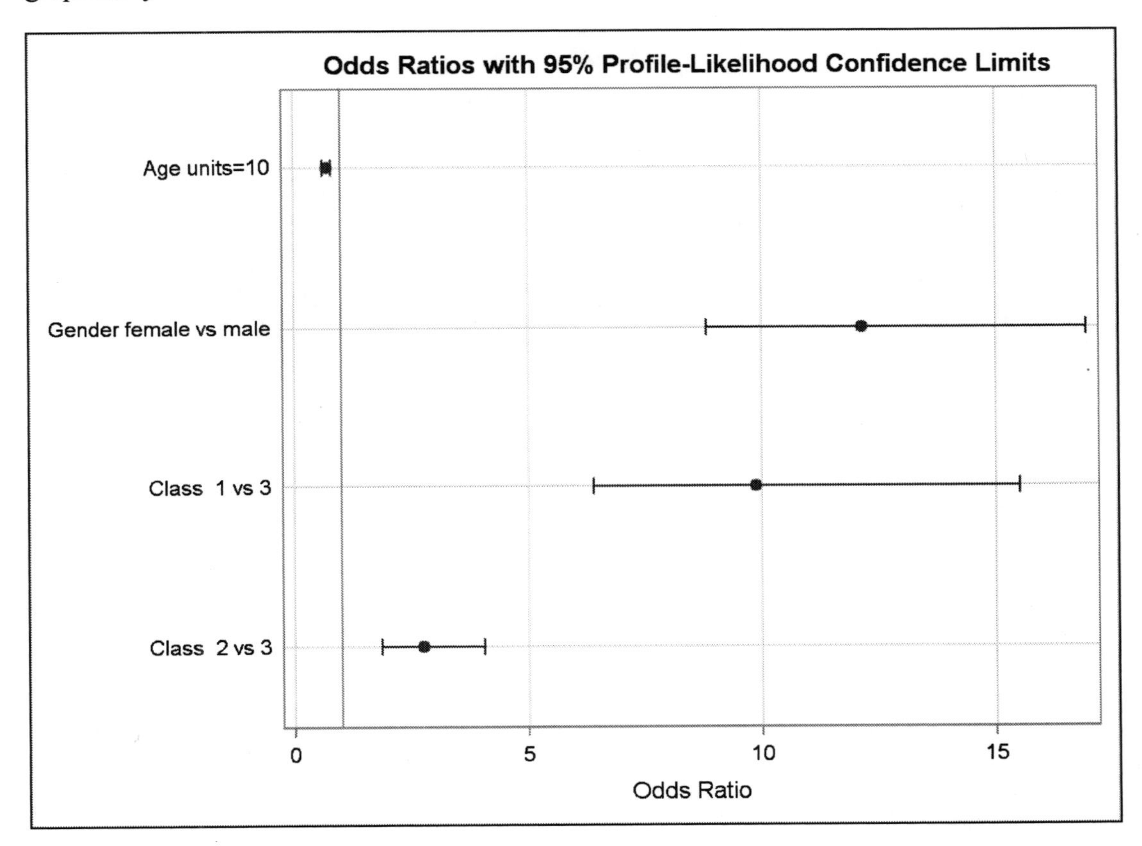

Finally, the Effects plot shows the probability of survival across all combinations of categories and levels of all three predictor variables.

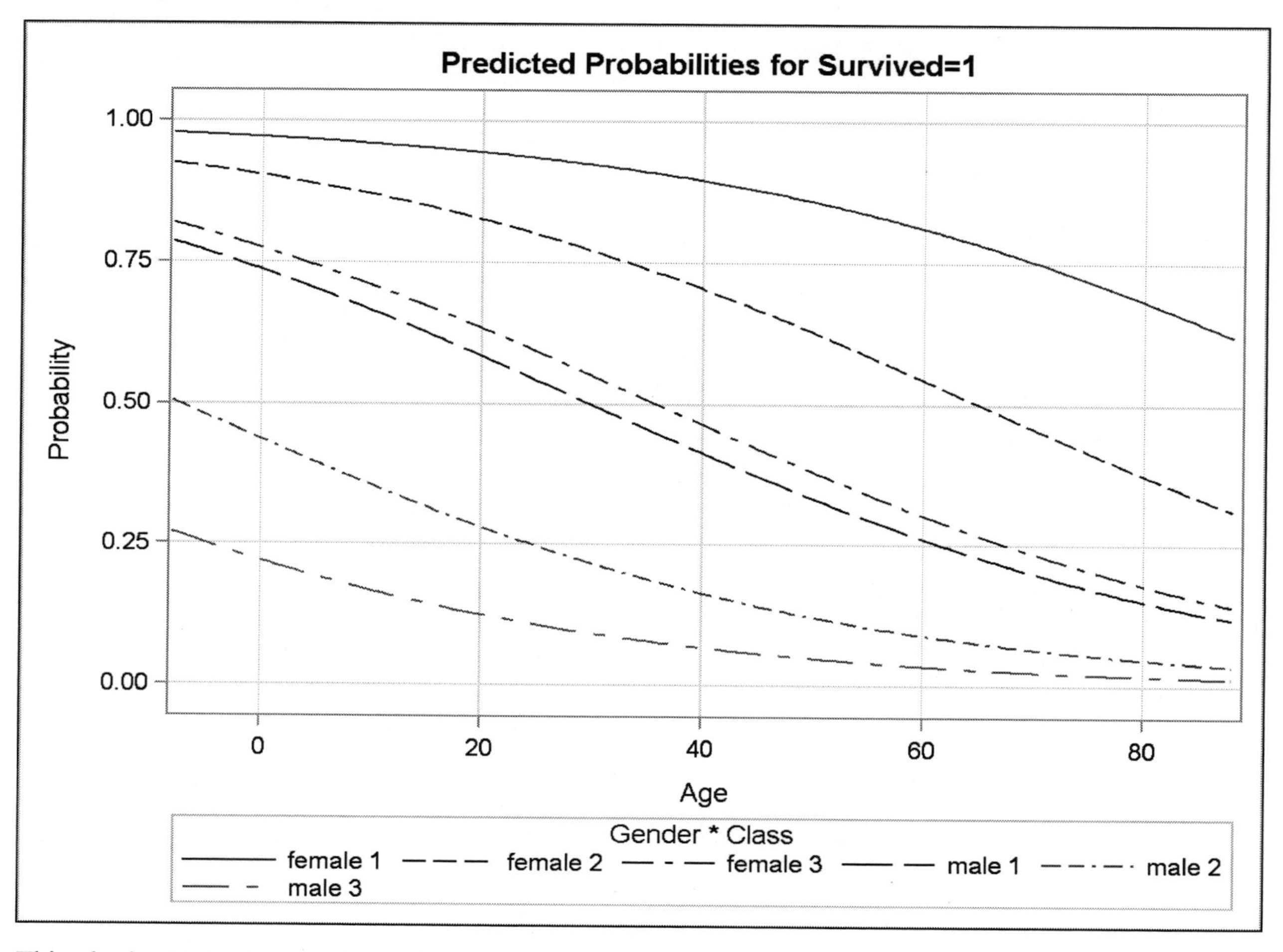


This plot is obtained by applying the parameter estimates from the logistic model to values of the predictors and then converting the predictions to the probability scale.

The plot indicates that at every age, all classes of women are predicted to survive at a greater rate than all classes of men. Holding **Age** and **Gender** constant, the descending order of predicted survival probabilities are first class, second class, and third class.

## Exercises

**3. Performing a Multiple Logistic Regression Analysis Including Categorical Variables**

Fit a logistic regression model using **sasuser.safety** with **Unsafe** as the outcome variable and **Weight**, **Region**, and **Size** as the predictor variables. Request reference cell coding with **Asia** as the reference level for **Region** and **3** (large cars) as the reference level for **Size**. Use the EVENT= option to model the probability of below-average safety scores. Request Profile Likelihood confidence limits and an odds ratio plot along with an effect plot.

**a.** Do you reject or fail to reject the null hypothesis that all regression coefficients of the model are 0?

reject

**b.** If you do reject the global null hypothesis, then which predictors significantly predict safety outcome?

Size 1

**c.** Interpret the odds ratio for significant predictors.

Size 1 Cars have 19.56 times the odds of being unsafe than a size 3 vehicle

### 5.06 Multiple Choice Poll

A variable coded 1, 2, 3, and 4 is parameterized with effect coding, with 2 as the reference level. The parameter estimate for level 1 tells you which of the following?

a. The difference in the logit between level 1 and level 2
b. The odds ratio between level 1 and level 2
c. The difference in the logit between level 1 and the average of all levels
d. The odds ratio between level 1 and the average of all levels
e. Both a and b
f. Both c and d

97

# 5.5 Stepwise Selection with Interactions

## Objectives

- Fit a multiple logistic regression model with main effects and interactions using the backward elimination method.
- Explain interactions using graphs.

101

## Overview

| Type of Response \ Type of Predictors | Categorical | Continuous | Continuous and Categorical |
|---|---|---|---|
| Continuous | Analysis of Variance (ANOVA) | Ordinary Least Squares (OLS) Regression | Analysis of Covariance (ANCOVA) |
| **Categorical** | Contingency Table Analysis or Logistic Regression | Logistic Regression | **Logistic Regression** |

102

## Stepwise Methods – Default Selection Criteria

| | PROC REG | | | PROC LOGISTIC | |
|---|---|---|---|---|---|
| | SLENTRY | SLSTAY | | SLENTRY | SLSTAY |
| FORWARD | 0.50 | ----- | | 0.05 | |
| BACKWARD | ----- | 0.10 | | | 0.05 |
| STEPWISE | 0.15 | 0.15 | | 0.05 | 0.05 |

103

If you are doing exploratory analysis and want to find a best subset model, PROC LOGISTIC provides the three stepwise methods that are available in PROC REG. However, the default selection criteria are not the same as in PROC REG. Remember that you can always change the selection criteria using the SLENTRY= and SLSTAY= options in the MODEL statement.

If you have a large number of variables, you might first need to try a variable reduction method such as variable clustering.

## Stepwise Hierarchy Rules

By default, at each step model hierarchy is retained. This means that higher level effects cannot be in a model when any of its lower level composite effects are not present.

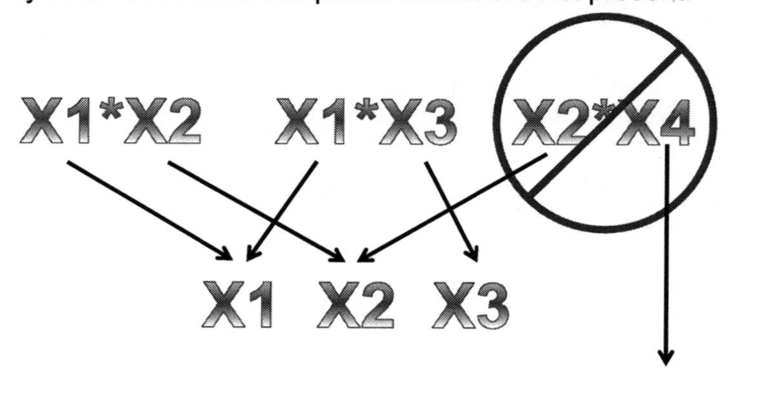


104

Model hierarchy refers to the requirement that, for any term to be in the model, all effects contained in the term must be present in the model. For example, in order for the interaction X2*X4 to enter the model, the main effects X2 and X4 must be in the model. Likewise, neither effect X2 nor X4 can leave the model while the interaction X2*X4 is in the model.

When you use the backward elimination method with interactions in the model, PROC LOGISTIC begins by fitting the full model with all the main effects and interactions. PROC LOGISTIC then eliminates the nonsignificant interactions one at a time, starting with the least significant interaction (the one with the largest *p*-value). Next, PROC LOGISTIC eliminates the nonsignificant main effects not involved in any significant interactions. The final model should consist of only significant interactions, the main effects involved in those interactions, and any other significant main effects.

For a more customized analysis, the HIERARCHY= option specifies whether the hierarchy is maintained and whether a single effect or multiple effects are allowed to enter or leave the model in one step for forward, backward, and stepwise selection.

The default is HIERARCHY=SINGLE. You can change this option by inserting the HIERARCHY= option in the MODEL statement. See the *SAS/STAT® 9.3 User's Guide* in the SAS online documentation for more information about using this option. In the LOGISTIC procedure, HIERARCHY=SINGLE is the default, meaning that SAS will not remove a main effect before first removing all interactions involving that main effect.

# Logistic Regression: Backward Elimination with Interactions

Example: Fit a multiple logistic regression model using the backward elimination method. The full model should include all the main effects and two-way interactions.

```
/*st105d07.sas*/  /*Part A*/
proc logistic data=sasuser.Titanic plots(only)=(effect oddsratio);
   class Gender(ref='male') Class(ref='3') / param=ref;
   model Survived(event='1')=Age|Gender|Class @2 /
         selection=backward clodds=pl slstay=0.01;
   units age=10;
   title1 'LOGISTIC MODEL (3): Backward Elimination '
          'Survived=Age|Gender|Class';
run;
```

The bar notation with the @2 constructs a model with all the main effects and the two-factor interactions. If you increase it to @3, then you construct a model with all of the main effects, the two-factor interactions, and the three-factor interaction. However, the three-factor interaction might be more difficult to interpret.

A more conservative significance level criterion was used because the sample size was relatively large and the interactions were not hypothesized a priori. Under these circumstances, there is an elevated risk of creating a model with effects that are significant only by chance. Lowering the significance criteria provides some protection.

Selected MODEL statement option:

SELECTION= specifies the method to select the variables in the model. BACKWARD requests backward elimination, FORWARD requests forward selection, NONE fits the complete model specified in the MODEL statement, STEPWISE requests stepwise selection, and SCORE requests best subset selection. The default is NONE.

| Model Information | |
|---|---|
| Data Set | SASUSER.TITANIC |
| Response Variable | Survived |
| Number of Response Levels | 2 |
| Model | binary logit |
| Optimization Technique | Fisher's scoring |

| | |
|---|---|
| Number of Observations Read | 1309 |
| Number of Observations Used | 1046 |

| Response Profile | | |
|---|---|---|
| Ordered Value | Survived | Total Frequency |
| 1 | 0 | 619 |
| 2 | 1 | 427 |

**Probability modeled is Survived=1.**

**Note:** 263 observations were deleted due to missing values for the response or explanatory variables.

All information to this point is the same as that from the previous model.

**Backward Elimination Procedure**

| Class Level Information | | | |
|---|---|---|---|
| Class | Value | Design Variables | |
| Gender | female | 1 | |
| | male | 0 | |
| Class | 1 | 1 | 0 |
| | 2 | 0 | 1 |
| | 3 | 0 | 0 |

The Model Fit Statistics and Testing Global Null Hypothesis tables at Step 0 are presented.

**Step 0. The following effects were entered:**

**Intercept Age Gender Age*Gender Class Age*Class Gender*Class**

| Model Convergence Status |
|---|
| Convergence criterion (GCONV=1E-8) satisfied. |

| Model Fit Statistics | | |
|---|---|---|
| Criterion | Intercept Only | Intercept and Covariates |
| AIC | 1416.620 | 937.714 |
| SC | 1421.573 | 987.241 |
| -2 Log L | 1414.620 | 917.714 |

**Step 1. Effect Age*Gender is removed:**

| Model Convergence Status |
|---|
| Convergence criterion (GCONV=1E-8) satisfied. |

| Model Fit Statistics | | |
|---|---|---|
| Criterion | Intercept Only | Intercept and Covariates |
| AIC | 1416.620 | 940.064 |
| SC | 1421.573 | 984.638 |
| -2 Log L | 1414.620 | 922.064 |

| Testing Global Null Hypothesis: BETA=0 | | | |
|---|---|---|---|
| Test | Chi-Square | DF | Pr > ChiSq |
| Likelihood Ratio | 492.5567 | 8 | <.0001 |
| Score | 424.3790 | 8 | <.0001 |
| Wald | 221.7387 | 8 | <.0001 |

| Residual Chi-Square Test | | |
|---|---|---|
| Chi-Square | DF | Pr > ChiSq |
| 4.3665 | 1 | 0.0367 |

**Step 2. Effect Age*Class is removed:**

| Model Convergence Status |
|---|
| Convergence criterion (GCONV=1E-8) satisfied. |

| Model Fit Statistics | | |
|---|---|---|
| Criterion | Intercept Only | Intercept and Covariates |
| AIC | 1416.620 | 945.832 |
| SC | 1421.573 | 980.501 |
| -2 Log L | 1414.620 | 931.832 |

| Testing Global Null Hypothesis: BETA=0 | | | |
|---|---|---|---|
| Test | Chi-Square | DF | Pr > ChiSq |
| Likelihood Ratio | 482.7886 | 6 | <.0001 |
| Score | 422.4668 | 6 | <.0001 |
| Wald | 237.1963 | 6 | <.0001 |

| Residual Chi-Square Test | | |
|---|---|---|
| Chi-Square | DF | Pr > ChiSq |
| 13.2931 | 3 | 0.0040 |

No (additional) effects met the 0.01 significance level for removal from the model.

The procedure stops after the two interactions involving **Age** are removed.

| Summary of Backward Elimination | | | | | |
|---|---|---|---|---|---|
| **Step** | **Effect Removed** | **DF** | **Number In** | **Wald Chi-Square** | **Pr > ChiSq** |
| 1 | Age*Gender | 1 | 5 | 4.3264 | 0.0375 |
| 2 | Age*Class | 2 | 4 | 8.8477 | 0.0120 |

The *p*-values associated with the two removed effects were below 0.05 and would therefore be retained, if the default SLSTAY criterion were used.

| Type 3 Analysis of Effects | | | |
|---|---|---|---|
| **Effect** | **DF** | **Wald Chi-Square** | **Pr > ChiSq** |
| Age | 1 | 32.5663 | <.0001 |
| Gender | 1 | 40.0553 | <.0001 |
| Class | 2 | 44.4898 | <.0001 |
| Gender*Class | 2 | 43.9289 | <.0001 |

| Analysis of Maximum Likelihood Estimates | | | | | | | |
|---|---|---|---|---|---|---|---|
| **Parameter** | | | **DF** | **Estimate** | **Standard Error** | **Wald Chi-Square** | **Pr > ChiSq** |
| Intercept | | | 1 | -0.6552 | 0.2113 | 9.6165 | 0.0019 |
| Age | | | 1 | -0.0385 | 0.00674 | 32.5663 | <.0001 |
| Gender | female | | 1 | 1.3970 | 0.2207 | 40.0553 | <.0001 |
| Class | 1 | | 1 | 1.5770 | 0.2525 | 38.9980 | <.0001 |
| Class | 2 | | 1 | -0.0242 | 0.2720 | 0.0079 | 0.9292 |
| Gender*Class | female | 1 | 1 | 2.4894 | 0.5403 | 21.2279 | <.0001 |
| Gender*Class | female | 2 | 1 | 2.5599 | 0.4562 | 31.4930 | <.0001 |

Notice that when a CLASS statement is used containing multiple variables, new rows are added to the parameter estimates table. These represent design variables that SAS creates in order to test the interactions.

As described in the ANOVA chapter, an interaction between two variables means that the effect of one variable is different at different values of the other variable. This makes the model more complex to interpret.

| Association of Predicted Probabilities and Observed Responses | | | |
|---|---|---|---|
| Percent Concordant | 85.0 | Somers' D | 0.703 |
| Percent Discordant | 14.7 | Gamma | 0.706 |
| Percent Tied | 0.4 | Tau-a | 0.340 |
| Pairs | 264313 | c | 0.852 |

The c value is a slight improvement over the previous model (c=0.840) that only included the main effects.

Odds ratios are not calculated for effects involved in interactions. Any single odds ratio for **Class** or for **Gender** would be misleading because the effects vary for each at different levels of the other variable.

| Profile Likelihood Confidence Interval for Odds Ratios | | | | |
|---|---|---|---|---|
| **Effect** | **Unit** | **Estimate** | **95% Confidence Limits** | |
| **Age** | 10.0000 | 0.681 | 0.595 | 0.775 |

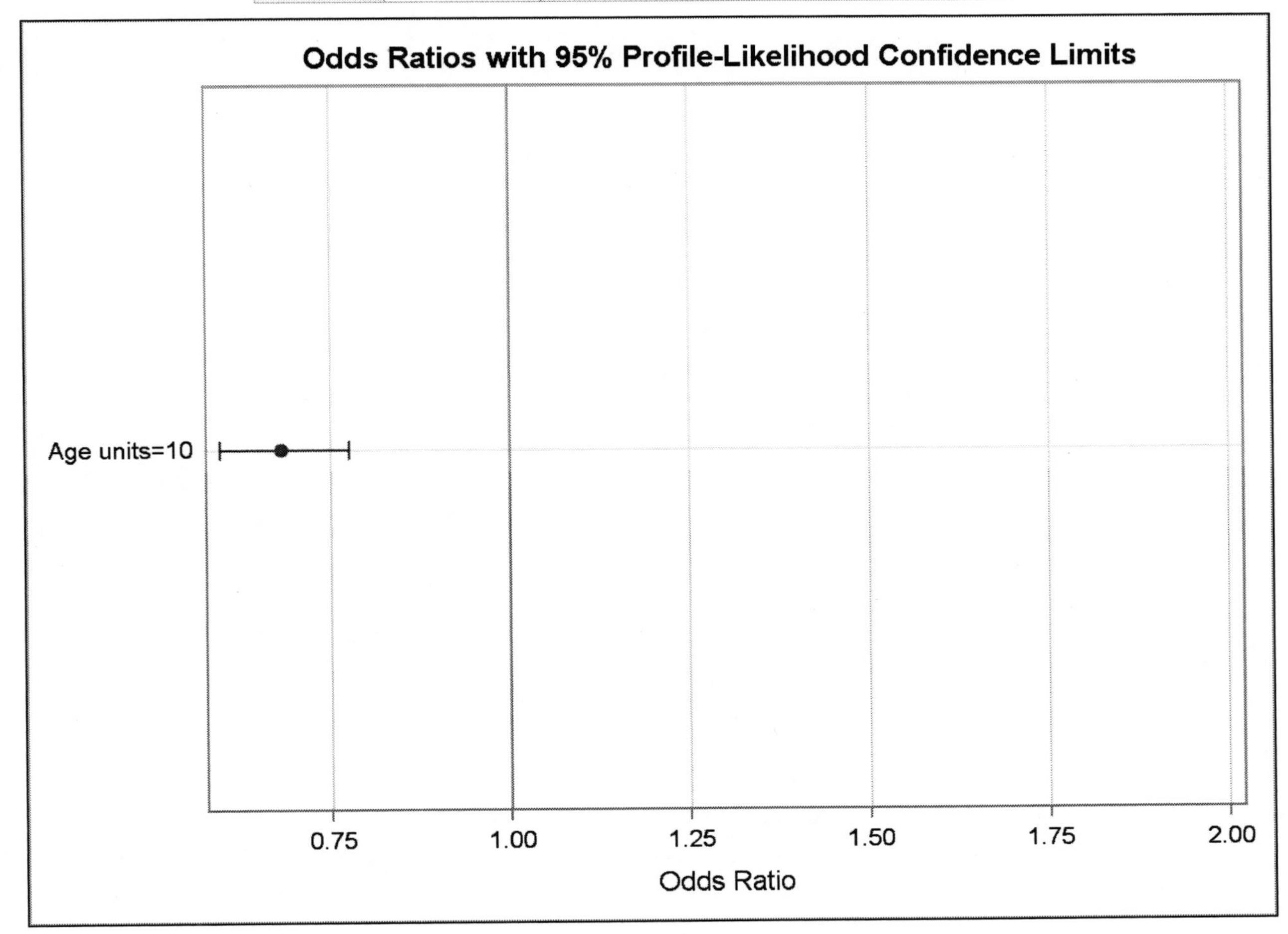


The odds ratio for **Age** in this model changed only slightly with the addition of the interaction term.

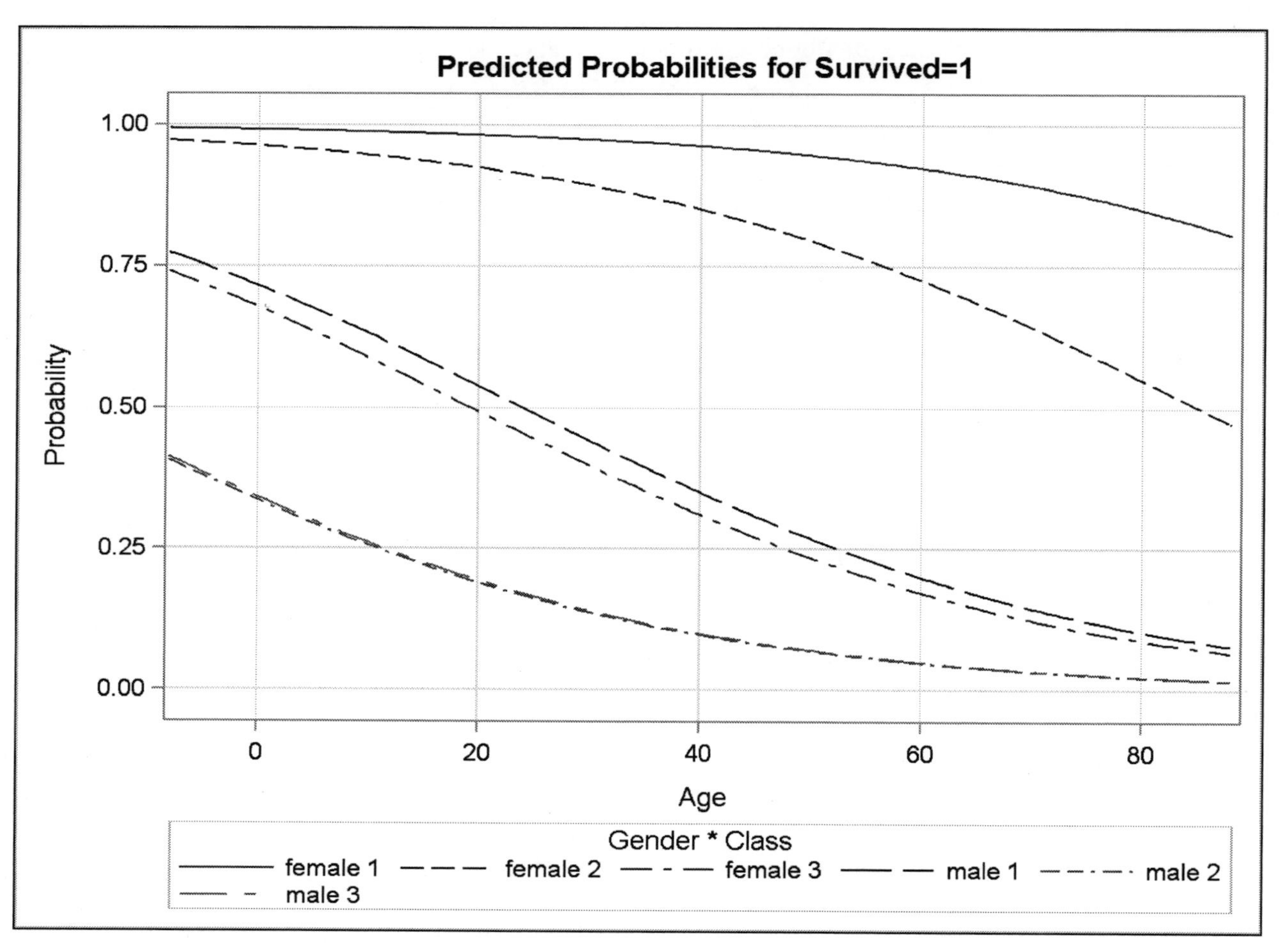


The effect plot shows the interaction. **Male** second class is closer to **male** third class (they have almost identical probabilities at every age) than **male** first class. **Female** second class is much closer to **female** first class than to **female** third class.

In order to estimate and plot odds ratios for the effects involved in an interaction, an ODDSRATIO statement can be used. An EFFECTSPLOT statement can help display the interaction, as well.

```
/*st105d07.sas*/  /*Part B*/
proc logistic data=sasuser.Titanic
              plots(only)=oddsratio(range=clip);
   class Gender(ref='male') Class(ref='3') / param=ref;
   model Survived(event='1')=Age Gender|Class;
   units age=10;
   oddsratio Gender / at (Class=ALL) cl=pl;
   oddsratio Class / at (Gender=ALL) cl=pl;
   oddsratio Age / cl=pl;
   title1 'LOGISTIC MODEL (3.1): Survived=Age Gender|Class';
run;
```

Selected PROC LOGISTIC statement PLOTS option:

RANGE= with suboptions **(<*min*><,*max*>) | CLIP**, specifies the range of the displayed odds ratio axis. The RANGE=CLIP option has the same effect as specifying the minimum odds ratio as ***min*** and the maximum odds ratio as ***max***. By default, all odds ratio confidence intervals are displayed. This option is helpful when one or more odds ratio confidence intervals are so large that the smaller ones become difficult to see on the scale required to show the larger ones.

Selected statement:

ODDSRATIO produces odds ratios for a variable even when the variable is involved in interactions with other covariates, and for classification variables that use any parameterization. You can also specify variables on which constructed effects are based, in addition to the names of COLLECTION or MULTIMEMBER effects.

Selected options for the ODDSRATIO statement:

AT specifies fixed levels of the interacting covariates. If a specified covariate does not interact with the variable, then its AT list is ignored. For continuous interacting covariates, you can specify one or more numbers in the value-list. For classification covariates, you can specify one or more formatted levels of the covariate enclosed in single quotation marks (for example, A='cat' 'dog'), you can specify the keyword REF to select the reference-level, or you can specify the keyword ALL to select all levels of the classification variable. By default, continuous covariates are set to their means, while CLASS covariates are set to ALL.

Partial PROC LOGISTIC Output

**Profile Likelihood Confidence Interval for Odds Ratios**

| Label | Estimate | 95% Confidence Limits | |
|---|---|---|---|
| Gender female vs male at Class=1 | 48.735 | 20.313 | 145.458 |
| Gender female vs male at Class=2 | 52.295 | 24.869 | 119.543 |
| Gender female vs male at Class=3 | 4.043 | 2.630 | 6.253 |
| Class 1 vs 2 at Gender=female | 4.621 | 1.590 | 15.350 |
| Class 1 vs 3 at Gender=female | 58.349 | 23.371 | 179.396 |
| Class 2 vs 3 at Gender=female | 12.626 | 6.330 | 27.317 |
| Class 1 vs 2 at Gender=male | 4.959 | 2.778 | 9.106 |
| Class 1 vs 3 at Gender=male | 4.841 | 2.960 | 7.978 |

| Profile Likelihood Confidence Interval for Odds Ratios | | | |
|---|---|---|---|
| **Label** | **Estimate** | **95% Confidence Limits** | |
| Class 2 vs 3 at Gender=male | 0.976 | 0.564 | 1.645 |
| Age units=10 | 0.681 | 0.595 | 0.775 |

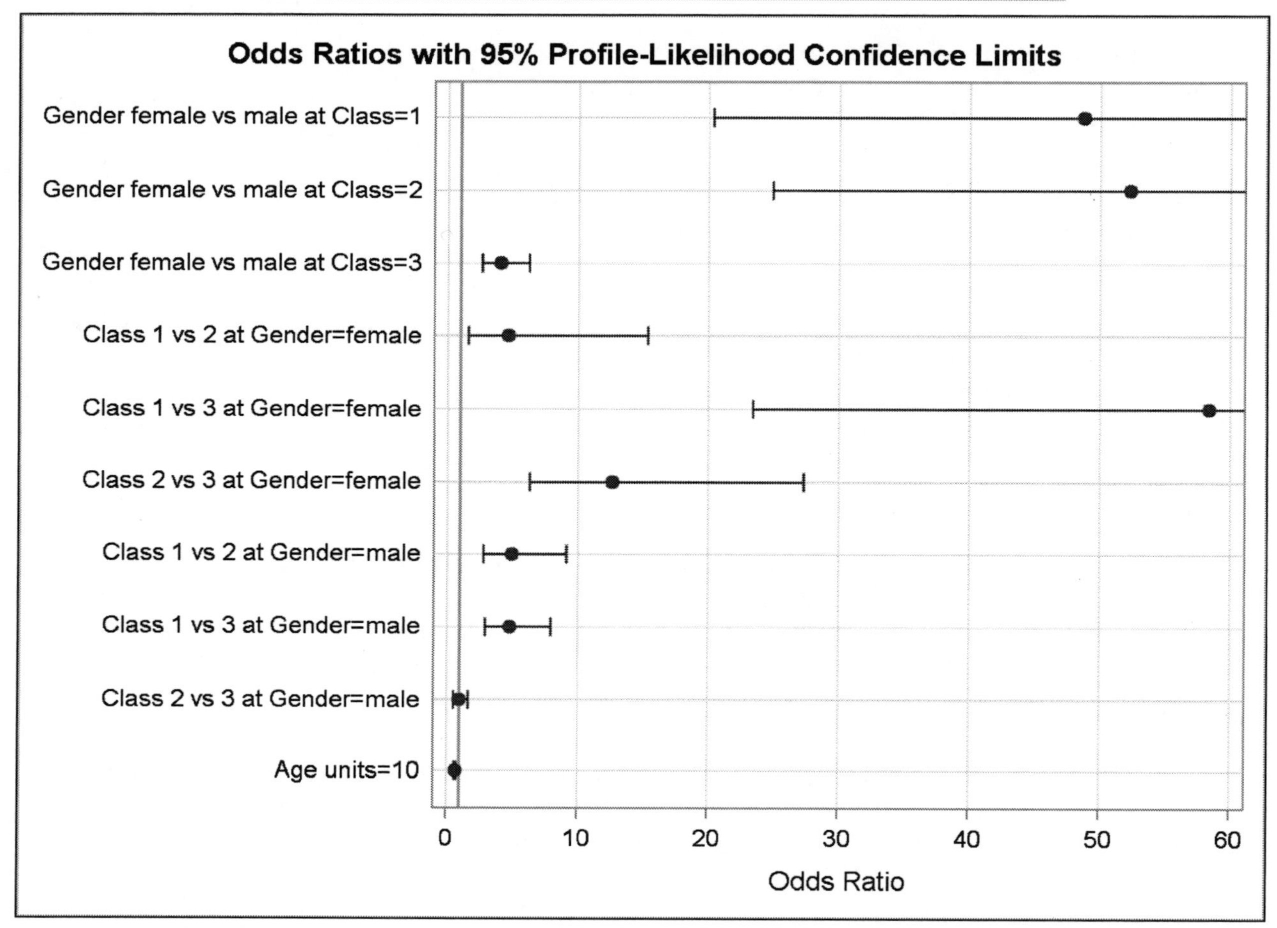


Notice the effect of the RANGE=CLIP suboption. The Odds Ratio axis is clipped just beyond the odds ratio estimate of Class 1 versus 3 at **Gender=`female`**. The upper bound of the associated 95% confidence interval is 179.396. Even with the range clipped, the **Age** confidence interval is barely discernible.

From this plot it is clear that the gender effect is different at different classes. (There is a stark difference in first and second classes, but not nearly as much in third class.) The class differences are also evidently different at each gender. For example, the odds ratio comparing first and third classes for females is far greater than the odds ratio comparing those same classes for males.

# Exercises

**4. Performing Backward Elimination**

Using the **sasuser.safety** data set, run PROC LOGISTIC and use backward elimination. Start with a model using ***only main effects***.

Use **Unsafe** as the outcome variable and **Weight**, **Size**, and **Region** as the predictor variables. Use the EVENT= option to model the probability of below-average safety scores.

Use the SIZEFMT format for the variable **Size**.

Specify **Region** and **Size** as classification variables using reference cell coding and specify **`Asia`** as the reference level for **Region** and **`Small`** as the reference level for **Size**.

Use a UNITS statement with -1 as the units for weight, so that you can see the odds ratio for lighter cars over heavier cars. Request any relevant plots.

**a.** Which terms appear in the final model?

**b.** Do you think this is a better model than the one fit with only **Region**?

The variable **Size** is coded (1, 2, 3), but the applied format requires that the formatted value be used in the CLASS statement for the REF= category.

```
value sizefmt 1='Small'
              2='Medium'
              3='Large';
```

# 5.6 Logit Plots (Self-Study)

## Objectives

- Explain the concept of logit plots.
- Plot estimated logits for continuous and ordinal variables.

109

## Scatter Plot of Binary Response Data

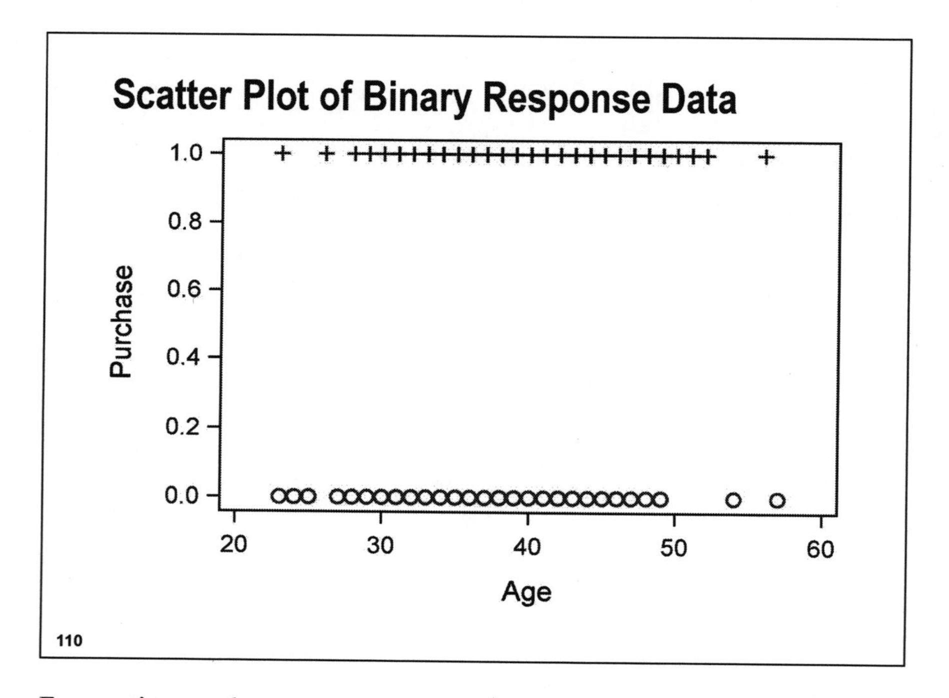


110

For continuous data, a recommended step before building a regression model is to analyze the bivariate relationships between the regressors and the response variables. The goal is not only to detect outliers, but also to analyze the shape of the relationships to determine whether there might be some nonlinear trend that should be modeled in the analysis. For binary response variables, a scatter plot contributes little to these ends.

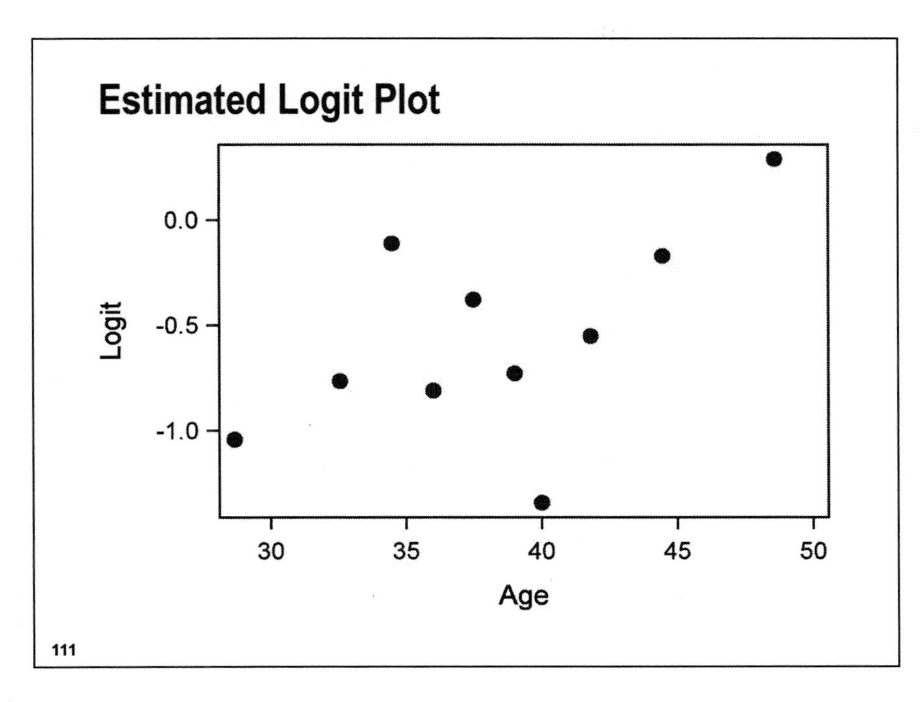


The logistic model asserts a linear relationship with the logit (not with the actual binary values). However, a logit for one observation will be infinite in either the positive or negative direction ($\ln(p/(1-p))=\ln(1/0)$ or $\ln(0/1)$). A recommendation, however, is to group the data into approximately equally sized bins, based on the values of the predictor variable. The bin size should be adequate in number of observations to reduce the sample variability of the logits. You can then assume that the average probability within each bin is approximately the value of the proportion in the bin with the event. The estimated logit is then approximately equal to ln(proportion/(1–proportion)).

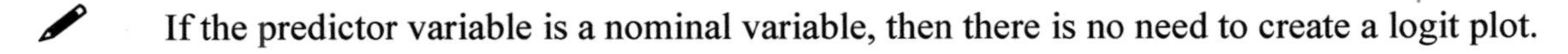
If the predictor variable is a nominal variable, then there is no need to create a logit plot.

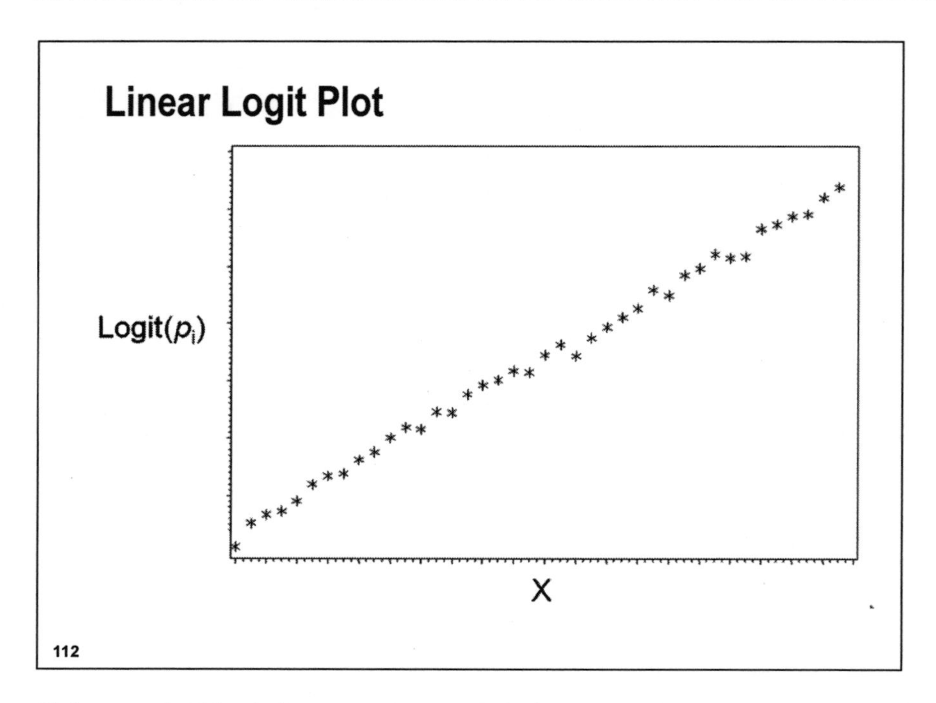


If the standard logistic regression model adequately fits the data, the logit plots should be fairly linear. The above graph shows a predictor variable that meets the assumption of linearity in the logit.

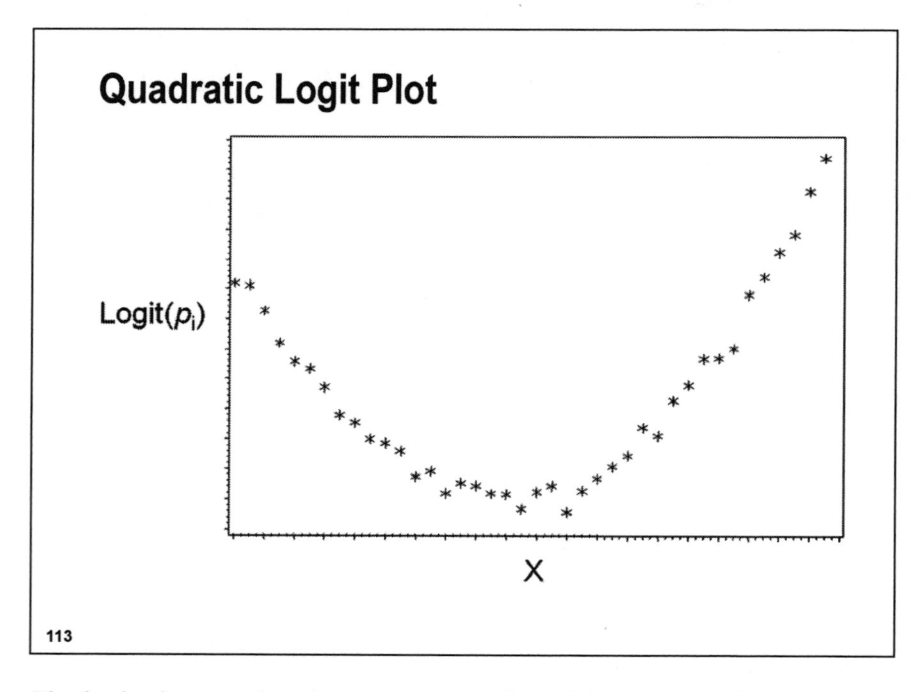


The logit plot can also show serious nonlinearities between the outcome variable and the predictor variable. The above graph reveals a quadratic relationship between the outcome and predictor variables. Adding a polynomial term or binning the predictor variable into three groups (two dummy variables would model the quadratic relationship) and treating it as a classification variable can improve the model fit.

## Estimated Logits

$$\ln\left(\frac{E_i+1}{C_i-E_i+1}\right)$$

where

$E_i$= number of events in bin

$C_i$= number of cases in bin

114

A common approach when computing logits is to take the log of the odds. The path from the definition of a logit to the formula above is shown below. *C* represents the total number in the bin and *E* represents the total number of positive events in the bin.

$$\left(\frac{P_i}{(1-P_i)}\right)=\left(\frac{\frac{E_i}{C_i}}{\left(\frac{C_i}{C_i}-\frac{E_i}{C_i}\right)}\right)=\left(\frac{E_i}{(C_i-E_i)}\right)$$

The logit is undefined for any bin in which the outcome rate is 100% or 0%. To eliminate this problem and reduce the variability of the logits, a common recommendation is to add a small constant to the numerator and denominator of the formula that computes the logit (Santner and Duffy 1989).

## Plotting Estimated Logits

Example: Plot the estimated logits of the outcome variable **Survived** versus the predictor variable **Class**. To construct the estimated logits, the number of passengers who survived and the total number of customers by each level of **Class** must be computed.

```
/*st105d08.sas*/  /*Part A*/
proc means data=sasuser.Titanic noprint nway;
   class Class;
   var Survived;
   output out=bins sum(Survived)=NEvent n(Survived)=NCases;
run;

data bins;
   set bins;
   Logit=log((NEvent+1)/(NCases-NEvent+1));
run;

proc sgplot data=bins;
   reg Y=Logit X=Class /
       markerattrs=(symbol=asterisk color=blue size=15);
   pbspline Y=Logit X=Class / nomarkers;
   xaxis integer;
   title "Estimated Logit Plot of Passenger Class";
run;
quit;
```

Selected PROC MEANS statement option:

| | |
|---|---|
| NWAY | causes the output data set to have only one observation for each level of the class variable. |

Selected PROC SGPLOT statements:

| | |
|---|---|
| REG | creates a fitted regression line or curve. |
| PBSPLINE | creates a fitted penalized B-spline curve. |

Selected options for REG or PBSPLINE statements:

| | |
|---|---|
| MARKERATTRS | controls the display of the marker values for data points on the plot. SIZE is measured in pixels. |
| NOMARKERS | removes the scatter markers from the plot. |

PROC MEANS creates a data set that contains a separate value for the requested statistics for each level of the CLASS variable. Because **Survived** is coded 0/1, SUM(**Survived**) returns the value for the count of ones within each level of **CLASS**. N(**Survived**) returns the number of nonmissing values of **Survived**, which is the total effective sample size within each level.

The logit is created in the DATA step, using the formula seen in the slide shown previously. In this case, **C** is represented by **NCases** and **E** is represented by **NEvent**.

PROC SGPLOT shows the data, a regression line, and a penalized B-spline curve. The regression line and the curve can be compared to each other to assess the linearity of the relationship between the logit and the predictor. If the curve approximates the regression line, this gives evidence of linearity.

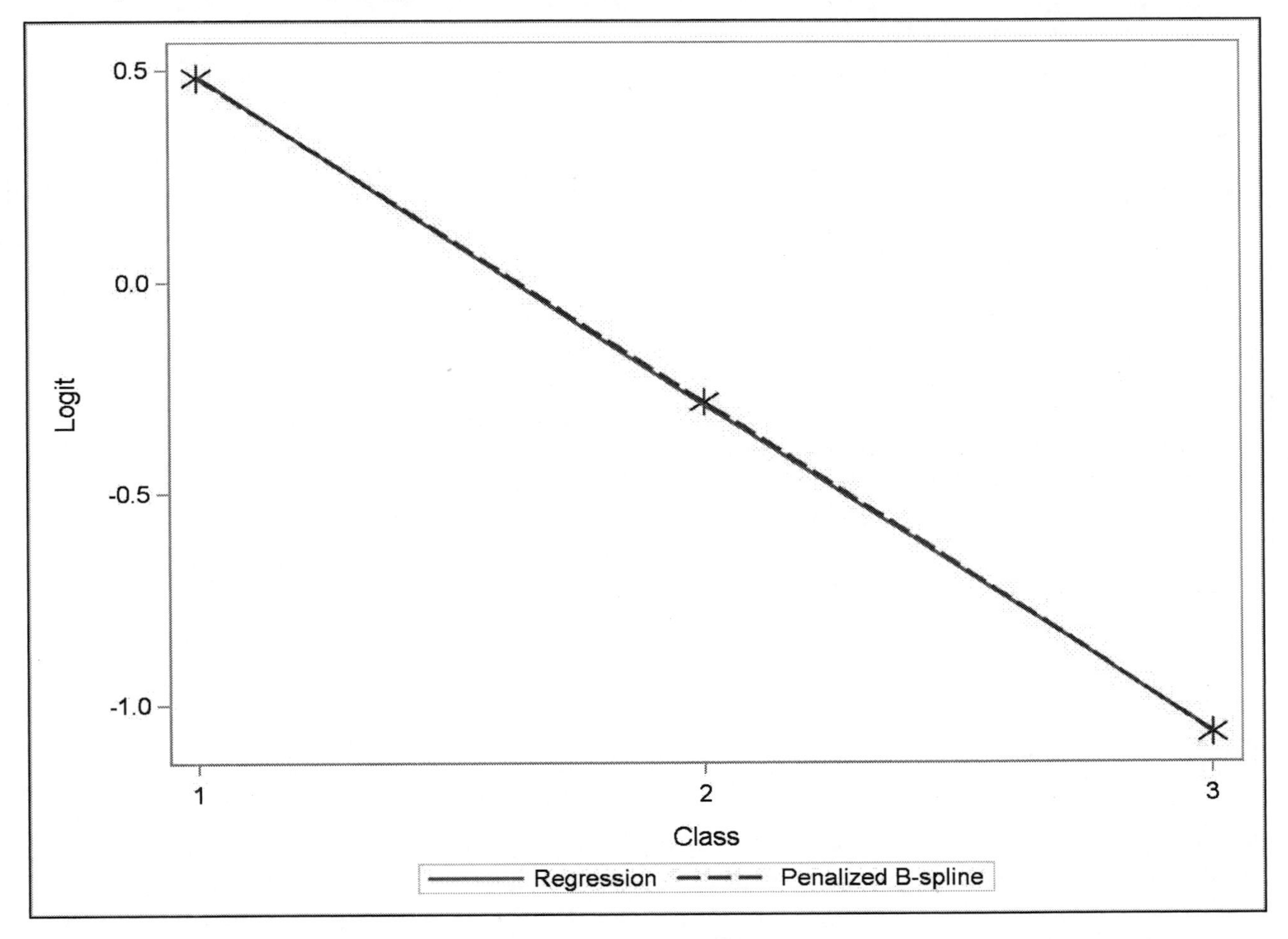


The logit plot for this ordinal variable is almost perfectly linear.

When a linear pattern is detected in a logit plot for an ordinal variable, the variable can be removed from the CLASS statement, implying that it would be considered the same as a continuous variable. The statistical advantage of doing so would be to increase model power, due to obtaining almost the same information using fewer degrees of freedom. However, theoretical justifications should always supersede such data-driven considerations.

Example: Plot the estimated logits of the outcome variable **Survived** versus the predictor variable **Age**. Because **Age** is a continuous variable, bin the observations into 50 groups to ensure that an adequate number of observations are used to compute the estimated logit.

```
/*st105d08.sas*/  /*Part B*/
proc rank data=sasuser.Titanic groups=50 out=Ranks;
   var Age;
   ranks Rank;
run;

proc means data=Ranks noprint nway;
   class Rank;
   var Survived Age;
   output out=Bins sum(Survived)=NEvent n(Survived)=NCases
          mean(Age)=Age;
run;

data bins;
   set bins;
   Logit=log((NEvent+1)/(NCases-NEvent+1));
run;

proc sgplot data=bins;
   reg Y=Logit X=Age /
       markerattrs=(symbol=asterisk color=blue size=15);
   pbspline Y=Logit X=Age / nomarkers;
   title "Estimated Logit Plot of Passenger's Age";
run;
quit;
```

Selected PROC RANK statement option:

GROUPS=*n* bins the variables into *n* groups.

Selected RANK procedure statement:

RANKS names the group indicators in the OUT= data set. If the RANKS statement is omitted, then the group indicators replace the VAR variables in the OUT= data set.

In the case of **Age**, you do not have a made-to-order bin variable, so you must create one. You can use the RANK procedure for this purpose. You have 1309 observations. It is recommended that you have approximately 20 to 30 observations per bin. At approximately 26 per bin, you could create 1309/26~50 bins. That will be the option value of GROUPS=.

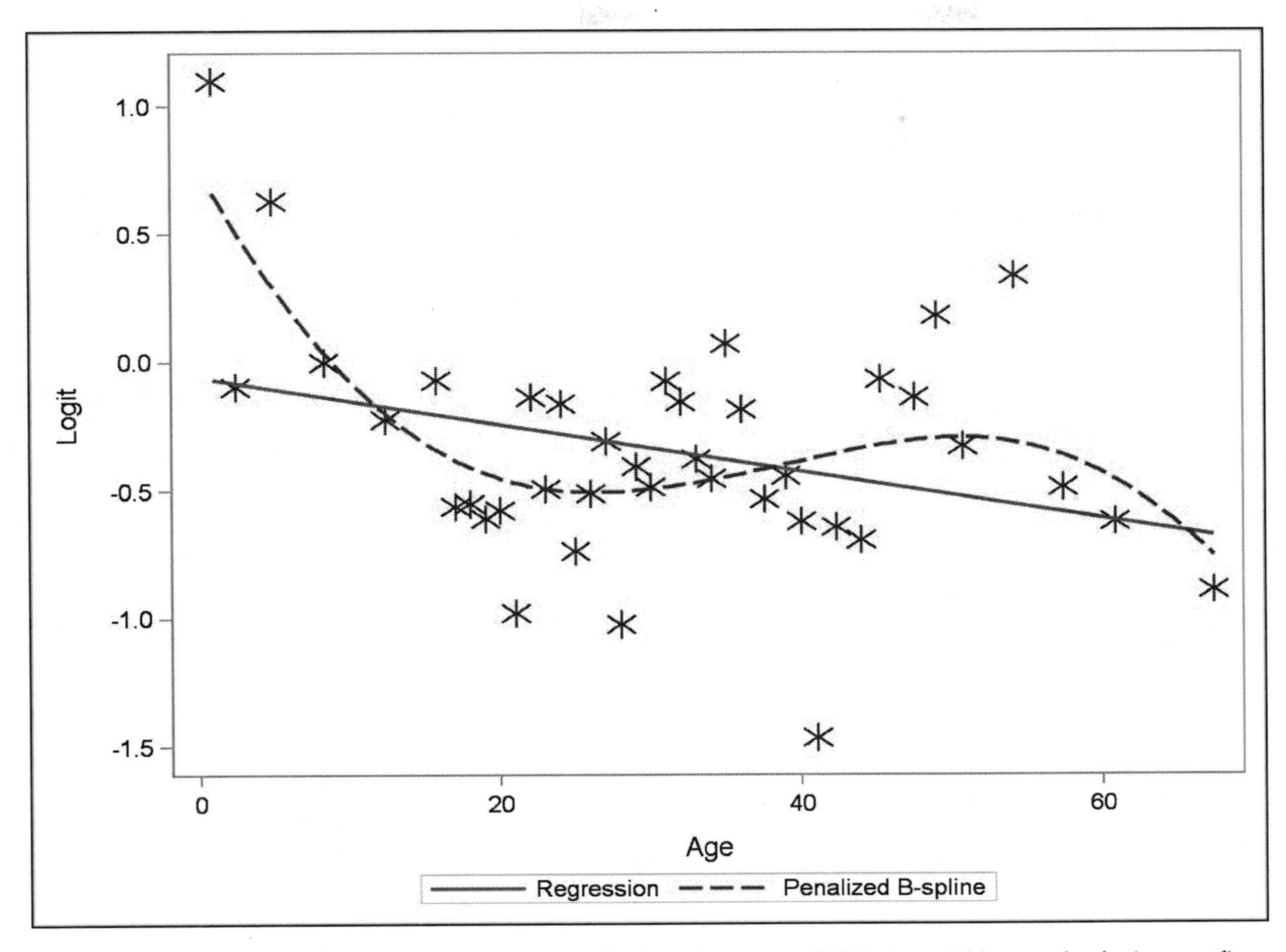


The estimated logit plot shows a deviation from linearity. One possibility is to add a quadratic (squared) or cubic (cubed) term for **Age**.

The estimated logit plot is a univariate plot and therefore can be misleading in the presence of interactions and partial associations. (Association between the response variable and the predictor variable changes with the addition of another predictor variable in the model.) If an interaction is suspected, a model with the interaction term and main effects should be evaluated before any variable is eliminated. Estimated logit plots should never be used to eliminate variables from consideration for a multiple logistic regression model.

# 5.7 Solutions

## Solutions to Exercises

1. **Performing Tests and Measures of Association**

   An insurance company wants to relate the safety of vehicles to several other variables. A score is given to each vehicle model, using the frequency of insurance claims as a basis. The data are in the **sasuser.safety** data set.

   **a.** Invoke the FREQ procedure and create one-way frequency tables for the categorical variables.

```
/*st105s01.sas*/  /*Part A*/
ods graphics off;
proc freq data=sasuser.safety;
   tables Unsafe Type Region Size;
   title "Safety Data Frequencies";
run;
ods graphics on;
```

| Unsafe | Frequency | Percent | Cumulative Frequency | Cumulative Percent |
|---|---|---|---|---|
| 0 | 66 | 68.75 | 66 | 68.75 |
| 1 | 30 | 31.25 | 96 | 100.00 |

| Type | Frequency | Percent | Cumulative Frequency | Cumulative Percent |
|---|---|---|---|---|
| Large | 16 | 16.67 | 16 | 16.67 |
| Medium | 29 | 30.21 | 45 | 46.88 |
| Small | 20 | 20.83 | 65 | 67.71 |
| Sport/Utility | 16 | 16.67 | 81 | 84.38 |
| Sports | 15 | 15.63 | 96 | 100.00 |

| Region | Frequency | Percent | Cumulative Frequency | Cumulative Percent |
|---|---|---|---|---|
| Asia | 35 | 36.46 | 35 | 36.46 |
| N America | 61 | 63.54 | 96 | 100.00 |

| Size | Frequency | Percent | Cumulative Frequency | Cumulative Percent |
|---|---|---|---|---|
| 1 | 35 | 36.46 | 35 | 36.46 |
| 2 | 29 | 30.21 | 64 | 66.67 |
| 3 | 32 | 33.33 | 96 | 100.00 |

1) What is the measurement scale of each variable?

| Variable | Measurement Scale |
|---|---|
| **Unsafe** | **Nominal, Ordinal, Binary** |
| **Type** | **Nominal** |
| **Region** | **Nominal** |
| **Weight** | **Ratio (Continuous)** |
| **Size** | **Ordinal** |

2) What is the proportion of cars made in North America?

**63.54 %**

3) For the variables **Unsafe**, **Size**, **Region**, and **Type**, are there any unusual data values that warrant further investigation?

**No.**

**b.** Use PROC FREQ to examine the crosstabulation of the variables **Region** by **Unsafe**. Generate a temporary format to clearly identify the values of **Unsafe**. Along with the default output, generate the expected frequencies, the chi-square test of association and the odds ratio.

```
/*st105s01.sas*/  /*Part B*/
proc format;
   value safefmt 0='Average or Above'
                 1='Below Average';
run;

proc freq data=sasuser.safety;
   tables Region*Unsafe / expected chisq relrisk;
   format Unsafe safefmt.;
   title "Association between Unsafe and Region";
run;
```

| Table of Region by Unsafe | | | |
|---|---|---|---|
| **Region** | **Unsafe** | | |
| **Frequency**<br>**Expected**<br>**Percent**<br>**Row Pct**<br>**Col Pct** | **Average or Above** | **Below Average** | **Total** |
| **Asia** | 20<br>24.063<br>20.83<br>57.14<br>30.30 | 15<br>10.938<br>15.63<br>42.86<br>50.00 | 35<br><br>36.46 |
| **N America** | 46<br>41.938<br>47.92<br>75.41<br>69.70 | 15<br>19.063<br>15.63<br>24.59<br>50.00 | 61<br><br>63.54 |
| **Total** | 66<br>68.75 | 30<br>31.25 | 96<br>100.00 |

**Statistics for Table of Region by Unsafe**

| Statistic | DF | Value | Prob |
|---|---|---|---|
| Chi-Square | 1 | 3.4541 | 0.0631 |
| Likelihood Ratio Chi-Square | 1 | 3.3949 | 0.0654 |
| Continuity Adj. Chi-Square | 1 | 2.6562 | 0.1031 |
| Mantel-Haenszel Chi-Square | 1 | 3.4181 | 0.0645 |
| Phi Coefficient | | -0.1897 | |
| Contingency Coefficient | | 0.1864 | |
| Cramer's V | | -0.1897 | |

| Fisher's Exact Test | |
|---|---|
| Cell (1,1) Frequency (F) | 20 |
| Left-sided Pr <= F | 0.0525 |
| Right-sided Pr >= F | 0.9809 |
| | |
| Table Probability (P) | 0.0334 |
| Two-sided Pr <= P | 0.0718 |

| Estimates of the Relative Risk (Row1/Row2) | | | |
|---|---|---|---|
| Type of Study | Value | 95% Confidence Limits | |
| Case-Control (Odds Ratio) | 0.4348 | 0.1790 | 1.0562 |
| Cohort (Col1 Risk) | 0.7578 | 0.5499 | 1.0443 |
| Cohort (Col2 Risk) | 1.7429 | 0.9733 | 3.1210 |

1) For the cars made in Asia, what percentage had a below-average safety score?

   **Region is a row variable, so look at the Row Pct value in the `Below Average` cell of the `Asia` row. That value is 42.86.**

2) For the cars with an average or above safety score, what percentage was made in North America?

   **The Col Pct value for the cell for `North America` in the column for `Average or Above` is 69.70.**

3) Do you see a statistically significant (at the 0.05 level) association between **Region** and **Unsafe**?

   **The association is not statistically significant at the 0.05 alpha level. The *p*-value is 0.0631.**

4) What does the odds ratio compare and what does this one say about the difference in odds between Asian and North American cars?

   **The odds ratio compares the odds of below average safety for North America versus Asia. The odds ratio of 0.4348 means that cars made in North America have 56.52 percent lower odds for being unsafe than cars made in Asia.**

Recall that odds ratios given in the Estimates of Relative Risk table are calculated comparing row1/row2 for column1. In this problem, this comparison is `Asia` to `N America` whose outcome is `Average or Above` in safety. The value 0.4348 is interpreted as the odds of having an `Average or Above` car made in `Asia` is 0.4348 times the odds for American-made cars. If you wished to compare `N America` to `Asia`, still using `Average or Above` for safety, the odds ratio would be the inverse of 0.4348, or approximately 2.3. This is interpreted as cars made in North America have 2.3 times the odds for being safe than cars made in Asia. This single inversion would also create the odds ratio for comparing `Asia` to `N America` but `Below Average` in safety. If you wished to compare `N America` to `Asia` using `Below Average` in safety, you would invert your odds ratio twice returning to the value 0.4348.

**c.** Use the variable named **Size**. Examine the ordinal association between **Size** and **Unsafe**. Use PROC FREQ.

```
/*st105s01.sas*/  /*Part C*/
proc freq data=sasuser.safety;
   tables Size*Unsafe / chisq measures cl;
   format Unsafe safefmt.;
   title "Association between Unsafe and Size";
run;
```

| Table of Size by Unsafe | | | |
|---|---|---|---|
| **Size** | **Unsafe** | | |
| **Frequency**<br>**Percent**<br>**Row Pct**<br>**Col Pct** | **Average or Above** | **Below Average** | **Total** |
| **1** | 12<br>12.50<br>34.29<br>18.18 | 23<br>23.96<br>65.71<br>76.67 | 35<br>36.46 |
| **2** | 24<br>25.00<br>82.76<br>36.36 | 5<br>5.21<br>17.24<br>16.67 | 29<br>30.21 |
| **3** | 30<br>31.25<br>93.75<br>45.45 | 2<br>2.08<br>6.25<br>6.67 | 32<br>33.33 |
| **Total** | 66<br>68.75 | 30<br>31.25 | 96<br>100.00 |

**Statistics for Table of Size by Unsafe**

| Statistic | DF | Value | Prob |
|---|---|---|---|
| Chi-Square | 2 | 31.3081 | <.0001 |
| Likelihood Ratio Chi-Square | 2 | 32.6199 | <.0001 |
| Mantel-Haenszel Chi-Square | 1 | 27.7098 | <.0001 |
| Phi Coefficient | | 0.5711 | |
| Contingency Coefficient | | 0.4959 | |
| Cramer's V | | 0.5711 | |

| Statistic | Value | ASE | 95% Confidence Limits | |
|---|---|---|---|---|
| Gamma | -0.8268 | 0.0796 | -0.9829 | -0.6707 |
| Kendall's Tau-b | -0.5116 | 0.0726 | -0.6540 | -0.3693 |
| Stuart's Tau-c | -0.5469 | 0.0866 | -0.7166 | -0.3771 |
| Somers' D C\|R | -0.4114 | 0.0660 | -0.5408 | -0.2819 |
| Somers' D R\|C | -0.6364 | 0.0860 | -0.8049 | -0.4678 |
| Pearson Correlation | -0.5401 | 0.0764 | -0.6899 | -0.3903 |
| Spearman Correlation | -0.5425 | 0.0769 | -0.6932 | -0.3917 |
| Lambda Asymmetric C\|R | 0.3667 | 0.1569 | 0.0591 | 0.6743 |
| Lambda Asymmetric R\|C | 0.2951 | 0.0892 | 0.1203 | 0.4699 |
| Lambda Symmetric | 0.3187 | 0.0970 | 0.1286 | 0.5088 |
| Uncertainty Coefficient C\|R | 0.2735 | 0.0836 | 0.1096 | 0.4374 |
| Uncertainty Coefficient R\|C | 0.1551 | 0.0490 | 0.0590 | 0.2512 |
| Uncertainty Coefficient Symmetric | 0.1979 | 0.0615 | 0.0773 | 0.3186 |

1) What statistic should you use to detect an ordinal association between **Size** and **Unsafe**?

   **The Mantel-Haenszel Chi-Square**

2) Do you reject or fail to reject the null hypothesis at the 0.05 level?

   **Reject**

3) What is the strength of the ordinal association between **Size** and **Unsafe**?

   **The Spearman correlation is -0.5425.**

4) What is the 95% confidence interval around that statistic?

   **The CI is (-0.6932, -0.3917).**

**2. Performing a Logistic Regression Analysis**

Fit a simple logistic regression model using **sasuser.safety** with **Unsafe** as the outcome variable and **Weight** as the predictor variable. Use the EVENT= option to model the probability of below-average safety scores. Request Profile Likelihood confidence limits and an odds ratio plot along with an effect plot.

```
/*st105s02.sas*/
proc logistic data=sasuser.safety plots(only)=(effect oddsratio);
   model Unsafe(event='1')=Weight / clodds=pl;
   title1 'LOGISTIC MODEL (1):Unsafe=Weight';
run;
```

| Model Information | |
|---|---|
| Data Set | SASUSER.SAFETY |
| Response Variable | Unsafe |
| Number of Response Levels | 2 |
| Model | binary logit |
| Optimization Technique | Fisher's scoring |

| | |
|---|---|
| Number of Observations Read | 96 |
| Number of Observations Used | 96 |

| Response Profile | | |
|---|---|---|
| Ordered Value | Unsafe | Total Frequency |
| 1 | 0 | 66 |
| 2 | 1 | 30 |

**Probability modeled is Unsafe=1.**

| Model Convergence Status |
|---|
| Convergence criterion (GCONV=1E-8) satisfied. |

| Model Fit Statistics | | |
|---|---|---|
| Criterion | Intercept Only | Intercept and Covariates |
| AIC | 121.249 | 106.764 |
| SC | 123.813 | 111.893 |
| -2 Log L | 119.249 | 102.764 |

| Testing Global Null Hypothesis: BETA=0 | | | |
|---|---|---|---|
| Test | Chi-Square | DF | Pr > ChiSq |
| Likelihood Ratio | 16.4845 | 1 | <.0001 |
| Score | 13.7699 | 1 | 0.0002 |
| Wald | 11.5221 | 1 | 0.0007 |

| Analysis of Maximum Likelihood Estimates | | | | | |
|---|---|---|---|---|---|
| Parameter | DF | Estimate | Standard Error | Wald Chi-Square | Pr > ChiSq |
| Intercept | 1 | 3.5422 | 1.2601 | 7.9023 | 0.0049 |
| Weight | 1 | -1.3901 | 0.4095 | 11.5221 | 0.0007 |

| Association of Predicted Probabilities and Observed Responses | | | |
|---|---|---|---|
| Percent Concordant | 55.2 | Somers' D | 0.474 |
| Percent Discordant | 7.7 | Gamma | 0.754 |
| Percent Tied | 37.1 | Tau-a | 0.206 |
| Pairs | 1980 | c | 0.737 |

| Profile Likelihood Confidence Interval for Odds Ratios | | | | |
|---|---|---|---|---|
| Effect | Unit | Estimate | 95% Confidence Limits | |
| Weight | 1.0000 | 0.249 | 0.102 | 0.517 |

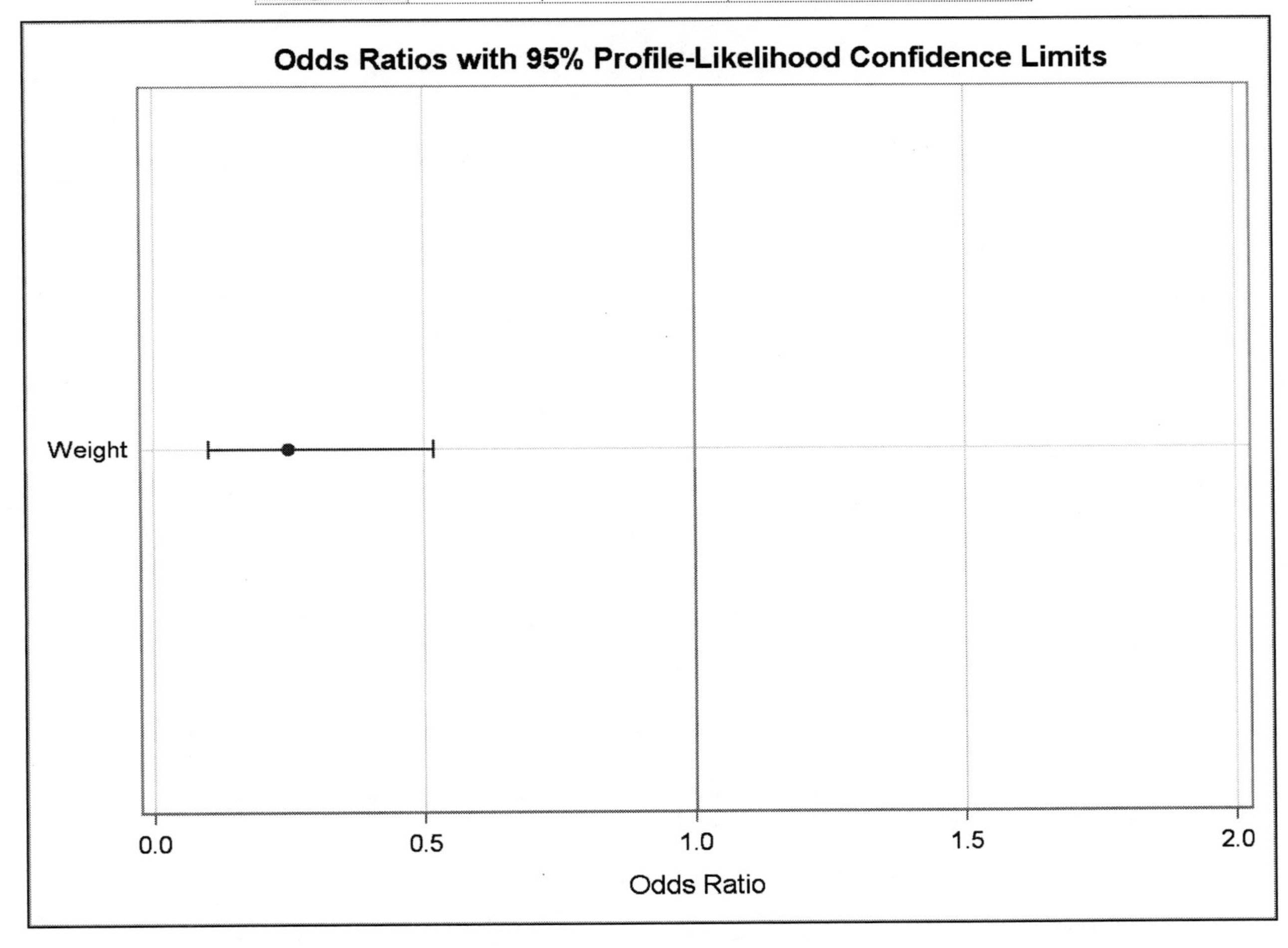

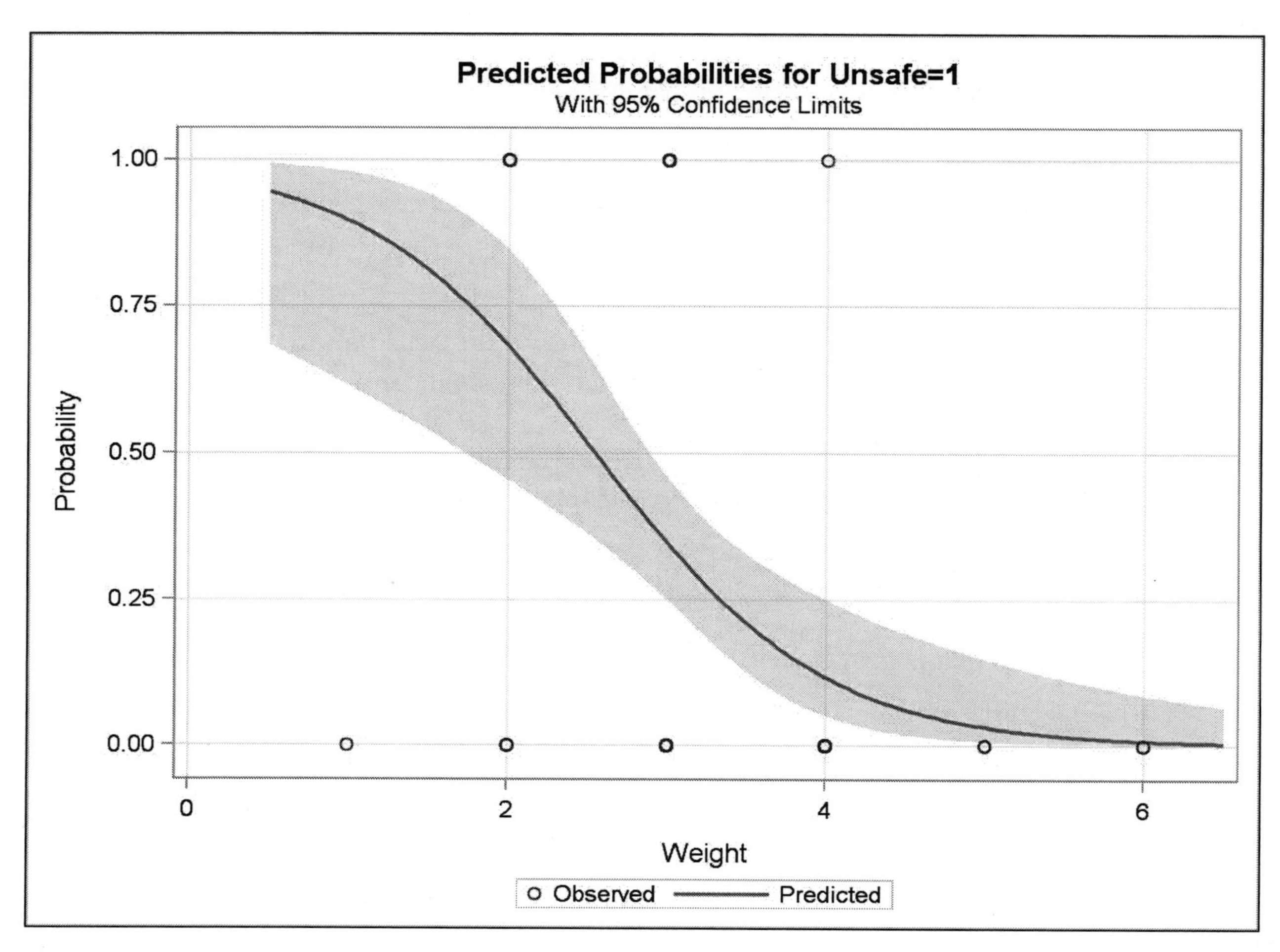


**a.** Do you reject or fail to reject the global null hypothesis that all regression coefficients of the model are 0?

**The *p*-value for the Likelihood Ratio test is <.0001 and therefore the global null hypothesis is rejected.**

**b.** Write the logistic regression equation.

**The regression equation is as follows:**

**Logit(Unsafe)=3.5422 + (-1.3901)*Weight.**

**c.** Interpret the odds ratio for **Weight**.

**The odds ratio for Weight (0.249) says that the odds for being unsafe (having a below average safety rating) are 75.1% lower for each thousand pound increase in weight. The confidence interval (0.102 , 0.517) does not contain 1, indicating that that the odds ratio is statistically significant.**

## 3. Performing a Multiple Logistic Regression Analysis Including Categorical Variables

Fit a logistic regression model using **sasuser.safety** with **Unsafe** as the outcome variable and **Weight**, **Region**, and **Size** as the predictor variables. Request reference cell coding with **Asia** as the reference level for **Region** and **3** (large cars) as the reference level for **Size**. Use the EVENT= option to model the probability of below-average safety scores. Request Profile Likelihood confidence limits and an odds ratio plot along with an effect plot.

```
/*st105s03.sas*/
proc logistic data=sasuser.safety plots(only)=(effect oddsratio);
   class Region (param=ref ref='Asia')
         Size (param=ref ref='3');
   model Unsafe(event='1')=Weight Region Size / clodds=pl;
   title1 'LOGISTIC MODEL (2):Unsafe=Weight Region Size';
run;
```

Partial PROC LOGISTIC Output

| Class Level Information | | | |
|---|---|---|---|
| **Class** | **Value** | **Design Variables** | |
| **Region** | **Asia** | 0 | |
| | **N America** | 1 | |
| **Size** | **1** | 1 | 0 |
| | **2** | 0 | 1 |
| | **3** | 0 | 0 |

| Model Convergence Status |
|---|
| Convergence criterion (GCONV=1E-8) satisfied. |

| Model Fit Statistics | | |
|---|---|---|
| **Criterion** | **Intercept Only** | **Intercept and Covariates** |
| **AIC** | 121.249 | 94.004 |
| **SC** | 123.813 | 106.826 |
| **-2 Log L** | 119.249 | 84.004 |

| Testing Global Null Hypothesis: BETA=0 | | | |
|---|---|---|---|
| **Test** | **Chi-Square** | **DF** | **Pr > ChiSq** |
| **Likelihood Ratio** | 35.2441 | 4 | <.0001 |
| **Score** | 32.8219 | 4 | <.0001 |
| **Wald** | 23.9864 | 4 | <.0001 |

a. Do you reject or fail to reject the null hypothesis that all regression coefficients of the model are 0?

**You reject the null hypothesis with a p<.0001.**

| Type 3 Analysis of Effects | | | |
|---|---|---|---|
| Effect | DF | Wald Chi-Square | Pr > ChiSq |
| Weight | 1 | 2.1176 | 0.1456 |
| Region | 1 | 0.4506 | 0.5020 |
| Size | 2 | 15.3370 | 0.0005 |

**b.** If you do reject the global null hypothesis, then which predictors significantly predict safety outcome?

**Only Size is significantly predictive of Unsafe.**

| Analysis of Maximum Likelihood Estimates | | | | | | |
|---|---|---|---|---|---|---|
| Parameter | | DF | Estimate | Standard Error | Wald Chi-Square | Pr > ChiSq |
| Intercept | | 1 | 0.0500 | 1.8008 | 0.0008 | 0.9778 |
| Weight | | 1 | -0.6678 | 0.4589 | 2.1176 | 0.1456 |
| Region | N America | 1 | -0.3775 | 0.5624 | 0.4506 | 0.5020 |
| Size | 1 | 1 | 2.6783 | 0.8810 | 9.2422 | 0.0024 |
| Size | 2 | 1 | 0.6582 | 0.9231 | 0.5085 | 0.4758 |

| Association of Predicted Probabilities and Observed Responses | | | |
|---|---|---|---|
| Percent Concordant | 81.9 | Somers' D | 0.696 |
| Percent Discordant | 12.3 | Gamma | 0.739 |
| Percent Tied | 5.8 | Tau-a | 0.302 |
| Pairs | 1980 | c | 0.848 |

| Profile Likelihood Confidence Interval for Odds Ratios | | | | |
|---|---|---|---|---|
| Effect | Unit | Estimate | 95% Confidence Limits | |
| Weight | 1.0000 | 0.513 | 0.201 | 1.260 |
| Region N America vs Asia | 1.0000 | 0.686 | 0.225 | 2.081 |
| Size 1 vs 3 | 1.0000 | 14.560 | 3.018 | 110.732 |
| Size 2 vs 3 | 1.0000 | 1.931 | 0.343 | 15.182 |

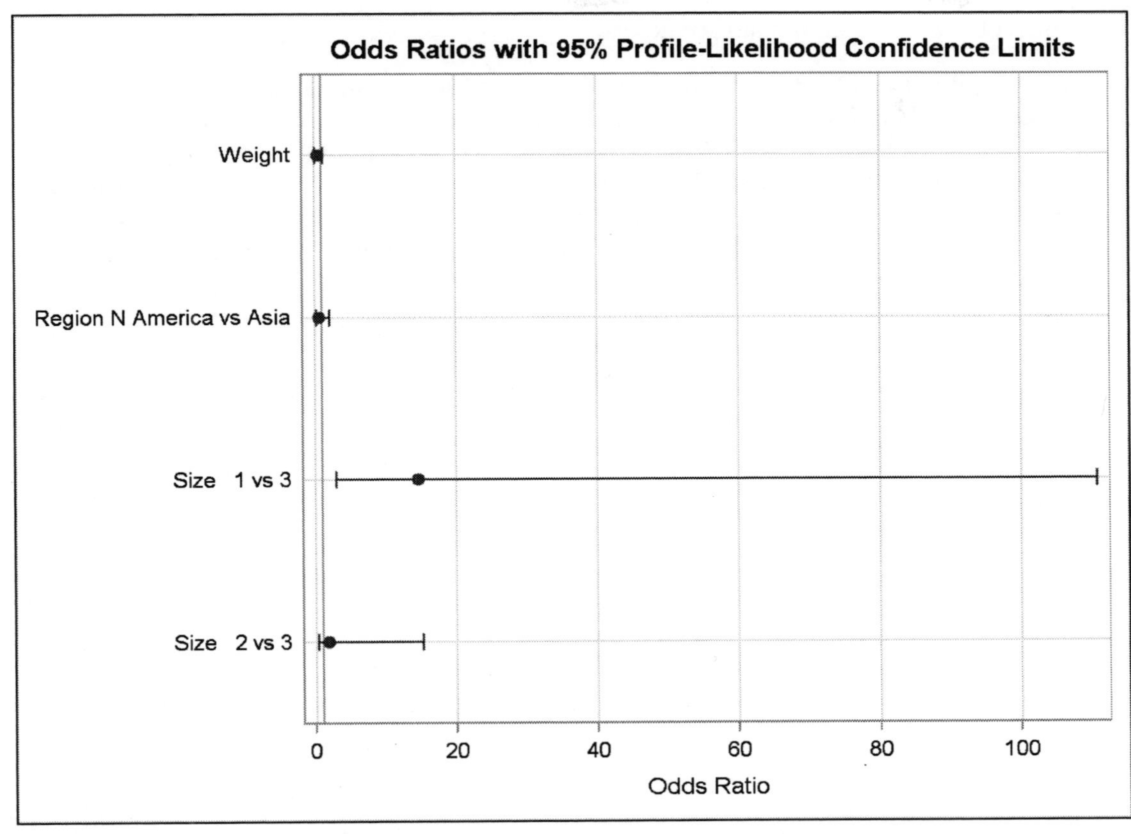
Odds Ratios with 95% Profile-Likelihood Confidence Limits
Weight
Region N America vs Asia
Size 1 vs 3
Size 2 vs 3
0
20
40
60
80
100
Odds Ratio

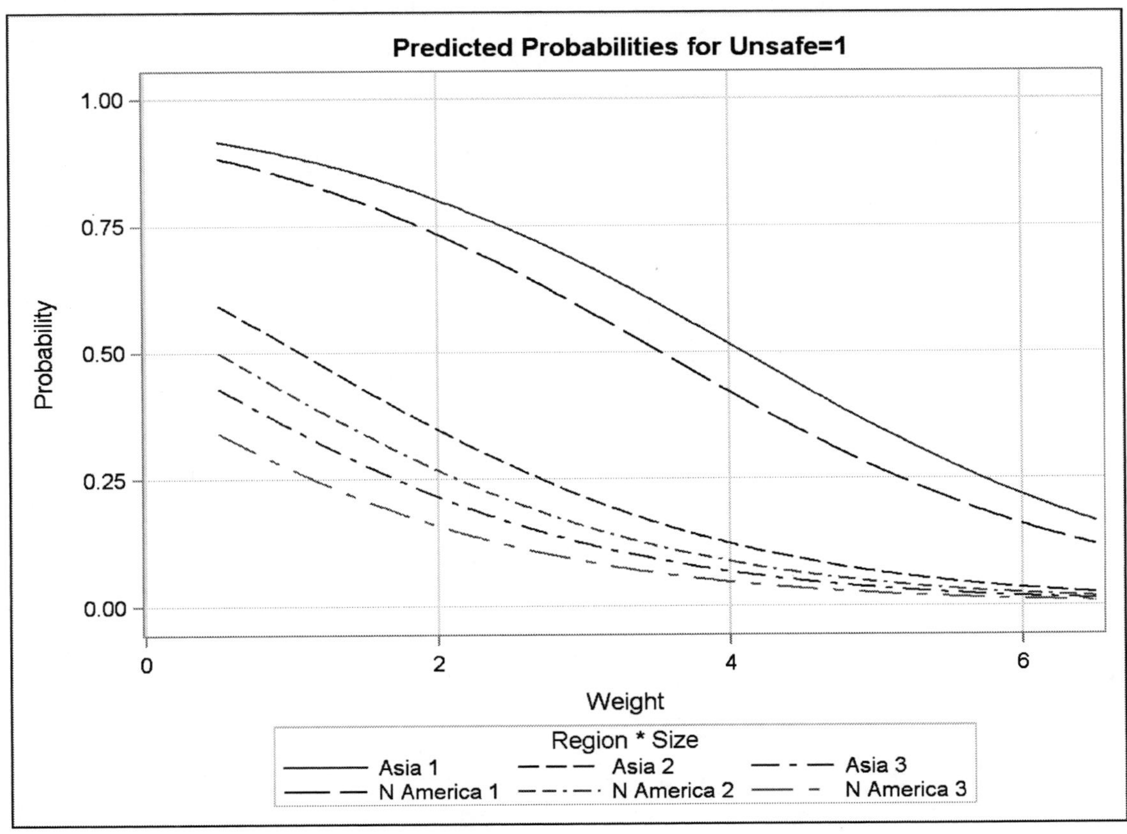
Predicted Probabilities for Unsafe=1
1.00
0.75
0.50
0.25
0.00
Probability
0
2
4
6
Weight
Region * Size
Asia 1
Asia 2
Asia 3
N America 1
N America 2
N America 3

c. Interpret the odds ratio for significant predictors.

**Only Size is significant. The design variables show that Size=1 (Small or Sports) cars have 14.560 times the odds of having a below-average safety rating compared to the reference category, 3 (Large or Sport/Utility). The 95% confidence interval (3.018, 110.732) does not contain 1, implying that the contrast is statistically significant at the 0.05 level. The contrast from the second design variable is 1.931 (Medium versus Sport/Utility), implying a trend toward greater odds of low safety for medium cars. However, the 95% confidence interval (0.343, 15.182) contains 1 and therefore the contrast is not statistically significant.**

## Solutions to Student Activities (Polls/Quizzes)

### 5.01 Multiple Answer Poll – Correct Answer

Which of the following would likely not be considered categorical in the data?

a. **Gender**
(b.) **Fare**
c. **Survival**
(d.) **Age**
e. **Class**

14

### 5.02 Multiple Answer Poll – Correct Answers

What tends to happen when sample size decreases?

a. The chi-square value increases.
(b.) The *p*-value increases.
c. Cramer's V increases.
d. The Odds Ratio increases.
(e.) The width of the CI for the Odds Ratio increases.

33

## 5.03 Multiple Answer Poll – Correct Answers

A researcher wants to measure the strength of an association between two binary variables. Which statistic(s) can he use?

a. Hansel and Gretel Correlation
b. Mantel-Haenszel Chi-Square
c. Pearson Chi-Square
(d.) Odds Ratio
(e.) Spearman Correlation

51

## 5.04 Multiple Choice Poll – Correct Answer

What are the upper and lower bounds for a logit?

a. Lower=0, Upper=1
b. Lower=0, No upper bound
(c.) No lower bound, No upper bound
d. No lower bound, Upper=1

$$\text{logit}(p_i) = \ln\left(\frac{p_i}{(1-p_i)}\right)$$

66

## 5.05 Multiple Choice Poll – Correct Answer

In the Analysis of Maximum Likelihood table, using effect coding, what is the estimated logit for someone at **IncLevel**=2?

a. -.5363
b. -.6717
c. -.6659
(d.) -.7563
e. Cannot tell from the information provided

91

## 5.06 Multiple Choice Poll – Correct Answer

A variable coded 1, 2, 3, and 4 is parameterized with effect coding, with 2 as the reference level. The parameter estimate for level 1 tells you which of the following?

a. The difference in the logit between level 1 and level 2
b. The odds ratio between level 1 and level 2
(c.) The difference in the logit between level 1 and the average of all levels
d. The odds ratio between level 1 and the average of all levels
e. Both a and b
f. Both c and d

98

# Appendix A References

# A.1 References

Agresti, A. 1996. *An Introduction to Categorical Data Analysis*. New York: John Wiley & Sons.

Allison, P. 1999. *Logistic Regression Using the SAS® System: Theory and Application*. Cary, NC: SAS Institute Inc.

Anscombe, F. 1973. "Graphs in Statistical Analysis." *The American Statistician* 27:17–21.

Belsey, D. A., E. Kuh, and R. E. Welsch. 1980. *Regression Diagnostics: Identifying Influential Data and Sources of Collinearity*. New York: John Wiley & Sons.

Chatfield, C. (1995), "Model Uncertainty, Data Mining and Statistical Inference," *Journal of the Royal Statistical Society*, 158:419–466.

Findley, D.F. and E. Parzen. 1995. "A Conversation with Hirotugu Akaike." *Statistical Science* Vol. 10, No. 1:104–117.

Freedman, D.A. 1983, "A Note on Screening Regression Equations," *The American Statistician*, 37:152–155.

Hocking, R. R. 1976. "The Analysis and Selection of Variables in Linear Regression." *Biometrics* 32:1–49

Hosmer, D.W. and Lemeshow, S. 2000. *Applied Logistic Regression 2nd Edition*, New York: John Wiley & Sons.

Johnson, R. W. 1996. "Fitting percentage of body fat to simple body measurements" *Journal of Statistics Education,* Vol. 4, No. 1.

Mallows, C. L. 1973. "Some Comments on $C_p$." *Technometrics* 15:661–675.

Marquardt, D. W. 1980. "You Should Standardize the Predictor Variables in Your Regression Models." *Journal of the American Statistical Association* 75:74–103.

Myers, R. H. 1990. *Classical and Modern Regression with Applications, Second Edition*. Boston: Duxbury Press.

Neter, J., M. H. Kutner, W. Wasserman, and C. J. Nachtsheim. 1996. *Applied Linear Statistical Models*, Fourth Edition. New York: WCB McGraw Hill.

Raftery, A.E. (1995), "Bayesian Model Selection in Social Research," *Sociological Methodology*.

Rawlings, J. O. 1988. *Applied Regression Analysis: A Research Tool*. Pacific Grove, CA: Wadsworth & Brooks.

Santner, T.J. and D. E. Duffy. 1989. *The Statistical Analysis of Discrete Data*. New York: Springer-Verlag.

Shoemaker, A. L. 1996. "What's Normal? – Temperature, Gender, and Heart Rate." *Journal of Statistics Education,* Vol. 4, No. 2.

Tukey, John W. 1977. *Exploratory Data Analysis*. Addison-Wesley, Reading, MA.

Welch, B. L. 1951. "On the Comparison of Several Mean Values: An Alternative Approach." *Biometrika* 38:330–336.

# Appendix B Sampling from SAS Data Sets

# B.1 Random Samples

## Selecting Random Samples

The SURVERYSELECT procedure selects a random sample from a SAS data set.

```
PROC SURVEYSELECT DATA=name-of-SAS-data-set
                  OUT=name-of-output-data-set
                  METHOD= method-of-random-sampling
                  SEED=seed-value
                  SAMPSIZE=number of observations desired in
                           sample
                  ;
<STRATA stratification- variable(s)>;
RUN;
```

Selected PROC SURVEYSELECT statement options:

DATA= identifies the data set to be selected from.

OUT= indicates the name of the output data set.

METHOD= specifies the random sampling method to be used. For simple random sampling without replacement, use METHOD=SRS. For simple random sampling with replacement, use METHOD=URS. For other selection methods and details about sampling algorithms, see the SAS online documentation for PROC SURVEYSELECT.

SEED= specifies the initial seed for random number generation. If no SEED option is specified, SAS uses the system time as its seed value. This creates a different random sample every time the procedure is run.

SAMPSIZE= indicates the number of observations to be included in the sample. To select a certain fraction of the original data set rather than a given number of observations, use the SAMPRATE= option.

Selected SURVEYSELECT procedure statement:

STRATA enables the user to specify one or more stratification variables. If no STRATA statement is specified, no stratification takes place.

Other statements and options for the SURVERYSELECT procedure can be found in the SAS online documentation.

Part A shows how to select a certain sample size using the SAMPSIZE= option.

```
/* st10ad01.sas */   /*Part A*/
proc surveyselect
   data= sasuser.Safety  /* sample from data table */
   seed=31475            /* recommended that you use this option */
   method=srs            /* simple random sample */
   sampsize=12           /* sample size */
   out=work.SafetySample /* sample stored in this data set */
;
run;

proc print data=work.SafetySample;
run;
```

If you do not provide a seed, you cannot reproduce the sample. It is recommended that you always include a seed when using PROC SURVEYSELECT.

| Selection Method | Simple Random Sampling |
|---|---|

| | |
|---|---|
| Input Data Set | SAFETY |
| Random Number Seed | 31475 |
| Sample Size | 12 |
| Selection Probability | 0.125 |
| Sampling Weight | 8 |
| Output Data Set | SAFETYSAMPLE |

| Obs | Unsafe | Size | Weight | Region | Type |
|---|---|---|---|---|---|
| 1 | 0 | 2 | 3 | N America | Medium |
| 2 | 0 | 2 | 3 | N America | Medium |
| 3 | 0 | 3 | 4 | N America | Large |
| 4 | 1 | 1 | 3 | N America | Sports |
| 5 | 0 | 3 | 5 | N America | Sport/Utility |
| 6 | 0 | 3 | 6 | N America | Sport/Utility |
| 7 | 0 | 2 | 3 | Asia | Medium |
| 8 | 0 | 2 | 3 | Asia | Medium |
| 9 | 1 | 1 | 3 | Asia | Small |
| 10 | 0 | 3 | 4 | N America | Large |
| 11 | 1 | 1 | 3 | Asia | Small |
| 12 | 0 | 2 | 3 | Asia | Medium |

Part B shows how to select a certain percentage of the original sample using the SAMPRATE= option.

```
/* st10ad01.sas */  /*Part B*/
proc surveyselect
   data= sasuser.Safety  /* sample from data table */
   seed=31475            /* recommended that you use this option */
   method=srs            /* simple random sample */
   samprate=0.05         /* sample size */
   out=work.SafetySample /* sample stored in this data set */
;
run;

proc print data=work.SafetySample;
run;
```

| Selection Method | Simple Random Sampling |
|---|---|

| | |
|---|---|
| Input Data Set | SAFETY |
| Random Number Seed | 31475 |
| Sampling Rate | 0.05 |
| Sample Size | 5 |
| Selection Probability | 0.052083 |
| Sampling Weight | 19.2 |
| Output Data Set | SAFETYSAMPLE |

| Obs | Unsafe | Size | Weight | Region | Type |
|---|---|---|---|---|---|
| 1 | 1 | 1 | 3 | N America | Small |
| 2 | 1 | 3 | 3 | N America | Sport/Utility |
| 3 | 0 | 2 | 3 | Asia | Medium |
| 4 | 0 | 3 | 4 | N America | Sport/Utility |
| 5 | 0 | 2 | 3 | N America | Medium |

# Appendix C Additional Topics

# C.1 Paired *t* Tests

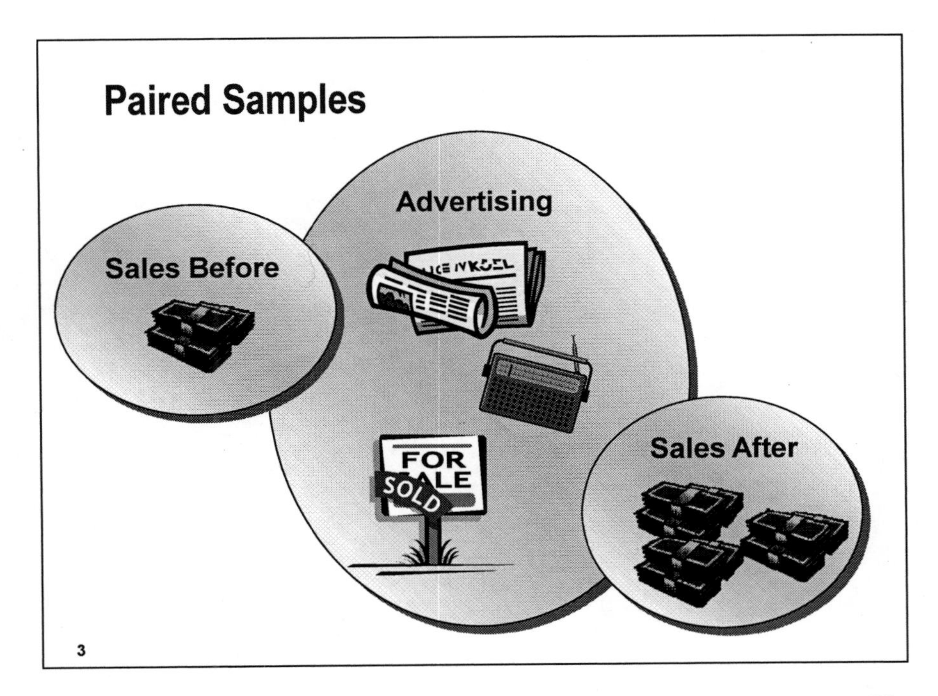


For many types of data, repeat measurements are taken on the same subject throughout a study. The simplest form of this study is often referred to as the *paired t test*.

In this study design,

- subjects are exposed to a treatment, for example, an advertising strategy
- a measurement is taken of the subjects before and after the treatment
- the subjects, on average, respond the same way to the treatment, although there might be differences among the subjects.

The assumptions of this test are that

- the subjects are selected randomly.
- the distribution of the sample mean differences is normal. The central limit theorem can be applied for large samples.

The hypotheses of this test are the following:

$$H_0: \mu_{POST} = \mu_{PRE}$$

$$H_1: \mu_{POST} \neq \mu_{PRE}$$

## The TTEST Procedure

General form of the TTEST procedure:

```
PROC TTEST DATA=SAS-data-set;
      CLASS variable;
      VAR variables;
      PAIRED variable*variable;
RUN;
```

4

Selected TTEST procedure statements:

CLASS specifies the two-level variable for the analysis. Only one variable is allowed in the CLASS statement.

VAR specifies numeric response variables for the analysis. If the VAR statement is not specified, PROC TTEST analyzes all numeric variables in the input data set that are not listed in a CLASS (or BY) statement.

PAIRED identifies the variables to be compared in paired comparisons. Variables are separated by an asterisk (*). The asterisk requests comparisons between each variable on the left with each variable on the right. The differences are calculated by taking the variable on the left minus the variable on the right of the asterisk.

## Paired *t* Test

Example: Dollar values of sales were collected both before and after a particular advertising campaign. You are interested in determining the effect of the campaign on sales. You collected data from 30 different randomly selected regions. The level of sales both before (**pre**) and after (**post**) the campaign were recorded and are shown below.

```
/*st10bd01.sas*/
proc print data=sasuser.market (obs=20);
   title;
run;
```

| Obs | pre | post |
|---|---|---|
| 1 | 9.52 | 10.28 |
| 2 | 9.63 | 10.45 |
| 3 | 7.71 | 8.51 |
| 4 | 7.83 | 8.62 |
| 5 | 8.97 | 10.03 |
| 6 | 8.62 | 9.45 |
| 7 | 10.11 | 9.68 |
| 8 | 9.96 | 9.62 |
| 9 | 8.50 | 11.84 |
| 10 | 9.62 | 11.95 |
| 11 | 10.29 | 10.52 |
| 12 | 10.13 | 10.67 |
| 13 | 9.11 | 11.03 |
| 14 | 8.95 | 10.53 |
| 15 | 10.86 | 10.70 |
| 16 | 9.31 | 10.24 |
| 17 | 9.59 | 10.82 |
| 18 | 9.27 | 10.16 |
| 19 | 11.86 | 12.12 |
| 20 | 10.15 | 11.28 |

The PAIRED statement used below is testing whether the mean of post-sales is significantly different from the mean of the presales because **post** is on the left of the asterisk and **pre** is on the right.

```
proc ttest data= sasuser.market;
   paired post*pre;
   title 'Testing the Difference Before and After a Sales Campaign';
run;
```

| N | Mean | Std Dev | Std Err | Minimum | Maximum |
|---|---|---|---|---|---|
| 30 | 0.9463 | 0.9271 | 0.1693 | -0.4800 | 3.3400 |

| Mean | 95% CL Mean | | Std Dev | 95% CL Std Dev | |
|---|---|---|---|---|---|
| 0.9463 | 0.6001 | 1.2925 | 0.9271 | 0.7384 | 1.2464 |

| DF | t Value | Pr > \|t\| |
|---|---|---|
| 29 | 5.59 | <.0001 |

The T Tests table provides the requested analysis. The *p*-value for the difference **post–pre** is less than 0.0001. Assuming that you want a 0.01 level of significance, you reject the null hypothesis and conclude that there is a change in the average sales after the advertising campaign. Also, based on the fact that the mean is positive 0.9463, there appears to be an increase in the average sales after the advertising campaign.

# C.2 One-Sided *t* Tests

## One-Sided Tests and Confidence Intervals

- Used when the null hypothesis is one of these forms:
  - $H_0$: $\mu \leq k$
  - $H_0$: $\mu \geq k$
- Can increase power
- Tests and confidence intervals produced in PROC TTEST using the following:
  - SIDES=U for Upper Tail Tests ($\mu_0 \leq k$) and CIs
  - SIDES=L for Lower Tail Tests ($\mu_0 \geq k$) and CIs

7

In many situations you might decide that rejection on only one side of the mean is important. For instance, a drug company might only want to test for positive differences between a new drug and a placebo and not negative differences. One-sided tests are a way doing this.

The students in Ms. Chao's class actually had another purpose when they collected the **Gender** information. They read about a study published in the 1980s about girls scoring lower on standardized tests on average than boys. They did not believe this still to be the case, particularly in this school. In fact, from their experiences, they hypothesized the opposite – that the girls' average score now exceeded the boys' average score.

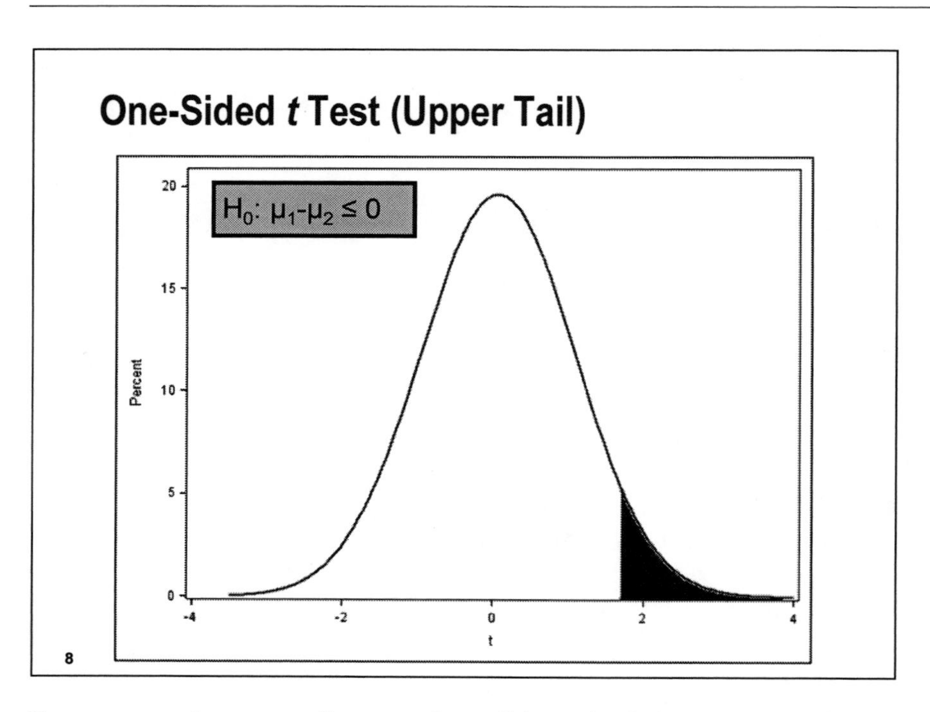


For two-sample upper-tail *t* tests, the null hypothesis is one not only of equivalence, but also of difference between two means. If you believe that the mean of girls is strictly greater than the mean of boys, this implies that you believe that the difference between the means for (Female - Male) is strictly greater than zero. That would then be your alternative hypothesis, $H_1$: $\mu_1$-$\mu_2 > 0$. The null hypothesis is then, $H_0$: $\mu_1$-$\mu_2 \leq 0$. Only *t* values above zero can achieve statistical significance. The critical *t* value for significance on the upper end will be smaller than it would have been in a two-sample test. Therefore, if you are correct about the direction of the true difference, you would have more power to detect that significance using the one-sided test. Confidence intervals for one-sided upper- tail tests always have an upper bound of infinity (no upper bound).

The $H_0$= option in PROC TTEST allows other values for the null hypothesis.

# One-Sided *t* Test

```
/*st10bd02.sas*/
proc ttest data=sasuser.TestScores
          plots(only shownull)=interval h0=0 sides=U;
   class Gender;
   var SATScore;
   title "One-Sided t-Test Comparing Girls to Boys";
run;
```

H0=0 is the default, but is written here explicitly for completeness. SIDES=U declares this to be an upper one-sided *t* test. Because **`Female`** comes before **`Male`** in the alphabet, the difference score in PROC TTEST will be for **`Female`** minus **`Male`** by default.

| Gender | N | Mean | Std Dev | Std Err | Minimum | Maximum |
|---|---|---|---|---|---|---|
| Female | 40 | 1221.0 | 157.4 | 24.8864 | 910.0 | 1590.0 |
| Male | 40 | 1160.3 | 130.9 | 20.7008 | 890.0 | 1600.0 |
| Diff (1-2) | | 60.7500 | 144.8 | 32.3706 | | |

| Gender | Method | Mean | 95% CL Mean | | Std Dev | 95% CL Std Dev | |
|---|---|---|---|---|---|---|---|
| Female | | 1221.0 | 1170.7 | 1271.3 | 157.4 | 128.9 | 202.1 |
| Male | | 1160.3 | 1118.4 | 1202.1 | 130.9 | 107.2 | 168.1 |
| Diff (1-2) | Pooled | 60.7500 | 6.8651 | Infty | 144.8 | 125.2 | 171.7 |
| Diff (1-2) | Satterthwaite | 60.7500 | 6.8436 | Infty | | | |

| Method | Variances | DF | t Value | Pr > t |
|---|---|---|---|---|
| Pooled | Equal | 78 | 1.88 | 0.0321 |
| Satterthwaite | Unequal | 75.497 | 1.88 | 0.0322 |

| Equality of Variances | | | | |
|---|---|---|---|---|
| Method | Num DF | Den DF | F Value | Pr > F |
| Folded F | 39 | 39 | 1.45 | 0.2545 |

Notice that the confidence limits for the difference between **`Female`** and **`Male`** are different than in the previous output, even though the Mean Diff is exactly the same. The upper confidence bound for the difference is now Infty (Infinity). For left-sided tests, the lower bound would be infinite in the negative direction. The *p*-value for the difference between **`Female`** and **`Male`** (0.0321) is now significant at the 0.05 level.

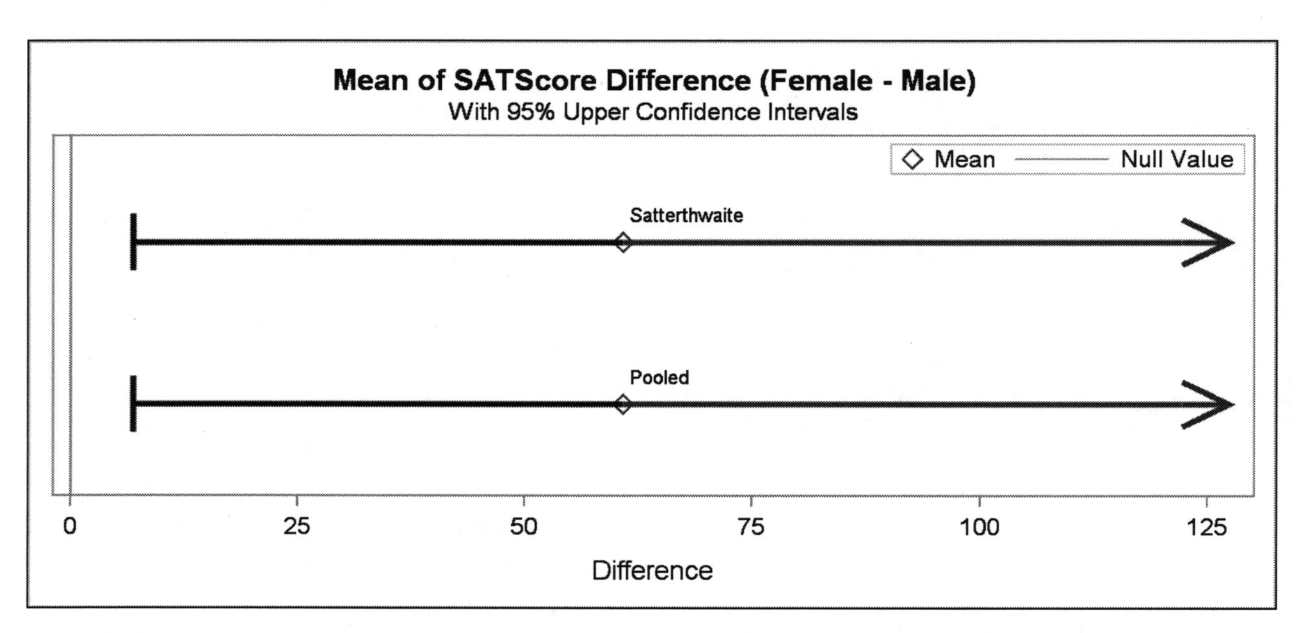


The Difference Interval plot reflects the one-sided nature of the analysis. This time, the confidence interval does not include zero. This implies statistical significance, which the *p*-value of 0.0321 confirms.

> The determination of whether to perform a one-sided test or a two-sided test should be made before any analysis or glancing at the data, and should be made bases on subject-matter considerations and not statistical power considerations.

## C.01 Multiple Choice Poll

What justifies the choice of a one-sided test versus a two-sided test?

a. The need for more statistical power
b. Theoretical and subject-matter considerations
c. A two-sided test that is nonsignificant
d. The need for an unbiased test statistic

11

# C.3 Nonparametric ANOVA

This section addresses nonparametric options in the NPAR1WAY procedure. Nonparametric one-sample tests are also available in the UNIVARIATE procedure.

## Nonparametric Analysis

*Nonparametric analyses* are those that rely only on the assumption that the observations are independent.

A nonparametric test is appropriate when

- the data contains valid outliers
- the data is skewed
- the response variable is ordinal and not continuous.

14

Nonparametric tests are most often used when the normality assumption required for analysis of variance is in question. Although ANOVA is robust with regards to minor departures from normality, extreme departures can make the test less sensitive to differences between means. Therefore, when the data is markedly skewed or there are extreme outliers, nonparametric methods might be more appropriate.
In addition, when the data follows a count measurement scale instead of interval, nonparametric methods should be used.

## Rank Scores

| Treatment | A | | | | | B | | | | |
|---|---|---|---|---|---|---|---|---|---|---|
| Response | 2 | 5 | 7 | 8 | 10 | 6 | 9 | 11 | 13 | 15 |
| Rank Score | 1 | 2 | 4 | 5 | 7 | 3 | 6 | 8 | 9 | 10 |
| | | | | | | | | | | |
| | Sum = 19 | | | | | Sum = 36 | | | | |

15

In nonparametric analysis, the rank of each data point is used instead of the raw data.

The illustrated ranking system ranks the data from smallest to largest. In the case of ties, the ranks are averaged. The sums of the ranks for each of the treatments are used to test the hypothesis that the populations are identical. For two populations, the Wilcoxon rank-sum test is performed. For any number of populations, a Kruskal-Wallis test is used.

## Median Scores

| Treatment | A | | | | | B | | | | |
|---|---|---|---|---|---|---|---|---|---|---|
| Response | 2 | 5 | 7 | 8 | 10 | 6 | 9 | 11 | 13 | 15 |
| Median Score | 0 | 0 | 0 | 0 | 1 | 0 | 1 | 1 | 1 | 1 |
| | Median = 9.5 | | | | | | | | | |
| | Sum = 1 | | | | | Sum = 4 | | | | |

16

Recall that the median is the 50th percentile, which is the middle of your data values.

When calculating median scores, a score of

- 0 is assigned, if the data value is less than or equal to the median
- 1 is assigned, if the data value is above the median.

The sums of the median scores are used to conduct the Median test for two populations or the Brown-Mood test for any number of populations.

## Hypotheses of Interest

$H_0$: all populations are identical with respect to scale, shape, and location.

$H_1$: all populations are not identical with respect to scale, shape, and location.

17

Nonparametric tests compare the probability distributions of sampled populations rather than specific parameters of these populations.

In general, with no assumptions about the distributions of the data, you are testing these hypotheses:

- $H_0$: all populations are identical with respect to shape and location
- $H_1$: all populations are ***not*** identical with respect to shape and location.

Thus, if you reject the null hypothesis, you conclude that the population distributions are different, but you did not identify the reason for the difference. The difference could be because of different variances, skewness, kurtosis, or means.

## THE NPAR1WAY PROCEDURE

General form of the NPAR1WAY procedure:

```
PROC NPAR1WAY DATA=SAS-data-set <options>;
     CLASS variable;
     VAR variables;
RUN;
```

18

Selected NPAR1WAY procedure statements:

CLASS specifies a classification variable for the analysis. You must specify exactly one variable, although this variable can have any number of values.

VAR specifies numeric analysis variables.

## Hospice Example

Are there different effects of a marketing visit, in terms of increasing the number of referrals to the hospice, among the various specialties of physicians?

19

Consider a study done by Kathryn Skarzynski to determine whether there was a change in the number of referrals received from physicians after a visit by a hospice marketing nurse. One of her study questions was, “Are there different effects of the marketing visits, in terms of increasing the number of referrals, among the various specialties of physicians?”

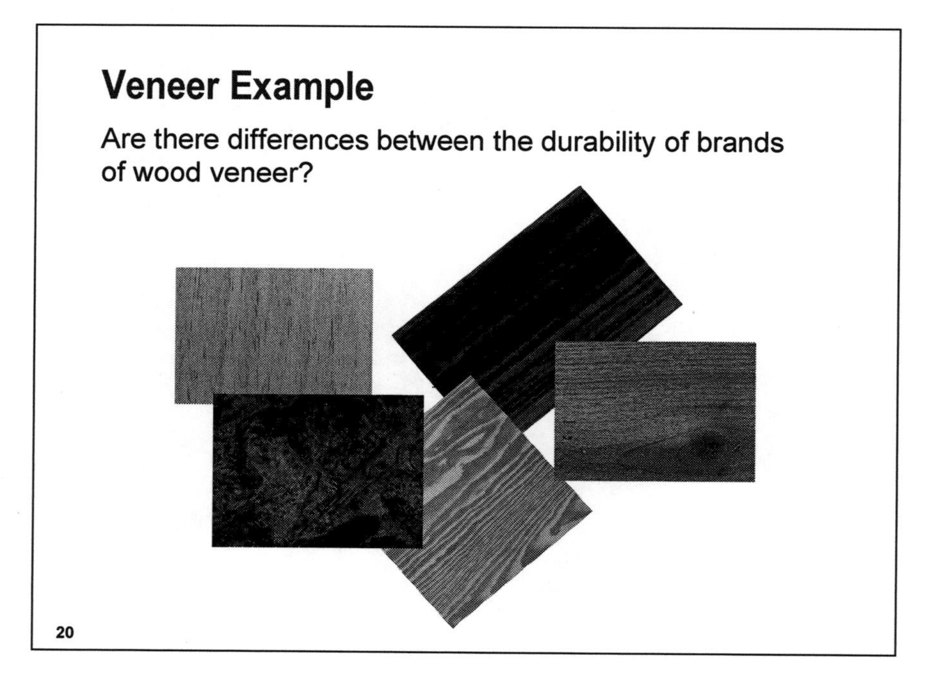


Consider another experiment where the goal of the experiment is to compare the durability of three brands of synthetic wood veneer. This type of veneer is often used in office furniture and on kitchen cabinets. To determine durability, four samples of each of three brands are subjected to a friction test. The amount of veneer material that is worn away due to the friction is measured. The resulting wear measurement is recorded for each sample. Brands that have a small wear measurement are desirable.

## The NPAR1WAY Procedure for Count Data

Example: A portion of Ms. Skarzynski's data about the hospice marketing visits is in the **st192.hosp** data set. The variables in the data set are as follows:

| | |
|---|---|
| **id** | the ID number of the physician's office visited |
| **visit** | the type of visit, to the physician or to the physician's staff |
| **code** | the medical specialty of the physician |
| **ref3p** | the number of referrals three months before the visit |
| **ref2p** | the number of referrals two months before the visit |
| **ref1p** | the number of referrals one month before the visit |
| **ref3a** | the number of referrals three months after the visit |
| **ref2a** | the number of referrals two months after the visit |
| **ref1a** | the number of referrals one month after the visit |

In addition, the following variables have been calculated:

| | |
|---|---|
| **avgprior** | the average number of referrals per month for the three months before the visit |
| **diff1** | the difference between the number of referrals one month after the visit and the average number of referrals before the visit |
| **diff2** | the difference between the number of referrals two months after the visit and the average number of referrals before the visit |
| **diff3** | the difference between the number of referrals three months after the visit and the average number of referrals before the visit |
| **diffbys1** | the difference between the number of referrals one month after the visit and the number of referrals three months before the visit |
| **diffbys2** | the difference between the number of referrals two months after the visit and the number of referrals three months before the visit |
| **diffbys3** | the difference between the number of referrals three months after the visit and the number of referrals three months before the visit. |

Print a subset of the variables for the first 10 observations in the data set.

```
/*st10bd03.sas*/
proc format;
   value vstfmt
      0='staff only'
      1='physician';
   value spcfmt
      1='oncologist'
      2='internal med'
      3='family prac'
      4='pulmonolgist'
      5='other special';
run;

proc print data= sasuser.hosp (obs=10);
   var visit code diffbys3;
   format visit vstfmt. code spcfmt.;
run;
```

| Obs | visit | code | diffbys3 |
|---|---|---|---|
| 1 | physician | family prac | 0 |
| 2 | physician | family prac | 1 |
| 3 | physician | oncologist | -1 |
| 4 | physician | family prac | -3 |
| 5 | physician | oncologist | 1 |
| 6 | physician | family prac | 0 |
| 7 | physician | oncologist | -1 |
| 8 | physician | oncologist | -1 |
| 9 | physician | internal med | 1 |
| 10 | physician | oncologist | 1 |

One of the analyses to answer the research question is to compare **diffbys3** (the number of referrals three months after the visit minus the number three months before the visit) for the different specialties.

Initially, you want to examine the distribution of the data.

```
proc univariate data=sasuser.hosp;
   class code;
   var diffbys3;
   histogram diffbys3 / normal kernel ncols=3;
   inset mean std skewness kurtosis
         normal(adpval="Anderson-Darling P"
                cvmpval="Cramer von Mises P"
                ksdpval="Komogorov-Smirnov P");
   probplot  diffbys3 / normal ncols=3;
   inset mean std skewness kurtosis;
   title 'Descriptive Statistics for Hospice Data';
   format code spcfmt.;
run;
```

Examine the histograms and normal probability plots for each group.

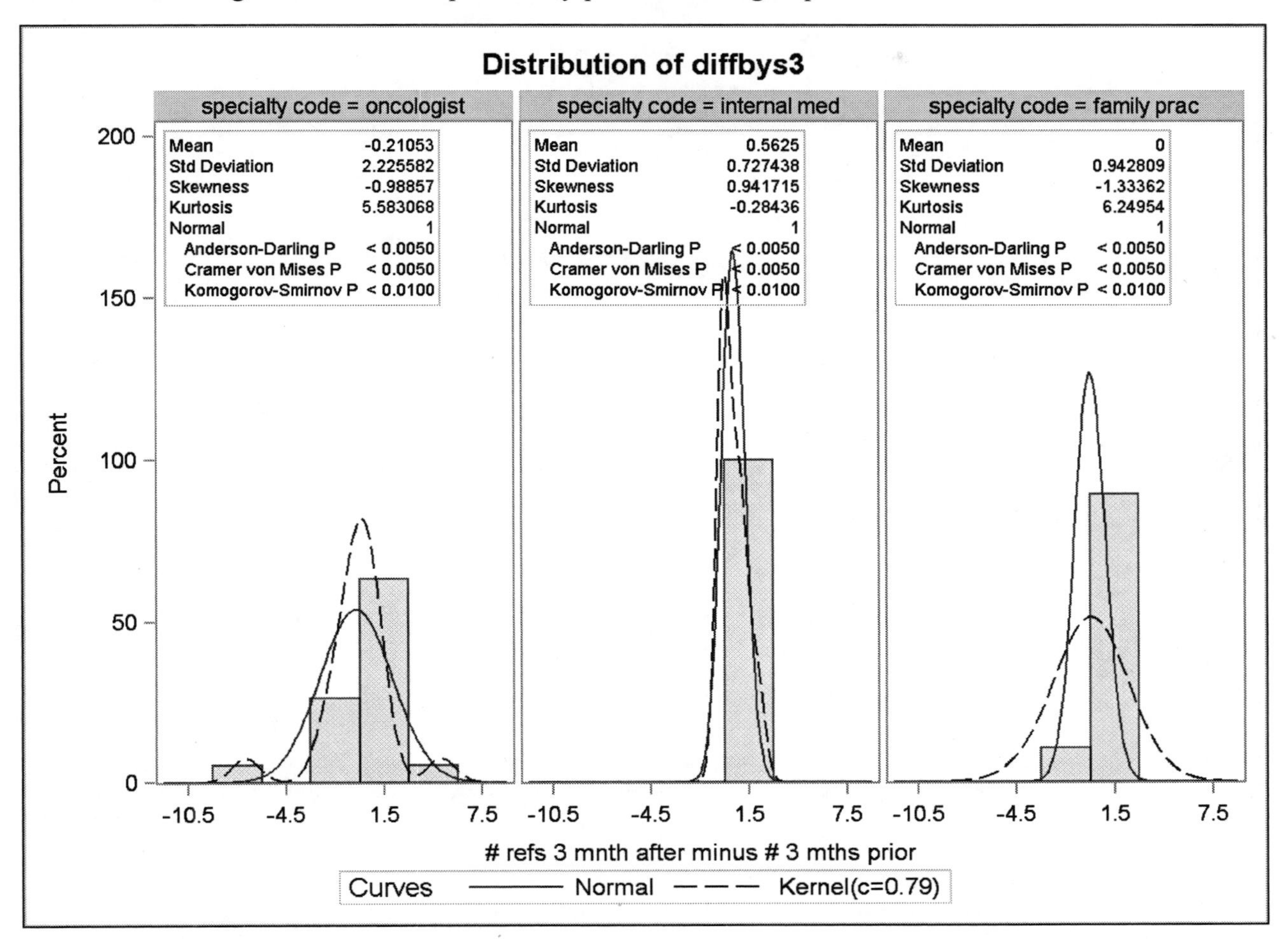


Based on skewness and kurtosis, the oncologists and family practice doctors data might not be normal. All three goodness-of-fit tests reject the null hypothesis that the data is normal.

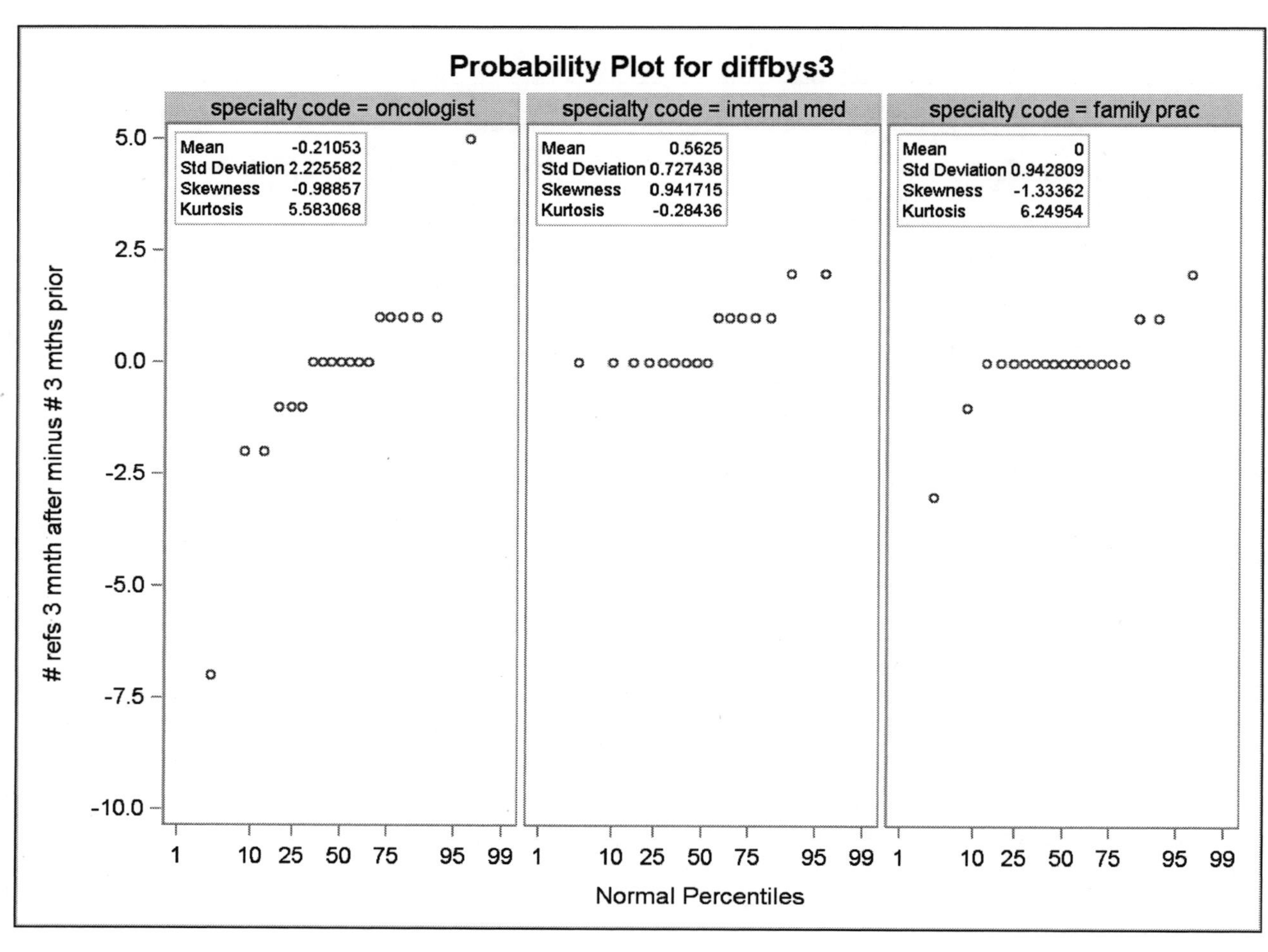


Internal medicine doctors appear to have only three values: 0, 1, and 2. The plots indicate that the data is not normal.

Family practice doctors appear to have mostly 0 values.

Both family practice doctors and oncologists have highly kurtotic distributions.

```
proc sgplot data=sasuser.hosp;
   vbox diffbys3 / category = code;
   format code spcfmt.;
run;
```

Now examine the PROC SGPLOT output.

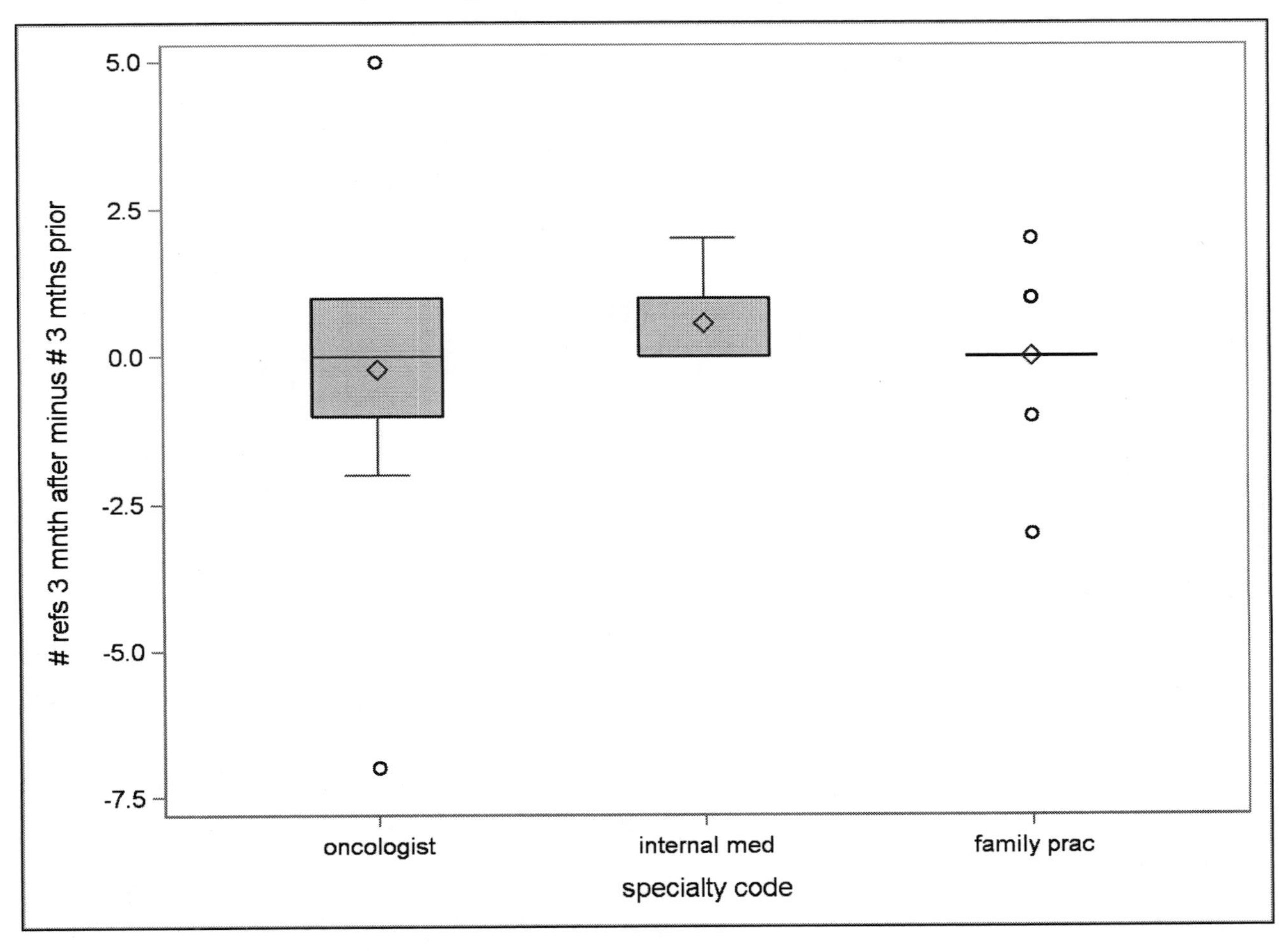


The box plots strongly support the conclusion that the data is not normal. Remember that the data values of **diffbys3** are actually counts and therefore ordinal. This suggests that a nonparametric analysis would be more appropriate.

For illustrative purposes, use the WILCOXON option to perform a rank sum test and the MEDIAN option to perform the Median test. This data was actually analyzed using the Rank Sum test.

```
proc npar1way data=sasuser.hosp wilcoxon median;
   class code;
   var diffbys3;
   format code spcfmt.;
run;
```

Selected PROC NPAR1WAY statement options:

WILCOXON requests an analysis of the rank scores. The output includes the Wilcoxon two-sample test and the Kruskal-Wallis test for two or more populations.

MEDIAN requests an analysis of the median scores. The output includes the median two-sample test and the median one-way analysis test for two or more populations.

| Wilcoxon Scores (Rank Sums) for Variable diffbys3 Classified by Variable code | | | | | |
|---|---|---|---|---|---|
| **code** | **N** | **Sum of Scores** | **Expected Under H0** | **Std Dev Under H0** | **Mean Score** |
| **family prac** | 19 | 478.50 | 522.50 | 49.907208 | 25.184211 |
| **internal med** | 16 | 538.00 | 440.00 | 47.720418 | 33.625000 |
| **oncologist** | 19 | 468.50 | 522.50 | 49.907208 | 24.657895 |
| **Average scores were used for ties.** | | | | | |

| Kruskal-Wallis Test | |
|---|---|
| **Chi-Square** | 4.2304 |
| **DF** | 2 |
| **Pr > Chi-Square** | 0.1206 |

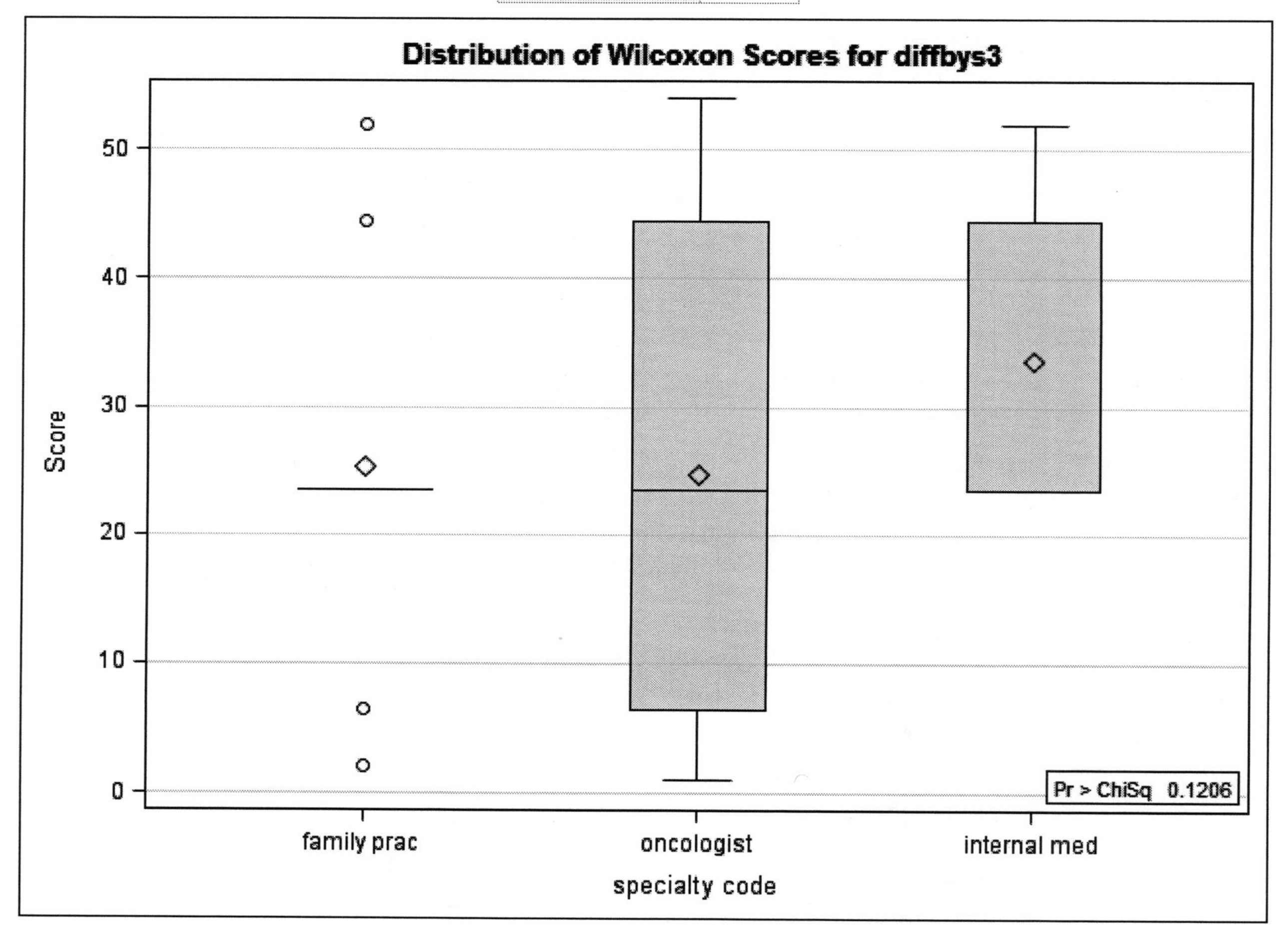

The PROC NPAR1WAY output from the WILCOXON option shows the actual sums of the rank scores and the expected sums of the rank scores if the null hypothesis is true. From the Kruskal-Wallis test (chi-square approximation), the *p*-value is .1206. Therefore, at the 5% level of significance, you do not reject the null hypothesis. There is not enough evidence to conclude that the distributions of change in hospice referrals for the different groups of physicians are significantly different.

Partial PROC NPAR1WAY Output

| Median Scores (Number of Points Above Median) for Variable diffbys3 Classified by Variable code | | | | | |
|---|---|---|---|---|---|
| code | N | Sum of Scores | Expected Under H0 | Std Dev Under H0 | Mean Score |
| family prac | 19 | 8.133333 | 9.50 | 1.232093 | 0.428070 |
| internal med | 16 | 10.300000 | 8.00 | 1.178106 | 0.643750 |
| oncologist | 19 | 8.566667 | 9.50 | 1.232093 | 0.450877 |
| Average scores were used for ties. | | | | | |

| Median One-Way Analysis | |
|---|---|
| Chi-Square | 3.8515 |
| DF | 2 |
| Pr > Chi-Square | 0.1458 |

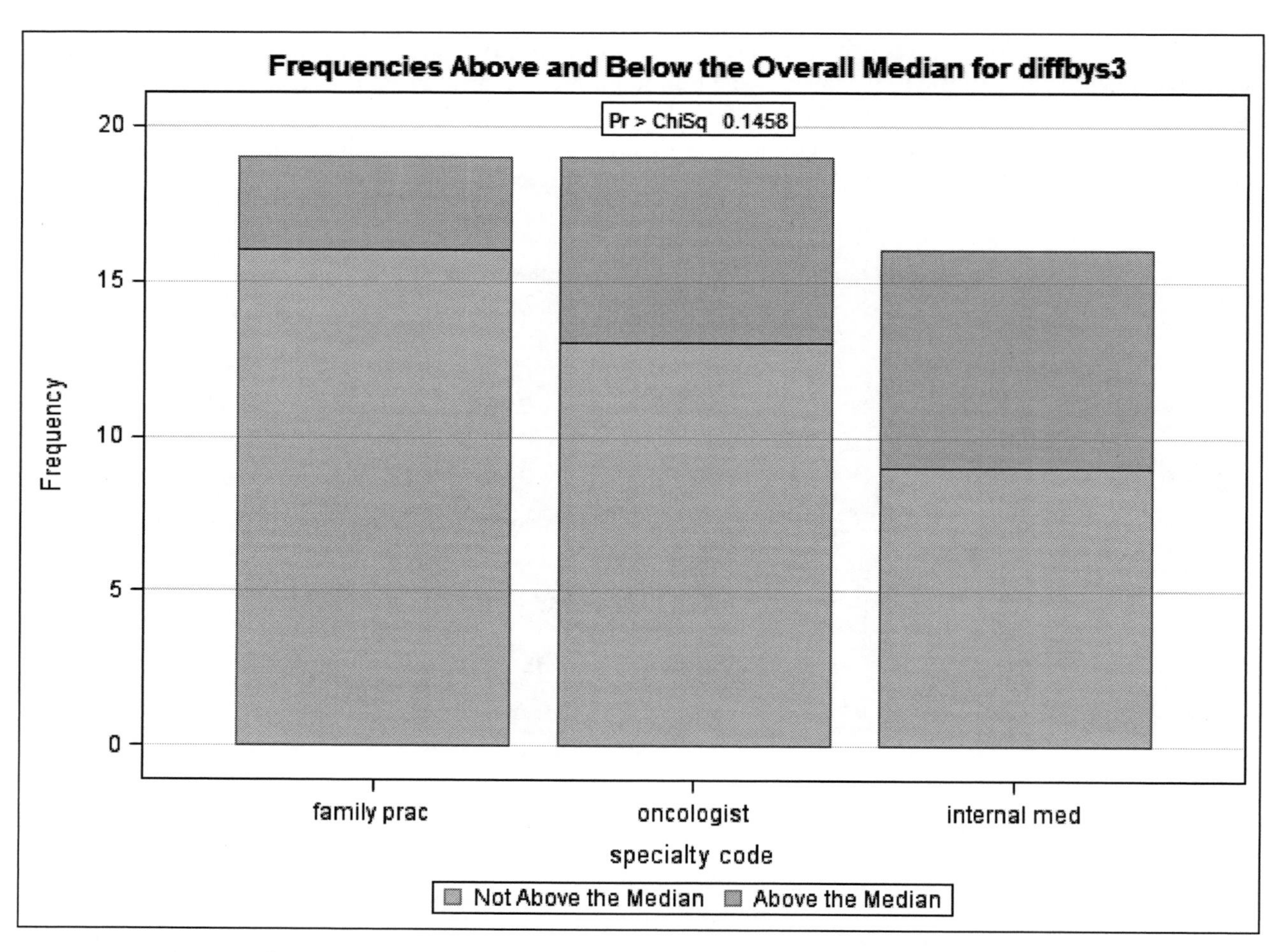


Again, based on the *p*-value of .1458, at the 5% level of significance, you do not reject the null hypothesis. There is not enough evidence to conclude that there are differences between specialists.

PROC NPAR1WAY produces a box plot similar to the one you created for exploratory data analysis. In addition, when you specify the MEDIAN option, a mosaic plot is generated and shows the number of observations above and below the median for each group:

# The NPAR1WAY Procedure for Small Samples

Example: For an experiment to compare the durability of three brands of synthetic wood veneer, perform nonparametric one-way ANOVA. The data is stored in the **st192.ven** data set.

```
/*st10bd04.sas*/
proc print data=sasuser.ven;
   title 'Wood Veneer Wear Data';
run;
```

| Obs | brand | wear |
|---|---|---|
| 1 | Acme | 2.3 |
| 2 | Acme | 2.1 |
| 3 | Acme | 2.4 |
| 4 | Acme | 2.5 |
| 5 | Champ | 2.2 |
| 6 | Champ | 2.3 |
| 7 | Champ | 2.4 |
| 8 | Champ | 2.6 |
| 9 | Ajax | 2.2 |
| 10 | Ajax | 2.0 |
| 11 | Ajax | 1.9 |
| 12 | Ajax | 2.1 |

Because there is a sample size of only four for each brand of veneer, the usual PROC NPAR1WAY Wilcoxon test *p*-values might be inaccurate. Instead, the EXACT statement should be added to the PROC NPAR1WAY code. This provides exact *p*-values for the simple linear rank statistics based on the Wilcoxon scores rather than estimated *p*-values based on continuous approximations.

Exact analysis is available for both the WILCOXON and MEDIAN options in PROC NPAR1WAY. You can specify which of these scores you want to use to compute the exact *p*-values by adding either one or both of these options to the EXACT statement. If no options are listed in the EXACT statement, exact *p*-values are computed for all the linear rank statistics requested in the PROC NPAR1WAY statement.

You should exercise care when choosing to use the EXACT statement with PROC NPAR1WAY. Computational time can be prohibitive depending on the number of groups, the number of distinct response variables, the total sample size, and the speed and memory available on your computer. You can terminate exact computations and exit PROC NPAR1WAY at any time by pressing the **Break** button in the SAS windowing environment or the **Stop** button in SAS Enterprise Guide, and choosing to stop computations.

```
proc npar1way data=sasuser.ven wilcoxon;
   class brand;
   var wear;
   exact;
run;
```

| Wilcoxon Scores (Rank Sums) for Variable wear Classified by Variable brand | | | | | |
|---|---|---|---|---|---|
| brand | N | Sum of Scores | Expected Under H0 | Std Dev Under H0 | Mean Score |
| Acme | 4 | 31.50 | 26.0 | 5.846522 | 7.8750 |
| Champ | 4 | 34.50 | 26.0 | 5.846522 | 8.6250 |
| Ajax | 4 | 12.00 | 26.0 | 5.846522 | 3.0000 |
| Average scores were used for ties. | | | | | |

| Kruskal-Wallis Test | |
|---|---|
| Chi-Square | 5.8218 |
| DF | 2 |
| Asymptotic Pr > Chi-Square | 0.0544 |
| Exact Pr >= Chi-Square | 0.0480 |

In the PROC NPAR1WAY output shown above, the exact $p$-value is .0480, which is significant at $\alpha$=.05. Notice the difference between the exact $p$-value and the $p$-value based on the chi-square approximation.

The following box plot is produced with ODS Statistical Graphics:

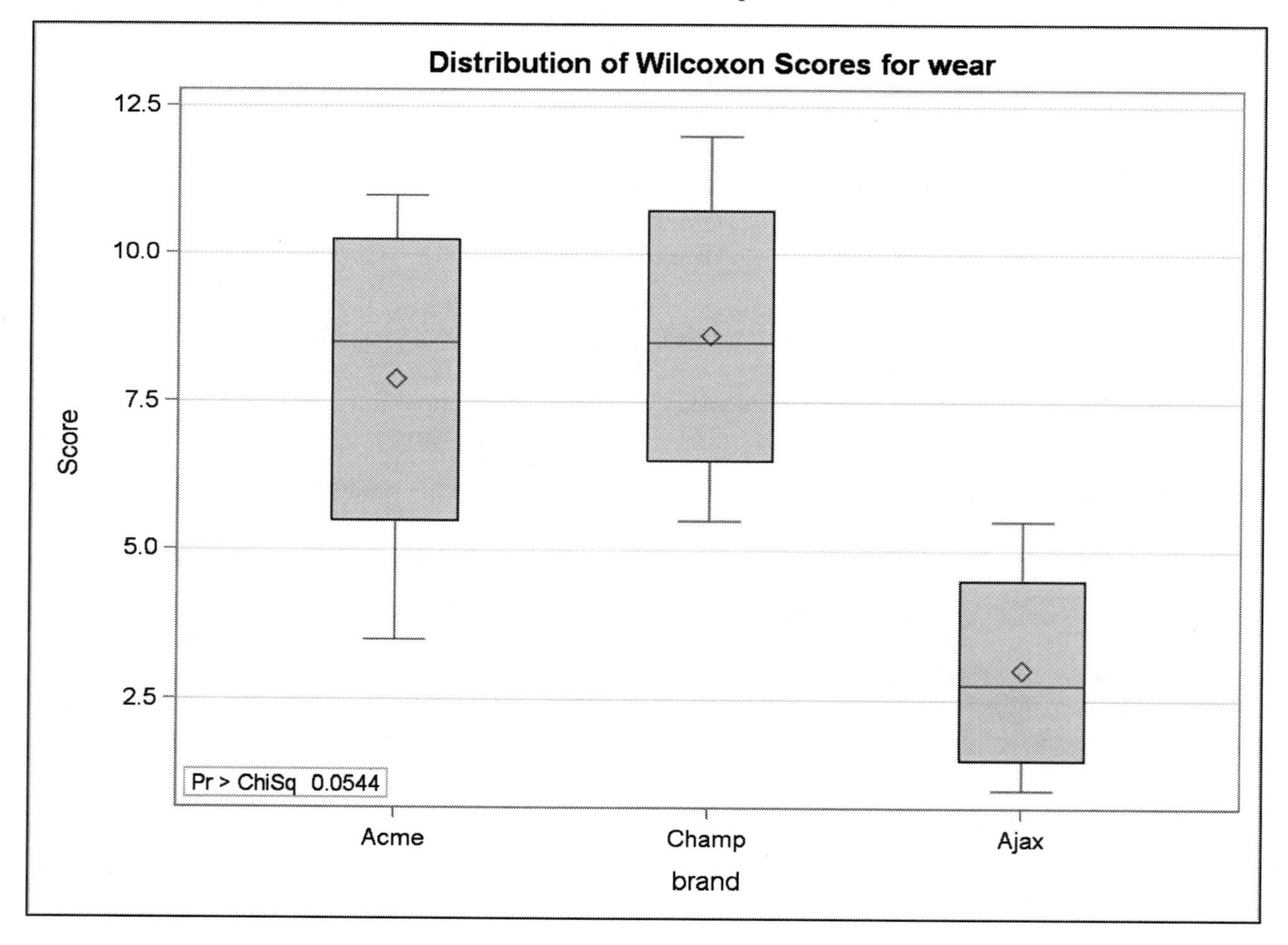

# C.4 Partial Leverage Plots

## Partial Leverage Plots

- Producing scatter plots of the response (Y) versus each of the possible predictor variables (the Xs) is recommended.
- However, in the multiple regression situation, these plots can be somewhat misleading because Y might depend on the other Xs not accounted for in the plot.
- Partial leverage plots compensate for this limitation of the scatter plots.

24

A *partial leverage plot* is a graphical method for visualizing the test of significance for the parameter estimates in the full model. The plot is basically a plot of the residuals from two partial regressions.

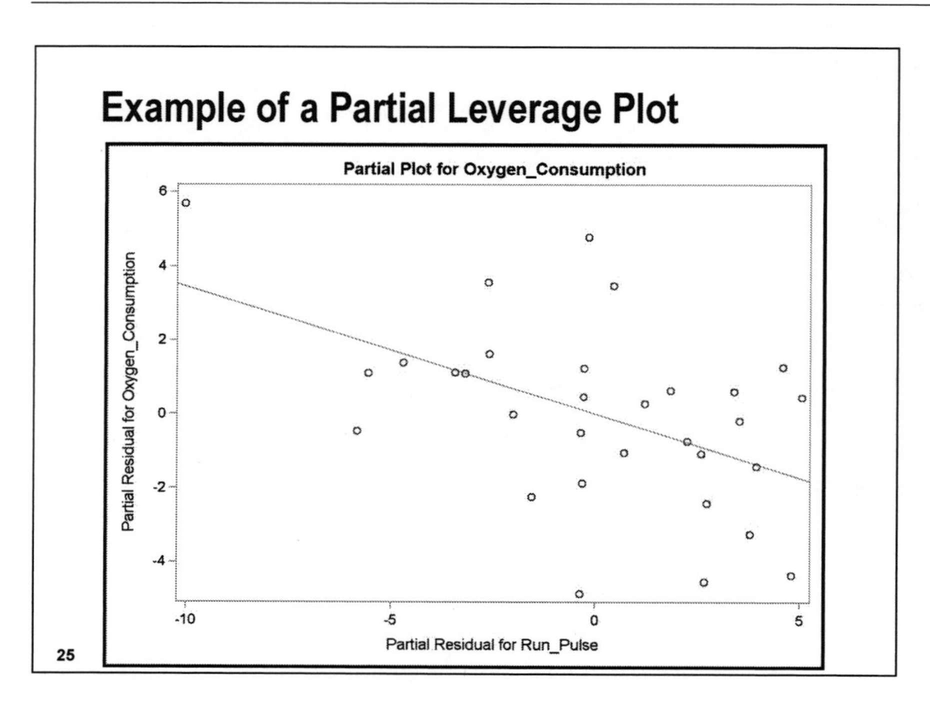


Partial regression leverage plots are graphical methods that enable you to see the effect of a single variable in a multiple regression setting, controlling for the effect of all other variables.

Partial leverage plots are produced automatically with ODS Statistical Graphics when you specify the PLOTS = PARTIAL option in the PROC REG statement.

## Partial Leverage Plots

Presume that you are performing a multiple linear regression with Y as the dependent variable, and X1, X2, and X3 as the independent variables.

To create a partial leverage plot for X2, do the following:

- Regress Y on X1 and X3. These residuals are the vertical axis of the partial leverage plot.
- Regress X2 on X1 and X3. These residuals are the horizontal axis of the partial leverage plot.

26

In the example shown, there are three partial leverage plots, one for each independent variable.

In general terms, for a partial leverage plot of the independent variable $X_r$,

- the vertical axis is the residuals from a regression of Y regressed on all Xs except $X_r$
- the horizontal axis is the residuals from a regression of $X_r$ regressed on all other Xs.

## Partial Leverage Plots

Example: Generate and interpret partial leverage plots for the full model and compare them to the fit plot from the simple regression model with **RunTime**.

```
/*st10bd05.sas*/
proc reg data=sasuser.fitness
         plots(only)=fitplot(nolimits stats=none);
   RUNTIME: model Oxygen_Consumption
                  = RunTime;
   title 'Simple Regression';
run;
quit;
```

Selected PLOTS= options:

NOLIMITS
suppresses the display of confidence and prediction limits.

STATS=NONE
suppresses the display of the model statistics box.

Partial Output

| Parameter Estimates | | | | | |
|---|---|---|---|---|---|
| Variable | DF | Parameter Estimate | Standard Error | t Value | Pr > \|t\| |
| Intercept | 1 | 82.42494 | 3.85582 | 21.38 | <.0001 |
| RunTime | 1 | -3.31085 | 0.36124 | -9.17 | <.0001 |

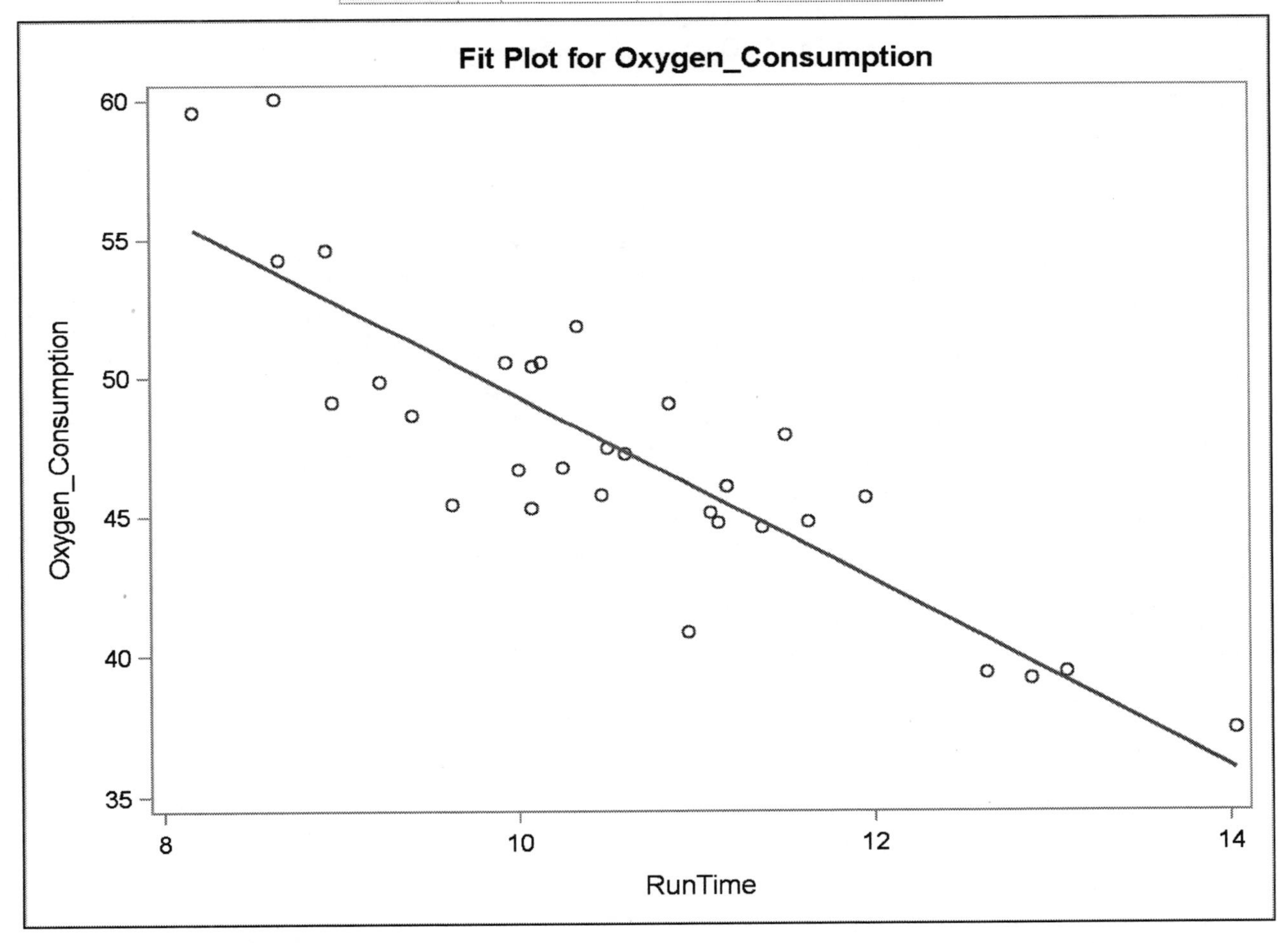


On its own, **RunTime** is a highly significant predictor of **Oxygen_Consumption** with a *p*-value <.0001. The observations fit tightly around the regression prediction line.

Now run the full model and look at the partial residual plot for **RunTime**.

```
proc reg data=sasuser.fitness
         plots(only)=partial(unpack);
    FULL: model Oxygen_Consumption
              = Performance RunTime Age Weight
                Run_Pulse Rest_Pulse Maximum_Pulse
              / partial;
    title 'Producing Partial Leverage Plots';
run;
quit;
```

Selected MODEL statement option:

PARTIAL
: generates partial leverage plots for all predictor variables in the model. If you also specify PLOTS=PARTIAL in the PROC REG statement, ODS Graphics are produced.

Partial Output

**Parameter Estimates**

| Variable | DF | Parameter Estimate | Standard Error | t Value | Pr > \|t\| |
|---|---|---|---|---|---|
| Intercept | 1 | 131.78249 | 72.20754 | 1.83 | 0.0810 |
| Performance | 1 | -0.12619 | 0.30097 | -0.42 | 0.6789 |
| RunTime | 1 | -3.86019 | 2.93659 | -1.31 | 0.2016 |
| Age | 1 | -0.46082 | 0.58660 | -0.79 | 0.4401 |
| Weight | 1 | -0.05812 | 0.06892 | -0.84 | 0.4078 |
| Run_Pulse | 1 | -0.36207 | 0.12324 | -2.94 | 0.0074 |
| Rest_Pulse | 1 | -0.01512 | 0.06817 | -0.22 | 0.8264 |
| Maximum_Pulse | 1 | 0.30102 | 0.13981 | 2.15 | 0.0420 |

The parameter estimate for **RunTime** is not significant in this model. The *p*-value is 0.2016.

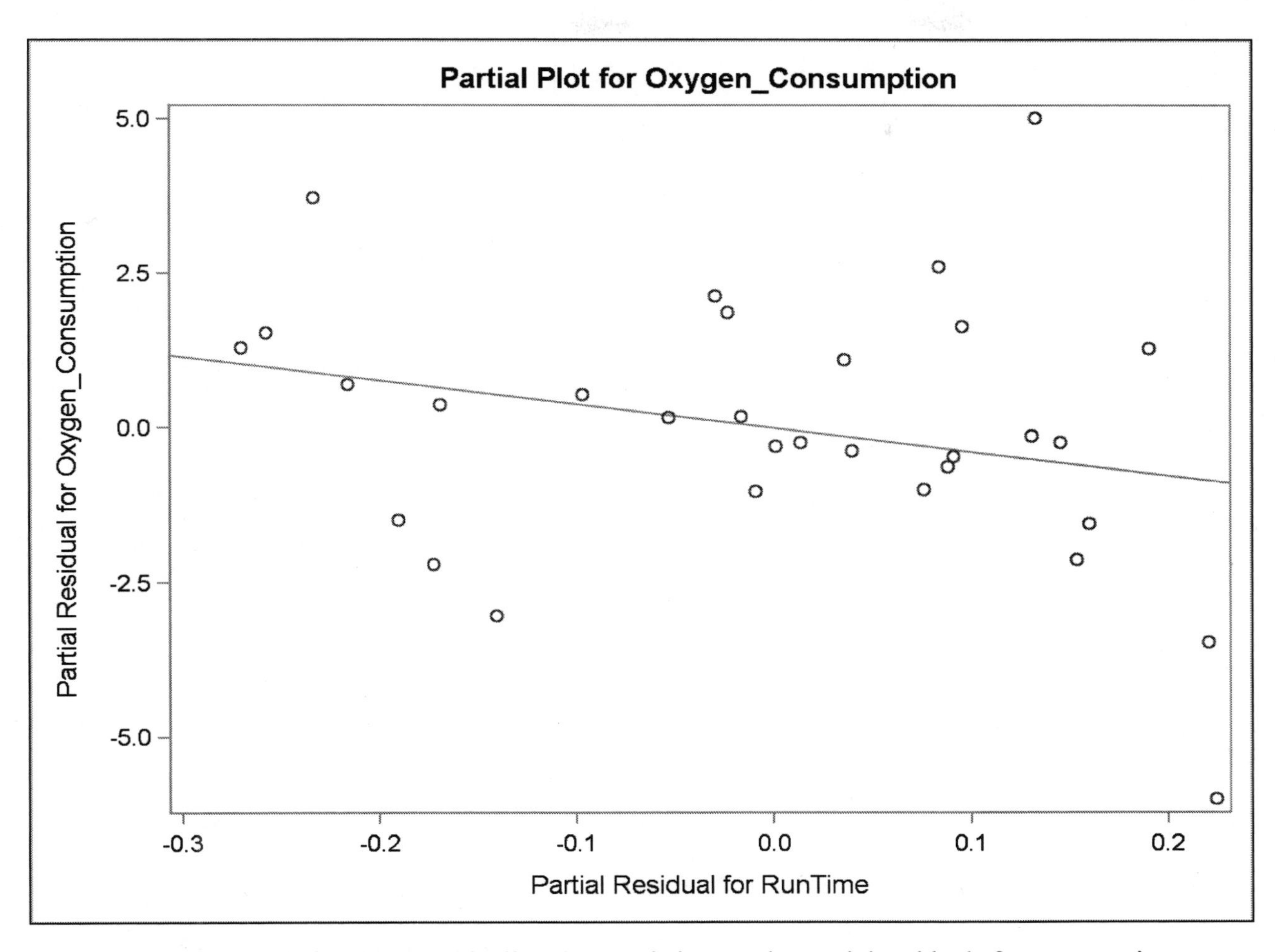


The plot shows this relationship graphically. The Y axis is now the partial residuals from regressing **Oxygen_Consumption** on all other predictors in the model. The X axis is the partial residuals from regressing **RunTime** on all other predictors in the model. The variance is much greater for observations around the partial regression line than for the simple regression line shown previously.

In addition to enabling you to visualize the adjusted relationships in a multiple regression model, partial residual plots can help you detect potential outliers. For instance, a potential influential outlier can be seen in the upper right corner of the plot. None was seen in the simple regression fit plot.

If you use the IMAGEMAP option and an ID statement, you can place your mouse over a data point to see the value of **Name** displayed as a tag on the plot.

# Appendix D Percentile Definitions

# D.1 Calculating Percentiles

## Using the UNIVARIATE Procedure

Example: Calculate the 25th percentile for the following data using the five definitions available in PROC UNIVARIATE:

1 3 7 11 14

For all of these calculations (except definition 4), you use the value $np = (5)(0.25) = 1.25$. This can be viewed as an observation number. However, there is obviously no observation 1.25.

**Definition 1** returns a weighted average. The value returned is 25% of the distance between observations 1 and 2. (The value of 25% is the fractional part of 1.25 expressed as a percentage.)

$$\text{percentile} = 1 + (0.25)(3 - 1) = 1.5$$

**Definition 2** rounds to the nearest observation number. Thus, the value 1.25 is rounded to 1 and the first observation, 1, is taken as the 25th percentile. If *np* were 1.5, then the second observation would be selected as the 25th percentile.

**Definition 3** always rounds up. Thus, 1.25 rounds up to 2 and the second data value, 3, is taken as the 25th percentile.

**Definition 4** is a weighted average similar to definition 1, except instead of using *np*, definition 4 uses $(n + 1)p = 1.5$.

$$\text{percentile} = 1 + (0.5)(3 - 1) = 2$$

**Definition 5** rounds up to the next observation number unless *np* is an integer, in which case an average of the observations represented by *np* and $(np + 1)$ is calculated. In this example, definition 5 rounds up, and the 25th percentile is 3.

# Appendix E Writing and Submitting SAS Programs in SAS Enterprise Guide

# E.1 Writing and Submitting SAS Programs in SAS Enterprise Guide

## Objectives

- Create and submit new SAS programs.
- Insert existing programs into a project.
- List programming statements to avoid.
- Generate a combined project program and log.

2

## SAS Enterprise Guide Program Editor

SAS Enterprise Guide includes a programming editor similar to the Enhanced Program Editor.

Additional functionality in the SAS Enterprise Guide 4.3 Program Editor includes the following:

- autocomplete
- dynamic syntax tooltips
- formatting programs to provide consistent spacing
- analyzing program flow

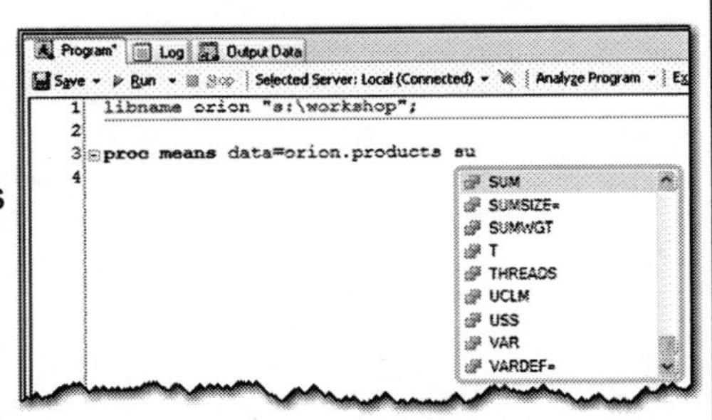


3

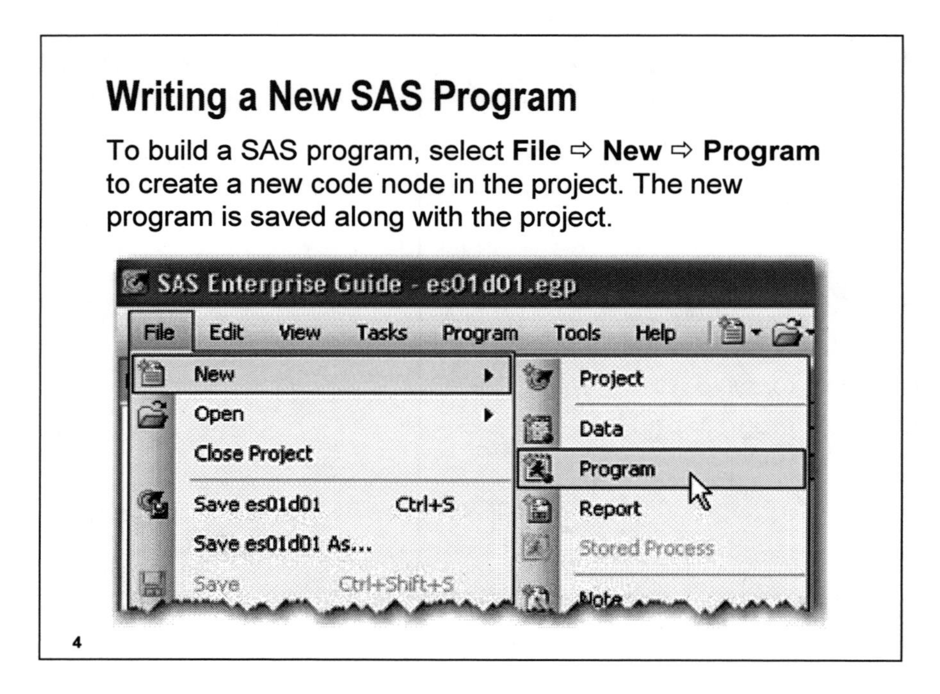


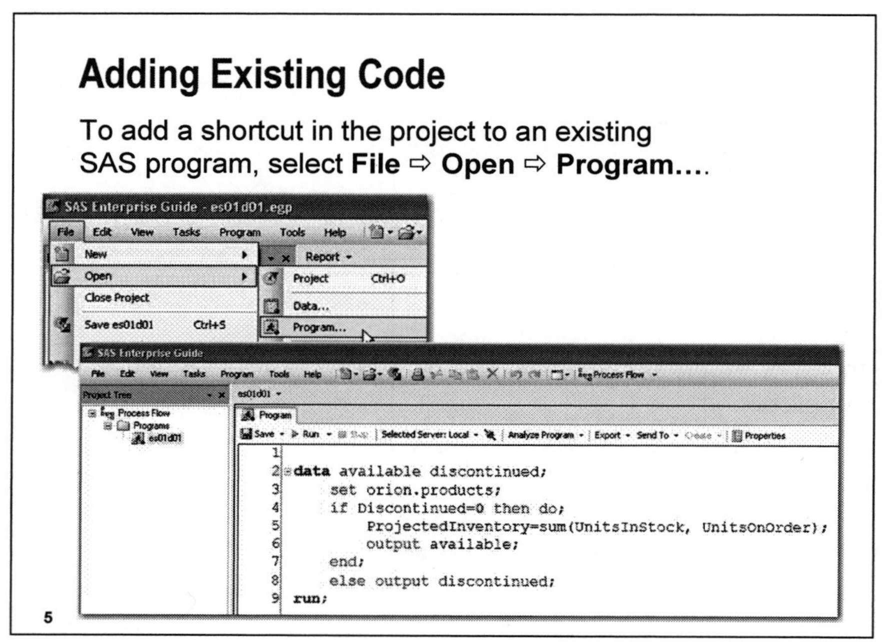


When you insert code, a shortcut to the file is added in the project, which means that changes made to the code in the project are also saved to the .sas file that you inserted. Also, if you make changes to the .sas file outside of SAS Enterprise Guide, the changes are reflected when you open or run the project again.

## Running SAS Code

A SAS program can be submitted using one of these techniques:

- Select **Run** or **Run Selection** from the toolbar.
- Select **Program** ⇨ **Run** or **Run Selection** from the menu bar.
- Right-click on the program and select **Run** or **Run Selection**.
- Press F8 or F3.

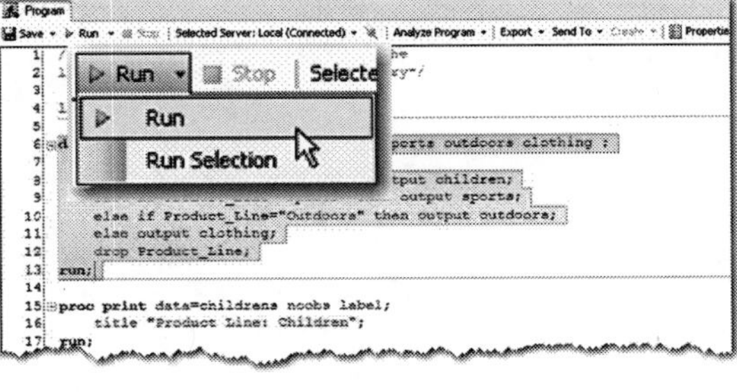


6

If SAS is available on multiple servers, you can select **Select Server** and designate the server on which the program should run.

If the data for a task is located on a server that is different from the server where the SAS code is run, then SAS Enterprise Guide copies the data to the server where the code actually runs. Because moving large amounts of data over a network can be time- and resource-intensive, it is recommended that the server that you choose to process the code be the same server on which the data resides.

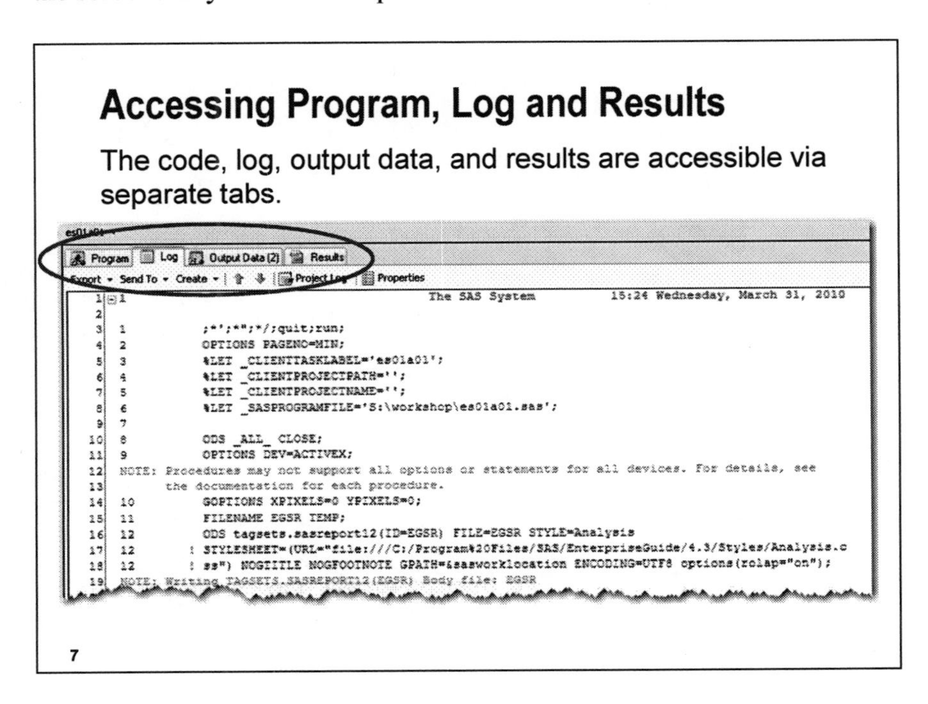

# Identifying Warning and Errors in the Log

The code icons in the project indicate whether there are warnings or errors in the SAS log.

Arrows on the Log tab enable quick navigation to the next warning or error.

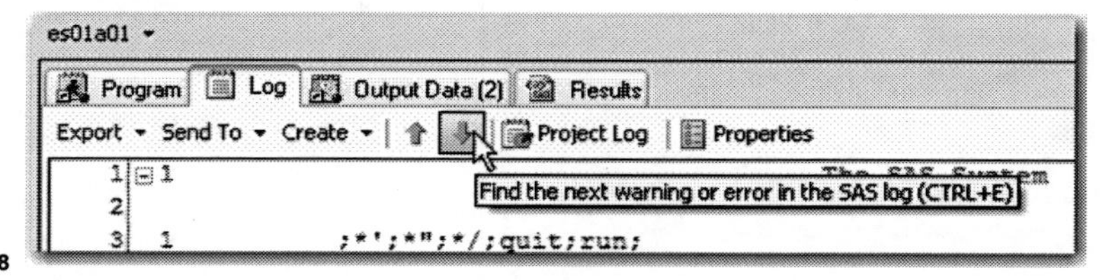


8

## Using the Program Toolbar

A toolbar above the program offers easy access to common actions, such as the following:

- saving the program
- running or stopping a program
- selecting the execution server
- analyzing the program for flow or grid computing
- exporting and e-mailing
- creating a stored process
- modifying program properties

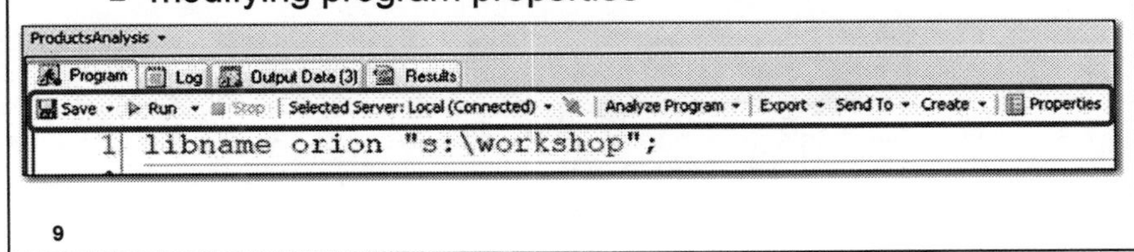


9

The Analyze Program button enables you to select one of these two options:

| | |
|---|---|
| ***Analyze Program Flow*** | SAS Enterprise Guide can create a process flow from a program. Using this process flow, you can quickly identify the different parts of the program and see how the parts are related. |
| ***Analyze Program for Grid Computing*** | When analyzing a program for grid computing, SAS Enterprise Guide identifies the parts of the program that are not dependent on one another. These parts can run simultaneously on multiple computers, which means that SAS Enterprise Guide returns the results more quickly. When SAS analyzes a program, lines of SAS/CONNECT code are added to your original program. Therefore, you must have a license for SAS Grid Manager or SAS/CONNECT to analyze a program for grid computing. |

Both options run the code behind the scenes to complete the analysis. If a data set is open in the SAS Enterprise Guide session, the analysis might fail. To view and close any open data sets, select **Tools** ⇨ **View Open Data Sets**.

## Embedding Programs in a Project

New SAS programs are embedded in the project so that it is saved as part of the .egp file.

When an existing SAS program is added to a project, a shortcut to the program file is created. You can also embed the program so that it is stored as part of the project file.

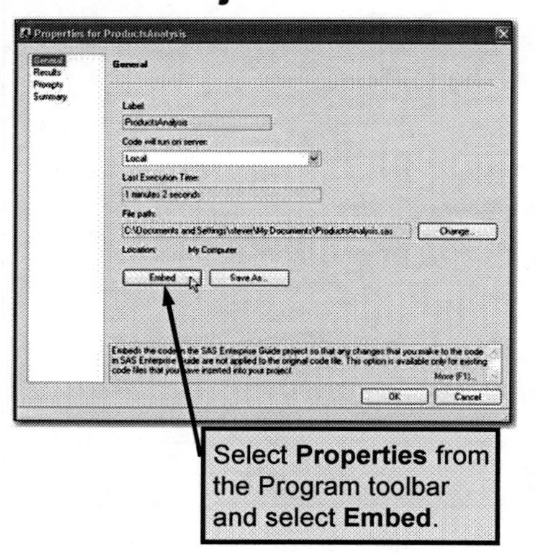


10

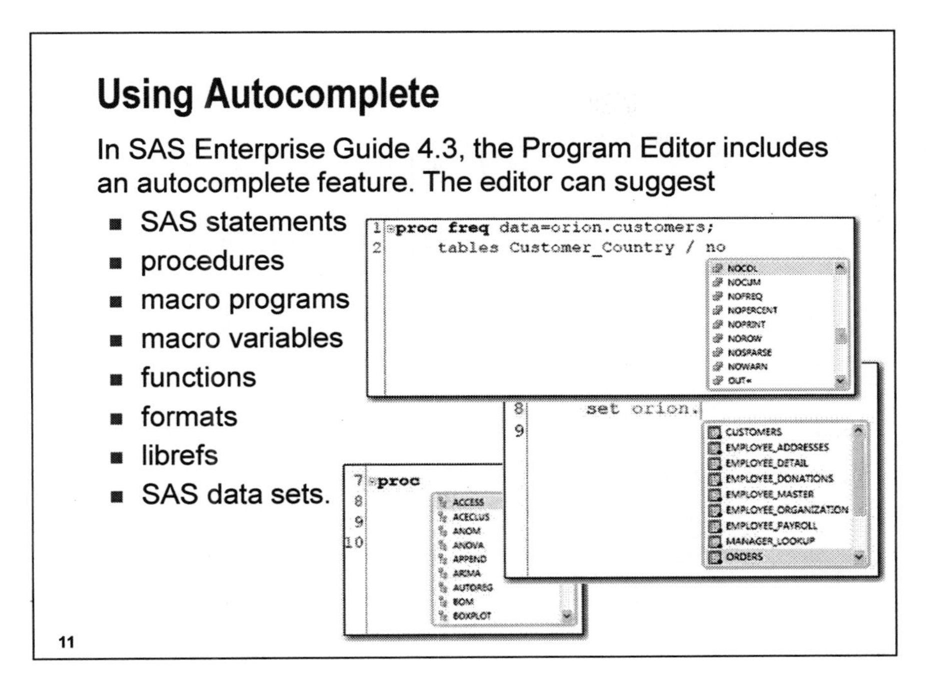


The autocomplete feature automatically suggests appropriate keywords. You can also manually open the Autocomplete window by using the following shortcut keys:

| Action | Keyboard Shortcut |
|---|---|
| Open the Autocomplete window for the keyword on which the cursor is currently positioned. In a blank program, this shortcut displays a list of global statements. | CTRL + space bar |
| Open the Autocomplete window that contains a list of the SAS libraries that are available with the current server connection. | CTRL + L |
| Open the Autocomplete window that contains a list of data sets that were created by using the DATA statement. | CTRL + D |
| Open the Autocomplete window that contains a list of SAS functions. | CTRL + SHIFT + F1 |
| Open the Autocomplete window that contains a list of macro functions. | CTRL + SHIFT + F2 |
| Open the Autocomplete window that contains a list of SAS formats. | CTRL + SHIFT + F |
| Open the Autocomplete window that contains a list of SAS informats. | CTRL + SHIFT + I |
| Open the Autocomplete window that contains a list of statistics keywords. | CTRL + SHIFT + K |
| Open the Autocomplete window that contains a list of SAS colors. | CTRL + SHIFT + C |
| Open the Autocomplete window that contains a list of style attributes. | CTRL + SHIFT + F4 |
| Open the Autocomplete window that contains a list of style elements. | CTRL + SHIFT + F3 |

## Customizing the Program Editor

The Program Editor can be customized by selecting **Program ⇨ Editor Options**.

Autocomplete can be customized or disabled on the Autocomplete tab.

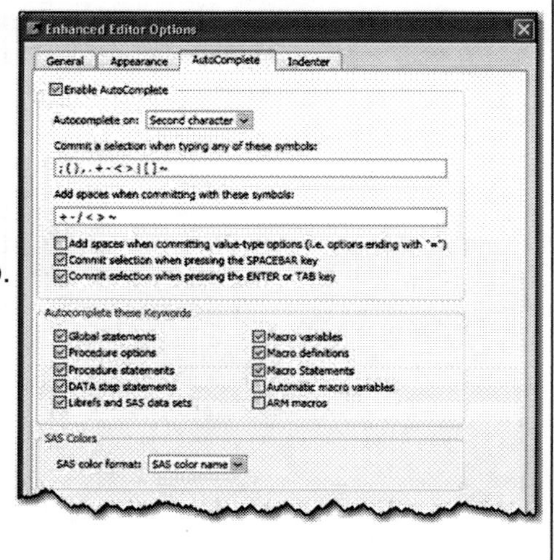


12

## Rearranging Windows

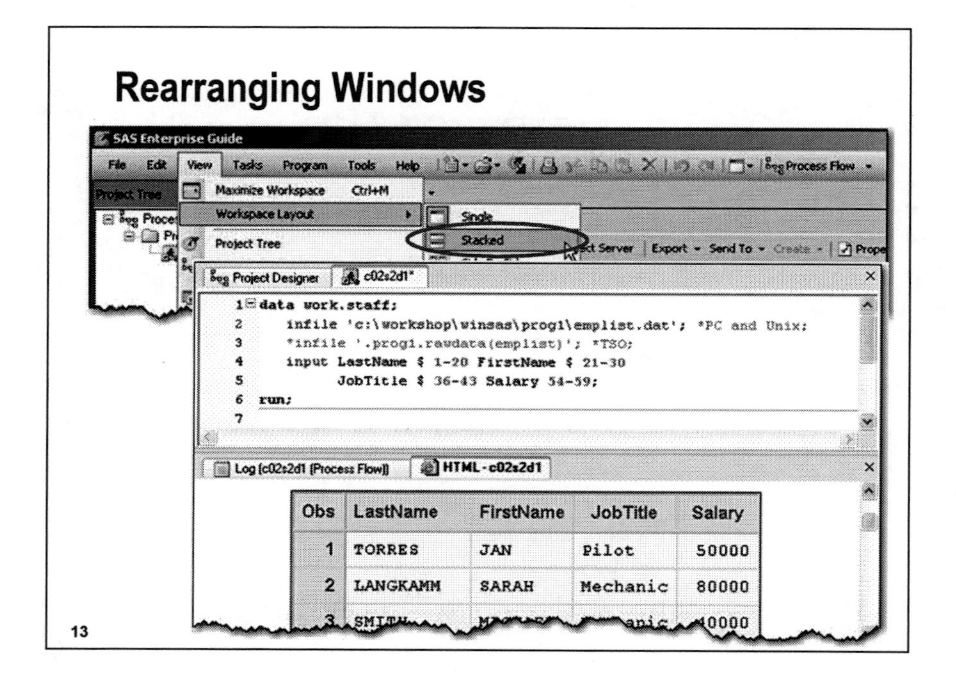


13

## Linking Items in the Process Flow

*Links* define the directional relationship between objects in SAS Enterprise Guide to create a process flow. Links can be either automatic or user-defined.

Links can enable you to force a particular flow between programs and point-and-click tasks in the project.

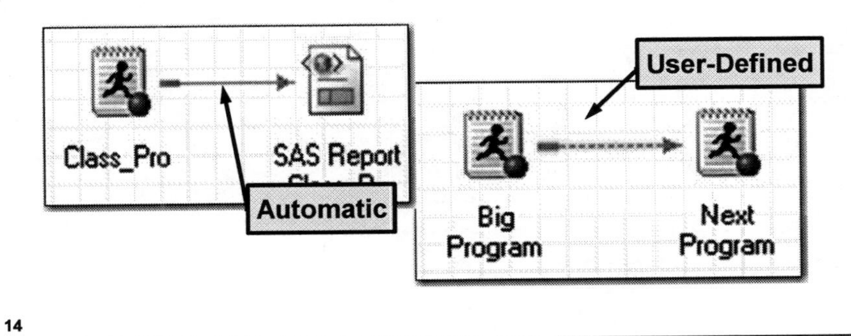


14

## Adding a SAS Program to a Project

1. Create a new project.
2. To open an existing SAS program, select **File** ⇨ **Open** ⇨ **Program…**. Navigate to the location of the course data and select **st10dd01.sas** ⇨ **Open**. A shortcut to the program is added to the project.

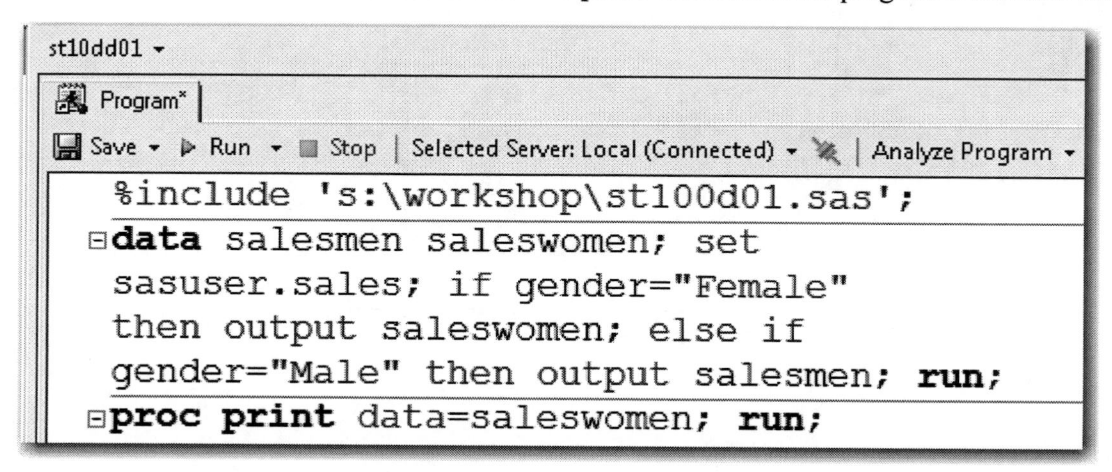

3. There is no indenting in this program to make it easier to read. Also, statements flow over onto new lines. Select **Edit** ⇨ **Format Code** to improve the spacing and organization of the code, or you can right-click on the program and select **Format Code**.

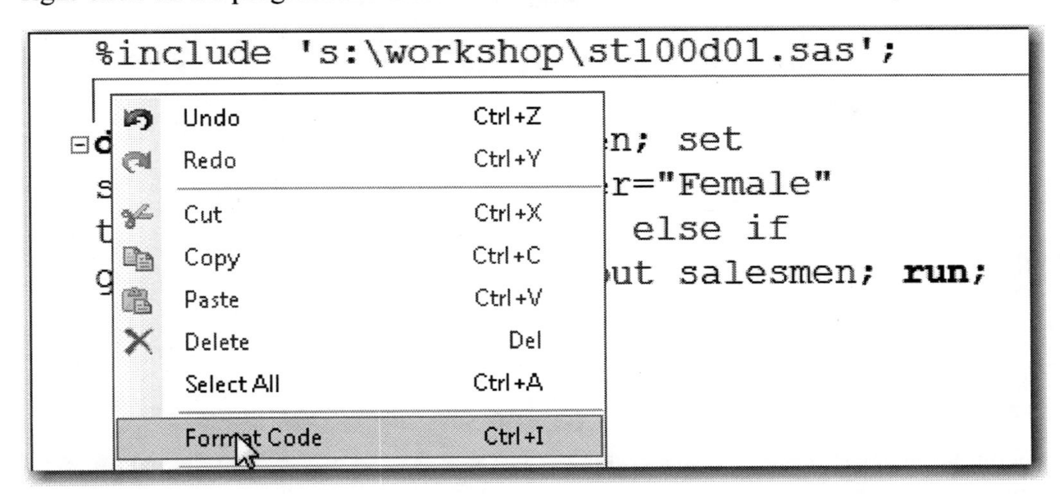


To modify the rules for formatting code, select **Program** ⇨ **Editor Options** ⇨ **Indenter**.

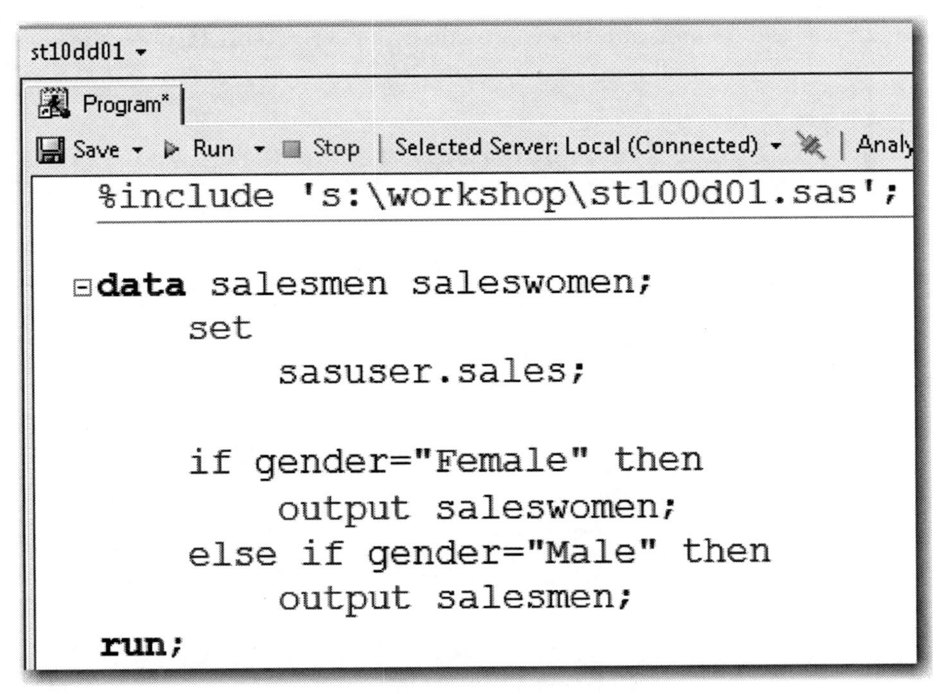


4. To execute the SAS program, select **Run** on the toolbar. A report is generated and lists the products in the **saleswomen** data set. Twenty-one are added to the project. Because **TestScores** was the first data set created, it is automatically placed on a new tab. All other data sets are accessible from the process flow.

| Obs | Purchase | Gender | Income | Age |
|---|---|---|---|---|
| 1 | 0 | Female | Low | 40 |
| 2 | 0 | Female | Low | 46 |
| 3 | 1 | Female | Low | 41 |

5. To include a frequency report to analyze the distribution of Purchase in the **Sales** data set, use the FREQ procedure in the SAS program. At the end of the program, type **pr**. A list of keywords is provided. Press the space bar to select the word **PROC** for the program.

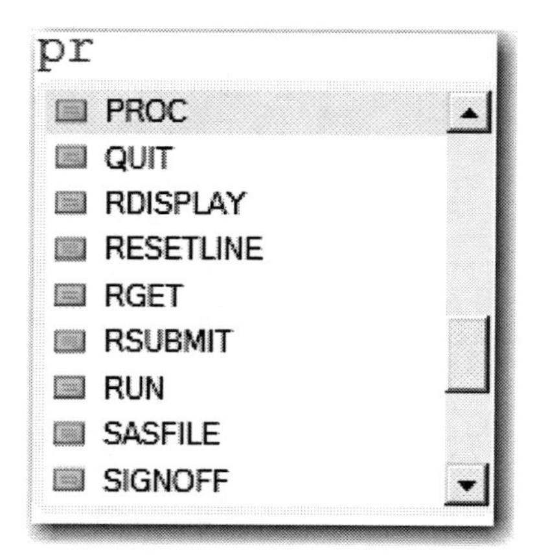


6. A list of procedure names is automatically provided. Type **fr** and press the space bar again to select **freq** for the program. Next, a list of valid options for the PROC FREQ statement is provided. Type **d** and press the space bar to select **data=**.

7. A list of data sets in the project and defined libraries is provided. Select **SASUSER**, press the space bar…

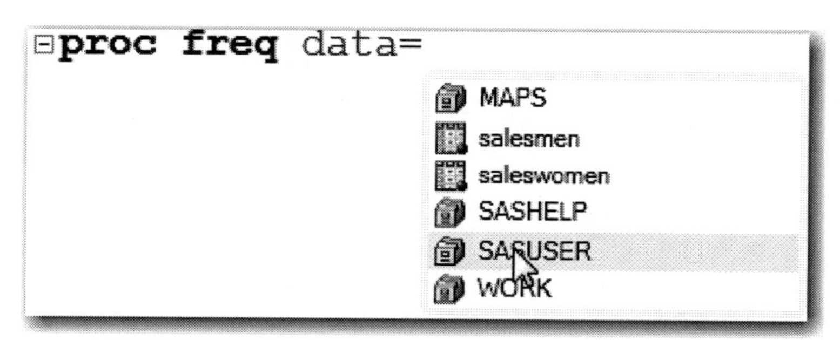


…and then select **SALES** for the data set.

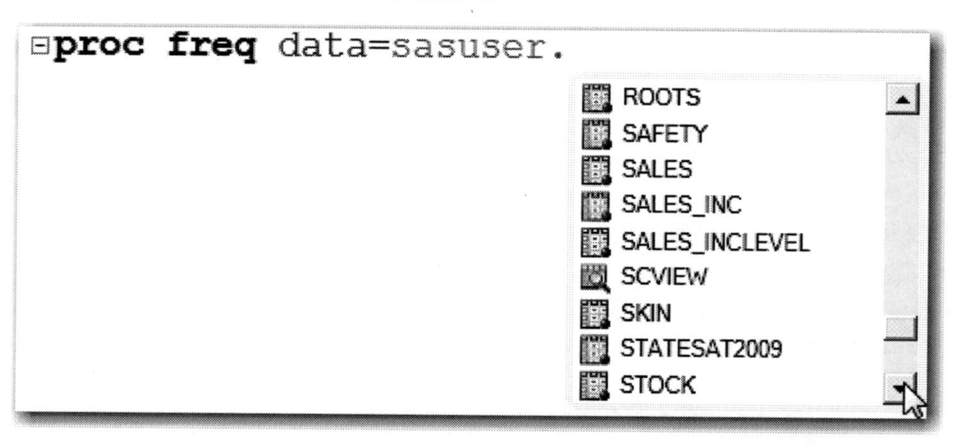

8. The list of valid options for the PROC FREQ statement appears again. Type **o**, select **order=**, and press the space bar. Type **fr** to select **FREQ** and then type a semicolon to complete the statement that appears as follows:

```
proc freq data=sasuser.sales order=freq;
```

9. Continue to use the autocomplete feature to write the remainder of the step:

```
proc freq data=sasuser.sales order=freq;
   tables Gender*Purchase / chisq relrisk;
run;
```

10. Highlight the PROC FREQ step in the program and select **Run ⇨ Run Selection**. Select **Yes** when you are prompted to replace the results.

Partial Results

| Table of Gender by Purchase | | | |
|---|---|---|---|
| **Gender** | **Purchase** | | |
| **Frequency<br>Percent<br>Row Pct<br>Col Pct** | **0** | **1** | **Total** |
| **Female** | 139<br>32.25<br>57.92<br>51.67 | 101<br>23.43<br>42.08<br>62.35 | 240<br>55.68 |
| **Male** | 130<br>30.16<br>68.06<br>48.33 | 61<br>14.15<br>31.94<br>37.65 | 191<br>44.32 |
| **Total** | 269<br>62.41 | 162<br>37.59 | 431<br>100.00 |

11. The program now includes three steps and creates multiple data sets and reports. To better visualize the flow of the program, return to the Program tab and select **Analyze Program ⇨ Analyze Program Flow**.

12. In the Analyze SAS Program window, select **Begin analysis**. Then type **Analysis of Associations** in the **Name of process flow to create** field and select **Create process flow** ⇨ **Close**.

   If a data set is open in the SAS Enterprise Guide session, the analysis might fail. To view and close any open data sets, select **Tools** ⇨ **View Open Data Sets…**.

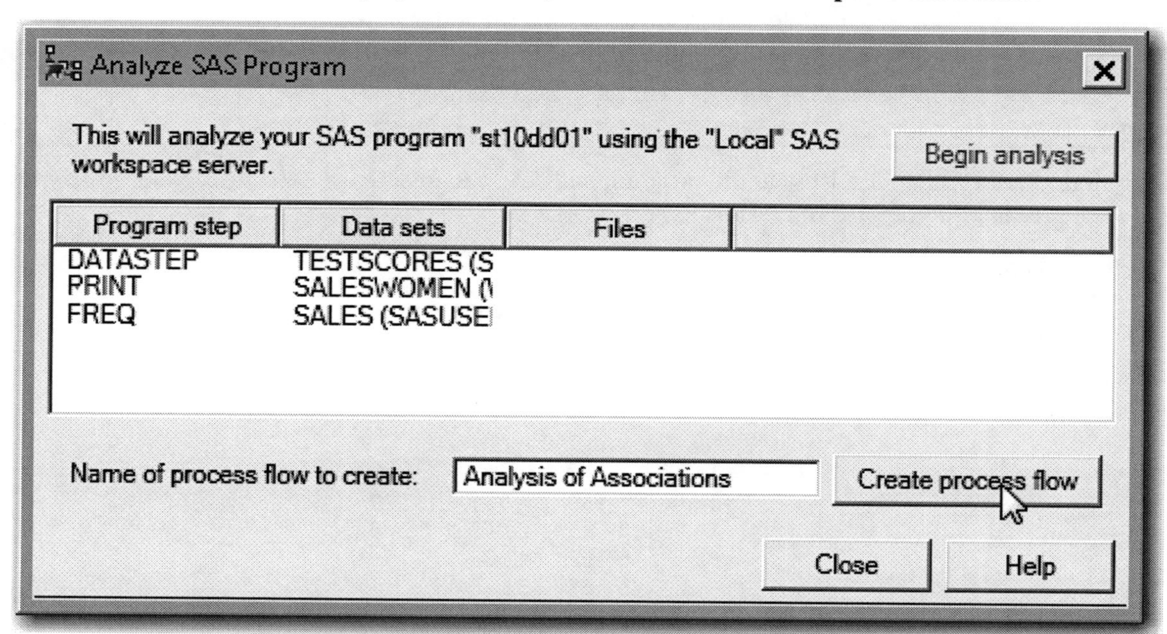


A new process flow is added to the project, and illustrates the flow of the steps in the program.

   To delete a process flow, right-click on the process flow in the Project Tree and select **Delete**.

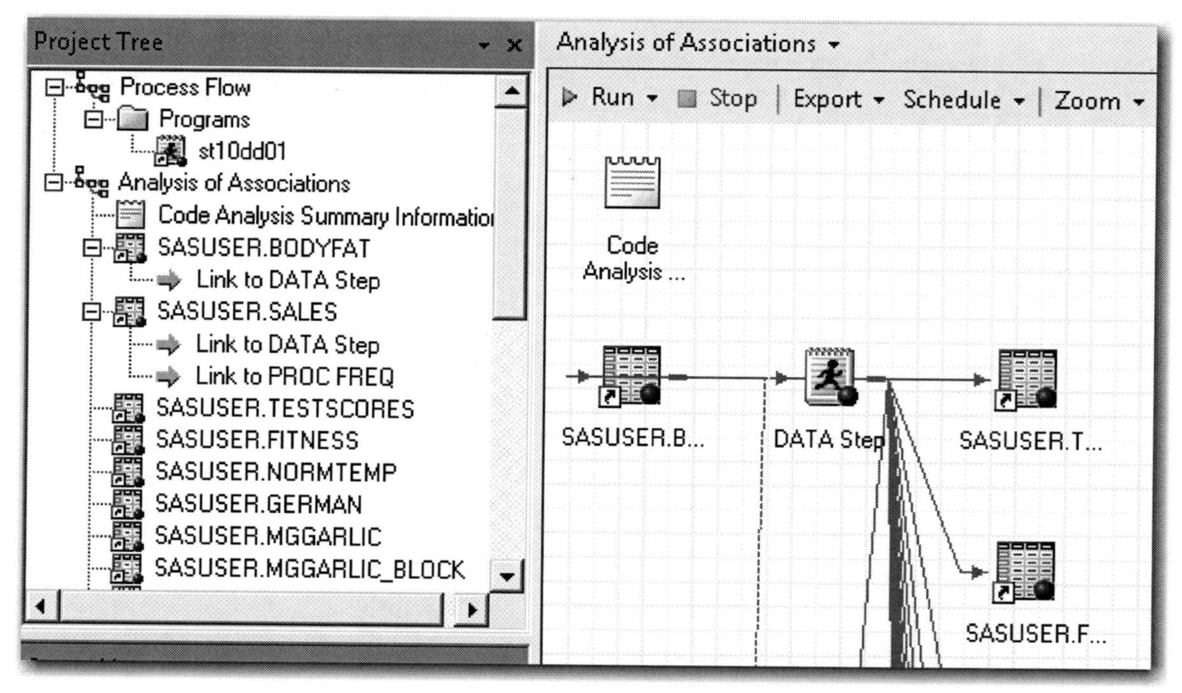

13. The Program Editor also includes syntax tooltips. Double-click on the **st10dd01** program in the Project Tree or Process Flow window. Hover the cursor over any keyword in the program. A tooltip displays syntax details for that particular step or statement.

    The F1 key also displays syntax help.

    You can view syntax tooltips by hovering the cursor over items in the autocomplete windows.

14. Save the modified program by returning to the Program tab and selecting **Save** ⇨ **Save As...**. Save the program as **st10dd01s** and select **Save**.

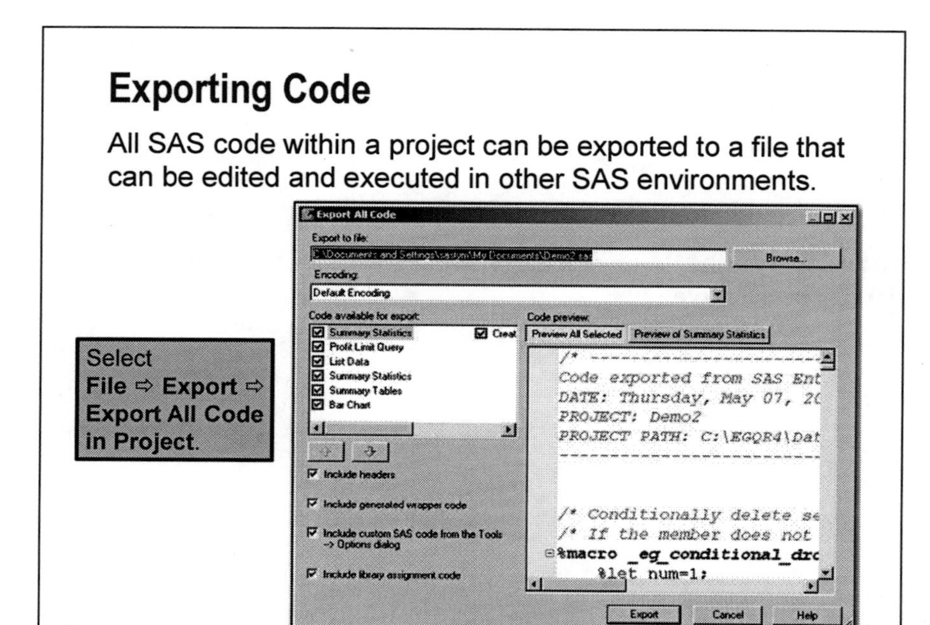
Exporting Code
All SAS code within a project can be exported to a file that can be edited and executed in other SAS environments.
Select
File ⇨ Export ⇨
Export All Code
in Project.
Export All Code
Browse...
Default Encoding
Code preview:
/* Code exported from SAS Ent
DATE: Thursday, May 07, 2(
PROJECT: Demo2
PROJECT PATH: C:\EGQR4\Dat
/* Conditionally delete se
/* If the member does not
%macro _eg_conditional_drc
%let num=1;
Export
Cancel
Help
16

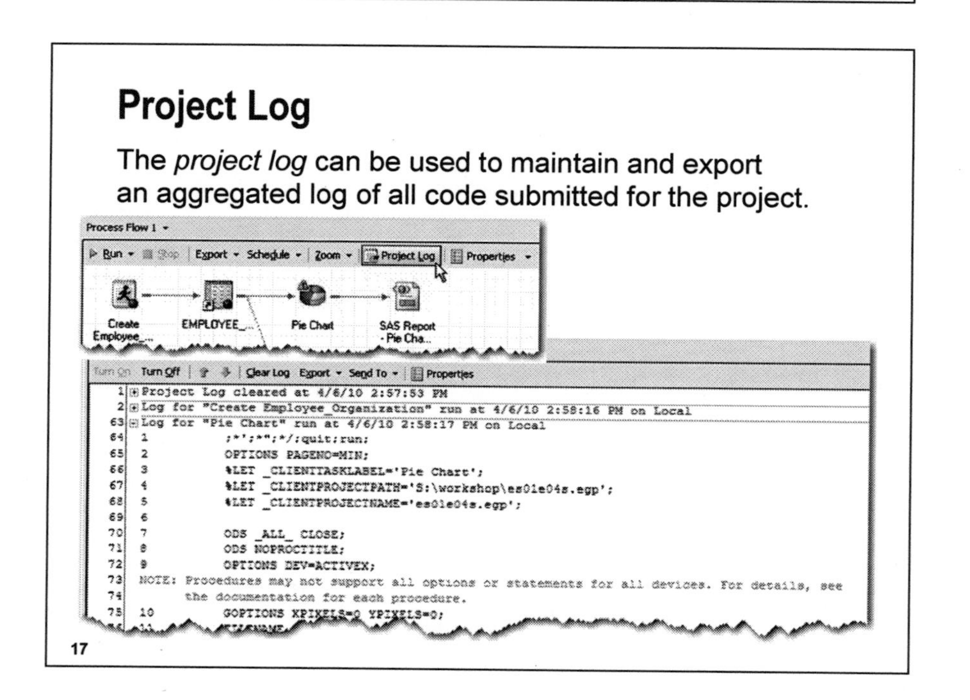
Project Log
The *project log* can be used to maintain and export an aggregated log of all code submitted for the project.
Process Flow 1
Run
Export
Schedule
Zoom
Project Log
Properties
EMPLOYEE_...
Pie Chart
SAS Report - Pie Cha...
Turn Off
Clear Log
Export
Send To
Properties
Project Log cleared at 4/6/10 2:57:53 PM
Log for "Create Employee_Organization" run at 4/6/10 2:58:16 PM on Local
Log for "Pie Chart" run at 4/6/10 2:58:17 PM on Local
OPTIONS PAGENO=MIN;
%LET _CLIENTTASKLABEL='Pie Chart';
%LET _CLIENTPROJECTPATH='S:\workshop\es01e04s.egp';
%LET _CLIENTPROJECTNAME='es01e04s.egp';
ODS _ALL_ CLOSE;
ODS NOPROCTITLE;
OPTIONS DEV=ACTIVEX;
NOTE: Procedures may not support all options or statements for all devices. For details, see the documentation for each procedure.
17

## Programming Statements to Avoid

Programs that run in the SAS windowing environment can also run successfully in SAS Enterprise Guide. Be aware of the following exceptions:

- Code that calls X commands or SYSTASK might not work unless this permission is granted by the administrator.
- Code that would normally cause a window or prompt to appear in the SAS windowing environment (DEBUG, PROC FSLIST, AF applications) does not work in SAS Enterprise Guide.
- Code that terminates the SAS process with ABORT or ENDSAS calls terminates the connection between SAS Enterprise Guide and the SAS server.

18

For more information about enabling X and SYSTASK commands, go to **blogs.sas.com/sasdummy/index.php?/archives/136-Using-the-X-and-SYSTASK-commands-from-SAS-Enterprise-Guide.html**.

# Recommended SAS® Titles

## Statistics 1: Introduction to ANOVA, Regression, and Logistic Regression

| ISBN | Title | Price (U.S. Dollars) |
|---|---|---|
| | **SAS® Press** | |
| 978-1-59047-080-0 | *Advanced Log-Linear Models Using SAS®* | $39.95 |
| 978-1-60764-664-8 | *Categorical Data Analysis Using the SAS® System, Third Edition (Available Spring 2012)* | TBD |
| 978-1-60764-379-1 | *Elementary Statistics Using SAS®* | $55.95 |
| 978-1-59994-725-9 | *The Little SAS® Book: A Primer, Fourth Edition* | $49.95 |
| 978-1-59994-641-2 | *Logistic Regression Using SAS®: Theory and Application, Second Edition (Available Spring 2012)* | TBD |
| 978-1-59994-660-3 | *Output Delivery System: The Basics and Beyond* | $55.95 |
| 978-1-58025-890-6 | *Regression and ANOVA: An Integrated Approach Using SAS® Software* | $69.95 |
| 978-1-59047-023-7 | *SAS® for Linear Models, Fourth Edition* | $61.95 |
| 978-1-59047-500-3 | *SAS® for Mixed Models, Second Edition* | $89.95 |
| 978-1-59047-882-0 | *SAS® Macro Programming Made Easy, Second Edition* | $59.95 |
| 978-1-60764-800-0 | *SAS® Statistics by Example* | $34.95 |
| 978-1-58025-725-1 | *SAS® System for Regression, Third Edition* | $43.95 |
| 978-1-60764-485-9 | *Statistical Graphics in SAS®: An Introduction to the Graph Template Language and the Statistical Graphics Procedures* | $37.95 |
| 978-1-59047-150-0 | *Step-by-Step Basic Statistics Using SAS®: Student Guide and Exercises (each book also sold separately)* | $99.95 |
| 978-1-59047-417-4 | *A Step-by-Step Approach to Using SAS® for Univariate and Multivariate Statistics, Second Edition* | $64.95 |

**Notes**

- Prices are subject to change without notice.
- To order, please visit **support.sas.com/bookstore**.
- SAS documentation is available to search, browse, or print **free** online at: **support.sas.com/documentation**.